THE AGRICULTURAL COMMODITY PROGRAMS

Two Decades of Experience

THE TWENTIETH CENTURY FUND

THE TRUSTEES of the Fund choose subjects for Fund studies and vote the appropriation to cover the expenses of each project. The authors, however, assume full responsibility for the findings and opinions in each report.

THE AGRICULTURAL COMMODITY PROGRAMS

TWO DECADES OF EXPERIENCE

Murray R. Benedict
Oscar C. Stine

NEW YORK • THE TWENTIETH CENTURY FUND • 1956

Library of Congress Catalog Card Number: 56–12417

PRINTED IN THE UNITED STATES OF AMERICA BY
THE LORD BALTIMORE PRESS, INC., BALTIMORE, MARYLAND

FOREWORD

THIS VOLUME is the last of three related works undertaken by the Twentieth Century Fund dealing with the farm problem in the United States. The first, *Farm Policies of the United States: 1790–1950,* published in 1953, set the issue in its historical context; the second, *Can We Solve the Farm Problem?,* published in 1955, dealt on a broad front with recent and current measures to meet the expectations of the farmers. The present volume, actually a continuation of the second, treats in detail the various programs on a commodity-by-commodity basis. Seemingly more specialized in approach than the other two, it has the particular interest which derives from showing the endlessly subtle variations, both of method and effect, which arise in the application of farm policy.

It may be asked why the Fund has shown so consistent a preoccupation over the past several years with the farm problem. In part, as is often the case, this preoccupation is a matter of circumstance. Dr. Murray R. Benedict, who has directed the research and has been the sole or principal author of all three reports, has shown himself an admirable guide—lucid, deeply informed, of a balanced judgment. To have tapped less than his total store would have seemed wasteful of what may be called a valuable natural resource. Yet there were obviously other reasons, linked with some of the basic dilemmas of modern democracy.

The Twentieth Century Fund has recognized the farm program as one of those areas where, in accordance with its established practices, objective surveys combined with the report of a representative committee could provide needed enlightenment. More than that, the Fund has recognized the farm problem in its relation to the technological developments which have concerned it so continuously. American agriculture has been transformed by scientific advances. Here, perhaps more clearly than elsewhere, we see the impact of technology upon older habits and methods of production; but here the results have a dimension not evident in industry. For the farmer since the beginning of the Republic has been considered the key figure in a free society. Merely to absorb the dispossessed or unemployed farmer in other trades, to industrialize and urbanize him, has gone against the grain of the American citizen. We have seen, consequently, a deliberate effort by the national government to counter "inevitable" trends—to introduce considerations of value into technological and economic processes.

There has obviously been demagogy and special pleading in connection with the farmer's case. Indeed, the belief that the small family farm is the indispensable element in democracy, that the farmer is the prototype of the free citizen, remains in large part an unexamined assumption. Yet the politician anxious to gain the farmer's support has not infrequently struck a responsive chord in a broad public; for the public feels instinctively that the continuance of farming in its more or less traditional forms is one of those menaced causes that are worth defending—one of those challenged hopes that are worth endeavoring to fulfill.

The conviction that there are in our society no technological imperatives, that man is still the master of the machines he creates, is indicated in the history of the continuing attempts to adjust policy to the changing methods of farming. Something comparable has been seen in the concern for preservation of small independent enterprises through the antitrust laws and other measures. This same deliberate, steady, humane shaping of policy to sustain what are considered democratic values may well become evident in virtually all areas of our rapidly changing society. If this is so, the need for values consciously held and philosophically validated is matched by the need for a constant re-examination of the changing ways by which powerful groups in our society exert their claims. The shaping of farm policy is a laboratory in which the mutual adjustment of economic compulsions and basic values can profitably be studied.

In offering these brief general reflections I do not mean to detract from the more specific attributes of Dr. Benedict's and Dr. Stine's study. The urgency of dealing with agricultural problems on the basis of actual conditions, with programs shaped to the diverse requirements of particular crops; the need of constant adjustment in programs; the degree to which unanticipated results frequently arise—these are among the considerations which Dr. Benedict and Dr. Stine suggest. Based on the thoroughgoing factual record and analysis of all the commodities in which government action has been important, the book should fill a significant gap in current agricultural studies.

AUGUST HECKSCHER, *Director*
The Twentieth Century Fund

330 WEST 42 STREET
NEW YORK 36, N. Y.
OCTOBER 1956

ACKNOWLEDGMENTS

NO BRIEF statement of acknowledgments can do justice to the many individuals who have helped with or participated in the preparation of this volume. However, a short résumé of the process by which it was developed will at least provide some general understanding of the sources of the material and of the nature and extent of the contributions made by the principal participants.

Chapters 1 and 2 are the work of Dr. Stine and his research assistant, Miss Patricia Gustafson, with some editorial revision in the later stages. Chapters 3, 4, 5 and 6 were prepared jointly by Drs. Stine and Benedict on the basis of early drafts written by Dr. Stine. The poultry and egg section of Chapter 6 is derived largely from a research memorandum prepared by Edward Karpoff of the U.S. Department of Agriculture.

Chapter 7 is based on an early manuscript, later considerably revised, which was prepared by Dr. David MacFarlane of MacDonald College, Quebec, in the summer of 1952. Chapter 8 was assembled and written by Dr. Benedict. All of Chapter 9, except the introductory section, is the work of Dr. Jerry Foytik of the Giannini Foundation of Agricultural Economics. Chapter 10 is based on a draft prepared by Dr. Stine and later revised and brought up to date by Dr. Benedict. Chapter 11 is a very severely condensed version of a much longer study prepared by Mr. Don Hammerbeg, State Milk Administrator of Connecticut. Dr. Benedict had responsibility for the final drafting of all of the chapters.

In addition to the principal participants, acknowledgment is due to many others who have assisted in one way or another. Miss Orpha Cummings, Librarian of the Giannini Foundation of Agricultural Economics, gave generous and able help in assembling needed documents and later in bringing some of the tables up to date. The excellent index of this volume, as of the other two in the series, was prepared by Dr. Elizabeth Kelley Bauer. Our thanks, and perhaps even more those of the users of the volume, are due her for her careful and painstaking work. Dr. Hans George Hirsch's criticisms and suggestions were very helpful in the revision of Chapter 7, as were also those of Dr. Boris Swerling of the Food Research Institute, Stanford University. Dr. John H. Davis, former General Manager of the National Wool Marketing Corporation, read the draft of Chapter 8 and made a number of helpful suggestions in regard to it. The authors are also indebted to Mr. Frank W. ImMasche, Mr. Reed Phillips and Mr. Walter L. Hodde, all of the U.S. Department of Agriculture, for helpful comments and suggestions with respect to that chapter.

Dr. David A. Clarke, Jr., of the Giannini Foundation was most helpful in reviewing the various drafts of Chapter 11. Many of his suggestions have been incorporated in it. Members of the Fruits and Vegetables Division, U.S. Department of Agriculture, read and criticized Chapter 9 and supplied from their unpublished records numerous corrections to the tables included in it. Many other persons in the Department of Agriculture, too numerous to mention here, were helpful in providing data, checking tables and making suggestions. Throughout, the administrators and staff of the Giannini Foundation helped in every way possible to facilitate the work and to make time available for it.

Recognition by the trustees of the Twentieth Century Fund of the need for a comprehensive survey of the experience gained in this dynamic period and their willingness to finance it made the study possible. We are deeply appreciative of the interest shown by the Fund's trustees and staff in initiating the study and of their continuing encouragement and able assistance in carrying it out.

Though these and other aids given are gratefully acknowledged the authors do not wish to imply responsibility on the part of anyone but themselves for the conclusions and analyses here presented. We have endeavored to provide an accurate and balanced account. The extent to which the results of the study fall short of that goal is, of course, a responsibility of the authors, not of those who assisted them.

MURRAY R. BENEDICT
OSCAR C. STINE

OCTOBER 1956

CONTENTS

TABLES

INTRODUCTION AND SUMMARY

Introduction and Summary

THE ECONOMIC disturbances created by World War I and the agricultural depressions of the 1920s and 1930s led to a marked change in the attitudes of farmers and the general public with respect to the role of the federal government in dealing with the problems of farmers. From 1930 on, similar changes were occurring in the relation of government to other economic groups but these lie outside the scope of this study and hence are not discussed.

Though the broad objective was that of improving farm incomes generally, most of the specific programs undertaken related to particular farm commodities, rather than to farms as economic units. Several reasons lay back of that emphasis: one, a commodity approach was considered more practical and more generally satisfying to farmers than one oriented to individuals or to the industry generally; two, the commodities and areas involved were those in which political pressure for direct and quick action was most vigorous and vocal; and, three, it was argued that if prosperity and stability could be achieved in respect to these important farm commodities, the aid thus given would strengthen the agricultural industry generally and help to some extent in the effort to revive economic activity throughout the national economy.

The policies and procedures adopted departed sharply from earlier attitudes and earlier methods of providing government aid, though most of the types of agricultural aid initiated previously were continued and strengthened. The new departures can best be described as an abandonment of the earlier policy of nonintervention in agricultural business affairs and a step in the direction of a managed and planned agricultural economy.

But neither of these changes was clearly defined or perhaps even fully accepted by those responsible for making them. In the early stages, especially from 1933 to 1935, much of the program was regarded as temporary: an emergency measure for getting agriculture into better balance with the rest of the economy, with an underlying assumption that once that was accomplished principal reliance would again be on the functioning of uncontrolled production and marketing processes.

However, the idea of continuing government intervention soon came to be widely accepted. The Soil Conservation and Domestic Allotment Act of 1936 and the Agricultural Adjustment Act of 1938 constituted a more specific recognition of the need for a continuing program to strengthen agriculture's position in an economy in which the returns to other groups were becoming less and less subject to the free play of competitive forces. Nevertheless, the free market structure and individual decisions in the production process continued to be the dominant features of American agriculture.

Government intervention has been a modifying influence rather than a substitute for earlier patterns of activity. State trading and direct government price fixing have not had any large part in the thinking of farm and congressional groups, except in wartime and even then only to the extent deemed necessary for successful prosecution of the war. However, the maintenance of high-level price supports does result in government price fixing and heavy involvement of the government in trading operations. Though that is true, it should be noted that state trading has been limited to a relatively few commodities. The agricultural markets generally have continued to be free and competitive.

Moreover, it is an oversimplification to say there was no government intervention before the 1930s. There was intervention but, without implying that the steps taken were inappropriate, the emphasis was largely negative. The government specified what could not be done, not what must be done. Much of the earlier legislation sought and obtained by the farm groups and by the general public was of that nature. Federal inspection of the slaughter of meat animals, the pure food laws and the campaign for the elimination of bovine tuberculosis were measures for the protection of consumers. The Packers and Stockyards Act, commodity exchange regulation, and the development of grain grading and federal licensing of warehouses were intended to protect farmers from exploitation, not to prescribe in detail how and by whom such businesses might be conducted. Some of these earlier programs were in the nature of aids to be used, rejected or ignored by the farmer as he might choose; among them were such services as crop and price reporting, agricultural research and extension education, and disease and pest control.

Though the new programs went considerably farther in the direction of government guidance or control they never were extended to all of American agriculture and, for the most part, rigorous and compulsory controls were applied in a somewhat gingerly way even to the crops and areas where these techniques were regarded as most appropriate and acceptable. The traditional preference of farmers, and of the American public generally, for freedom to produce, process, sell or buy with a minimum of government interference was still very strong though farmers were coming to be more and more skeptical of the merits of a completely unregulated, competitive system for agriculture—the more so since many types of business and most labor groups were clearly moving toward self-imposed or governmental restraints on competition.

Effects of Depression and War

The depression decade did not provide a favorable setting for the expected reversion to freer trading and unregulated production. The long period of substandard prices and business activity tended instead to enlarge and consolidate the areas and types of control. The 1940s provided economic opportunities for relaxation of controls but at the same time brought into effect price guarantees and other measures that farmers were reluctant to relinquish, even when prices and incomes were at highly satisfactory levels. These measures in turn operated to inhibit the types of readjustment that would have made possible a retreat from intervention on the part of the government without creating price and income problems that many of the farm groups were unwilling to face.

The result was a continuance of extensive government participation in the production and marketing processes relating to some commodities, notably cotton, wheat, tobacco, rice and some of the dairy products, and almost complete reversion to pre-1930s marketing and pricing procedures for a large part of the agricultural industry, including such major segments as beef cattle, hogs, poultry and most of the minor perishable crops. As of this writing, the issues are still in controversy. Strong political groups are seeking to reverse the drift toward greater reliance on competition and unregulated prices while other strong political groups, and economic forces, are working in the direction of removing or modifying some of the governmental restraints and guarantees now in effect. The outcome almost certainly will not be a return to the marketing and production policies of the pre-1930s era. In keeping with the almost worldwide trend toward increased protection of the individual against the vicissitudes of price and income declines that are beyond his control, it seems clear that some form of price and income support will be retained at least for the politically important crops.

The principal subject of controversy is the level of such supports, not whether supports shall or shall not be provided. No important political group advocates complete abandonment of safeguards against disastrously low prices for farm products. One school of thought would look to the maintenance of price floors, allowing considerable leeway for automatic adjustments to determine the actual level of prices received, while the other favors the maintenance through positive government action of "satisfactory" prices, together with strong controls on production which would adjust it to approximately the amounts that can be sold at the prices specified.[1] There is also controversy over the methods by which either of these types of support shall be made effective. Nonrecourse loan programs, government purchases, export subsidies, supplementary payments, acreage and marketing controls, and even reliance on general monetary and fiscal policies, are advocated or opposed.

For some few products, notably fluid milk, a continuing program of regulated marketing without subsidy but with federal or state control

1. Or, alternatively, procedures for letting products flow onto the market at lower prices with government payments making up the difference. There are, of course, many variants of these positions, which, for the sake of simplicity, are here stated in somewhat extreme form.

seems to have become well established over much of the country. This differs from similar procedures developed prior to 1933 mainly in that Secretary's orders or state legislation bring all producers and handlers into the system whereas participation was on a voluntary basis before the government programs were initiated. In some of the state-controlled markets the prices to consumers are also established by the control agencies, but the prices so established do not appear to differ greatly from those arrived at in the federally controlled markets or where no government control exists. For a few of the minor crops, including some of the perishables, similar programs have been developed and have achieved some standing but they do not appear to be so well established or so generally accepted as those in the fluid milk markets.

Farm Price Policy Not Settled or Consistent

Thus it is apparent that farm price-support policy in the United States is far from being settled or consistent. Further modifications and changes of direction can be expected in the years ahead. The direction of change will no doubt be considerably influenced by the nature of the supply-demand balance that develops as a result of government action and natural forces. If demand continues strong, as in the past fifteen years, and if weather conditions should prove less favorable, prices might be high enough to reduce the pressure for government intervention and encourage a return to increased reliance on traditional production and marketing procedures.

On the other hand, any serious setback in business activity or a continuing surplus will undoubtedly sustain or strengthen the demand for government action to support farm prices. In that event, the controversial issue will probably be whether to support prices in the market and attempt to deal with a continuing problem of excess stocks or to supplement returns to farmers by means of direct government subsidies (as is currently being done in Britain) or, alternatively, to introduce more rigorous and coercive controls on production. A third approach which seems to be emerging is that of attempting to speed the transfer of production resources out of agriculture, by means of "soil-bank" retirements of crop land not needed currently and encouragement to farm manpower to move into other and presumably more profitable types of employment.

Whatever direction is taken, it seems clear that agriculture will not be left so completely at the mercy of chance fluctuations in demand and supply as it was before the 1930s. Almost certainly some provision for the retention of price floors will be continued whether these be at high or low levels. There will probably be some device for absorbing and later releasing redundant supplies that arise from temporary upsurges in yield and production. In addition, the government seems firmly committed, on a bipartisan basis, to a vigorous effort to maintain substantially full employment and high demand and to reopen where feasible the external markets for U.S. farm products.

Experience Gained a Valuable Asset

In deciding on future policy, there is much to be learned from the rich and varied experience of the period here described in attempting to strengthen and stabilize the American agricultural economy. Even the most cursory survey of that experience makes it evident that some of the procedures have worked better than others and that a method which works reasonably well for one commodity may be quite impractical or unsatisfactory for others. It is apparent too that all of the procedures used in that period give rise to difficult problems of administration, of equity as between groups of producers, of fairness to consumers and taxpayers, and of relationships with other governments and with other producing and consuming areas.

It is with a view to making available in compact and convenient form the record of this mammoth experiment in economic management for one of the nation's largest industries that this book and the companion volume [2] have been written. Even so extensive a survey as this cannot, of course, describe in detail such a far-reaching, varied and changing program, extending over a period of more than twenty years and affecting dozens of different products and hundreds of thousands of farms and farmers. The attempt instead has been to trace the activities relating to the various commodities in broad outline and to bring out the more significant lessons that may be drawn from them. Many persons have helped with the task,[3] some by preparing research memoranda which have been used in writing the various chapters, others by supplying needed data and others by reading and criticizing the drafts of individual chapters at various stages in their preparation.

Necessarily, the authors have had to select, interpret and analyse the data as they see them. Others may arrive at different interpretations and conclusions and later, more detailed studies benefiting from a longer perspective may lead to modifications which the authors themselves would be quite willing to accept. However, it is hoped that the factual record here presented will contribute to a more informed and logical approach to the farm problem in the years immediately ahead. That must be the warrant for a study undertaken while the experiment is still under way and before the hand has been played out.

The authors have not approached the problem as advocates of some particular policy or procedure but rather have sought to describe and explain the pertinent events and actions. It is hoped that the account may be useful to all of those charged with the responsibility of shaping

2. Murray R. Benedict, *Can We Solve the Farm Problem?: An Analysis of Federal Aid to Agriculture,* Twentieth Century Fund, New York, 1955.

3. See "Acknowledgments," pp. vii-viii.

the farm policies of the future even though their personal attitudes and philosophies may differ markedly and may lead to different conclusions. The aim has been also to provide a readable and nontechnical summary for the reader interested only in obtaining a better understanding of this complex and important group of problems.

The present volume assumes some knowledge on the part of the reader of the many institutional arrangements set up to carry out the various programs. These are described in the companion volume, *Can We Solve the Farm Problem?: An Analysis of Federal Aid to Agriculture*.[4] Obviously such descriptions could not be included on a commodity-by-commodity basis without extensive and wearisome repetition. Such agencies as the Federal Farm Board, the Agricultural Adjustment Administration, the Commodity Credit Corporation and the Soil Conservation Service played a part in many different commodity programs. The legislation authorizing them, their forms of organization and their methods of operation are reported on in the companion volume and are referred to only incidentally in the analyses given here.

THE PROGRAMS AND THEIR RESULTS

Since many readers may find the great number of products and types of aid confusing, the following brief summary is intended as a guide to the chapters of this volume. The reasons for the actions taken and the descriptions of conditions in the various markets and producing areas can, of course, be obtained only from the more extended discussions in the commodity chapters themselves.

Most of the commodity programs relate to three quite different sets of conditions: (1) a period of deep depression with a heavy excess of production, very low prices and acute distress in the farm areas; (2) the war period when prices and production were high and when the principal emphasis was on increased production rather than on curtailment; and (3) a postwar period of general prosperity and relatively high farm prices when, however, production was beginning to outrun consumption, giving rise to fears of another depression in agriculture despite unprecedentedly high levels of employment and national income, and when the need for extensive readjustment in the kinds and amounts of production was beginning to be apparent.

The devices used fall roughly into six categories: (1) attempts to create an improved system of marketing based on producer-controlled cooperative marketing agencies; (2) holding operations designed to stabilize the flow of nonperishables onto the market; (3) efforts to cut back and hold down farm production with a view to bringing supplies into better adjustment with demand; (4) measures designed to transfer buying power from consumers or the Treasury to the farm groups; (5)

4. See note 2.

marketing agreements intended to stabilize the industry and strengthen prices; and (6) efforts to hold prices up to the high levels achieved during the war and postwar years by means of government loans and purchases. Included with these were various supplementary programs having for the most part similar or related objectives. Among them were such measures as export subsidies, the food stamp plan, incentives for increased production in the war years, and soil conservation payments made for the purpose of transferring income, adjusting production and building up soils.

For some of the commodities, several or even most of these devices were used or tried. For others only one or two were considered appropriate and workable. For a few, principally the beef cattle industry, no large-scale program was undertaken, excepting emergency purchase of cattle in the drought areas in the 1930s.

Cotton and the Cotton Programs

In the period here under review extensive and important changes were occurring in the cotton-producing areas. Some resulted from the specific programs undertaken by the government, others from forces that would have affected the industry profoundly even if there had been no direct intervention by the government. The two together brought about more significant readjustments and shifts in cotton production than had occurred in the nearly three quarters of a century between the close of the Civil War and the launching of the New Deal programs.

In the decades just prior to 1930, a cotton surplus was beginning to develop. It became more evident and serious as a result of the sharp reduction in cotton consumption in the early years of the depression. The first efforts to deal with it through the Farm Board's Cotton Stabilization Corporation were palliative and had no very significant effect on the industry. The failure of that program, however, contributed to the adoption of the more vigorous and positive programs of the succeeding years. It had become apparent that, without rigorous controls, the industry would produce more cotton than could be sold at prices that would sustain any acceptable level of prosperity in the cotton areas of the Southeast. From the time of the Civil War that region had been in a state of almost chronic depression because of the heavy reliance on cotton, the low price of that commodity and the underemployment of its labor.

The government's cotton program in the early years involved vigorous efforts to cut back acreage and production. These were soon supplemented by loan programs designed to maintain prices at levels well above those that would have prevailed in the absence of acreage controls and loans. These methods proved moderately effective so long as the loan rates were not put so high as to prevent movement of the cotton. Cash receipts from the sale of cotton were increased substantially and, in addition, sizable government payments were made to the growers. Cotton acreage was cut back some 20 per cent in 1933 and was further reduced in later years. By the early 1950s the acreage grown was not much more than half as large as in the late 1920s and early 1930s, but about as much cotton was being produced as before.

The program was considerably modified from 1936 on as a result of the invalidation of parts of the Agricultural Adjustment Act of 1933. That action eliminated the rigorous and relatively effective acreage and production controls established under the 1933 act and the supplementing Bankhead Cotton Control Act. In 1937 a sizable increase in acreage and a large yield resulted in the production of a 19-million-bale crop. This was far more than the market would absorb at prices comparable with those that had been maintained under the programs of the earlier years.

The Commodity Credit Corporation then became the major factor in preventing a new and serious price slump. It acquired nearly a third of the crop and also took over substantial quantities from the 1938 crop. Most of this accumulation was carried over under loan or in government ownership until the end of World War II. The operation was similar in nature to the acquisitions of the Farm Board's Cotton Stabilization Corporation but on a larger scale and with more adequate and more flexible financing which made possible a much longer period of withholding and liquidation.

The upsurge of production in 1937 led to congressional action to re-establish provisions for rigorous controls on acreage and for quotas on marketings, these being now more broadly applicable than the specific legislation for cotton and tobacco in the earlier legislation. Plantings were held in check during the war years by the strong demand for other farm products and the shortage of labor, but little progress was made in liquidating the large carry-over from the late 1930s. In the early postwar years unexpectedly strong demand coupled with a very moderate level of production led not only to a rapid reduction of stocks but to a sharp increase in price. By 1948, nearly all of the CCC inventories and loan commitments had been closed out. However, the high level of price support maintained, declining prices for competing products and record yields gave rise to a substantial increase in production and a new build-up of excess stocks, mostly in the hands of the Commodity Credit Corporation. The industry was again faced with the prospect of a period of heavy carry-overs and glutted markets.

The gloomy outlook of early 1949 and 1950 led to the reimposition of acreage controls in 1950. This coupled with lower yields and a sharp increase in demand in the summer of 1950 led to a severe shortage of cotton supplies throughout the world in 1950–51. Prices went to all-time highs and it became necessary to ration supplies to domestic mills and to foreign buyers. However, the tight supply situation was short-lived.

Acreage controls were abandoned for the 1951 and 1952 seasons and production increased substantially. No serious disposal problems arose until 1953, but from then on through 1955 the size of cotton holdings in the hands of CCC or under loan to it became a matter of serious concern.

Acreage and marketing controls were reimposed in 1954 and 1955 and the situation appeared for a time to be stabilizing. However, the August 1, 1955 carry-over was up to 11.1 million bales, about the same as the heavy stock held in 1945, which was approximately equal to a full year's domestic consumption and exports. On top of this, the yield in 1955 was phenomenally high (over 400 pounds per acre, which was more than double the customary yields of the early 1930s).

The cotton problem, though less acute and perplexing than that in wheat, had again come to be of major concern in the management of U.S. production and stocks. The situation was similar to that of the late 1930s except that the domestic and world economies were far more healthy and active than in the pre-World War II period. Downward revision of price supports to improve the competitive position of U.S. cotton in the world markets, foreign sales at loss-taking prices or further severe cutbacks in acreage appeared to be in prospect.

Collateral Effects of the Cotton Program

Though this simple and brief account of the main features of the cotton program gives a general idea of its nature and scope, it does not explain or describe important and more lasting effects of the government activities relating to cotton. The acreage grown was reduced and stabilized. By 1941 it was some 13.5 million acres smaller than in 1932, a reduction of about 37 per cent. In the postwar years the acreages planted remained at or near the 1941 level. Most of the reduction occurred in the older cotton states, an area that had long been too heavily dependent on a one-crop agriculture. It made possible and attractive a shift toward a better-balanced and more diversified agriculture which now seems to be sufficiently well established to constitute a permanent and desirable change. Incomes in one of the lowest-income segments of agriculture were increased and funds were made available for needed investment in agriculture and for improvements in methods of production. Some progress was made in the consolidation of undesirably small farming units.

These results did not all flow from the cotton program. Some were due to forces that would have made their influence felt anyway. Increased industrial activity provided jobs for excess labor; the war created new job opportunities and drew men off into the army and the war industries. The continuance of high employment and prosperity in the postwar years added strength and continuity to that movement. But along with these, there were significant influences that grew out of the program itself. The curtailment of cotton acreage freed land for other uses and thus provided strong incentives for more diversified types of agriculture. The soil conservation program provided education, guidance and financial incentives for significant efforts to check and reverse the long downward trend in the quality and fertility of the soils of the area.

These almost certainly are more important and lasting achievements than the direct price and income changes brought about by the program. However, the actions taken by the government were apparently a significant stabilizing influence especially in periods when supplies suddenly became overabundant as in 1937 and when demand slacked off quickly as in 1938. While these very considerable achievements on the plus side must be recognized, there are, of course, some offsetting disadvantages. The levels of price support maintained have probably had some adverse effect on the position of U.S. cotton in the world markets and on the competitive relationships with synthetic fibers. As of this writing, heavy stocks of cotton are still on hand and their liquidation seems likely to be both difficult and expensive. Also, it must be conceded that the transition to a sounder type of agriculture in the older cotton belt states is by no means complete and that the money costs of the changes brought about have been heavy. They would have been heavier if wartime and postwar inflation had not made possible the liquidation at a profit of stocks that might otherwise have resulted in heavy losses.

Nevertheless, the cotton program seems to have achieved a more genuine and lasting readjustment in southern agriculture than any other of the many farm programs undertaken in that area. The difficulties in the way of modifications needed to overcome the most evident defects of the program do not seem as formidable as in some of the other commodity programs.

The Tobacco Program

The tobacco program was similar in many ways to the one for cotton. Both involved rigorous controls on production in the early period. Both pertain to types of agriculture in which incomes are and have been notoriously low. Both resulted in rather substantial increases in the incomes of growers. The differences appear more largely in the over-all effects of the programs on the areas concerned.

Whereas the cotton program contributed to rather significant changes in the structure and character of the agriculture of the cotton states, no similar change can be attributed to the tobacco program. The acreages in tobacco usually are too small for even large percentage decreases or increases to affect importantly the nature of the farming enterprise as a whole or the agricultural activities of the region. The program has, in fact, tended to reduce individual acreages grown, to increase the number of small-scale producers and probably to lessen the efficiency of production. A collateral effect which has led to considerable criticism is the tendency for tobacco allotment rights to be capitalized into the values or rentals of the lands concerned, thus becoming vested rights that tend to defeat the program's original purpose of channeling more buying power into the hands of the operating tobacco producers.

On the other hand, the tobacco program has proved relatively effective in raising and maintaining prices and its cost to the federal government has not been high. Processors undoubtedly have paid higher prices than they would have done had there been no program. Owing to the peculiarities of the industry and the large portion of the consumer price that consists of taxes it is difficult to demonstrate conclusively that the program has resulted in significantly higher prices to consumers. Objections arise more from unwillingness to accept the principle of providing government collaboration in the maintenance of a producer monopoly than from actual demonstrated adverse effects on the consumer. It is, of course, generally recognized that the buyers of tobacco have long had bargaining advantages because of the concentration of tobacco processing in the hands of a very small number of firms which could therefore use monopolistic power in their dealings with the growers.

The success of the program has been to some extent due to the very rapid increase in the consumption of tobacco, particularly in the cigarette industry. Also, because it is based on historical price relationships, the program has introduced some maladjustments into the price relationships of the different types of tobacco. The conclusions here stated apply mainly to the flue-cured and burley types. The programs adopted have tended to keep the dark tobaccos overpriced and overexpanded as compared with the flue-cured and burley types, for which demand was increasing. Were it not for political considerations, maladjustments of that kind probably could be fairly easily corrected. On the whole, the tobacco program seems to be rather firmly established and to have strong congressional and grower support.

Wheat Program One of the Most Troublesome

The wheat program was originally conceived in terms similar to those relating to cotton. The underlying problem here also was one of heavy oversupply, large accumulations and low prices. The original plan of curtailing acreage was largely inoperative during the middle 1930s because of very severe droughts that reduced production even more than was contemplated by those in charge of the program. Except for some build-up of excess stocks in the late 1930s, the problem did not become serious until well after the close of World War II. Heavy war and post-war demand made full production and a considerable expansion of acreage desirable. Demand was sufficiently strong to absorb at good prices all that could be produced.

When the wartime and reconstruction demand eased off in the late 1940s, the true nature of the problem began to emerge more clearly.

A considerable downward adjustment of wheat acreage was undoubtedly needed but the wartime guarantees, based on price relationships of the pre-World War I period, overpriced wheat in comparison with other farm products. Costs of production had been reduced much more than for most other farm commodities. Furthermore, the lands shifted into wheat production had few alternative uses and reversion to grass and livestock involved very heavy costs to the growers.

The price supports guaranteed in the war period and continued thereafter provided strong incentives for continuing to produce wheat on a scale comparable to that of the war and early postwar years. Consequently, there was strong resistance to the making of needed adjustments and extensive political support for the positions taken by the grower groups. At the same time, yields continued high and even increased, thus tending to offset such adjustments in acreage as were made.

The result was a continuing build-up of stocks in the hands of the Commodity Credit Corporation and increasing concern as to how these stocks were to be liquidated. Acreage controls were instituted in 1954 and 1955 but high yields caused production still to be somewhat in excess of requirements for bread use, exports, and normal feed and seed use. The unbalance on the production side had been reduced but not eliminated. The problem of liquidating a billion bushels or more of CCC-owned wheat still remained.

It was complicated by rapid recovery in the agricultural economies of the major wheat-consuming countries and similar oversupplies in competing wheat-exporting countries. Heavy subsidies on U.S. exports were being provided by way of the International Wheat Agreement and some wheat was being made available for disaster relief abroad, but the liquidation and adjustment problems still were among the most perplexing ones facing government administrators as of the end of 1955.

In the wheat areas, no significant, constructive influence on the overall agricultural economy, similar to that noted for cotton, had been exerted. The wheat areas were, in fact, more out of balance and more vulnerable to adverse weather conditions than when the program was started. There were, of course, important and justifiable reasons for the difference. Cotton acreage was not expanded in the war years as a means of furthering the national war program. Also, most of its major acreage adjustment had been carried out in the 1930s.

Nevertheless, the continuing overstimulation of wheat production in areas particularly prone to drought was creating a danger to wheat producers themselves as well as a perplexing problem for the government and its administrative agencies. Price guarantees could not provide much help to the farmer whose wheat crop failed. The fixed level of price support was in fact likely to increase income instability rather than to lessen it. As of 1955, no considerable progress had been made in the solution of this difficult problem. Wheat acreage still was excessive, inactive stocks were high and the prospects of a receptive foreign market for the excess were not bright. The cost of the program had been high, some $2 billion between 1930 and 1953, with other large losses already incurred or in prospect.

Oilseed Programs Diverse and Costly

Government intervention in the oilseed industries and markets has been extensive and relatively high in cost. Much of it came about because of the cutting off of supplies from the Pacific area and the increased requirements resulting from war. Peanuts, however, were handled under one or another type of government program nearly all through the 1930s, beginning with 1934. The interrelationship between peanuts and cotton in some areas has made for increased pressure on the peanut markets when cotton production was cut back and for an easier situation in peanuts when conditions were favorable for an increase in cotton acreage.

The principal objective of the depression decade programs was to protect and stabilize the market for "edible" nuts, that is, for nuts used as peanuts, not as peanut oil. That market is relatively inelastic. Hence any considerable increase in the supply of nuts flowing into it could reduce prices drastically. Efforts were therefore centered on holding out of the edible nut market quantities in excess of the amounts that market would absorb at prices considered acceptable. The remainder was diverted to the much wider vegetable oil market by means of diversion purchases, two-price arrangements and other devices. Conservation payments were made for diverting land from peanut production and, later, acreage allotments and marketing quotas were used in the effort to hold down production.

War conditions made an expansion of peanut production desirable and the wartime programs were designed to stimulate output rather than to restrain it. The need for more vegetable oils also resulted in an equalizing of the prices paid for peanuts used for oil with the prices of those for direct use as edible nuts. The price of peanuts for oil was held high in the early postwar years by the shortage of vegetable oils in western Europe and the strong export demand for U.S. supplies.

Production controls were again put into effect in 1949 with a view to speeding the adjustment necessitated by the decline of western European demand. Price supports were continued at about the wartime levels in terms of parity. By that time CCC purchases were the principal method of support. Though acreage was cut back in 1948 and much more sharply in 1949, CCC losses were heavy on the 1948 crop. They were reduced to moderate levels by the early 1950s. However, a heavy oversupply of vegetable oils as a whole resulted in large CCC losses on peanuts in fiscal 1954 ($23.5 million).

Nearly all of the various methods of price support were applied in the peanut programs of the 1930s and 1940s. Purchase and resale for diversion to oil was the method most widely used. While that procedure worked out rather smoothly, it was an expensive one for the government and its apparent effectiveness was due rather largely to the abnormal demand for vegetable oils during the years 1942–1947. The efforts to meet the problem by means of a two-price plan which would take account of the lower value of nuts used for oil proved unsatisfactory to both growers and government administrators. By 1955 the situation had reverted to one much like that of the late 1930s, with peanuts grown chiefly for edible nut use and with principal reliance on acreage allotments and marketing quotas as a method of maintaining prices at relatively high levels without incurring heavy losses to CCC on its price-support operations.

The programs relating to the other oilseed crops were, in the main, a result of the strong demand for vegetable oils that developed in the war years. Cottonseed became important as a source of oil and the channeling of seed into that use was encouraged. However, the amount of seed produced was not greatly affected, for the output of seed is related to the amount of cotton grown. Since cotton was not in short supply, there was little reason to expand production except as a means of increasing oil supplies.

In the early postwar years, the price of cottonseed was above support levels and disposal of supplies presented no serious problems. With price support at a high level, surpluses began to appear in the 1951 season and continued through the 1952, 1953 and 1954 seasons despite a sizable reduction in the level of support in 1953. Heavy losses on CCC purchases were incurred in fiscal 1954 and 1955 on stocks that had been building up since 1952.

Soybeans have become in recent years the most important vegetable oil crop in the United States. However, the large increase of the 1930s came about without government aid. No price-support program for soybeans was inaugurated until 1941 and then it was for the purpose of increasing production of soybean oil, not primarily as an aid to farmers. During the war years, soybean production was increased and prices were stabilized though at rather high cost to the government. However, the government subsidy resulted mainly from government purchases at higher than ceiling prices and resale at ceiling prices, as a means of keeping prices stable. Thus it can be regarded as primarily a consumer subsidy or war expense.

Soybean prices rose above support levels after decontrol and continued above for the first two years following the war. Because of the strong export demand, no serious problems arose in supporting and stabilizing the price during the years 1949–1953, though production was high. There was some accumulation of stocks thereafter but no large loss had resulted as of the time of this writing. However, were it not for the support of the vegetable oil market through CCC purchases of cottonseed oil, the soybean support program would undoubtedly have given more trouble and resulted in larger losses.

The flaxseed price-support program was also primarily a wartime operation. As a stimulator of production it was not too successful in the war years. There was no serious problem of price support for flaxseed during the late 1940s. Demand was strong, prices were above support levels and production was higher than in 1945. The level of price support was reduced in 1950 and 1951 and raised again in 1952.

The 1953 acreage was increased in spite of government recommendations that it be cut by 10 to 15 per cent. As a consequence, price-support operations for the 1953–54 season resulted in a loss of more than $50 million. The support level was reduced to 70 per cent of parity in 1954, but further increases in acreage and production resulted in another heavy loss ($23 million) on that year's operations. A further reduction in support level (to 60 per cent of parity) was made in 1955, but acreage continued at about the high 1948 and 1949 levels because of the continuing pressure for reduction in the acreage sown to wheat, a competing crop. Flax production still appeared to be somewhat out of balance but probably not enough to cause serious difficulties in making the acreage adjustments needed.

Corn and Livestock Programs Only Moderately Effective

The principal market for corn consists of the livestock to which it is fed. Since more than two thirds of the corn grown is fed on the farms where it is produced, controls applied at the marketing stage for corn as grain tend not to be overly effective. It is also difficult to apply and enforce acreage allotments or marketing quotas since the crop does not have to pass through ginning or marketing processes such as those used for cotton, tobacco and wheat, where marketing quotas can be made effective. Because of these peculiarities of the industry the control programs for corn have been both milder and less effective than for some of the other crops.

No specific programs relating to corn and hogs were undertaken in the Farm Board period. When the Roosevelt administration came into power in 1933 both corn and hogs were in long supply and prices were very low. Though some effort was made to curtail the acreage and production of corn, it was soon recognized that the corn and hog economies were so closely interrelated that they must be handled together. Furthermore, it was apparent that it would be impossible to raise enough money from processing taxes on corn to carry out an effective program relating to corn alone. The early program adopted was therefore a joint one, designed to reduce quickly the hog population as well as the production of corn. The principal source of funds for carrying it out was to be a processing tax on hogs.

By means of a pig-sow slaughter campaign and special relief purchases of hogs and pork, the hog population was reduced moderately and corn production was cut back to some extent though not as much as planned. Corn prices strengthened somewhat in the fall of 1933, partly because of a smaller crop but also because production of other coarse grains had been severely diminished by droughts. There was some expectation that crop controls would become more effective in 1934 and also that farm prices generally would improve. The hog market took on a somewhat better tone though prices did not improve much until the following year.

The most important feature of the 1933 corn program from the standpoint of its effect on later farm programs was the nonrecourse loan arrangement announced by the Commodity Credit Corporation in the fall of 1933. Provision was made whereby farmers could obtain loans on corn sealed on the farm at levels that were higher than the prices then prevailing in the market. If the price later rose above the loan rate, the farmer could pay off the loan and reclaim the corn. If the price remained below the loan level, he could surrender the corn to the Corporation and the Corporation would absorb the loss on it. The plan worked out unexpectedly well owing largely to the severe drought of 1934. Corn prices advanced sharply in 1934 and most of the corn loans were repaid, the corn being repossessed and fed on the farms where grown. The operation not only put much-needed cash into the corn areas in 1933 but also served to some extent as a stabilizer of feed supplies. The success of this first nonrecourse loan program led to much wider use of that device in later years.

During the years 1934–1936 droughts plus the program for restraining hog and corn production, and some general improvement in demand, brought corn and hog supplies and demand into better balance. The Supreme Court's decision of January 1936 which invalidated the main features of the Agricultural Adjustment Act brought to an end this first phase of the corn-hog program. Thereafter, until World War II, main reliance was on soil conservation payments made as inducements for a reduction of corn acreage and on such support of prices as could be provided (for corn, not for hogs) through the nonrecourse loan procedure of the Commodity Credit Corporation.

During the same period some assistance was given to the livestock industry of the western states by extensive purchases of starving animals in the severely depleted range areas. This, however, was an emergency program and did not develop into any continuing arrangement for giving aid to the growers of livestock.

The drought of 1936 reduced corn supplies so much that stocks were seriously deficient and the price rose to a dollar a bushel. The permitted re-expansion of wheat and cotton kept corn acreage down in 1937 and there was no important recurrence of surpluses until 1938 when CCC began to accumulate stocks under its nonrecourse loan program.

Though acreage allotments were continued for corn grown in the "commercial" corn areas and some moderate downward adjustment was achieved, yield increases kept production above planned levels. More and more the main reliance for aid to corn growers was on CCC's nonrecourse loan program. The result was a heavy build-up of CCC holdings, which reached its peak in 1940. A burdensome stock situation appeared to be in the making but the onset of war turned these troublesome stocks into an asset.

Yields were good throughout the war years and no important new problems arose until 1948 when the mandatory 90 per cent of parity loan program started off a new period of heavy accumulations by CCC. By October 1950 they had reached a record level of 650 million bushels, including loans and commitments. However, nongovernmental holdings were declining and the 1950 and 1951 crops were somewhat smaller. This, together with the upsurge in demand caused by the war in Korea, made possible some reduction in holdings though they were still high at the end of 1951.

Larger crops in 1952 and 1953 carried CCC commitments to a new high of 760 million bushels. Acreage allotments were re-established in 1954 but CCC stocks continued to increase, reaching about 900 million bushels by October 1, 1955, while total carry-over amounted to more than a billion bushels. As of the beginning of 1956 some reduction in the level of support appeared to be in prospect and special efforts were being made to reduce the overabundant stocks. The rate of accumulation had been slowed but production and use still were not fully in balance. The situation did not appear to be unmanageable, however, provided needed adjustments in the program could be made and if, as might well happen, weather conditions should prove less favorable for a year or two.

For livestock there were no important governmental programs after the drought-area purchases of the middle 1930s except the price-support, price-control and feed subsidy programs of the war years. After decontrol livestock prices moved up to well above parity and remained high until the wartime price-support guarantees expired. Beef cattle prices fell off sharply in 1949 but moved up again in 1950 and 1951. A new wave of selling and further liquidation of the large beef cattle inventory occurred in 1953 but did not result in any large-scale intervention by the government in the beef economy. Grower sentiment on the whole was not favorable to government interference in the cattle industry.

The Butter and Cheese and Poultry and Egg Programs

The principal government programs relating to butter, cheese and poultry and eggs were an outgrowth of the war, except for a rather limited operation in butter during the Farm Board period and sizable relief purchases carried out during the 1930s, mostly with Section 32 funds. The distortions created by the abnormal demand of the war period were responsible for much of the difficulty encountered in manufactured dairy products in the early 1950s. The problems that developed in the butter industry would no doubt have arisen anyway but they were advanced in time and made more acute by the shifts that occurred during the war years.

The full employment and high incomes of that period enabled a great many families to buy more and better food than they had been able to buy previously, and military requirements were high. Fluid milk consumption increased markedly, thus reducing the availability of butter for which the demand also increased. As a result, margarine came into far wider use than before. Later (in 1950), the virtual elimination of the federal tax on colored margarine and some easing of state restrictions on its sale and use, together with improvements in the product itself, increased the shift. Many people who had become accustomed to using margarine when butter was in short supply and severely rationed continued to use the cheaper product now that their prejudice against it had been broken down. Consequently the butter industry found itself in a greatly changed competitive situation, with a sharply curtailed market for its product.

Other major changes created postwar problems for the industry. A large dried milk and dried egg capacity had been built up as a means of supplying lend-lease and military requirements. This left a heritage of overequipped plants, changed marketing patterns and government commitments to support prices. Whereas the dairy industry had been heavily subsidized during the war in an effort to induce larger production, there was now a need for rapid cutbacks that could not be easily made.

A considerable part of the expanded capacity for dried milk production should logically have been looked upon as a war cost and written off promptly as were many of the factories built to produce guns, tanks and so on. However, the price supports required by law, which treated nearly all of the farm products in a uniform way, resulted in continuous overstimulation of dried milk and dried egg production in the postwar years. The Secretary of Agriculture did not have authority to reduce the level of support on dried milk until 1950. By that time, burdensome and costly accumulations were beginning to build up. Until then, the great need for relief shipments to Europe and the liberal funds provided by the U.S. government for this purpose helped to keep stocks down to manageable proportions.

The support level was reduced in 1950 but stocks continued to be embarrassingly heavy. Abnormal types of disposal, some of them very wasteful, were resorted to but dried milk still was proving an expensive and troublesome feature of the farm program as late as 1955.

The dried egg problem was similar to that in dried milk. The industry was greatly expanded during the war years and the price guarantees caused it to continue in an overexpanded condition for some years after the close of the war. The price-support operations proved even more expensive than those relating to dried milk but were brought to a close at an earlier date. The program was liquidated in 1953.

While much of the heavy postwar cost of the dried egg program was a hangover from the war years when dried eggs constituted a very important part of the food shipments to Britain, it could and should have been brought under control much sooner than it was. The later operations were wasteful as well as very expensive. However, the fault lay largely in the legislation rather than in the administration of the program. No large outlet for dried eggs exists in peacetime. The mandatory continuance of high price supports until 1950 brought into being quantities that had to be disposed of in one way or another. In some of the years, wasteful and uneconomic methods of disposal were the only ones available. The continuance for so long a period of a heavily expanded war industry was as illogical as a similar operation in the production of army uniforms or guns and tanks would have been.

There is reason to think that egg producers would have found it about as easy to make needed readjustments soon after the war as in the early 1950s when the discontinuance of the program made such action necessary. When free of wartime disturbances or extreme depression the industry has shown great ability to make relatively quick adjustments in output and it has been operating fairly smoothly without government assistance since 1953.

Serious problems did not arise in the government's butter and cheese operations until well after the close of World War II. When heavy accumulations began to pile up in 1953 and 1954 the butter and cheese inventory soon became one of the most discussed and expensive features of the farm program. These products, unlike cotton and wheat, could not be held indefinitely and the type of storage required was expensive. The level of price support was reduced from 90 per cent of parity to 75 per cent in April 1954, probably a year later than it should have been. Strenuous efforts to reduce the burdensome stocks were made especially in the 1955 season. The large government holdings were reduced substantially by donations at home and abroad and sales at reduced prices. The situation so far as the federal government was concerned was brought into better balance. However, there were still difficult problems to be faced by the industry. Further readjustments in price relationships as among the various manufactured dairy products seemed likely to be necessary and probably some downward adjustment in production. It seemed unlikely that exports could be maintained at or near the levels attained in 1955–56 without continuing resort to dumping operations that were bound to be disturbing to friendly relations with other butter producing and exporting countries. For cheese, the situation was somewhat similar to that of butter though less acute. The industry was not faced with a rapid shift of demand to a substitute product but would of course be affected by any general decline in the price of and demand for butter.

Program for a Deficit Crop—Sugar

The problems and the program with respect to sugar differed materially from those of most of the other farm products. Here there was no domestic surplus in the ordinary sense. The United States had long been a deficit area, heavily dependent on foreign supplies drawn mostly from Cuba. Until 1934, the principal and almost the only form of government aid provided was that afforded by the tariff. In an effort to raise prices to U.S. growers the tariff on sugar was increased sharply in the 1920s and in 1930. That approach not only proved ineffective as a means of raising and stabilizing prices to U.S. growers; it resulted in serious distortions of the whole sugar economy including that of Cuba, a country in which the United States had important strategic, economic and political interests.

For reasons more fully stated in Chapter 7, the most severe impact of the increased tariff on sugar was on the Cuban sugar economy. Instead of raising prices in the United States its main effect was to lower the returns to Cuban growers. In addition, it caused a rapid expansion of production in the U.S. offshore areas, Hawaii, Puerto Rico and, at that time, the Philippine Islands. The program adopted in 1934 was designed in part to overcome these difficulties while providing to U.S. mainland growers at least as much support and stabilizing influence as had been afforded by the tariff.

Quotas on imports to the U.S. mainland were established with a view to stabilizing supplies and prices within that area. In addition, an excise tax was levied on all sugar used by the American public, the proceeds to be used in benefit and adjustment payments to U.S. sugar growers. The tariff on imported sugar was reduced but the quotas applied placed limits on the amounts that could be imported. The effect was to stabilize the supplies available to U.S. mainland consumers, to strengthen the Cuban economy and to check the rapid shift of production from Cuba to the U.S. offshore areas.

The excise tax and benefit payment program seems not to have materially increased the returns to U.S. growers. It has, however, made available some funds for encouraging adjustments in acreage and production if that should become desirable. As of 1955, the effects on U.S. mainland production had not been large. However, the benefit payment provision did make possible the establishment of economic incentives for complying with the minimum-wage and child labor provisions contained in the legislation.

Strategic considerations have played an important role in the shaping of the program. Cuba is the closest and most important offshore producing area. Since the U.S. mainland is, and will probably continue to be, heavily dependent on Cuba for a good portion of its supplies, it is considered important to help maintain a strong and healthy sugar economy there and to keep the relations between the two countries cordial and cooperative. These incentives are reinforced by the traditional interest of the United States in the well-being of the Cuban nation and its people.

Over the period 1934–1954, the over-all effect of the program seems to have been to introduce considerable stability into a situation that was rapidly becoming chaotic and to check the deterioration of economic conditions in Cuba. The program contains monopoly features and possibilities of misuse which are somewhat disquieting to those who favor efforts to bring about freer world trade. Experience during the first twenty years, however, does not seem to reveal much tendency toward use of the restrictive features in antisocial ways or toward price increases out of line with those which would have prevailed under the earlier policy based on protective tariffs. That policy did, of course, provide some subsidy to U.S. sugar producers at the expense of the consumer but in an uncertain and ineffectual way. A principal objection to the current program is that it does not necessarily contribute to a logical solution of the larger world problem of oversupplied and unstable sugar markets. Nevertheless, as of 1955, the program seemed to be comparatively well established and not likely to be changed materially in its broad outlines.

Similarities and Dissimilarities in the Wool Program

Wool, like sugar, is a deficit commodity so far as the United States is concerned. However, the programs relating to the two commodities have been quite unlike because of differences in the production processes and marketing structure and in the circumstances out of which they arose. Until the 1930s, the wool growers like the sugar producers relied heavily on protective tariffs as a method of aiding and protecting their industry. Though tariffs were usually high, that type of aid proved ineffective in stabilizing prices or assuring stability to the industry.

Wool, even more than sugar, has been strategically important in war periods and in both world wars was brought largely under government control. An extremely severe price decline followed World War I and was expected after World War II. Prices fell to extremely low levels in the early 1930s as well. For slumps of that kind, brought about mainly by changes in demand rather than supply, the tariff was of little help in maintaining prices.

In the early 1930s, under Farm Board auspices, some effort was made to improve and stabilize the wool market by strengthening producer cooperation. That undertaking proved disappointing as a stabilizing device and wool selling reverted to essentially the pre-1930s pattern until

World War II. The situation changed quickly with the outbreak of war. Strategic considerations soon overshadowed longer-term objectives. State trading of one kind or another replaced most of the ordinary marketing procedures. Heavy stocks of wool were acquired by both the U.S. and British governments. Prices to U.S. growers were established at moderately favorable levels and the U.S. government became for a time the sole buyer of domestically produced wools.

With the close of the war, the U.S. and British governments found themselves with heavy stocks of wool on hand and faced a difficult and lengthy period of liquidation. Wise and skillful handling of British Commonwealth stocks, together with an unexpectedly strong demand, resulted in the successful liquidation of a carry-over stock of some 5 billion pounds (about three times the amount normally carried over) without serious disturbance to the market. However, U.S. stocks of domestically grown wool moved sluggishly if at all and continued to be a source of concern to U.S. growers. Foreign wools were preferred by the mills on the basis of quality and methods of preparation.

The U.S. government therefore continued to support wool prices at the wartime levels by means of CCC purchases. Eventually, authorization was given for CCC to sell at prices competitive with imported wools, with the government taking the loss. At the same time, U.S. wool production was declining rapidly as a result of unfavorable cost-price relationships despite the fact that the price was held at what would previously have been regarded as fairly satisfactory levels. By 1950, the U.S. war stocks had been liquidated and nearly all of those held by the "Joint Organization," the agency set up to liquidate British Commonwealth stocks.

With stocks down to or even below normal levels, wool prices rose sharply after the outbreak of war in Korea, to nearly twice what they had been a year earlier. In the following year they dropped back again to levels below those prevailing in the first half of 1950. Thereafter, with a congressional directive that wool prices be supported at 90 per cent of parity so long as the quantity produced was less than 360 million pounds, CCC began to accumulate wool that was difficult to dispose of without loss.

After considerable study of the problem, the Congress passed in 1954 a National Wool Act, which approached the problem in a quite different way. Wool was to be allowed to find its price in the commercial markets without reference to the level of support guaranteed by the government. Hence there would be little or no burdensome accumulation in government hands. The government, however, pledged itself to supplement the amounts so received by the growers with direct government payments that would equal the difference between the amounts received and the returns pledged by the government. In the first year of operation under this plan the government guaranteed an average return equal to about

106 per cent of parity. This was designed to encourage increased production and to offset to some extent the adverse cost situation facing sheep producers. As of 1955 there was as yet no experience to go on in estimating the effects and suitability of the new program.

Specialty Crops—Main Reliance on Marketing Agreements

For the specialty crops, particularly the perishables, the procedures outlined in the preceding pages were clearly unsuitable and were not used. To the extent that government aid was provided for growers of these crops, the principal device used was a government supervised and sponsored marketing agreement supplemented by licenses or Secretary's orders. Considerable additional aid was provided by means of purchases and subsidies financed out of Section 32 funds or from appropriations made in connection with the foreign-aid programs. Many of these contributions were in the form of surplus-reducing purchases for use in the food stamp, school lunch and relief programs. In a few cases, export subsidies were provided.

The marketing agreement and license or Secretary's order programs have yielded a considerable body of experience as to situations in which such methods are likely to be effective and the procedures that do and do not work well. On the whole their significance as a price-raising device has not been large. In many cases they have, however, contributed to more orderly movement of commodities and the elimination of waste by holding off the markets low-quality or otherwise unsuitable portions of crops.

The marketing agreement programs appear to have proved more attractive to growers of nuts and dried fruits than to the producers of highly perishable products such as melons, fresh fruits and vegetables. There are some exceptions. For example, the California citrus agreements have apparently had strong grower support. In part, limited use of the marketing agreement procedure in the fresh fruit and vegetable industry was due to legislative restrictions written into the Marketing Agreement Act in 1935. For example, the act prohibited marketing agreements and Secretary's orders for most of the canning crops and some others. The more active grower interest in this type of program for the semiperishables was due partly to the fact that surpluses of these crops could more readily be held out of the normal markets and carried over to another season, or diverted to lower uses or exported at subsidized prices. The fact that government subsidies could be and were used more effectively in disposing of such surpluses has also no doubt contributed to the apparently greater success of the nut and dried fruit programs.

The marketing agreement and order type of program appears to have a place in the over-all approach to the farm problem but its potentialities for raising prices substantially to growers, or to consumers, do not appear to be very great. Nevertheless, with further experimentation and particularly with more adequate analysis of results, the stabilizing possibilities of such devices may prove to be more attractive to growers than in the past. Many of the features included in some of the earlier agreements have been found undesirable and are now almost always omitted. Thus the knowledge of what is and what is not likely to be practical and effective is undoubtedly greater than when the programs were first initiated. For example, attempts to maintain posted lists of prices on perishables and to regulate marketing charges appear to be of dubious merit. In addition, it seems to be generally agreed that control of the programs, nominally at least, must be in the hands of the growers. Except for such direct subsidies as have been provided, the programs have not involved heavy expense to the government. As a means of introducing more orderly procedures into these very unstable markets the marketing agreement approach appears to warrant further experimentation and study.

The Potato Program—Unpopular and Expensive

Of the various price-support programs carried on during the postwar period the one relating to potatoes was undoubtedly the most unpopular and the most costly for the time covered and the size of the industry. The program was mainly an outgrowth of commitments made in the war period and carried too long without the modifications needed under a changed set of circumstances.

A Potato Control Act was passed in 1935 but did not come into effect because of the Court decision in the Hoosac Mills case, which was handed down shortly thereafter. However, the authorization to use Section 32 funds for surplus removal, which was passed at the same time, did make possible some modest aid to potato growers in the late 1930s. The most significant surplus removal operation of that period was in 1940 when the government bought up some 21 million bushels, of which 16 million were diverted to livestock feed and starch production. One feature of the 1935 act was to cause great difficulty in later years: the base period specified for computing parity prices of potatoes was 1919–1929 (the same as that for tobacco) instead of 1909–1914 as for most other farm products. But the consumption of potatoes was not increasing as was the demand for tobacco. The parity price goal thus established was some 25 per cent above what it would have been otherwise. Support prices based on this high "parity price" criterion proved very stimulating to the industry. With yields increasing at the rate they were, support at 90 per cent of parity would undoubtedly have resulted in an oversupply of potatoes even if parity were not artificially high.

The later developments were largely the result of fears that wheat supplies might become inadequate during the war years and thus compel greater reliance on potatoes as a source of carbohydrates. Increased production of potatoes was asked for and this automatically put them under the 90 per cent of parity price guarantees required by the Steagall Amendment and later legislation. The wartime legislation required continuance of this level of support for two years after the close of the war. During the period covered by these commitments, phenomenal gains were made in yield per acre, partly in response to the very favorable prices guaranteed by the government. Acreage was cut back, but not fast enough to offset the gains in yields. The level of support was reduced from 90 per cent to 60 per cent of parity as soon as that could be done legally, but even the 60 per cent level of support, in terms of the artificially high parity base, still assured a price attractive to growers.

Since potatoes are neither storable from year to year nor suitable for other uses on any large scale and since even large reductions in price would not result in much increase in consumption, there was little that could be done with the surplus except to destroy it, or channel it to livestock feeding or other uses in which the returns would be very small. Since the government was committed to taking over the surplus at relatively high prices consumers did not get cheap potatoes, huge quantities were destroyed and the cost to the government was exceedingly heavy.

As a whole the program cost the federal government some $630 million, which, instead of contributing to the welfare of agriculture in a period of depression, was added to farm incomes at a time of very high prosperity and when there was no war on. Public opposition to the program became so vigorous that government supports were discontinued in 1951 and the industry reverted to its previous status.

Fluid Milk Program Adapted to Peculiarities of the Market

The fluid milk program differed markedly from those described above. This was due both to the peculiarities of the fluid milk markets and to the kinds of arrangements developed earlier without government participation. The demand for fluid milk is relatively stable throughout the year whereas the supply fluctuates widely from season to season. The industry must therefore produce in the flush season considerable quantities of milk that cannot be sold at fluid milk prices. This surplus or Class 2 milk is channeled into various types of manufactured dairy products. It had become customary, even before the government programs were authorized, for producers to be paid on a blended-price, or perhaps seasonal, basis, depending on the proportion used as Class 1 milk and the amount of Class 2 milk supplied. In many of the larger markets these arrangements had grown up through the organization of cooperative bargaining or selling associations designed to increase the bargaining power of the producers as against those of the distributors.

The Agricultural Adjustment Act authorized producers and distributors to enter into marketing agreements whereby all suppliers and handlers would be required to participate in these arrangements. In other words, the system implied the establishment of government sponsored and supervised monopolistic arrangements, with the consumer interest presumably protected by the restraints prescribed by the government representatives.

The program as a whole passed through two principal stages. The first consisted of a brief period in which principal reliance was on marketing agreements. These were found rather generally unsatisfactory and unworkable. Instead, the drift was toward the use of marketing orders issued by the Secretary of Agriculture, which specified the prices to be paid to producers but not, as in the period of marketing agreements, the resale prices at which the handlers would sell to consumers. Enforcement was in the hands of a milk market administrator assigned to each market by the Secretary of Agriculture.

These arrangements have become rather well established in the markets under federal supervision. In a number of the states somewhat similar supervision of the marketing arrangements is provided by the state government under state law. Where state law does not require participation in the program, the adoption of a federal program is voluntary so far as any given market is concerned. If a specified majority of the producers favors the establishment of a federal program, and the Secretary of Agriculture approves, all producers and distributors in that particular market automatically come under the terms of the order.

The system that has developed, under both federal and state laws, seems to have become well established and widely accepted. It has contributed to more orderly handling of a type of market that is particularly prone to price wars and other chaotic conditions. There is controversy over whether it results in some exploitation of the consumer. Such exploitation, if it exists, probably is not on any large scale since the pricing and other arrangements made must be approved by government officials who presumably are responsible to the public as well as to the industry. The procedures used do not differ markedly from those in unregulated markets and probably do not involve a significantly larger element of monopoly. Some students contend, in fact, that the public interest is more adequately protected in the regulated than in the unregulated markets. The direct cost to the government is not large.

The Commodity Programs as a Whole

There are few broad generalizations that can safely be made about the numerous and diverse commodity programs undertaken by the federal government during the past two decades. One is that no one type of program can be applied to all commodities or even to any very large group of them. Each major commodity, and many of the minor ones, has so many peculiarities of its own that any program designed to improve its position needs to be carefully and specifically worked out to fit the existing conditions.

The lack of such product differentiation was one of the principal defects of the system of postwar guarantees established during the war years. A separate and more flexible arrangement for the greatly expanded industries like dried milk, dried eggs, potatoes and wheat would have led to more rapid adjustment and to large savings in public expenditure. This is not to say that such individual crop legislation could practically have been undertaken in the war period. It obviously could not. It does point up the fact, however, that generalized legislation applying to a number of commodities should be very carefully scrutinized in periods when more deliberate consideration is possible.

Though extremely difficult politically, some regional and type differentiation is needed even for various parts of what is ordinarily considered a single commodity. For example, it is not logical to apply the same percentage cuts in acreage to the spring wheat area, where overproduction is only moderate or perhaps nonexistent, as to a region of substantial overproduction like the hard winter area or the Pacific Northwest. The problems of the cotton-producing areas of the Southeast and of the western states are also sufficiently distinct to warrant some differentiation of programs. Similarly, the difficult adjustments facing the butter-producing areas may warrant special treatment.

Among the major crops, acreage controls and marketing quotas are more practical and effective for crops like cotton or tobacco, which must be processed, than for crops like corn and oats, which may be used on the farms where grown.

Most of the programs now in operation were developed as a means of dealing with two of the most uncharacteristic periods in the nation's history, one a prolonged and severe depression, the other a period in which war requirements were dominant. The time seems now to have arrived for devising more carefully considered and specialized programs designed to meet the needs of farmers, and of the general public, under a different set of conditions. During the years in which the existing programs were taking shape, considerable progress was made in adapting them to the problems of this diverse and complex industry, but there still is much to be done in developing a well-balanced and constructive long-term program that will give to agriculture an appropriate share of the national income and at the same time take due account of the national interest and of our changing position in international affairs.

In general, the trend toward more detailed specification by the Congress of the procedures to be followed and the price relationships to be maintained has tended to increase the difficulties of administration and to introduce more rigidity than is desirable from the standpoint of the public and of the industry. For example, greater freedom of action at the administrative level would have made possible more realistic handling of the cotton surplus of the late 1930s, the oversupply of potatoes, dried milk and dried eggs in the postwar period, and the heavy accumulations of butter, cheese, wheat and cotton which have created such perplexing problems in recent years.

There has been some relaxation of the extreme rigidities of the early postwar years, but as yet no clear and comprehensive policy has emerged. Excessive preoccupation by the Congress with detailed and specific provisions relating to particular crops and enterprises tends frequently to inhibit or retard readjustments that would be in the long-time interest of both farmers and the public. It also precludes or de-emphasizes the much needed effort to work out and popularize consistent and constructive over-all policies relating to the place of agriculture in the national economy, and the amounts and kinds of public aid that should be provided for it.

During the 1930s the laws passed left room for considerable administrative discretion in determining the kinds of aid to be given and the levels of price support to be maintained. Few would contend that the decisions made were always wise and appropriate, but, on the whole, an extremely difficult and complex situation was dealt with imaginatively and with a high sense of responsibility. The trend since then has been for the Congress itself to take on more and more of the task of specifying the procedures to be used and the levels of support to be provided instead of delegating this authority under appropriate general directives.

The division of responsibility between the Congress and the administrators of the programs obviously presents difficult problems. Too much delegation, especially if not carefully and continuously supervised by the Congress, can open the way to excessive bureaucratic power, discrimination in favor of or against certain groups, and so on. The Supreme Court has long exercised a restraining influence on such delegation of powers and has frequently checked the drift in that direction as being in excess of the limitations set up in the Constitution. Nevertheless, as the economy has grown more complex, an increase in the amount of delegation of functions formerly considered specifically legislative has come to be generally recognized as inescapable.

Federal Reserve Board and Treasury management of monetary policies and Interstate Commerce Commission regulation of railroad rates are cases in point. These have long been recognized as too complex or too fast-moving to be handled adequately by direct congressional action. No similar degree of discretion has been permitted for the administrators of such agencies as the Commodity Credit Corporation, except in the 1930s, a period in which much of the most forward-looking and realistic action for the betterment of conditions in agriculture occurred.

Agriculture's position in an economy which is becoming more and more rigidified by growth in the size and power of other organized groups is a difficult one. Its tendency to overexpand production and to defer needed adjustments when put on a price basis that it regards as equitable is well recognized and extremely difficult to deal with. How to determine what is an equitable balance between farmers and other groups in an economy which has become so highly organized is, of course, difficult in the extreme, but some guiding principle is required even if only a policy of trying to ameliorate the hardships inherent in an industry that is so highly competitive.

An approach entirely in terms of prices is clearly inadequate. Stable prices in agriculture may mean very unstable incomes. Furthermore, if production is not to be guided and adjusted by price changes, some other form of guidance must be provided. Thus the problem is that of somehow channeling into agriculture a reasonably adequate share of the total national income without at the same time maintaining it as an overexpanded and relatively inefficient part of the economy. The other alternative appears to be to undertake to shift enough resources out of agriculture so that it will obtain in the market, in most years, a return comparable in real terms with those achieved by other groups.

That problem is not being adequately considered or discussed. It will not be met by an approach wholly in terms of price supports whether high or low. Also, it is not a party matter. The agricultural program, practically from its inception, has been in the main a bipartisan one. The conditions to which the farm program should now be oriented are those of the future, so far as we can foresee them, not those of the past. We must be willing to abandon traditional patterns where that is logical and to continue and strengthen those types of activity that are suited to present-day conditions, or to devise new ones if necessary. Much of what has been done will stand as an appropriate and logical approach to the problem. Some features of the program clearly are outmoded and should be relegated to the field of historical interest, not retained merely because we can't think of some better way to do the job.

THE AGRICULTURAL COMMODITY PROGRAMS

Two Decades of Experience

1

Cotton

A COTTON surplus problem was beginning to develop at the outbreak of the first world war. Though the demand for other products and the invasion of the boll weevil cut back production temporarily, the problem reappeared in the 1920s as new areas in the West came into production and as farmers learned how to combat the boll weevil. The great depression beginning in 1929 emphasized the vulnerability of the cotton industry with its high level of production in relation to demand and its dependence on foreign as well as domestic markets.

The economies of most of the southern states had been built primarily on cotton. It was the great cash crop. It required little capital and utilized a large amount of unskilled hand labor. The cropper system had developed out of the slave-plantation form of organization. Both the cropper and the landlord relied from year to year on the returns from cotton. The great fluctuations in cotton prices and yields were therefore a serious handicap to progress in the economy of the South.

In fact, practically all business activities in the cotton states were related to and largely dependent on the size of the cotton crop and on the ability of cotton producers to purchase goods and services. Consequently, the prospect of overproduction and low prices presented a dilemma not only to the producers but also to those engaged in processing and handling cotton and to many others as well.

It had been recognized for decades that the living conditions of most of the South's agricultural population, especially of the cotton croppers, were far from satisfactory and that they could not be much improved without raising the level of incomes. Farmers in the South had long been urged by agricultural leaders, particularly by extension workers, to diversify production, to produce more for home use and to develop other products for market. The great depression precipitated action.

Significance of the Cotton Programs

Cotton has been one of the most important crops to be dealt with in the farm programs developed in the period since 1930. Price supports have been provided at strategic points with some degree of success, especially in times of market weakness. Producers' incomes from cotton have been larger during periods of business depression than they would otherwise have been, and the government has made significant income contributions to cotton producers in the form of rental, benefit, parity and conservation payments.

Farmers have been required to reduce cotton acreage, but most of them have been able, through better methods of cultivation and increased use of fertilizer, to increase yields per acre to such an extent that production and incomes have been maintained at relatively high levels. The government requirements in respect to the utilization of land taken out of cotton, and the conservation payments made, have helped materially in bringing about the kinds of diversification long advocated by educators and others and thus have contributed to the development of a more stable agriculture throughout most of the cotton belt.

The importance of cotton in the national economy, and especially in the economy of the South, has declined. Nationally, the acreage in cotton is less than half what it was in the early 1930s. Production, however, is roughly comparable to that of the 1920s and higher than in most years of the 1930 and 1940 decades. Part of the loss of acreage and production in the cotton belt has been offset by increases in the irrigated areas of the western states. Foreign production has expanded and the upland staple of the South no longer has a virtual monopoly of world markets. Substitutes have been developed to replace cotton in many fabrics, both in the domestic and in foreign markets. In the United States the development of substitutes has held in check the expansion of cotton consumption so it has not kept pace with the growth of population and with increasing industrialization.

Nevertheless, in recent years, cotton producers have made substantial gains in income and in living conditions as compared with producers of other farm products. In the long run, the net loss or gain from the cotton programs depends primarily on the returns to producers from alternative uses of resources as well as on the returns from cotton in the remaining available market.

Effects on the Industry

The federal programs have demonstrated the effectiveness of contracts or agreements with individual farmers, supplemented by financial inducements and marketing quotas, in controlling the acreage planted to cotton and in bringing about readjustments that could not be accomplished by educational efforts alone. They have also demonstrated that government support in times of market weakness can stabilize prices more effectively than can be done by cooperative marketing organizations. While the cost of the cotton program to the government is difficult to determine accurately, it is probable that the net gain to the government of approximately $267 million on price-support operations in cotton for the period 1933–1955 has about counterbalanced the costs of administration.[1] The

1. This, however, does not take account of a loss of some $41 million on export differentials which was a result of the price-support program.

additional appropriations for rental and benefit payments and parity payments may be regarded as public contributions designed to raise income levels and improve living conditions on farms in the cotton-producing states. The soil conservation payments also include an element of relief, but they can be considered in large measure a contribution to the national welfare.

Other important points to consider in weighing the gains and losses from the program are its effects on farm tenure, on efficiency in the use of production resources and on market organization. The control program apparently has not had much effect on landlord-tenant relationships. Other factors, including increased opportunities for other employment, rising wage rates and mechanization, have contributed to the reduction in number of croppers and the enlargement of farm units. The use of historical bases in allotting acreage and establishing marketing quotas has tended to prevent desirable shifts in the areas of production and to restrain somewhat the adoption of improved production practices. However, the abandonment of controls during the war period permitted shifts and improvements that had been inhibited under the earlier programs.

The Commodity Credit Corporation has affected the functioning of the private marketing system significantly in some periods. It has at times taken considerable quantities of cotton off the markets, through loans and accumulation of stocks, and has later fed these withheld stocks back into the market. However, the marketing system itself has not been much changed as a result of these operations.

There has been no follow-through on the national policy of strengthening cooperatives which was inaugurated under the Agricultural Marketing Act of 1929 (the Federal Farm Board). Under the programs of 1933 and after, the cotton cooperative marketing associations were treated in the main like other private marketing agencies. Apparently the cotton program, as administered over the past two decades, has not had any large significance as a promoter of improved market organization and increased marketing efficiency.

The role of the federal government in maintaining orderly production and marketing and conserving agricultural resources appears to have come to be widely accepted. However, one of the current problems is that of whether the administration of the programs can be improved so as to facilitate desirable shifts in areas of production and increase efficiency in production and marketing and still maintain a reasonable degree of price and income stability.

CONDITIONS IN THE BASE PERIOD

For cotton, the prewar years 1910–1914 were a period of high-level production and declining prices. During the first decade of the 1900s, the price of cotton had advanced with the rise of the general price level from the depression low of the 1890s. The average price at New York increased from 6 cents per pound in 1898 to 14.7 cents in 1909. In the same years, harvested acreage and production increased about 50 per cent. A good crop in 1910 checked the rise in prices and a new record crop in 1911 turned the tide.

During the previous ten years, both domestic consumption and exports had been increasing and were largely responsible for the rise in prices. However, the cotton producers of the United States had developed such a volume of production that a surplus could appear in the event of any significant depression at home or any disturbance to the foreign market. Foreign production also had been increasing. The price of cotton remained fairly stable for the 1909–1913 marketing seasons in spite of the fact that the general price level continued to advance in those years. In that period, southern cotton farmers were producing two thirds of the cotton grown in the world, were exporting two thirds of their production and were shipping to northern mills half of the cotton retained at home.

While economic conditions in the South had greatly improved with the advance in the price of cotton after 1898, the average incomes of cotton producers, and of other gainfully occupied persons in the South, were still low in relation to the average earnings of the gainfully employed in other parts of the country. The bulk of the cotton crop was produced by croppers and tenants who subsisted from year to year on whatever income was derived from their share of the crop. When a slump in business activity or a financial crisis depressed the price of cotton, the income of most producers was quickly absorbed in paying debts and in living expenses. They had to be carried through the planting season for the next crop by plantation owners.

The high degree of dependence of the croppers and tenants on the returns from the annual cotton crop with its erratic price movements was generally deplored. Producers were urged to grow more foodstuffs for home use and to produce other crops or livestock products for market as a hedge against a price depression in cotton. However, the lack of capital and of skills for other kinds of farming tended to keep most of the farm labor of the South in the production of cash crops such as tobacco and cotton.

THE WAR PERIOD AND RECOVERY

A record crop harvested in 1914 just as war erupted in Europe broke the cotton market. The farm price dropped from an average of 12.4 cents in July to 6.5 cents in November. Exports and consumption were maintained at a fairly high level for the season, but there was a large increase in carry-over and the farm price for the season averaged only a little more than 7 cents as compared with 12.5 cents for the previous season. Even in a peacetime market, the record production of 16 million bales would not have been absorbed without a significant fall in prices; the outbreak of war added to the disturbance.

Improvement in the markets for other products and relatively lower prices for cotton caused plantings to be reduced and held to a lower level through the war years. In the meantime the boll weevil had become a menace to the crop throughout much of the cotton belt, reducing yields significantly. However, advancing prices in the war period brought an increase in plantings. They were about at the prewar level in 1918. The depression of 1920 reduced cotton prices, but subsequently there was a quick recovery to the parity level and above. Farmers began to learn how to deal with the boll weevil. Production recovered from the low of a little less than 8 million bales in 1921 to 16 million bales in 1925. This large crop was harvested from a record area of more than 44 million acres. Another record crop harvested in 1926 broke prices early in the season to the 1920 depression level. This blow aroused interest in protection or relief for the cotton farmers.

Cotton producers were urged to adjust production to demand by shifting land and other resources to alternative lines of production. In response to the lower prices, they reduced plantings in 1927 by nearly 15 per cent. This cut, together with low yields, reduced the crop to less than 13 million bales. Prices advanced to more than 20 cents per pound. High prices in turn brought plantings up again to about 44 million acres and resulted in a crop large enough to reduce prices. Crops continued relatively large and prices kept on declining.

Cotton producers joined with other producers in pressing for government protection or relief from declining prices. The federal government was very reluctant to assume responsibility for relief. However, Congress did respond to the continued pressure and enacted legislation acceptable to the Administration in 1929. The program was intended primarily for support of the cooperatives in more orderly marketing. The cooperatives were expected to reduce the early-season price depressions from large crops by distributing marketings more evenly through the season and holding over some of the excess supplies from years of large crops to years of small crops. The government offered financial support to the cooperatives and, in case of necessity, additional support to the market through the establishment of a Cotton Stabilization Corporation.

FARM BOARD PROGRAM AND OPERATIONS, 1929–1932

Cotton price-support operations by the Federal Farm Board began with the break in prices in October 1929. The Board then announced a policy of making loans on seasonal pool cotton sufficient to enable cooperative associations to support the market at about 16 cents per pound. The cooperative associations received loans on 1,241,509 bales. However, in spite of this support the average farm price declined from 17.6 cents in October to 11.9 cents at the end of the season in July 1930.

To protect the market for the next crop, the Board organized the Stabilization Corporation in June 1930, which purchased the cotton held by the associations. The average cost of the holdings was 16.3 cents per pound. The Board announced that it would hold this cotton through the season and authorized the associations to loan 90 per cent of the current market value on the new crop with three-year maturity. Prices continued downward from an average at the farm of about 11 cents in August to about 8 cents at the end of the season. The cooperatives accumulated about 2 million bales in that season and the Stabilization Corporation added a few bales to its holdings, making the total carry-over of the cooperatives and the Corporation at the end of the season about 3,384,000 bales.

The 1931 crop was large and the carry-over excessive. Prices continued to decline from a farm average of 6.1 cents in August to 4.6 cents in June 1932. The Board carried through but did not add to its holdings. Banks were encouraged to make loans for the season. About 3 million bales were held by the borrowers, making about 7 million bales in all held off the market in the 1931–32 season. In summing up its experience in its third annual report, the Board stated that it had financed the removal of nearly 3.5 million bales from current sales, but underconsumption had added 10 million bales to the unused supply.

Efforts to Reduce Farm Board Stocks

At the beginning of the 1932 season the Board agreed to extend its commitments to July 1933 on condition that the acreage planted to cotton would be reduced substantially. The area reported in cultivation in July was about 6.7 per cent less than a year earlier and 18 per cent less than in July 1929. Lower prices and the drive for readjustment had taken 7.9 million acres out of cotton between 1929 and 1932. Moreover, early conditions indicated lower yields and a crop considerably smaller than the one harvested in 1931. Prices advanced moderately in July from the low point reached in June. The Board announced a policy of selling up to 650,000 bales during the season beginning August 1, 1932. Congress voted 500,000 bales for Red Cross relief. Consumption and exports increased sufficiently to absorb the new crop and reduce carry-over. Prices remained above the low point reached at the end of the previous season and returns to farmers averaged about 20 per cent over those of 1931–32. However, the stock of old cotton that remained on hand was considered too large.

The Board recognized that market price stabilization efforts alone could not be very effective without greater adjustments in production than had been effected. It was clear that advice to reduce cotton acreage or to shift resources to other production could not be effective in view of the general price decline, since the prices of other products had declined as much as or more than cotton prices.

What the Farm Board accomplished, in brief, was to check, but only temporarily, price declines in the early parts of the 1929 and 1930 marketing seasons. The volume financed was not sufficient to have much effect on season average prices in the face of the general decline in prices and the continuing decline in business activity and cotton consumption. Had the Board followed a more conservative policy in making loans on the 1929 and 1930 crops, advancing only 75 per cent instead of 90 per cent of current values, its resources probably could have been used more effectively in supporting prices at lower levels in 1931 and 1932 and without significant loss. Perhaps such a conservative policy would not have been acceptable in 1929, but by 1931 an offer of a 10-cent loan on cotton would have been gladly accepted. But could a government agency in 1929 anticipate such an extended price decline and business depression, and could it reserve strength to operate an effective program only in periods of greatest price weakness?

THE EMERGENCY ADJUSTMENT PROGRAM, 1933–1936

The Agricultural Adjustment Act of 1933 included specific provisions for taking over and distributing the stocks of cotton accumulated under the Farm Board by the cooperatives and the Stabilization Corporation. The remaining Farm Board holdings of cotton were turned over to the Farm Credit Administration to be sold to the Secretary of Agriculture at 5 cents per pound and to be made available by the Secretary of Agriculture to cotton producers in lieu of cotton plantings to be plowed up. About 844,000 bales were donated to the Red Cross.

More significant for the future were the general provisions of the act enlarging the responsibility of the government for emergency relief and readjustment. Three main types of procedure were to be used: first, measures to restrict production and marketing in order to raise market prices; second, measures to hold off the market temporarily any surpluses which might develop in spite of production controls (carried out, mainly in later years, by the Commodity Credit Corporation); and, third, direct payments to farmers for compliance with government programs. These payments, of course, added to the incomes received from sales or from virtual sales in the form of nonrecourse loans from CCC.

The 1933 Season

The 1933 spring plantings had been large, and a program was outlined to induce farmers to plow up a substantial part of the planted cotton acreage. The financial incentives offered included a fixed cash rental for acres plowed up plus an option to purchase cotton on the basis of 6 cents per pound in an amount equal to the quantity of cotton which would presumably have been produced on the land taken out of cultivation. The incentives were successful in reducing the acreage grown from an estimated 40,788,000 to a harvested acreage of 29,978,000, a reduction of about 25 per cent.

It was expected that the value of the crop could be increased by reducing production and that the amount grown could be reduced enough to clear the market of the accumulated stocks without further acquisitions. An earlier analysis of the relation of supply to price and crop values indicated that a 10 per cent reduction in output would normally result in a 16 per cent increase in price. It would follow that the 25 per cent reduction in acreage to be harvested would, with average yields, reduce the crop enough to raise the price by about 40 per cent.

However, higher yields resulted in a 1933 crop as large as that harvested in 1932 and nearly as large as the 1930 crop. In fact it was only about 12.5 per cent lower than the average production in the five years preceding this heavy reduction in acreage. Undoubtedly, favorable weather was largely responsible, but farmers may have contributed somewhat to higher average yields by plowing up a larger proportion of the low-yielding acres than of the better land and, secondly, by putting more labor into cultivating and harvesting the remainder of the crop. It has been estimated that without the program the crop would have been larger by about 3 million bales. With this larger crop the average farm price would have been held to about 7 cents per pound as compared with 6.5 cents for the previous crop.[2]

Price and Income Gains

Producers actually realized about 10.2 cents per pound (on the average) for the 1933 crop, an increase of 3.5 cents over what they realized for a crop of about the same size a year earlier. The average farm price advanced from 6.3 cents per pound in April to 10.7 cents in July. It was affected primarily by prospects of a reduction in the crop and by the devaluation of the dollar.[3] Improvements in the general business situation and advances in the general price level, influenced to some extent by these same prospects, also contributed to the advance in cotton prices. The market weakened somewhat after July with the prospect of a high-yielding crop and a slowing up of business activity.

In October the Commodity Credit Corporation was organized. It offered a loan of 10 cents per pound for cotton grading low middling ⅞ inch and over. When announced, the loan was slightly above the equivalent market price, though it was only 69 per cent of parity. The market strengthened after the announcement of the loan. Later, improvements in demand advanced the market to above the loan level and only a small portion of the crop entered the loan.

2. The carry-over had been reduced by about 1.5 million bales. That, together with the improvement in business activity, would have supported the price slightly above the level of the previous season.

3. The rise in the spot price of American cotton at Liverpool from April to July was only one penny and by November the price in pence was back to the April level. An obvious effect of the devaluation was to increase the price of American cotton in relation to the prices of some of the foreign cottons in countries in which the currencies had been devalued greatly, and earlier than in the United States.

At the loan level the cotton that had been carried over from previous seasons became available to the market and thus contributed toward stabilizing prices at about the loan level. Domestic consumption and exports for the season were somewhat less than in the previous season. However, consumption and exports exceeded production, the producer pool was sold out and the total carry-over was reduced moderately.

Cash receipts from the sale of the 1933 crop were nearly 40 per cent above those from the 1932 crop. Undoubtedly, the most significant factor in maintaining the price above that which would have resulted without the program was the reduction in crop through a 25 per cent reduction in acreage. This reduction probably contributed about 2.5 cents to the increase in prices to producers. Establishing a support price slightly above the market during a period of weakness, and withholding stocks from the market when the price was below the loan level, probably added nearly a cent per pound.

Rentals paid on acres plowed up and profits on the cotton option pool added about $179 million to the cash receipts of cotton farmers during this first season under the program. This was equivalent to adding about 3.8 cents to the price of cotton lint. These additional payments raised the cash receipts of farmers to about $896 million, nearly double the receipts in the previous season.

The Programs of 1934–1936

The power to control production was strengthened by the Bankhead Act early in 1934. That act provided for a tax to be levied on cotton at the gin, but producers were to be exempted from the tax in amounts corresponding to their respective allotments of the desired national production. The tax was designed to prevent noncontracting producers from profiting from a general reduction in production without contributing to it, and to prevent contracting producers from increasing production by increased use of fertilizer and in other ways. Exemptions were issued to both contracting and noncontracting farmers. These exemptions permitted the ginning of specified quantities of cotton. In case a producer received an exemption for a quantity in excess of his actual production, he could transfer this excess to another producer to permit him to gin more cotton than was originally allotted to him. This was in effect a transferable production allotment plan. The tax on cotton marketed in excess of the allotments was to be at the rate of half of the current market price but not less than 5 cents per pound. Originally the act was to apply only to the 1934 crop, but it proved popular with cotton producers and was extended until repealed in 1936.

Acreage control, together with production restrictions effected through the ginning tax, held plantings below the acreage allotments through the 1934 and 1935 seasons. Less favorable weather and restrictions on ginnings helped to hold production to planned levels. The 1936 crop was planted after some features of the act had been declared unconstitutional and the ginning act had been repealed, but voluntary contracts succeeded in holding the acreage harvested to about the 1933 level and production to about the amount produced in 1933.

In summary, the controls provided in the emergency Agricultural Adjustment Act held the harvested cotton acreage through the 1933–1936 seasons to a level more than 25 per cent below the acreage harvested in the period of Farm Board operations. In spite of the high yields in 1933, offset as they were by drought in 1934, production was reduced by more than 20 per cent. The cutback of production supported prices and provided an opportunity for disposing of a large part of the excessive carry-over that had accumulated by 1932.

The Role of the Commodity Credit Corporation

The Commodity Credit Corporation played a significant though less important role in raising and maintaining prices and incomes to producers in this emergency period. The success with loans in the first season and the higher current market prices at the beginning of the 1934 season led to an advance of the loan rate to 12 cents. That proved to be a mistake from the standpoint of moving the crop. The market dropped back to the support level. Although the crop was reduced by drought to less than 10 million bales, nearly half of it was placed under loan. Domestic consumption and exports declined. Though the total carry-over at the end of the season was slightly less than at the beginning of the crop year, the bulk of it was left in the hands of the Corporation. By the end of the season, the stocks under loan had been increased from about a million bales to more than 4 million bales. The private trade had unloaded a large part of its stocks and CCC was left holding the bag.

The loan offered on the 1935 crop was reduced to 10 cents per pound, about 62 per cent of parity. Producers were offered an adjustment payment of the difference between 12 cents per pound and the current market price, to encourage movement of the crop. Under these conditions, consumption and exports increased. The price moved above the loan rate. Only 1 per cent of the new crop entered the loan and all of it was redeemed. Producers received nearly $40 million as price adjustment payments in addition to rental and benefit payments for that season's crop.[4]

Reducing the loan rate for the 1935 crop below that of the 1934 crop involved a possible loss on the cotton already under loan. In April 1936, producers were offered an opportunity to redeem cotton under loan at approximately .75 cent per pound less than loan value. The privilege was extended through 1936 and into 1937. Producers redeemed 2,740,000

4. These payments were not charged to CCC but were made from Section 32 funds which had been authorized in the Agricultural Adjustment Act amendments of August 1935.

bales with a loss to the Corporation of about $14 million. Additional redemptions of 227,000 bales left a total of 1,665,000 bales under loan.

The loan program through the 1933–1936 seasons involved a net loss which is difficult to estimate. The accumulated investment of 12 cents per pound, and carrying charges on 1,665,000 bales from the 1934 crop, gave the holdings a book value of $109,854,000.[5]

Cost of the Program

The emergency cotton program was to have been largely if not entirely financed by excise taxes levied on the first processing of cotton and closely related substitutes. A tax of 4.2 cents per pound net weight was established in August 1933. The rate represented the estimated difference between the actual price and the parity price computed as of June 1933. The funds derived from the tax were used to make rental and benefit payments and to contribute to other costs relating to the program.

Revenues from the processing tax ceased in January 1936 when this feature of the act was declared unconstitutional. The net receipts from this source from August 1933 through December 31, 1935 were $246,-800,000. The total cost of the cotton program for the three seasons was estimated by Richards to be about as follows (in millions):[6]

Rental and benefit payments	$351.4
'Option' cotton (48.8+15.0)	63.8
Administrative expenses	33.8
Price adjustment payments	50.0
Cotton loans	66.0
Total	$565.0

The funds from the processing tax on cotton and related competing products were therefore not sufficient to cover the rental and benefit payments and amounted to less than half of the estimated cost of the program in the first three years. The ginning tax, designed primarily as a control measure, did not yield revenue sufficient to cover expenses

5. Average Commodity Credit Corporation loan rates and average prices for middling ⅞ inch cotton at the 10 spot markets during this period were as follows (in cents):

Crop Season	Average Loan Rate	Average Price of 10 Markets			Per Cent of Crop Entering Loan
		Season High	Season Low	Season Average	
1933	10.0 [a]	12.3	8.8	10.17 [b]	15.2
1934	12.0	13.1	11.5	12.36 [b]	48.9
1935	10.0	12.6	10.6	11.09	1.1
1936	[c]	13.7	12.0	12.36	[c]

a. Applicable for all cotton LM and better, ⅞ inch and longer.
b. Includes unredeemed loan cotton at estimated loan value.
c. No loan program.
(U.S. Bureau of Agricultural Economics, *Statistics on Cotton and Related Data*, Statistical Bulletin 99, June 1951, pp. 130, 239.)

6. Henry I. Richards, *Cotton and the AAA*, The Brookings Institution, Washington, 1936, p. 236.

of administration. Consequently, more than half of the cost of the program in the first three seasons was supplied by the government from other revenue sources.

The effect of the processing tax on consumption, on returns to producers and on costs to consumers was a matter of much concern. An analysis of results, made after the tax was declared unconstitutional, indicated that processors and distributors of cotton products passed the tax on to consumers. The demand for cotton goods is so inelastic that the higher cost probably reduced domestic consumption by only about 400,000 to 500,000 bales per year. Such a curtailment of domestic consumption probably reduced the farm price by not more than a half cent per pound.[7] Since exports were exempt from the tax, the reduction in domestic consumption and prices would tend to encourage exports. Also, since the price of raw cotton constitutes only a small part of the price paid by the consumer for products manufactured from cotton, the increase in costs to consumers as a result of the program was apparently small.

A later estimate than that made by Richards shows total government payments for the emergency control period amounting to $536 million. That estimate does not include some items of expense, such as administrative expenses, which are included in the Richards estimate. (See Table 1.)

Cash Returns to Farmers

Income results are of course more important to farmers than price results. While it is practically impossible to determine net income results from these operations, it seems evident that the cash return to farmers was increased significantly but not as much as prices were increased. It is particularly important to note that the estimated gross cash income from marketings, not including benefit payments, exceeded what would have been obtained without the program in the first two seasons but was lower in the 1935 and 1936 seasons. The average price of lint cotton was increased about 35 per cent, whereas cash receipts from lint were increased only 4 per cent. Government payments raised the gross income to about 23 per cent over what it would have been without any program. (See Tables 2 and 3.)

The decrease in production under the AAA program was not sufficient to reduce significantly the supply of cotton available to foreign consumers who were in a position to buy. As indicated earlier, the processing tax probably encouraged rather than discouraged foreign takings of American cotton. However, the price advances beginning with 1933 and the withholding of stocks from the market undoubtedly lent some

7. See U.S. Treasury Department, Bureau of Internal Revenue, *An Analysis of the Effects of the Processing Taxes Levied under the Agricultural Adjustment Act*, 1937, pp. 33–35.

TABLE 1

COTTON: CONTRIBUTION OF GOVERNMENT PAYMENTS TO GROSS CASH INCOME, 1933–1936

(*Millions*)

Marketing Season	Government Payments [a]	Receipts from Marketings		Total Cash Receipts	Government Payments as Per Cent of Total Receipts
		Cotton	Cottonseed		
1933–34	$179 [b]	$663	$ 53	$896	20
1934–35	115	596	111	822	14
1935–36	160 [c]	590	108	858	19
1936–37	82	764	141	987	8
4-year average	134	653	103	891	15

Source: Derived from an unpublished analysis prepared by Maurice R. Cooper of the U.S. Bureau of Agricultural Economics, *Estimates Pertaining to Cotton, with and without an Agricultural Adjustment Program, 1933–34 to 1936–37,* June 2, 1938.

a. A net gain of $25 million by producers from loans in this period has not been distributed by seasons.
b. Includes profits on cotton options.
c. Includes price adjustment payments of nearly $40 million.

TABLE 2

COTTON: ESTIMATED EFFECT OF PROGRAMS ON PRICES AND RECEIPTS FROM MARKETINGS, 1933–1936

Marketing Season	Price to Producers				Cash Receipts for Lint		
	With Program	Without Program	Increase: Amount	Increase: Per Cent	With Program	Without Program	Percentage Increase or (−) Decrease
	(*Cents per Pound Lint*)				(*Millions*)		
1933–34	10.2	7.0	3.2	46	$663	$580	14
1934–35	12.4	7.9	4.5	57	596	537	11
1935–36	11.1	8.22	2.88	35	590	605	−3
1936–37	12.3	10.85	1.45	13	764	794	−4
4-year average	11.5	8.49	3.01	35	653	629	4

Source: Derived from an unpublished analysis prepared by Maurice R. Cooper of the U.S. Bureau of Agricultural Economics, *Estimates Pertaining to Cotton, with and without an Agricultural Adjustment Program, 1933–34 to 1936–37,* June 2, 1938.

TABLE 3

COTTON: INCREASE IN GROSS CASH FARM INCOME ATTRIBUTABLE TO THE AGRICULTURAL ADJUSTMENT PROGRAM, INCLUDING PAYMENTS,[a] 1933–1936

(*Millions*)

Marketing Season	With Program	Without Program	Increase	
			Amount	Per Cent
1933–34	$896	$626	$270	43
1934–35	822	636	186	29
1935–36	858	708	150	21
1936–37	987	905	82	9
4-year average	891	721	170	23

Source: Derived from an unpublished analysis prepared by Maurice R. Cooper of the U.S. Bureau of Agricultural Economics, *Estimates Pertaining to Cotton, with and without an Agricultural Adjustment Program, 1933–34 to 1936–37,* June 2, 1938.

a. Also includes estimated income from loans.

encouragement to an expansion in production and marketings of foreign growths. In that period the production and consumption of foreign cottons increased only about 10 per cent. Some part of that increase can be attributed to reduced production of American cotton and to the domestic price-support program.

At the outset, the program was authorized and operated as a depression emergency program. It was argued, and generally accepted, that the government was justified in advancing funds and subsidizing cotton producers as a means of contributing to recovery in agriculture and that the program was therefore in the national interest. At first it was expected that the excise taxes on processing would provide the funds necessary to carry out the program. The excise tax functioned about as expected in one respect: the tax was paid by consumers without much effect on consumption. However, the revenues produced failed to cover the cost of the program. The nullification of the tax by the Supreme Court decision of January 1936 eliminated this source of funds for the 1936 season and thereafter. What remained after the adverse court decision and the enactment of new legislation was authority to negotiate directly with farmers for desired adjustments, to continue price and income support programs to the extent that they would be financed by direct appropriations from general federal revenues, and to develop a national conservation program involving appropriate adjustments in cropping. Both the legislative and administrative branches of the government were moving to convert from an emergency recovery basis to a long-time continuing program.

THE LONGER-TERM PROGRAM

Market prospects for the 1937 season seemed to be the best since the onset of the great depression. The 1936 crop had been marketed at the highest average price since 1929. Industrial activity had returned to the 1929 level, thus completing a major business cycle. The domestic consumption of cotton had recovered from depression levels and in fact exceeded any previous record. Exports, however, lagged.

The cotton adjustment program for 1937 was similar to that of 1936. However, the higher level of prices received for the 1936 crop stimulated optimism on the part of farmers and government administrators. A goal of 32,750,000 acres was set for the 1937 crop with the expectation that it would yield 13.5 million bales. But the optimism of farmers encouraged them to plant a little more than the goal. The July 1 estimate of cotton land in cultivation was 34,471,000 acres. Farmers had set aside for diversion only about half as many acres as in the 1936 season. A large yield per acre produced a record crop of 18,946,000 bales.

Again the loan program contributed significant support at a weak point. The crop was big at home and foreign production was also large. The situation was further complicated by the onset of a business recession. The average farm price dropped from 12.4 cents per pound in July 1937 to 9 cents in September. Without the support program the price would have fallen much lower. Though the loan program prevented a drastic price decline, it simultaneously created another problem. CCC had made loans on about 5.6 million bales which, for the most part, were still on hand and not likely to be moved without heavy loss to the government and a severe impact on the market.[8]

Depression in 1938

The Commodity Credit Corporation, still having some 1934 cotton on hand, conservatively established the 1938 loan rate at 9 cents per pound for ⅞ staple length or longer. Though the loan rate was only at 53 per cent of parity, it proved to be high in relation to the current market demand. As the business recession developed in the latter half of the season domestic consumption declined. Since foreign crops were also large, the export volume remained low. Prices settled at about the loan rate, averaging only 8.4 cents for the season, and more than 30 per

8. Actually, of course, legislation passed in 1938 prohibited sales of government-acquired cotton at less than the amount invested in it, so the result of the program was to add substantially to the stocks on hand. However, the procedure followed was, in the main, a logical one in dealing with so large an excess supply. The defect in the program was mainly in the failure to adjust production in succeeding years and to provide more flexible arrangements for gradual liquidation of the stocks held. The total carry-over, government and private, at the beginning of the 1938 season was 11.5 million bales. (*Agricultural Statistics, 1945,* p. 76.) It was to go even higher, to 13 million bales, in the following year.

cent of the crop was put under loan. Only a few bales were redeemed and both the producers and the government were again buried under a pile of cotton.

As a further aid to growers, a deficiency appropriation of August 25, 1938 authorized the expenditure of $130 million from Section 32 funds. For each of the fiscal years 1938 and 1939, $65 million was set aside for price adjustment payments to producers on cotton grown in 1937. The purpose of the appropriation was to assure producers 12 cents per pound for that crop, 3 cents over the loan level. Payments were to be made to individual producers on 60 per cent of their base production as established by the 1937 program. There was a provision in the 1938 act that any cotton still held by producers on June 30 of that year would be assumed to have been sold at the official average price as of that date. Though no price adjustment payments were made in the 1937 marketing season, payments amounting to $103 million were made in the 1938 marketing season on cotton grown in 1937. These were intended as additions to the income from the 1937 crop.

Marketing Quotas Again

The problems arising out of the huge cotton crop of 1937 led to a more rigid control program for 1938. Marketing quotas, authorized by the 1938 act, were voted shortly after its passage.[9] The allotment for the season was reduced to 27.5 million acres and was designed to produce about 10 million bales. Producers cut plantings to about 25 million acres and harvested about 12 million bales. Marketing quotas were voted again in December 1938 and in 1939, to apply to the 1939 and 1940 crops.

The marketing quotas and the incentives for diverting acreage were very effective in controlling cotton plantings until war conditions made acreage controls unnecessary. The program administrators continued to allot about 27 million acres of cotton but the area in cultivation, as of July 1, in the 1938–1940 seasons averaged only about 25 million acres, about 60 per cent of the level before controls. Yields were higher; production averaged about 12 million bales, a reduction of only some 20 per cent. Domestic consumption increased but exports were reduced. The carry-overs continued to exceed 10 million bales in spite of the reduction in the size of crops.

Loans by CCC

The act of 1938 included specific legislation with respect to loan rates, conditions under which the loans were to be authorized and the disposal

9. The first quota vote was taken March 12, 1938. Of about 2,300,000 growers eligible to vote, about 1,527,000 voted and 92.1 per cent of these voted "yes." However, the "yes" vote was only 60 per cent of the "eligible" voters. Nearly 2,672,000 cotton farmers received price adjustment payments in 1939.

of cotton acquired by CCC. The loan rates specified for cotton were a minimum of 52 per cent of parity and a maximum of 75 per cent. This range was in line with rates that had been set administratively for the 1933–1935 and 1937 crops. Loans were to be offered when the price fell below 52 per cent of parity or when the estimated production was in excess of a normal year's domestic consumption and exports.[10]

The price of cotton at the beginning of the 1938 marketing season was below 52 per cent of parity. CCC therefore announced a basic loan rate of 8.3 cents per pound for middling ⅞ inch cotton, which was estimated to reflect 52 per cent of parity. Exports declined to such a low level that domestic consumption and exports together amounted to about 1.5 million bales less than the reduced crop. About 39 per cent of the crop (4.5 million bales) was placed under loan. The farm price averaged close to the loan level, with some improvement toward the end of the season. The loan was extended and most of the cotton under loan was carried over to the next season.

At this point the volume of cotton in the carry-over under loan and in producers' pools reached a record level of more than 11 million bales. The world carry-over of American cotton rose to an all-time high of more than 14 million bales, nearly a million bales over the previous record at the bottom of the depression in 1932. This carry-over was more than sufficient to provide for normal consumption and exports for a year without any new crop cotton.

At the beginning of the 1939 season the price of cotton was above 52 per cent of parity. With normal yields the cotton in cultivation would not produce more than the volume required for normal consumption and exports. However, the Administration decided to offer a loan at the same rate as for the 1938 crop, 8.3 cents. Since the parity index had declined somewhat, this rate was equivalent to 56 per cent of parity. (For loan rates, prices and percentages of crop under loan in these years, see Table 4.)

An advance in prices above the loan level, beginning in May 1939, was due primarily to the fact that the large amounts held by the Corporation left only small quantities of free cotton available in the current market. An upturn in domestic industrial production contributed to an increase in demand for cotton, which strengthened the market. The very large loan stocks held by CCC could not be released until the price was high enough to cover the 1938 loan and carrying charges. Advancing prices finally brought most of the 1938 cotton back into the market. Domestic consumption and exports increased and exceeded the 1939 crop by about 2.5 million bales. Under these conditions only a small quantity of the 1939 crop was put under loan and it was redeemed

10. The act defined a normal year's consumption and exports as the average of the last ten years, adjusted for current trends. The carry-over was taken into account in determining the level of allotment. A normal supply was defined as a normal year's consumption and exports plus 40 per cent.

TABLE 4

COTTON: AVERAGE COMMODITY CREDIT CORPORATION LOAN RATES AND AVERAGE PRICES FOR MIDDLING ⅞ INCH AT THE 10 SPOT MARKETS, 1937–1940

(*Cents*)

Crop Season	Average Loan Rate	Price Received by Farmers: Season High	Season Low	Season Average	Per Cent of Crop Entering Loan
1937	9.0 [a]	10.6	7.8	8.41 [b]	30.6
1938	8.3	8.9	8.0	8.60 [b]	38.6
1939	8.7	11.6	8.6	9.09	.3
1940	8.9	14.2	9.1	9.89 [b]	25.9

Source: U.S. Bureau of Agricultural Economics, *Statistics on Cotton and Related Data,* Statistical Bulletin 99, June 1951, pp. 130, 239.

a. Applicable for all cotton M and better, ⅞ inch and longer.
b. Includes unredeemed loan cotton at estimated loan value.

Note: The average rate for loans actually made is not necessarily the same as the officially announced loan rate for M and better ⅞ inch cotton as there are variations in grade and length of staple.

before the end of the season. The carry-over of Corporation loan stocks was reduced by more than 2 million bales.

The 1940 crop season opened with a less favorable outlook for exports. War conditions in Europe were shutting off markets for cotton. The price declined sharply from July to August. A loan rate to average 8.9 cents for ⅞ middling, equivalent to 56 per cent of parity, was announced. Prices dropped back close to the loan level and a large portion of the crop, about 26 per cent, went under loan. By the end of the season, increasing domestic consumption had contributed to an advance in prices that was sufficient to induce producers to redeem nearly all of the 1940 cotton that had been put under loan early in the season.

Aid Provided through the Surplus Commodities Corporation

The Federal Surplus Commodities Corporation made a significant contribution to the utilization and movement of surplus cotton in the 1938, 1939 and 1940 seasons. The accumulation of large stocks under loan from the 1934 and 1937 crops, together with the great reduction in exports in the 1938 season, stimulated resort to various measures for disposing of surplus cotton. In the 1935 marketing season, FSCC had used some Section 32 funds for purchase of cotton to donate to relief agencies. That operation was revived in the 1938 season and was expanded greatly in the next two seasons. The largest expenditure was for the purchase of cotton and materials for use in manufacturing mattresses and comforters to be distributed by relief agencies. It is estimated that the cotton absorbed in that way amounted to about 654,000 bales. A stamp plan to help low-income families purchase more cotton goods was financed from the same funds. Expansion of industrial uses was subsidized to some extent. It is estimated that the stamp plan and subsidization of industrial uses resulted in the absorption of about 94,000 bales.

Most of that consumption would have been foregone had it not been for the subsidies provided by the government. These programs probably made a net contribution to consumption equivalent to at least 700,000 bales. The cotton utilized in the FSCC programs was purchased in the open market, either directly by the Corporation or by the agencies utilizing the cotton. This contributed significantly to the movement of the current crops.

FSCC turned also to the export front for an outlet for some of the surplus cotton. The Agricultural Adjustment Act of 1938 had removed a legislative limitation that prohibited the use of funds for payments in connection with the exportation of *unmanufactured cotton*. The low level of exports in the 1938 season and its effect on the government's position with respect to cotton holdings led to actions designed to move more cotton in the 1939 season. In July 1939, the Corporation offered a subsidy of 1.5 cents per pound on cotton exports. This, together with the outbreak of war in Europe, stimulated a heavy movement of cotton. The subsidy rate was reduced in December and abandoned in January. Yet exports amounted to 6.5 million bales, 3 million in excess of the amount moved in the previous season. It is estimated that the subsidy may have added as much as 1.5 million bales to the export movement of cotton in the 1939 season.

The increases in exports and domestic consumption attributable to FSCC added about 2.2 million bales to the domestic consumption and exports of cotton through the 1938, 1939 and 1940 marketing seasons. This helped in moving the current crops but did not touch the heavy hangover from the 1934 and 1937 crops. Prices had not advanced to a level high enough to cover the loans and carrying charges invested in cotton from those crops.

What to Do with the Surplus?

CCC was authorized in the act of 1938 to take over cotton under loan and assume all obligations of the producer with respect to the loans, including accrued interest and carrying charges to the date of transfer. But the Corporation was not authorized to take any loss in disposing of cotton. With a view to protecting the producer pools and the opportunity of the producer to redeem his cotton and sell it, the Congress had provided that the sale price must cover not only the cost involved in taking over the 1937 cotton but also the price adjustment payments on that cotton. In further protection of the current market, the law stipulated that after July 31, 1939 the Corporation was not to sell more than

300,000 bales of cotton in any calendar month or more than 1.5 million bales in any calendar year.

Despite these limitations on sales, the Administration decided to take over in August 1939 the 1,665,000 bales in the 1934 producer pool and the 5,256,000 bales remaining under the 1937 loans. The decision was made at that time because of prospects for a barter deal with Great Britain to trade some cotton for rubber. That could be managed in such a way as to circumvent the legislative restrictions and move some of the long-held cotton. In the deal that was consummated, 600,000 bales of cotton were traded for rubber, which was eventually sold for more than enough to cover the investment in the cotton.

The Second Depression under Production Control

The four cotton marketing seasons 1937–1940 carried through a second cycle of economic depression under production control. In comparison with the first period of control the acreage was further reduced but yields increased so that average production was about as high as in the earlier period. Support prices were held to lower levels and prices were held close to support levels. After the first year, cash receipts from marketing cotton were lower than in the first period of control. Larger direct government payments made to farmers maintained total cash receipts slightly above the level of 1933–1937. At the end of the period the government had a larger investment in a larger stock of cotton.

During this period, foreign production of cotton and rayon displaced a significant amount of American cotton in foreign consumption. The production of foreign cotton averaged 2 million bales over that of the 1933–1936 period, and rayon production 2.4 million bales. The result was an annual average reduction of 2 million bales in foreign mill consumption of American cotton. It was a continuation of the developments noted in the previous period. The acreage planted to foreign cotton reached its highest level in 1937 and receded somewhat from that level under the impact of relatively low prices following the 1937 season. Under these conditions it seems doubtful that the price-support levels in the United States had much effect on foreign production of cotton in the 1938–1940 period. Yet the withholding of a large volume of American cotton from the market sheltered foreign producers to some extent from the full effect of a world surplus of cotton.

How Much Did the Program Affect Prices?

Estimates as to what the production, price and income would have been without governmental intervention become more difficult as the program is carried farther beyond the free-market base. Had the surplus from the 1934 crop been unloaded in the 1936 season, the price would not have been quite so high, and not quite so stimulating to overplanting in 1937. Starting with the 1936 price level, without the diversion contracts, the 1937 crop would have been larger and, without loan support, the price would have been lower. Perhaps the farm price would have been reduced as much as 3 cents, from 8.4 cents to 5.4 cents. The average farm price would have remained at a very low level for the 1938 season and probably would have advanced in the 1939 and 1940 seasons as a result of increasing domestic demand. The farm price for the four seasons probably would have averaged about 6 cents, or about a third less than the average realized with the program. The larger volume of marketings probably would not have significantly affected the total receipts, in comparison with what was received from the smaller crops.[11] Government payments made a significant contribution, adding about 20 per cent to the cash receipts of farmers in that period.

If the objective was to stabilize prices and incomes, the greatest mistake in this period was in the program relating to the 1937 plantings. Where price and income stabilization is a principal objective, caution is necessary in a boom period. While the very favorable season could not have been foreseen, some recession from boom was certainly in prospect for the marketing of that crop and there was an adequate carry-over of cotton from the previous period. While the loan rate seemed to be conservative in relation to prices for the previous season, the expansion of plantings, the indicated large crop, some prospect of recession and the experience with the 1934 crop should have suggested a somewhat lower loan rate. Perhaps the least justifiable action from an economic viewpoint was the legislation that appropriated funds for price adjustment payments intended to bring the price up to about 12 cents per pound. Fortunately the price adjustment payments were made in the 1938 season at the bottom of the depression and contributed significantly to raising the incomes received by producers in that season. In effect, the programs for this period stabilized prices to producers but contributed only moderately toward stabilizing incomes.

Recovery from the acute depression of the 1938 season, aided by the development of defense measures in the 1939 and 1940 seasons and reinforced to some extent by special measures for encouraging consumption, resulted in a substantial recovery of income to cotton producers. In the 1940 season the price advance was only moderate, from 9.09 cents to 9.89 cents. Receipts from marketing cotton lint increased from $537 million to $621 million. Receipts from the sale of cottonseed and the supplemental income derived from government payments lifted the total cash receipts for the 1940 season to $917 million. That was less than the total income received in the 1937 season (see Table 5), but it had greater purchasing power than the incomes received for the crops harvested just prior to the beginning of the great depression.

11. As in the earlier period, the larger volume of accumulated stocks, available if prices rose enough above loan levels to pay carrying charges, limited the price response to curtailment of the size of crop.

TABLE 5

COTTON: PRODUCTION, PRICES AND RECEIPTS FROM MARKETINGS AND GOVERNMENT PAYMENTS, 1937–1940

Crop Year	Production	Average Farm Price	Receipts from Marketings: Cotton	Receipts from Marketings: Cottonseed	Government Payments	Total Cash Receipts	Government Payments as Per Cent of Total Cash Receipts
	(Million Bales)	*(Cents per Pound)*	*(Millions)*		*(Millions)*		
1937–38	19	8.41 [a]	$796	$129	$192 [b]	$1,117	17
1938–39	12	8.60 [a]	514	93	143	749	19
1939–40	12	9.09	537	86	215	838	25
1940–41	13	9.89 [a]	621	97	198	917	21
4-year average	14	9.00	617	101	187	905	20

Source: U.S. Bureau of Agricultural Economics, *Statistics on Cotton and Related Data,* Statistical Bulletin 99, June 1951, pp. 5, 130, 342.

a. Includes unredeemed loan cotton at estimated loan value.
b. Includes parity payments paid early in the following calendar year.

The Prewar Cotton Program in Summary

At this point it may be of interest to sum up generally the experience and results of the prewar Agricultural Adjustment programs relating to cotton. By 1936 these programs had succeeded in curtailing production sufficiently to clear up most of the accumulated cotton and to raise prices. However, the invalidation of some of the features of the Agricultural Adjustment Act in January 1936 made it necessary to revise the program. Moreover, by that time it had become apparent that a more permanent program was needed as protection against surplus production and depressions. The longer-term program was designed not only to protect prices and incomes of producers in depressions and to dispose of surpluses on hand but, more important, to adjust production so as to bring it more into line with economic requirements and to conserve agricultural resources.

The huge cotton crop of 1937, in the face of reduced export requirements and a business recession, forced the government to give more attention to disposal of surpluses and readjustments in the use of resources. Incomes were maintained primarily by payments as price adjustments, conservation payments for compliance with acreage allotments and parity payments to make up to some extent for the low levels of loan rate. In addition to these payments made directly in relation to cotton, other payments were made to cotton producers to encourage the production of more foodstuffs for home use and of feedstuffs for livestock, partly as a means of encouraging soil-conserving practices.

The program was criticized vigorously on two points: (1) for the emphasis on reduced production, and (2) for administrative arrangements that were said to retard desirable readjustments. Processors and distributors of raw cotton naturally objected to curtailment of the amounts to be handled. Others criticized curtailment of production on moral rather than economic grounds. Curtailing production without redirecting the use of resources had a tendency to increase unemployment. The number of farms growing cotton was reduced. Unemployment and underemployment of labor were increased. Not much could be done to correct that situation without some increase in the opportunity for alternative employment of both the labor and the natural resources of the South.

Legislative direction and administrative expediency were important factors in carrying out a program which was subject to the criticism that it retarded desirable adjustments. The use of historical bases for making allotments was primarily a matter of expediency to avoid the great responsibility for making decisions for each farm in relation to its present resources and future opportunities. The restrictions on the use of land withdrawn from cotton production were primarily a recognition of interregional conflicts with respect to surplus production. A notable example of legislative restriction was the provision that the crops grown on land withdrawn from cotton production should not be used to expand the dairy industry in the South. However, in spite of restrictions, some progress in readjustment was realized.

The census of 1940 gave evidence of improvements and adjustments in the ten cotton belt states. The population on farms remained about the same as in 1930 but some increase was reported in the electrification of farms and in the use of tractors. The number of farms that reported the growing of cotton was reduced by 20 per cent and cotton acreage by 50 per cent, but the amount of cropland harvested was down only 6 per cent. Cotton yields had increased so much that the amount of cotton produced in 1940, on the reduced acreage, was only about 10 per cent less than in 1930. Some of the cotton acreage had been shifted to other cash crops such as peanuts, soybeans and vegetables for sale. The cash income from these sources had increased significantly in relation to the income from cotton.

More important was the shift to the production of feed crops and forage. Part of the cropland taken out of cotton had been shifted to hay and pasture, which contributed to the production of more livestock. These adjustments in the use of resources helped to restore the purchasing power of the farm income of the cotton belt states to the predepression level. The cash farm income from all sources, including government payments in the 1939 and 1940 seasons, averaged about

$2 billion, only about 80 per cent of the predepression level, but the prices of things bought by farmers were also down, to about 80 per cent of what they had been in 1929. The significance of the readjustment is indicated by the fact that in recent years cotton has accounted for less than 30 per cent of the total farm income of the cotton belt states whereas in the predepression years more than half of it was derived from sales of cotton and cottonseed.

As the United States entered the second world war, the supplies of cotton on hand were more than sufficient to provide adequately for any foreseeable emergency. Increasing yields indicated that reserves of soil fertility had been enlarged significantly. Other resources in the South were sufficient not only to maintain cotton production at an adequate level but also to expand the production of foodstuffs and other agricultural materials needed in the war emergency.

COTTON AND THE WAR

The outbreak of the second world war in Europe soon contracted export outlets but stimulated the domestic demand for cotton. Expanding industrial activity increased not only the industrial utilization of cotton but also the consumer demand for cotton textiles. Furthermore, war conditions in Europe curtailed the exports of cotton textiles from the European manufacturing countries and thus provided an additional outlet for textiles produced in the United States. Later, as the United States prepared to enter the war, the equipment of soldiers added materially to the domestic demand for cotton. Mill consumption increased at a rapid rate and prices rose to parity early in the 1941 season.

Increasing demand for foodstuffs arising out of war conditions in Europe and preparations for defense in the United States provided an opportunity for shifting more agricultural resources into the production of foodstuffs and of some industrial raw materials other than cotton. The improvement in prices and in the outlook for marketing alternative products led producers to continue to reduce cotton acreage. Pressure for change increased as the United States entered the war.

Allotments and marketing quotas were in effect at the outbreak of war, but farmers soon were planting considerably less than the allotments. The allotments for the 1942 and 1943 seasons were about the same as for the 1941 season but farmers reduced plantings substantially in the 1943 season. Payments were made for compliance with allotments in the 1942 and 1943 seasons. In fact, producers who overplanted in 1942 were required to plow up 348,000 acres of cotton already planted, as a matter of legal requirement, notwithstanding the fact that total plantings were far below the allotted acreages. Under these conditions, controls were subject to many criticisms and, finally, marketing quotas and allotments were abandoned. Producers continued to reduce plant-

TABLE 6

COTTON: ALLOTMENTS AND PLANTINGS, 1938–1945

(1,000 Acres)

Year	Allotments	Plantings as of July 1[a]
1938	27,500	25,018
1939	27,897	24,683
1940	27,545	24,871
1941	27,392	23,130
1942	27,400	23,302
1943	27,200 [b]	21,900
1944	22,277 [c]	19,990
1945	20,507 [c]	17,588

Sources: Allotments data from annual reports of the Agricultural Adjustment Administration and successor agencies; and plantings data from U.S. Agricultural Marketing Service, *The Cotton Situation,* June-July 1951.

a. Includes for 1938–1942 such acreages as were plowed up in order to conform with farm acreage allotments. These acreages were (in thousands): 1938, 425; 1939, 433; 1940, 572; 1941, 434; 1942, 348.

b. Though the allotment was 27.2 million acres, farmers were urged to hold total cotton acreage down voluntarily to 22.5 million acres, as a means of making further substitutions of war crops wherever possible.

c. Announced acreage goal; allotments discontinued in 1943.

ings without official encouragement until after the end of the war. (See Tables 6 and 7.)

Early in the war period the administrators considered measures designed to encourage shifts out of cotton production, including restrictions on the use of fertilizer and lower deferment priorities for cotton workers. However, southern members of Congress insisted that there should be no discrimination against cotton. It was argued that in some areas cotton would in fact contribute as much as or more than any other crop to the needed production of oil and feedstuffs.

Southern congressmen were continuously on the lookout for ways of safeguarding the interests of cotton producers after the war. Legislation was passed in order to protect farmers against the loss of acreage allotments as a result of shifts, contractions or abandonments in the war period. It was provided that farmers who shifted cotton acreage to "war crops" would not as a result be assigned smaller allotments after the war. The interest in maintaining the position of cotton was also reflected in the raising of loan levels from 85 to 95 per cent of parity and finally in the provision that the President should use his powers to obtain parity prices for cotton.

Conservation payments were continued in considerable volume through the war period. Parity payments made directly on cotton were discontinued when the price advanced to parity in the 1941 season, and

TABLE 7

COTTON: PAYMENTS UNDER AGRICULTURAL ADJUSTMENT, AGRICULTURAL CONSERVATION AND PARITY PAYMENT PROGRAMS, BY PROGRAM YEARS, 1933–1943

(*Thousands*)

Year	Adjustment or Conservation	Price Adjustment and Parity	Total
1933 [a]	$181,025	—	$181,025
1934 [a]	115,226	—	115,226
1935 [a]	120,451	—	120,451
1936	86,884 [b]	$ 39,771 [c]	126,655
1937	68,742 [b]	—	68,742
1938	142,595	123,000 [d]	265,595
1939	118,817	96,195	215,012
1940	102,564	95,752	198,316
1941	97,251	87,706	184,957
1942	80,167	— [e]	80,167
1943 [f]	74,204	—	74,204

Source: Annual reports of the Agricultural Adjustment Administration and successor agencies.

a. All 1933, 1934 and 1935 payments were rental and benefit payments and were made under provisions of the Agricultural Adjustment Act of 1933.

b. Made under the Soil Conservation and Domestic Allotment Act of 1936 from a special appropriation to "enable the Secretary of Agriculture to meet all obligations and commitments . . . heretofore incurred under the provisions of the Agricultural Adjustment Act . . ." (Public Law 440, 74th Cong., approved Feb. 11, 1936).

c. Price adjustment payments made on account of the 1935 crop under the 1935 Cotton Price Adjustment Act to offset in part reduction in loan rate and to encourage the movement of the current crop. Payments were from Section 32 funds.

d. Price adjustment payments made under the 1937 Cotton Price Adjustment Act to make up to producers of the 1937 crop the difference between the loan rate for that season and 12 cents per pound.

e. Parity payments were discontinued after 1941 because the price of cotton advanced to the parity level.

f. Allotments and quotas were discontinued; consequently payments for compliance were discontinued after this season.

conservation payments for compliance directly related to the cotton crop were discontinued in 1943 with the abandonment of allotments and quotas. However, payments for the carrying out of conservation practices on farms complying with the programs in effect were maintained at about the same level as at the beginning of the war period. This was an important factor in developing and maintaining high crop yields.

Prices Outran Supports

To insure that cotton would share in the war-stimulated advance in prices, Congress passed a series of amendments to the act of 1938 so as to provide higher loan rates, but price advances ran ahead of the rising support levels. The first step was taken early in 1941 through an amendment directing that loans be offered on cotton and other basic commodities at 85 per cent of parity. This was to apply to the 1941 crop, but by the beginning of the season the average farm price was above the loan level; in fact, the price reached parity in the first month of the season. The level of support for cotton and other commodities was raised again, to 90 per cent of parity, in the Stabilization Act of 1942. That act was amended early in 1944 to provide special treatment for cotton. The amendment established a loan rate of 92.5 per cent of parity for the 1944 and subsequent crops and for two seasons after the end of the war.

A final boost in the loan rate on cotton was made in the Surplus Property Disposal Act passed later in 1944, which provided for loans at 95 per cent of parity for the 1944 crop only. In the extension of the Stabilization Act there was another provision which required the President to use available resources to insure producers of certain commodities a price equal to whichever was higher, parity or the highest price received for the commodity between January 1, 1942 and September 15, 1942. For cotton the parity price was the higher and CCC entered the open market in September 1944 to purchase 1944 crop cotton at 100 per cent of parity.

The advances in loan rates on cotton were criticized as an encouragement of cotton production in spite of the overhanging large stocks and the greater need for food supplies. However, cotton prices had responded to war conditions as they had in the first world war period. As usual, the prices of raw materials required in the production of textiles advanced with increasing demand and the development of inflationary conditions. Price controls which restrained cotton price advances in that period probably had more effect on the prices received than did the loan rates prescribed by the Congress. The levels of price to which cotton was held under textile ceilings did not encourage an expansion in production. In fact, as indicated earlier, farmers continued to reduce plantings and to shift resources to other lines of production in spite of the advancing support levels.

War Role of the CCC

The Commodity Credit Corporation played an important role in handling cotton and stabilizing prices through the war period. The large stocks in inventory and under loan at the beginning of the war provided adequate supplies against any emergency. The Corporation was in a position to contribute toward stabilizing prices simply by selling cotton when pressures threatened to push the price of raw cotton above price ceilings. On the other hand the loans were a guarantee against prices falling much below parity.

The result was remarkable stability of prices. At the beginning of the 1942 season the farm price averaged 18 cents per pound. It had advanced only to an average of 21 cents by the start of the 1945 season. In each of the war years, producers put considerable quantities of cotton under loan even though prices were above the loan level. Some was redeemed before the end of the marketing season and some was carried over into the next season. Parity was creeping up slowly even under price control, and the producer could gain by carrying cotton under loan from one season to another.

The Corporation also performed other useful services relating to cotton in the war period. It served as a procurement agency as well as a distribution agency. Losses were taken as a result of export differentials, which amounted to about $35 million, and on some foreign cotton purchases in the amount of more than $5 million. Cotton and linters purchased on government account amounted to more than $1 million. However, these expenditures are not properly chargeable to the price-support program. Attention is called to them merely as a recognition of the fact that in the war period the Corporation performed many other services in addition to that of maintaining farm incomes by holding cotton and some other commodities off the market.

The high level of consumption and the advance to parity in the 1941 season provided an opportunity for CCC to reduce its inventory. Consumption plus exports in the 1941 season amounted to over 12 million bales, which was more than the amount produced in that year. Furthermore, under the conditions then existing, the trade was becoming interested in carrying larger stocks. Out of CCC stocks 900,000 bales were shipped to the United Kingdom under lend-lease and 300,000 bales were exported commercially. The domestic market took 1.1 million bales.

The CCC inventory was thus reduced from about 6 million bales in September 1941 to a little less than 4 million bales by June 1942 and to about 3.5 million bales by September 1942. During the next three seasons current production was adequate to provide the amounts required for domestic consumption and exports. Inventories were further reduced moderately until the Corporation was instructed to purchase cotton at parity in the 1944 season.

Carry-Over Increased Again

With an opportunity to sell to CCC at 100 per cent of parity, producers redeemed much of the cotton they had under loan and sold it to the Corporation. The Corporation increased its inventory from about 2.5 million bales in March 1944 to nearly 5.4 million bales in June 1945. At the end of the 1944 marketing season the carry-over of stocks held by the Corporation in inventory and under loan amounted to nearly 7 million bales and the total carry-over of American cotton in the United States was about 11 million bales.

At this point there began to be great concern about the cotton situation when the war should come to an end. It was recognized that the normal peacetime consumption would be smaller than the amounts used during the war and there was some doubt about the recovery of the foreign market. An act approved on April 12, 1945 relaxed restrictions on the sale of cotton. The act of 1938 had provided that all costs must be recovered and that no more than 1.5 million bales could be sold from CCC stocks in any one year. The act of April 1945 suspended these restrictions until the expiration of the postwar two-year period in which supports were to be maintained at 92.5 per cent of parity. During the period of such suspension the Corporation was permitted to sell at not less than parity but it could accept lower prices on sales made for new or by-product uses or for export. Following the approval of this act the Corporation took steps to reduce its inventory.

Fortunately, from the standpoint of the Corporation, the 1945 crop was considerably reduced. Farmers planted less, and lower yields reduced the crop to less than 10 million bales. A diversion program moved a small amount of cotton into domestic consumption. Export subsidies moved a larger volume.[12] Exports increased from 1.9 million bales in the 1944 season to nearly 3.7 million bales in the 1945 season. As a result, the Corporation was able to unload practically all of its accumulated stocks. It began the season with nearly 7 million bales and ended with less than a million bales.[13] Some of the cotton unloaded at that time had been carried through from the 1937 crop. It is interesting to note also that the trade was willing to take over and carry larger stocks. The total carry-over in the United States at the end of the 1946 season was about 7 million bales, the bulk of it in private trade channels.

Net Results of the War Period

The Corporation realized a substantial profit on cotton that had been carried through many years. The realized net gain on domestic cotton through the 1941–1945 seasons amounted to more than $218 million. The rubber barter deal added a profit of $11 million. Against these gains should be charged export differential costs of about $27,650,000. The other cotton operations about balanced out, gains against losses, leaving a net over-all gain for CCC on lint cotton during the war period of about $200 million.

Cotton producers received approximately parity prices through the

12. Export payments made at the end of the 1944 season amounted to $33 million and those made at the end of the 1945 season amounted to $32 million. In addition $17 million of Section 32 funds was used in providing export subsidies on cotton in the 1945 season. Cotton registered for export in the 1945 season amounted to 2.2 million bales.

13. The Corporation had available from inventory, from purchases and in producer pools 6,243,000 bales. Sales amounted to 5 million bales and sales in process to 1,100,000 bales, leaving only a very small amount of cotton not sold or under contract to sell.

war years. Receipts from marketings were maintained at a high level. Government payments made a significant contribution in the first season but were reduced when prices reached parity and eliminated with the abandonment of allotments in 1943. Income from other sources also increased during the war. In comparison with the prewar period 1937–1940, the income from livestock and other crops was larger. In the cotton belt the average receipts from cotton and cottonseed declined from 25 to 24 per cent of the total income whereas the proportion received from livestock products increased from 24 to 29 per cent.

The census of 1944 recorded significant changes in the agriculture of the cotton belt states. There was a reported decrease in farm population of 25 per cent. Military and labor drafts had reduced the number of farms, but by only about 5 per cent as compared with 1939, and the area in crops was reduced only 1 per cent. The number of farms with electricity and tractors had nearly doubled. The number of farms reporting cotton production was reduced by nearly 25 per cent. The shift to food crops is indicated by increases in the production of peanuts, rice and wheat. A larger volume of livestock production was supported by increases in pasture and in feed crops. Thus, under pressure, cotton producers had made significant shifts in production and had greatly increased the productivity per worker.

Controls Not Needed in Early Postwar Years

Fortunately, no control programs were required for the purpose of restricting production in the first three seasons after the armistice. The business recession which had been expected to follow the end of military operations was mild and short-lived. Another short crop was harvested in 1946. The decontrol of textile prices in 1946 permitted cotton prices to rise above parity. The President's proclamation of the cessation of hostilities, made on December 31, 1946, meant that the 92.5 per cent support level for cotton would be continued during the 1947 and 1948 seasons. Deferred domestic demand for increased mill consumption strengthened the domestic market, and financial aid provided to speed the recovery of cooperating countries contributed to increased exports. Stocks were drawn down to the lowest level since 1929. Producers responded slowly to the higher prices. In 1947 the acreage planted was brought back to about the 1941 level. A more favorable season produced a crop about equal to the requirements for domestic consumption and exports, with prices close to parity.

Loans were offered at 92.5 per cent of parity in accordance with legal requirements, but since prices were above parity very little cotton was put under loan in those years. Consequently there was not much accumulation of loan stocks at the end of the 1947 marketing season. Prices and incomes reached record levels in these early postwar seasons without any important government aid.

Congressional Study of the Cotton Problem

In the meantime the agricultural committees of the Congress and the U.S. Department of Agriculture continued to consider the problem of adjustments. It was recognized that prices and the demand for cotton were temporarily inflated by war and postwar conditions. After the 1944 hearings, a Cotton Research Committee was organized by the National Cotton Council and that Committee reported to the Cotton Subcommittee of the House Agriculture Committee early in July 1947.[14]

In analyzing prospects, the Committee assumed that prices in general would readjust downward to about the 1943 level and that national full employment would be maintained, with national income at about $160 billion. It assumed, further, that readjustments toward greater efficiency in the agriculture of the South would continue to increase productivity per farm worker and to reduce costs per unit.

One of the conclusions reached was that if the price of cotton remained on a competitive basis without production controls about 13 million bales could be produced and marketed at 12 to 14 cents per pound, but if the price was to be maintained at approximately the parity level it would be necessary to control production and the market could be expected to take only about 6 million bales annually, at about 20 cents per pound. The Committee expected that at the lower price level cotton probably could compete more successfully with synthetic fibers and that a sizable volume of exports could be maintained. However, if the price were to be maintained at about parity, exports would be practically eliminated by competition from foreign cottons and from rayon production abroad, while the synthetics would continue to encroach upon the domestic market for cotton, reducing the volume taken to the low level of about 6 million bales.

Following these hearings, the Department of Agriculture undertook to present to the agricultural committees of Congress facts and analyses designed to aid in the development of a long-range agricultural program. In these hearings, it was assumed that the price-support program for the basic commodities, including cotton, would be continued but that the program would be modified so as to improve the competitive position of cotton and permit greater flexibility in methods of disposing of such quantities of it as would be put under loan or taken over by CCC. Production controls were recognized as probably necessary in emergencies, but it was hoped that with a support program adjusted to meet competition and a continuation of the readjustments in production that had been occurring during the war years the need for controls would be minimized.

14. *Study of Agricultural and Economic Problems of the Cotton Belt,* Hearings before the Special Subcommittee on Cotton of the Committee on Agriculture, House of Representatives, 80th Cong., 1st sess., July 7 and 8, 1947.

New Legislation

The first legislative action to provide a basis for postwar programs was contained in the Agricultural Act of 1948, approved early in July of that year. The act extended support of the basic commodities, including cotton, at 90 per cent of parity through the 1949 season. Amendments to the Agricultural Adjustment Act of 1938, to take effect for the 1950 season, were designed to prepare the way for some downward adjustment in support levels whenever surpluses accumulated and to relax the regulations governing CCC sales of stocks.

The new method of computing parity prices would have the effect of reducing the parity price for cotton because of the fact that the prices of other farm products had been rising relative to the price of cotton. The act provided that in such a case transition from the old to the new parity base would be made at the rate of 5 per cent a year after 1949.

The Agricultural Act of 1949 postponed the application of the modernized parity index through the four years following 1950. For that period, the parity price for cotton and other basic commodities was to be computed in the same manner as before the revision of the parity formula. However, by 1954 the higher level of cotton prices in the postwar years, in relation to the prices of other farm commodities, had increased the parity price for cotton even when computed by the modernized formula.

The loan rates prescribed for cotton in the 1948 act were to be not less than a schedule of minima related to the percentage of normal which the current production and carry-over would amount to. The lowest minimum level was 60 per cent of parity for a current supply amounting to more than 130 per cent of the normal supply. As the percentage of current supply in relation to normal supply declined, support prices could be increased to a maximum of 90 per cent of parity.

Another amendment to the Agricultural Adjustment Act of 1938, approved in August 1949, revised the regulations regarding acreage allotments and marketing quotas. In that amendment, the Secretary of Agriculture was directed to proclaim a marketing quota for any year in which he determined that the total supply of cotton in the current marketing year would exceed the normal supply. The marketing quota was to be not less than 10 million bales or one million bales less than the estimated consumption and export requirements for the season, whichever was smaller. The proclamation was to be made not later than October 15 and a referendum for approval or disapproval of it was to be held by December 15. As in the earlier legislation, the marketing quotas were related to the acreage allotments. Plantings in the preceding five years, not including 1949, were to be used in determining acreage allotments, with allowance for acreage reductions made in the war period and for substitutions of war crops for cotton.

The Agricultural Act of 1949 continued the 90 per cent upper limit on price-support loans but adjusted the schedule upward to provide a minimum of 75 per cent support for a supply of more than 130 per cent of normal. Loans were continued at the 90 per cent level.

The normal supply of cotton was defined as the current consumption and exports plus 30 per cent. To illustrate, in a season in which the current domestic consumption was 10 million bales and exports 5 million bales, an addition of 30 per cent, or 4.5 million bales, was allowed for carry-over, making the normal supply 19.5 million bales.

Changes made by the act of 1949 in the conditions relating to the sale of cotton by CCC were very important in providing for a more flexible program. CCC had been handicapped by limitations on the quantities it could sell as well as on the price at which sales could be made. The 1949 act provided for sales at 5 per cent above the current support price plus a reasonable carrying charge. Cotton could, nevertheless, be sold for new types of use, for export or for lower uses without restrictions as to quantity or price. The Corporation was required to give consideration to establishing such policies with respect to prices, terms and conditions as would not discourage or deter manufacturers, processors or dealers from acquiring and carrying normal inventories.

RETURN TO CONTROLS

At the beginning of the 1948 season, almost all inventories and loan pools had been closed out. Domestic consumption of cotton had declined in that season to the lowest level since 1939. Exports had increased by more than 2 million bales but not enough to offset the decline in domestic consumption and the increase in supply.

The high level at which the price of cotton was supported in the 1948 season—92.5 per cent of parity (about 28.8 cents a pound)—together with a sharp decline in the prices of many other farm products, stimulated an increase in plantings. The area in cultivation on July 1, 1948 was reported to be about 23 million acres, a return to the level planted in 1942. A record yield of 311 pounds per harvested acre resulted in a crop that amounted to nearly 15 million bales, 3 million bales above that of 1947. The end-of-season carry-over was increased from 3 million bales to 5 million, most of it (3.8 million bales) in the hands of the Commodity Credit Corporation.

To further darken prospects, a general price decline developed in the latter half of the marketing season. The index of the average price of all farm products was above 300 in January 1948. From that time on, there was a downward trend in farm prices generally. The farm price of cotton declined from 35 cents in May 1948 to 30 cents in August, which brought it down to 97 per cent of parity.

The situation confronting those concerned with the cotton program began to resemble the one which the Farm Board had faced in 1929. Stocks were beginning to accumulate. It was obvious that the price of cotton was high enough to encourage increased plantings, especially with the prices of alternative products declining. The 1948 act did not provide for allotments and controls under the supply conditions existing in the 1948 season, but, in anticipation of increased plantings for the 1949 crop, the Congress passed in March an act providing that the acreage planted to cotton in 1949, and the yields for that season, should not be used in computing acreage allotments and marketing quotas in any subsequent year.[15] Notwithstanding this legislation, the area planted was increased to 27.7 million acres, the largest since 1937.

The loan level for the 1949 crop was reduced to 90 per cent of parity (27.2 cents per pound for middling ⅞ inch cotton). The farm price of cotton adjusted to that level. Fortunately, both consumption and exports increased, and only 20 per cent of the larger crop entered the loan. Most of it was redeemed before the end of the season. The private trade took over more of the stocks, and the holdings under CCC loans were reduced moderately, to about 3.5 million bales. Yet the total carry-over was increased by about 1.5 million bales by the end of the 1949 season.

At this point the position of CCC began to seem hazardous. The decline in prices from the high level at the beginning of 1948 had resulted in the placement of large volumes of the basic commodities under loan. Although some of the 1948 crop loans were liquidated within the year, the carry-over from that season into the next constituted a heavy investment in inventories and current loans. The total CCC investment at the end of the 1948–49 fiscal year was $2,373 million, including $609 million invested in cotton. That was a very heavy investment with which to face a new marketing season. The 1949 season added to the heavy load. In June 1950, CCC requested and obtained an increase in borrowing power from $4.75 billion to $6.75 billion.[16] By that time its total investment had increased to $3,434 million.

In the meantime, in accordance with the provisions of the amendment approved in August, the Secretary had determined that the supply of cotton for the 1949 season exceeded the normal supply and that marketing quotas should be applied to the 1950 crop. A referendum was held in December and producers voted in favor of quotas.[17] In accordance with other provisions of the amendment, the announced allotment was

15. Public Law 28, 81st Cong., 1st sess., approved March 29, 1949.

16. Later actions by the Congress in 1954 and 1955 raised the borrowing power of the Commodity Credit Corporation first to $8.5 billion, then to $10 billion and later to $12 billion.

17. The record of marketing quota votes is interesting. In every referendum, more than two thirds of those voting voted "yes." However, the number voting was always substantially less than the number of producers. In some years the "yes" vote was less than a majority of the total number of producers, as indicated by the nearest census count of farms producing cotton.

to total 21 million acres, with a marketing quota of 11.7 million bales. Again farmers planted less than the allotment. The area in cultivation as of July 1, 1950 was 18,921,000 acres. Yields were lower and only 10 million bales were produced. The outbreak of war in Korea gave a great stimulus to the market. Prices advanced sharply. Consumption and exports exceeded production. War again provided an opportunity for unloading CCC stocks.

Supplies Inadequate in 1950–51

The small 1950 crop, together with the sharp increase in demand, caused supplies to be very tight in the 1950–51 season in spite of the heavy carry-over from the 1949 program. As of June 30, 1950, CCC held 3.4 million bales of upland cotton valued at $580 million.[18] This was almost wholly 1948 crop cotton that had been pooled for the account of growers on August 1, 1949. In addition CCC had outstanding loans on the 1949 crop amounting to $121 million.

Virtually all of the cotton held by CCC or under loan to it was disposed of during the 1950–51 fiscal year and the Corporation realized a net gain of some $28 million as a result of the rapid rise in prices.[19]

While this sharp decrease in cotton production and the much stronger demand which grew out of the Korean War relieved the Commodity Credit Corporation of a potentially troublesome stock situation that had been building up since 1948, it was not without drawbacks so far as the industry was concerned. The 1950 cutback of production turned out to be more drastic than was desirable from a national or an industry standpoint. Even with the relatively large carry-over at the beginning of the 1950 crop season, there was not enough cotton available to supply the increased domestic and foreign demand. Limitations were put on exports and there was some rationing of supplies to U.S. mills. Prices went to all-time highs in the United States and to fantastic levels in some of the foreign countries that customarily looked to the United States for supplies.

The season average price to U.S. growers rose from 28.6 cents in 1949 to 40 cents in 1950, and prices of more than double that amount were reported in some foreign markets. Both the high prices and the uncertainty as to availability of U.S.-grown supplies undoubtedly had some tendency to stimulate efforts by some foreign countries to become more self-sufficient or to grow larger quantities of cotton for export.

18. There was a relatively small continuing program for American Egyptian (long-staple) cotton, which is not included in the figures given here. The carry-over in CCC ownership as of June 30, 1950 was only 582 bales valued at $169,000.

19. See U.S. Production and Marketing Administration, *Review of Operations—Commodity Credit Corporation—Fiscal Year 1950*, pp. 4, 5, and table summarizing Cotton Branch program activities, and *ibid.*, fiscal 1951, pp. 4, 5, and Cotton Branch table.

A further stimulus to cotton production in the newer, western cotton-producing areas of the United States was provided and some further impetus to the development of capacity for producing competing synthetics both in the United States and abroad. Some, at least, of the representatives of cotton producers considered so sharp an increase in prices as unstabilizing to the industry and undesirable from an industry standpoint.

The shortage that developed was not due to inadequate carry-overs. It came about as a result of an unduly drastic cutback of acreage (from 27.4 million to 17.8 million), somewhat lower yields and a large but unforeseeable increase in demand. The cutback of acreage was not primarily a result of government action in applying acreage allotments, since the acreage grown was substantially smaller than that allotted. The experience did demonstrate, however, that seemingly large government-held stocks can disappear rather quickly under some conditions and that moderately heavy stocks may be desirable in the national interest in times of great uncertainty in world affairs.

Controls Abandoned in 1951

Since cotton stocks were low and demand still strong, no allotments or marketing quotas were announced for the 1951 season. Price supports at 90 per cent of parity (about 28 cents per pound) were continued as provided by the legislation then in effect. However, since the support level was well below the market price, the price supports provided did not affect the situation in any important way. The season average price to farmers in 1951 was 37.88 cents and in 1952 it was 34.59 cents.

However, the high prices of the 1950 season and the abandonment of controls did result in a sharp increase in acreage and production. Harvested acreage increased by more than 50 per cent (from 17.8 million to 26.9 million) and production was some 50 per cent higher than in 1950. With shortages still to be made up and a continuing strong demand, no surplus developed. Prices remained high, though somewhat lower than in 1950.

There were no serious problems from the standpoint either of CCC or the cotton producers in the 1951 and 1952 fiscal years. The 90 per cent of parity support rate in 1952 was about 30.5 cents, as a result of a rising general price level, but still was well below the market price. In that year, the support arrangements also, for the first time, included purchase agreements. Loans were made on 1.1 million bales in the amount of some $172 million, but virtually all of the loans were repaid at or before maturity. As of the end of the 1952–53 fiscal year, CCC held only 236,000 bales valued at $32.7 million. However, exports of cotton fell off sharply in 1952 and there were indications of coming problems if cotton production continued at the 1951–52 level of about 15 million bales.

Surpluses in the 1953 and 1954 Seasons

By 1953, the cotton problem was again much the same as in 1948 and 1949. Production continued heavy and demand, especially export demand, was falling off. Exports in the 1952 season amounted to 3.0 million bales as compared with 5.5 million in 1951 and 4.1 million in 1950. They had been as high as nearly 5.8 million bales in 1949. In the period 1929–1933, exports averaged above 7 million bales per year and mounted to 8.7 million bales in the 1931 season.[20]

The loan rate on 1953 cotton was 30.8 cents. New loans amounting to $1,121 million were made on 41.5 per cent of the cotton produced (as compared with 15 per cent of the 1952 crop put under loan). About 23 per cent of the loans had been repaid by the end of the fiscal year, leaving a balance outstanding, on 1953 cotton, of $861 million, about three times the corresponding figure for the 1952 crop.

The 1953 yield and production were high. Though the acreage harvested was less than in 1949, 1951 and 1952, yields were higher and the outturn was larger than in those years. Yields were at an all-time high of 324 pounds per acre, almost double the customary yields of the early 1930s. The result was a total output of 16.5 million bales, which was well above the amount required for domestic production and exports.

Acreage controls were reimposed in 1954. The total allotment of 17.9 million acres, announced in October and November 1953, was later raised to 21.4 million. The increase resulted from the passage of Public Law 290 (January 30, 1954), which modified the allotments previously announced. The heaviest percentage cuts were in the western states. The over-all average called for a reduction of 16 per cent from the acreage grown in 1953. The increased allotment was not fully planted. The estimated acreage in cultivation on July 1 was about 22 per cent less than a year earlier.

The 1954 production on 19.8 million acres was about 13.7 million bales, which was enough to result in a further increase in carry-over of 1.4 million bales. With that addition, the August 1, 1955 carry-over was up to 11.1 million bales, approximately a full year's supply for domestic consumption and exports. It was the largest carry-over since 1945, when stocks amounted to 11.2 million bales. Of this total, CCC held 8.1 million bales. The total carry-overs (private and CCC) had been increasing from August 1, 1951 but did not become large enough to be a matter of serious concern until the 1953 and 1954 seasons. However, CCC holdings had been increasing continuously not only in amount but as a percentage of total holdings.[21]

20. U.S. Department of Agriculture, *The Cotton Situation,* November 1955, p. 23.

21. Data here and above are from U.S. Agricultural Marketing Service, *The Cotton Situation,* August 26, 1955, p. 5.

Program Modifications in 1954 and 1955

Under the Agricultural Act of 1954, approved on August 28, the Secretary of Agriculture could, for the first time since 1942, provide supports on basic crops at less than 90 per cent of parity, subject to the conditions specified in the various legislative acts. The rate for 1955 could range from 82.5 to 90 per cent of parity and presumably thereafter from 75 to 90 per cent as provided in the 1949 act.

However, various other legislative and administrative actions modified these provisions and affected the cotton situation in a number of ways. The Agricultural Act of 1954 directed the Commodity Credit Corporation to set aside specified quantities of certain commodities held by it with a view to disposing of them through noncommercial channels. The total set-aside, for all commodities, was not to exceed $2.5 billion in value. For cotton, the set-aside was to be a minimum of 3 million bales and a maximum of 4 million bales. In accordance with this directive, 3 million bales of upland cotton were set aside early in 1955 and could not thereafter be included in computing supply percentage, as related to normal, in determining the level of price-support loans.

In view of that, the support level for the 1955 crop was put at 90 per cent of parity (31.7 cents per pound) for upland cotton, and acreage allotments and marketing quotas were announced. The support level for long-staple cotton, which was in large supply and subject to the provisions of the Agricultural Act of 1949, was put at 75 per cent of parity (55.2 cents). The total acreage allotment was put at 18.1 million, 3.3 million smaller than the 1954 allotment. The largest reductions (about 20 per cent) were in Oklahoma and Georgia.

During the 1953, 1954 and 1955 seasons the prices received by farmers were determined mainly by the levels of support provided and by the selling policies under which CCC operated. Spot cotton for mill use was at times on the short side despite the large government holdings. The season average price to farmers in 1953 was 32.25 cents; the 1954 price, 33.7 cents; and the price as of September 15, 1955, 33.77 cents. Thus the price actually received was in each of the years slightly above the support level.[22]

At the same time efforts were being made to increase exports. Public Law 480, passed on July 10, 1954, authorized the Secretary of Agriculture to accept up to $700 million in foreign currencies as repayment for surplus agricultural commodities shipped abroad to friendly nations. The maximum authorized for such transactions was later increased to $1.5 billion.[23] In addition, the Mutual Security Act of 1954 permitted

22. Some part of this differential may also have been due to differences in quality between the cotton actually sold and the grades specified as the basis for price supports.

23. The same act authorized gifts of surplus U.S. farm products for famine relief at home and abroad and for other purposes in an amount not to exceed $300 million. However, this part of the act had little bearing on the cotton situation.

the use of up to $350 million for export of surplus farm products for foreign currencies, and some further operations of that kind were carried out by the Foreign Operations Administration, partly with funds appropriated under Section 550 of the Mutual Security Act of 1951. During the fiscal year beginning July 1954 the expenditures on cotton amounted to $280 million and financed the export of 1.5 million bales.[24]

1955 Crop Larger Than Expected

A phenomenally high yield of cotton in 1955 (416 pounds per acre, which was much above any previously recorded) resulted in a 14.7-million-bale crop. This brought the total 1955–56 supply up to 25.7 million bales, an all-time record. Mill consumption was expected to reach 9.2 million bales and exports about 2.5 million, which would leave 14 million bales in the carry-over.

The most significant problems facing growers and the government were how to liquidate the surplus stocks that had accumulated and adjust production more nearly in line with current requirements for domestic consumption and exports.

CHANGES AND DEVELOPMENTS, 1933–1955

Cotton Acreage Reduced and Stabilized under Controls

Between 1932 and 1941, cotton plantings were reduced by about 20 million acres. Also, the annual variations in plantings were much less than in the years when the crop was not under control though prices continued to influence plantings to some extent. When the support price of cotton was relatively high, plantings pressed against allotments, but as alternative opportunities for the use of the land improved, plantings fell away from allotments.

A period of freedom from controls, which began in 1944, demonstrated that other crops and livestock had established a firm position as replacements for cotton on much of the land east of the Mississippi River. That shift had been encouraged by restrictions on cotton planting, on the one hand, and by conservation payments, agricultural extension efforts and the development of better markets for alternative products on the other. The postwar developments, particularly in 1949 and 1951, suggest that the eastern cotton belt may have passed the stage of needing continuous controls to hold down or stabilize cotton plantings.

With freedom from controls there was a significant shift in acreage and production toward the West. Total 1949 plantings exceeded the 22-million-acre average of the ten years ending in 1948 by more than 6 million acres. Half of the increase was in Texas and Oklahoma. It

24. See *The Cotton Situation,* January 30, 1956. Some funds were also being made available in the form of loans from the Export-Import Bank.

consisted largely of a shift into west Texas but resulted in part from the loss of wheat acreage in northwest Texas and in Oklahoma. Another million-acre increase occurred on the irrigated lands of New Mexico, Arizona and California. These changes were, in the main, shifts of cotton production to new areas with lower costs of production per unit. The recovery and further expansion in those areas in 1951, after a year of control, was a move in the same direction. No large further expansion in Oklahoma and Texas seems likely even without controls, since water and weather place fairly definite limits on the acreage available for cotton production.

Yields Not Subject to Control

Under control, yields have increased and have continued to be highly variable. One of the most significant factors in determining yields in the eastern cotton belt is the application of fertilizer. In the early years the control programs included provisions for keeping down the amounts of fertilizer used, but these restraints were soon abandoned. Acreage restrictions contributed to the increase in yields; there were strong inducements for farmers to withdraw from cultivation the lower-yielding acres while at the same time price supports encouraged increased applications of fertilizer as a means of obtaining more cotton per acre. Moreover, the conservation programs tended to build up the fertility of the soil by encouraging the rotation of crops. Improved cultural practices also helped to increase yields. In areas where cotton continued to be the best-paying crop, at support levels, and where increased applications of fertilizer were profitable, there were remarkable improvements in yields. In the state of Mississippi, for example, increased yields offset the reductions in acreage so that production in the early 1950s averaged higher than in the years before controls were applied.

The combination of factors operating to improve yields increased the average yield per harvested acre from 174 pounds in the years prior to the inauguration of the program to 222 pounds in the first period after controls were initiated and to more than 300 pounds for the period 1946–1955. During this latter period controls were not in effect continuously. However, the stimulus for the increase had come about largely as a result of controls, and the conservation payments provided gave continuing encouragement to growers to increase cotton yields. By 1945–1955, yields had increased on the average by about 70 per cent as compared with those that were customary in the years before the cotton program was put into effect. Though yields have been increased, the program has made little if any contribution to their year-to-year stabilization, as is apparent from the data given above. In the years 1945 to 1955, yields ranged from as low as 236 pounds to as high as 416 pounds even when controls were in operation.

Acreage allotments and marketing quotas are effective in controlling acreage but not yields. Since the quotas are related to the production from the allotted acres, total production may be larger or smaller than plans call for because of variations in yield. The upward trend in yields has resulted in some increase in production even with acreage under control.

Effects of CCC Operations and Government Payments

The Commodity Credit Corporation has had an important price-stabilizing influence by extending loans to producers to enable them to postpone sales when faced with declining prices and business depression. Prices were raised in 1933 and were maintained in the 1933–1935, 1937–1940 and 1948–1949 seasons at levels that were higher than they would have been otherwise. The rising price level and war inflation contributed to the realization of higher prices for cotton carried through several seasons. Growers profited from loans on the cotton that was carried in pools until prices were high enough to more than cover loans and carrying charges. These gains both to the farmers and to CCC were due in large part to the inflationary tendencies that characterized the period here under review. In a period of declining prices like that of 1929–1932 such holding of stocks would, of course, result in heavy losses of the kind experienced by the Federal Farm Board.

Government payments made directly to producers for compliance with programs contributed significantly to the increase and maintenance of grower incomes. Rental and benefit, conservation, price adjustment and parity payments on cotton through the 1933–1943 seasons amounted to about $1,630 million. Though the price adjustment and parity payments, amounting to $442 million, were made as aids toward approximating parity price returns to farmers, they also served as incentives to induce compliance under the programs.

Consumption and Exports Affected Mainly by Economic Conditions

Large crops resulting from high yields may have to be marketed in times of declining prices and business depression, as in 1931 and 1937. In a business depression, reducing the price of cotton has little effect on consumption, primarily because the cost of the raw material constitutes only a small part of the cost of the final product. Also, many consumers may defer the purchase of cotton fabrics for one or more seasons.

Synthetics and Foreign Production

Before the great depression rayon was an insignificant factor in the market. The price was high and the annual consumption averaged less than one pound per capita. Domestic cotton consumption in the same period averaged about 27 pounds per capita. The price of rayon came down to the level of cotton prices at the beginning of World War II. The quality of that fiber also was improved in such a way as to make it a strong competitor of cotton in many uses. Since 1943, rayon has been cheaper than cotton and its uses have been extended in many directions in competition with cotton.

Between 1933 and 1953 rayon consumption in the United States increased from the equivalent of about 500,000 bales of cotton to an amount that would take the place of more than 3.5 million bales of cotton. Of that increase, about a million bales were added before World War II while the price of rayon was being adjusted downward to the level of cotton prices. Another million bales were added in the five years 1942–1947 as cotton prices advanced above the level of rayon prices. Thereafter, with cotton prices considerably higher, rayon consumption was increased by another million bales by 1953.

The domestic mill consumption of man-made fibers increased from 7.3 pounds per capita in 1949 to 11.2 pounds in 1955. Cotton consumption per capita increased from 25.7 pounds in 1949 to 31.5 in 1951 because of the outbreak of war in Korea and thereafter declined to 25.4 pounds in 1954 and 26.3 pounds in 1955. Thus the competition from rayon has not reduced per capita cotton consumption but it apparently has tended to check its expansion.[25]

Consumer surveys indicate that both rayon and cotton have preferential values in certain uses. In the war period the use of cotton was extended in some industrial materials while rayon was extended in others. Both seem to have firmly established markets. Yet it is evident that they are competitive.

Relative prices are undoubtedly a significant factor in determining the extension of marginal uses of both cotton and rayon. Rayon staple fiber has been cheaper than its cotton fiber equivalent since 1943. In 1949 rayon staple fiber was about 37 cents per pound, which was equivalent in yarn value to cotton then priced at about 39 cents. In 1955 the price of the rayon fiber had declined to about 36 cents per pound whereas the price of comparable cotton was more than 40 cents per pound. This decline in the price of rayon staple fiber in relation to the price of cotton is undoubtedly a factor in increasing the consumption of rayon.

Increased production and consumption of rayon in foreign countries continued to hold in check, if not to reduce, the export demand for American cotton. Foreign production of rayon increased to the equivalent of nearly 4.5 million bales between 1929 and 1941, and thus contributed to the reduction in U.S. exports of cotton. During the war years,

25. Cotton consumption reached a level of 41 pounds per capita in 1942, but that was a result of heavy military requirements. Rayon consumption did not show a corresponding rise.

rayon production in foreign countries declined, but after the war it recovered and expanded. By 1954 foreign production had reached a new record level of 8,355,000 bales.

The foreign mill consumption of cotton of all growths had recovered to the highest prewar levels by 1951 and has increased since then to new record levels. The larger production of cotton in foreign countries has provided the basis for the increase in consumption. Between 1949 and 1954 the production of foreign cotton increased by 6 million bales. Foreign production and consumption of synthetic fibers increased in the same period by the equivalent of 4 million bales of cotton. The expansion of foreign cotton and rayon production helped to reduce the exports of American cotton from 5,769,000 bales in 1949 to 3,446,000 in the 1954 season.

Foreign cotton production now seems likely to continue to increase in volume and to improve in quality, thus increasing the competition with American cotton. Before World War II, the strongest competition was in Brazil, where cotton was replacing coffee. The expansion of cotton production in Brazil has been checked but in the meantime Mexico has become an important producer and exporter. Production is increasing to a significant extent in several Central American countries, in Turkey and several other countries in Asia, and in parts of Africa. The continued maintenance of a relatively high price level for American cotton in foreign markets would encourage further expansion in many of these areas.

In view of the prospect for increased production of rayon in foreign countries and the maintenance of a high level of foreign cotton production, the prospect of increasing or even of maintaining the current volume of exports of American cotton does not appear bright unless or until there is a significant increase in over-all textile consumption in foreign countries.

Incomes of Cotton Producers

The predepression dollar income from cotton was restored early in the war period. The receipts from cotton marketings had been reduced from $1,442 million in 1929 to $484 million in 1932. The support program helped materially in raising the cash income from cotton to about $916 million in the first year of operations. In that year government payments constituted 20 per cent of the total. By 1943 the dollar income from cotton was back up to the 1929 level. However, the number of farms producing cotton in the cotton belt had been reduced by 20 per cent, so the income per cotton producer was materially higher than in 1929. By 1949 the income from cotton was much higher than in 1929 and was shared by an even smaller number of farmers.

The increased income in the cotton belt from other sources is even more significant than the increase in dollar income from cotton. The forced reduction in cotton and the shift to other products decreased the proportion of gross farm income received from cotton and cottonseed from a predepression level of 50 per cent to about 25 per cent by the early 1950s. Livestock and livestock products have become more important than cotton as a source of income; the average receipts from marketings in the ten cotton belt states in the years 1949–1951 were more than double the average for the period 1924–1929. Though farm prices and incomes in the cotton belt have declined from the levels reached in the postwar years, they have not declined as much as those in some of the other agricultural regions.

In conclusion, cotton producers have made significant readjustments in the use of their resources. They have greatly increased productivity, and the diversity of production has helped to stabilize incomes. However, they are facing serious problems in holding markets for their cotton in competition with synthetic fibers and with cotton produced abroad. They also have the problem of adjusting production to what the markets will take.

2

Tobacco

TOBACCO has been one of the most important cash crops of North America since colonial times. In recent years it has ranked fourth, after cotton, wheat and corn, as a source of cash receipts from marketings.

Though tobacco provides only about 8 per cent of the total cash receipts from crops and only 4 per cent of the cash income from all farm products, it is very important in the agricultural economies of several states. It is of some significance as a source of farm income in a few of the northern states, particularly in Connecticut, Pennsylvania, Wisconsin and Ohio, and is second only to cotton in the South. It provides about one tenth of the cash receipts of the cotton belt states. More than half of the cash income from crops in North Carolina and a third of that in Kentucky is derived from tobacco. Tobacco is also an important source of income in South Carolina, Virginia, Tennessee, Georgia and Maryland. In fact, the increased income received for tobacco has contributed more than that of any other crop to the improvement of economic conditions in several southern states since the outbreak of World War II.[1]

Much of the tobacco produced is exported. Conditions in the foreign markets as well as in the United States are therefore very important to tobacco growers. Though tobacco exports constitute only about 8 per cent of the total value of U.S. agricultural exports, the foreign market takes about 25 per cent of the tobacco crop.

Weak Bargaining Position of Growers

The free-market price of tobacco fluctuates greatly from season to season because of variations in production as well as in demand. Domestic consumption is more stable than production. Tobacco is storable for relatively long periods. Processors customarily accumulate stocks and keep on hand more than the amount required to supply their yearly needs. Stocks may accumulate from a series of high-production seasons to such an extent that buyers for domestic processors become rather indifferent to the supplies offered. Producers, however, must sell current crops as they become available and thus they may be in a very inferior

1. See U.S. Bureau of Agricultural Economics, *The Tobacco Situation,* May 1952, p. 38.

bargaining position. Also, accumulations abroad and international trade disturbances may cause significant changes in the annual purchases for export.

Tobacco growers are small independent operators. As a rule, they are not in a position to hold crops from one season to another. Most of them are in urgent need of cash from their crops as soon as they are harvested. Few growers have facilities for storage or proper conditioning for sale at some later date. In the past, efforts to develop voluntary producer cooperative agencies for providing necessary funds and facilities and effective bargaining arrangements have generally failed after short periods of trial. On the other hand, the buying of tobacco both for domestic processing and for export has for years been highly concentrated in a few firms. Consequently there has been a long history of conflict between producers and buyers growing out of the efforts made by the producers to maintain or increase their bargaining power as compared with that of the buyers.

The most intense struggle between tobacco producers and buyers developed around the turn of the century. The American Tobacco Company, incorporated in 1890, had extended its control over domestic manufacturing until by 1910 it controlled more than 75 per cent of all tobacco products except cigars. It had also developed foreign connections and had become an important factor in buying for the foreign market. In the meantime, tobacco prices had fallen to the lowest level on record. The average price of tobacco in Kentucky in 1898 was only 4 cents per pound. Production was reduced and prices advanced to 6 cents but they held at about that level through the next four years.

These conditions gave rise to bitter feeling against the American Tobacco Company and stimulated producers to organize for the purpose of reducing acreage and increasing their bargaining power. An organization called the Dark District Planters' Association was formed in the dark-tobacco district of Kentucky and Tennessee. It was succeeded in 1904 by the Planters' Protective Association. Beginning in December 1905, in the "Black Patch" of Kentucky and Tennessee, masked, armed and mounted men raided several towns and burned factories and warehouses. They also attacked growers who refused to join the Planters' Association.

Later, the campaign was extended to the burley areas. The Burley Tobacco Society secured control of large parts of the crops of 1906 and 1907 and held them for higher prices. With warehouses full and two stored crops on hand, they decided to cut out the 1908 crop. That crop was greatly reduced. Prices increased and the accumulated stocks were finally sold at more satisfactory levels. In the meantime, the American Society of Equity in Wisconsin had organized twenty local associations, which built warehouses to handle their crops. Under its auspices an Interstate Tobacco Growers' Protective Association was organized in

Virginia and North Carolina. The objectives of these organizations were to control planting or restrict acreages and withhold stocks from the market as a means of increasing their bargaining power with the tobacco buyers. They achieved some degree of success under their policy of fixing prices and waiting for the buyers to come to them.[2]

The dissolution of the American Tobacco Company, by decree of the Supreme Court in 1911, had no significant effect on the position of tobacco growers, for the successor companies were able to maintain the concentration of bargaining power in the hands of the manufacturers. Some of the cooperative associations continued to operate for some years, but their strength waned as prices advanced with the increase of demand in the World War I period.

Renewed Interest in Cooperation in the 1920s

A break in prices began in 1920. The average price for all tobaccos declined from a record high of 31 cents per pound for the 1919 crop to 17 cents for the 1920 crop. In Kentucky, prices dropped from 24 cents to 11 cents; in North Carolina, from 49 cents to 21 cents. This setback again stimulated cooperative organization. Organizers were temporarily successful in signing up many growers and forming what seemed to be strong associations. The Burley Tobacco Growers' Cooperative Association, incorporated in 1921, reported a sign-up of about 75 per cent of the burley crop. The Tobacco Growers' Tri-State Cooperative Association, incorporated early in 1922, reported that more than half of the flue-cured, dark fire-cured and dark air-cured growers of Virginia, North Carolina and South Carolina had signed up with the association. These cooperatives concentrated more on market controls than on production controls.

A substantial cutback of production, in response to the depression, contributed to a prompt price recovery from the low levels of 1920. Production was reduced about one third in 1921 as compared with 1920 and the average farm price advanced from 17.3 cents per pound for the 1920 season to 22.8 cents for the 1922 season. While this was considerably below the high level reached in 1919, it was double the prewar average, though the crop was about a fourth larger than those of the prewar period. Moreover, the price of tobacco was still high in relation to the prices of alternative crops. A higher level of domestic and foreign demand maintained prices near the 1921–22 level for most seasons until 1930, when a new record crop and the beginning of a major

2. William H. Nicholls, *Price Policies in the Cigarette Industry*, Vanderbilt University Press, Nashville, 1951, p. 214. See also "Beginnings of Cooperative Tobacco Marketing," Division of Cooperative Marketing, Federal Farm Board, October 1931, pp. 4–5, mimeo.

The area in tobacco in Kentucky was reduced from 430,000 acres in 1906 to 275,000 in 1908. Prices averaged 7.7 cents in 1906 and 9.1 cents in 1908. An average of 10.6 cents was paid for the large crop of the next season.

business depression reduced the average farm price to less than 13 cents per pound.

The cooperative associations that came into being around 1920 increased their membership for a few years and they handled a large part of the crops of their members. After 1923, however, the percentage of the crop they handled began to decline. The most important factors in their decline and subsequent failure appeared to be the lack of power to force members to deliver their crops to them and the relatively satisfactory level of prices. The attitude of buyers was also a factor. They seemed to prefer to buy at auctions rather than to negotiate with the agents of the cooperatives.[3] Producers who were in great need of cash could obtain only a relatively small share of the current values of their crops as advances from the cooperatives, whereas at the independent auction sales they could obtain current market values, which were increased to some extent by the action of the cooperatives in withholding supplies from the market.

TOBACCO UNDER THE FEDERAL FARM BOARD

The Federal Farm Board legislation and programs of 1929 seemed made to order for tobacco growers. One of the officials of the Burley Tobacco Growers' Cooperative Association was appointed to membership on the Board but his cooperative remained inactive. There were only two small tobacco cooperatives in operation when the Board was organized. Apparently the failure of the cooperative movement in the early 1920s and the sustained demand for tobacco without their support discouraged further cooperative developments and a prompt response to the opportunities offered by the Board. Doubtless the cooperative experience of the early 1920s also caused the Board to be cautious about undertaking tobacco stabilization operations without the prospect of stronger controls over production.

However, the harvesting of larger tobacco crops in 1929 and 1930, in the face of an oncoming business depression, again stimulated interest in cooperative activity and in government aid. The Farm Board conducted educational and advisory programs to encourage tobacco cooperatives and offered some financial aid.

The first new organization was in South Carolina, for the 1930 crop. The farm price for that crop was about a third lower than for the 1929 crop. The Board advanced funds to aid in handling the 1930 crop but the 1931 crop was also large and prices were lower. The cooperative did not operate in 1931 but prices advanced enough later to make it possible for the Farm Board to recover the loan on the 1930 crop.

Accumulating stocks and low prices in other areas stimulated action

3. Nicholls, *op. cit.*, p. 218. See also T. J. Woofter, Jr., *The Plight of Cigarette Tobacco,* University of North Carolina Press, Chapel Hill, 1931, pp. 8–12, 93–95.

in the 1931 and 1932 seasons. The farm price of fire-cured types dropped from 13.3 cents per pound for the 1929 season to 5.1 cents for the 1931 season. In Kentucky and Tennessee prices again reached the low level which in the early 1900s had produced "night riders" and "cutout" campaigns. The Farm Board advanced funds to aid in the organization of several grower co-ops to handle fire-cured tobacco. In all, the Board advanced $6 million, of which $3 million was repaid to it. The Farm Credit Administration eventually collected the balance. The Reconstruction Finance Corporation also extended loans to these tobacco cooperatives and accumulated a considerable volume of collateral, which was subsequently (in 1936) turned over to the Commodity Credit Corporation.

Tobacco buyers were more successful than growers in cooperating, coordinating activities and following the leaders. A leading tobacco firm advanced the price of cigarettes in October 1929 and again in June 1931, despite lower leaf costs and declining consumer purchasing power. Others promptly followed. Apparently the advance was intended to increase the revenues available for advertising. The net profits on the equities of the four leading tobacco manufacturers increased from 17 per cent to over 19 per cent in 1930 and 1931. In dollars, the net profits of these four concerns exceeded the cash receipts of growers for all tobacco sold for domestic consumption and exports in 1932.

Tobacco manufacturers for the domestic market learned, however, that there are limits to monopoly power and that even advertising cannot sell more tobacco to consumers in times of severe depression. Tobacco consumption declined. Some consumers responded to the increase in cigarette prices by shifting to roll-your-own and pipe smoking. The production and consumption of economy brands increased, bringing some competition into the leaf markets from adventurous smaller operators. The profits of the leading companies declined, and by 1933 they were ready to make adjustments to changing conditions. They reduced the prices of their products and were willing to cooperate with the government and growers in stabilizing the leaf market.

Growers, under pressure of the lower prices of 1931, had reduced voluntarily the area harvested from about 2 million acres to about 1.4 million. The crop was reduced by more than a third. However, the demand also had been reduced; both exports and consumption had declined. The smaller crop of 1932 still was slightly in excess of consumption and exports. Prices advanced somewhat but there was some further accumulation of stocks. The advance in prices was not sufficient to offset the reduction in volume marketed. The gross income from the 1932 crop was only about 40 per cent of the predepression level. Early in 1933, while the emergency agricultural legislation was being formulated, representatives of growers worked with members of the U.S. Department of Agriculture to outline programs for tobacco.

EMERGENCY AGRICULTURAL ADJUSTMENT ACT

Inclusion of tobacco in the list of basic commodities in the Agricultural Adjustment Act of 1933 provided an opportunity to apply production control and marketing agreement measures for the relief of tobacco growers. The only significant issue that developed in deciding whether to include tobacco was the question of the base period to be used in determining "fair exchange value." The voluntary crop reduction in 1932 had resulted in a rise of prices to about the pre-World War I average level, but it was recognized that war and postwar conditions had materially increased the demand for tobacco. This increase in demand had resulted in some significant shifts in production and in changes in price relations which were reflected in postwar price levels. In view of these considerations, the predepression ten-year period 1919–1929 was designated as the base period for tobacco, though the parity base used for most other farm products was 1910–1914.

Use of the prewar 1910–1914 base for tobacco would have indicated that the average price received for the 1932 crop was about at parity, but this was producing a very low level of income. The use of the postwar 1919–1929 base raised the base level about 60 per cent over what it would have been on the prewar base. Another point considered in adoption of the postwar base was that the statistical basis for determining price parities by types of tobacco had been greatly improved in the postwar years. The demand for the different types had shifted since the prewar period. The use of the postwar base period reflected this shift and provided a relatively higher exchange value for the types in greater demand.

The development of a program for tobacco was complicated by the fact that production and consumption are highly specialized. Tobacco is really a group of crops with distinctive characteristics and uses. The substitution of different kinds of tobacco in the several different uses is so limited that excessive accumulations of stocks of some kinds may occur at the same time that there is a scarcity of others. In fact, changes in the trend of demand for the several different kinds of tobacco had affected both prices and supplies.

The Agricultural Adjustment Act provided an opportunity for recognizing significant differences and for developing programs suited to the different types. It provided that "any regional or market classification, type or grade" of a "basic commodity" could be treated separately as a "basic commodity." [4] The Department of Agriculture had established in 1919 seven distinct classes of tobacco and had developed statistics relating to them. The classes were officially designated as flue-cured, fire-cured, air-cured, cigar filler, cigar binder, cigar wrapper and miscel-

4. Section 11, Agricultural Adjustment Act of 1933, Public Law 10, 73d Cong., approved May 12, 1933.

laneous domestic.[5] In practice, these classes are variously subdivided. For example, in common use, burley, Maryland and Virginia sun-cured types are separated from the air-cured class. Tobacco grown in Puerto Rico also is classified and is sometimes included in the cigar filler and cigar binder classes of the continental tobaccos.

Characteristics of the Different Classes

Flue-cured was the most important of the tobacco crops. It was produced in the southeastern states, with the heaviest concentration in North Carolina, Virginia and South Carolina. On the average, this crop amounted to about half the total U.S. production. Its principal domestic use was in cigarettes and more than half the crop was exported. The demand for it in both the domestic and foreign markets had been increasing.

Burley was by far the most important type of the air-cured tobaccos. It constituted about a fourth of the total U.S. crop. At that time burley was used to a significant extent in various kinds of pipe smoking and chewing tobacco. It was beginning to be used extensively in the manufacture of cigarettes but very little of it was exported. The production was concentrated in Kentucky with extensions into Tennessee, North Carolina, Virginia, West Virginia, Ohio and Indiana.

Maryland tobacco somewhat resembles burley. The volume of production was relatively small and fairly stable. Some of it was used in cigarettes and a considerable amount was exported.

The fire-cured class of tobacco, produced mainly in the western parts of Kentucky and Tennessee, was next in importance to burley in production and second only to flue-cured in exports. The principal domestic use was in the manufacture of snuff. It was used to some extent in pipe smoking mixtures and in chewing tobacco. Demand, both domestic and foreign, for this kind of tobacco had been declining.

The dark air-cured tobacco grown in Kentucky, Tennessee and southern Indiana and the Virginia sun-cured produced in Virginia have qualities which make them adaptable domestically for use principally in chewing tobacco and snuff. Small quantities were used in smoking mixtures. Both the domestic and foreign consumption had been declining.

Cigar tobaccos are commonly classified in three groups—fillers, binders and wrappers. They are produced in widely scattered areas ranging from the Connecticut Valley of New England south to Georgia and Florida and west to Wisconsin and Minnesota, primarily for domestic consumption. The demand had declined to some extent.

Pursuant to authority given in the Agricultural Adjustment Act, the

5. "Classification of Leaf Tobacco Covering Classes, Types, and Groups of Grades," U.S. Department of Agriculture, *Service and Regulatory Announcement No. 118*, November 1929.

Secretary of Agriculture designated the following classes or types as basic commodities:

flue-cured, types 11–14
burley, type 31
Maryland, type 32
fire-cured, types 21–24
dark air-cured, types 35–36
cigar, types 41–56

Some types were not included at that time in the list of basic commodities. Virginia sun-cured was omitted from the dark air-cured class, and the cigar types excluded cigar wrappers. The designation of basic commodities was intended primarily to authorize the application of processing taxes to those classes and types. Other programs were to be developed for the tobaccos not included in the list.

Shortly after the Adjustment Act was signed, the Department's Tobacco Committee reported on the condition of the tobacco industry and offered suggestions for programs. The report stressed the necessity of adjusting production to clear the accumulated stocks and restore a normal balance between supplies and requirements. Attention was called to the possibility of using marketing agreements to obtain better prices to producers. Representatives of growers and processors and of agricultural colleges as well were invited to confer with members of the Department to consider proposals for relief.

Cigar Tobaccos

The principal recommendation of the Department committee was that early efforts should be confined largely to cigar tobaccos. Because of a sharp decline in consumption, a large accumulation of stocks, and very low prices, the need for adjustment in the cigar tobacco districts was considered most pressing. Furthermore, it appeared more feasible to establish control quickly over the cigar tobaccos than over other classes because cigar types are planted somewhat later and production is more highly concentrated.

Cigar fillers and binders were in the most distressed condition. The acreage harvested and the production of these types had continued to increase in the 1929–1931 seasons even though consumption was declining and stocks were accumulating. Declining prices caused many growers to cut acreage in 1932 and unfavorable crop conditions reduced production in some areas. Consumption increased, but not enough to have much effect on stocks. Prices continued to decline. The average farm price for cigar fillers fell from about 13 cents per pound in the 1929 season to less than 5 cents in the 1932 season and binders fell from 20 cents to 7 cents. The low prices and smaller crops in the 1932 season resulted in very low incomes. The gross income for these two classes of tobacco fell from $26 million in the 1929 season to only $8 million for the 1932 crop.

The fact that the accumulated stocks of cigar filler and binder were sufficient to supply average domestic consumption for a period of three years was an important consideration in developing a program for these tobaccos. The acreage had to be reduced enough to clear the market of excessive stocks. The program, announced in July 1933, provided for establishing a base acreage for each grower from which the acreage harvested was to be reduced by 50 per cent. If a grower had made substantial reductions in the preceding years, that was to be taken into account in establishing the base acreage. If he had planted for 1933 harvesting more than 50 per cent of that base, he was to plow up or not harvest the excess acreage.

The result was that the acreage of cigar filler tobacco harvested in 1933 was reduced 50 per cent, and of cigar binder nearly 50 per cent, as compared with 1932. Production was reduced correspondingly, even slightly more. But since consumption also dropped to a low level, stocks were reduced only moderately and the advance in prices was also very moderate. Receipts from marketings declined, but payments from processing taxes made substantial contributions to incomes.

No production or marketing quotas were provided for the cigar filler and binder tobaccos. Growers were permitted to market the production from allotted acres but were prohibited from increasing yields by adopting unusual "cultural practices" or by applying more fertilizer than they used in 1932.

The moderate reduction in stocks and the established low level of production prepared the way for price improvements in the seasons that followed. The acreage contracts for 1934 and 1935 required the same reduction from base as in 1933. In 1934, growers in some areas made even greater reductions than were required of them. Consumption increased after the 1933 season and stocks were reduced. With prices advancing generally, the prices of these classes of tobacco also advanced and by 1936 were more than double those of 1932. The payments from processing taxes, together with the advance in prices, brought a substantial recovery in incomes.

Programs in Other Areas

A somewhat different program was developed for the Puerto Rican growers of filler and binder tobaccos. The 1933 contracts with these growers required them to harvest only one crop from the acreage planted whereas some of them customarily harvested more than one. The terms of the contracts for the 1934 and 1935 crops also required substantial reductions in the amounts harvested.

The cigar wrapper tobaccos, not included in the designated basic commodity list, were in a better position than the binders and fillers. Production had been sharply decreased from 1929 through the 1932 season and prices had declined much less. The prices of these tobaccos were, in fact, close to parity. However, there were heavy accumulations of stocks to be moved into consumption. The acreage increased moderately after 1933 with consumption increasing and prices rising.

The Georgia-Florida shade growers had reduced acreage to a low level in 1933 and no further reduction was required by the program developed for this type of tobacco. However, they were required to forego harvesting some leaves of the plants and to limit marketings to not more than a specified quantity per acre. Because this type of tobacco was subject to processing taxes, rental and benefit payments were made to growers for compliance with their contracts. A revision of the contract in the 1934 season provided for acreage allotments and limitations on the number of pounds to be sold. However, the conditions of the contract permitted some increase in acreage and production in 1934 over the low level of 1933.

The shade growers of the Connecticut Valley, in cooperation with representatives of the processors and the Department of Agriculture, developed a significantly different program which required no reduction in acreage or production. The acreage and production of shade-grown wrapper tobacco in that area had already been reduced by about 50 per cent from the 1929 level. The program was designed to stabilize production and provide an opportunity for moving the excess accumulated stocks. From the outset it was a stabilization program. It was, moreover, not considered temporary but was to operate until terminated by the Secretary or at the request of 75 per cent of the handlers.[6] In some respects it was a forerunner of the subsequent development of operations by cooperatives designed to carry out price-support programs.

Representatives of the Connecticut Valley Shade Growers' Association worked out with the Department a program providing for control of production and marketing under a marketing agreement and order. The plan provided for allotment of acreage to individual growers, official grading, allotment of quotas among handlers and the establishment of minimum prices by grades. A control committee, consisting of representatives of growers and handlers, was to be established to supervise the operation of the agreement, subject to approval by the Secretary of Agriculture. Processing taxes were not to be imposed and rental and benefit payments were not to be made.

Finally, a marketing agreement was negotiated covering the stemming grades of cigar leaf, which are used in the manufacture of scrap chewing and smoking tobaccos. The agreement required four contractors to

6. This arrangement was terminated on August 14, 1941.

purchase directly from growers or cooperative associations specified minimum quantities at minimum prices ranging from 6 to 8.5 cents per pound. Apparently these agreements were carried out without difficulty.

No Program for Flue-Cured in 1933

No production control for the 1933 crops of other tobaccos was considered, because market prospects seemed relatively favorable; but the low prices paid at the opening of the flue-cured auction markets in Georgia and the Carolinas stimulated action to obtain higher prices during the marketing season. Prices paid in Georgia and South Carolina in August averaged only about 10 cents per pound, which was 7 cents below parity and no higher than the low price of the 1932 season. The auctions were closed by state authorities to await the development of an effective federal program.

Increased production in conjunction with reduced exports and smaller domestic consumption was depressing the flue-cured markets. Production had been reduced more than half from 1930 to 1932 but an advance in prices from about 8 cents in 1931 to nearly 12 cents in 1932 had led to increased plantings and higher yields, which had doubled the crop. The stocks at the beginning of the season were not unduly high, but the new crop would materially exceed probable exports and carry-over. Under these conditions the best measure obviously was to take steps to insure that surplus production would not be continued through the next season.

The Agricultural Adjustment Administration proceeded promptly to develop with producers an acreage reduction program for the 1934 and 1935 crops and, with buyers, a marketing agreement program to raise prices for the 1933 crop. Within a few weeks 95 per cent of the flue-cured growers had signed contracts for the control of production. This influenced buyers to enter into an agreement to pay the "fair exchange value," an average of 17 cents per pound, for the remainder of the season.[7]

The auctions were reopened shortly in the flue-cured areas and buyers carried out their agreements. The marketing agreement was successful in raising and maintaining prices for the larger 1933 crop above the average paid for the 1932 crop. Some increase in the national income made it possible for processors to sell more products, and the devaluation of the dollar provided some encouragement of exports. The season average price was increased from 11.6 cents to 15.3 cents and receipts from marketings by a larger percentage. Subsequently, growers who had sold tobacco at lower prices, before the agreement became effective, received supplemental payments.

7. The agreement required buyers to take at least as much as they had bought in the previous year and not to increase the price of their products more than was necessary to cover increased costs.

Situation in the Burley Areas

In the burley areas, the 1933 prospect was for a large increase in supplies and for prices considerably lower than those of 1932. Stocks had been accumulating until they amounted to about three times the annual consumption. Moreover, a price advance in 1932 over the very low level of 1931 had led to increased plantings and to a prospective crop considerably in excess of annual consumption.

A burley marketing agreement for the 1933 crop, and the producer sign-up for control of the 1934 and 1935 crops, were developed before the opening of the 1933 marketing season. The grower sign-up provided an inducement for buyers to enter into the marketing agreement. Under the agreement, the principal buyers, reluctant to take all of the large crop in prospect, finally agreed that each of them would take at least as much as had been used in the previous season and would pay an average price of 12 cents a pound. Two companies contracted to take specific amounts that were later reduced when the crop proved smaller than was expected.

Burley prices to producers for the season averaged only 10.5 cents per pound, as compared with 12.5 cents for the previous season, but the larger crop resulted in some increase in receipts from marketings. The reason why the average price was less than that agreed on is not obvious, but it was probably due to lower than average quality. Without the agreements, prices probably would have declined to the 1931 average of about 9 cents per pound.

The Dark Tobaccos

By the time the dark-tobacco markets opened in December, the principal domestic users of these types had agreed to proposals for marketing agreements similar to those developed for the flue-cured and burley tobaccos. The production of dark tobacco had been reduced to about the current levels of domestic consumption and exports, but stocks were excessive in relation to domestic requirements. Large amounts of these tobaccos were normally exported but the volume of exports also had been reduced. About 80 per cent of the acreage was signed up for control of the 1934 crop, and domestic manufacturers agreed to buy the 1933 crop at prices somewhat higher than had been paid for the 1932 crop. Prices had dropped to low levels. Control contracts were offered to growers to hold production down to levels that would provide for moving surplus stocks.

Three separate dark-tobacco agreements were developed, one with the principal manufacturers of pipe smoking and chewing tobaccos, one with snuff manufacturers, and a third with by-product manufacturers. In the first of these, manufacturers agreed to purchase at least as much

as they had used in the preceding season and to pay minimum avera
prices of not less than 7 cents for some specified types and 7.5 cents fo
Virginia sun-cured. The snuff manufacturers agreed to purchase specified amounts at minimum prices ranging from 7.5 cents to 14 cents. The by-product agreement provided an outlet for grades that could not be sold on the market at the agreed minimum prices. Thus minimum prices and quantities were specified in the agreements. Exporters did not enter into the agreements but they did undertake, informally, to make their prices and volumes of purchase conform to the terms of the agreements.

The result of these agreements, together with the devaluation of the dollar and some improvement in the general demand situation, was to increase dark-tobacco prices and incomes from marketing in the 1933 season by about 50 per cent over those of the previous season. An increase in consumption of the fire-cured types resulted in some reduction of stocks. The stocks of dark air-cured were also reduced moderately as a result of a crop that was somewhat smaller than the amounts required for domestic consumption and exports. These developments helped to strengthen demand for the crop of the following year.

All of the six tobacco agreements entered into provided only for the fixing of minimum quantities and prices on the 1933 crops and only for tobacco used domestically. The purchases made under these agreements amounted to nearly half of the total tobacco crop. Buyers for export voluntarily cooperated on prices paid. Thus price support was extended to about 90 per cent of the total crop. A total crop that was about 35 per cent larger was marketed at prices that averaged about 24 per cent higher than for the 1932 season. Gross income was increased by about two thirds over that of the previous season. The agreements, supported by grower contracts to control production in the next season, contributed substantially to this increase in prices and income.

The tobacco buyers were unwilling to continue the agreements through the 1934 season. In the meantime, the production control programs had been fully developed and had come into operation. Plantings for the 1934 crops were brought into close alignment with objectives. Prices at the opening markets of 1934 were above parity.

CONTROLS AND EXCISE TAXES

Processing taxes to provide revenues to cover the costs of operating the programs, and for rental and benefit payments, were levied on the first processing of tobacco beginning in October 1933. For each class or type, with the exception of cigar leaf, the rate was established at about the full difference between the average price received in the 1932 season and the computed "fair exchange value." The rates ranged from 1.7 cents co to 4.2 cents on flue-cured. In the case of cigar f 6 cents was considered to be so great that a tax ect consumption. Consequently, the rate was set ce.

Maryland rate was reduced to zero because prices atter part of the 1933 marketing season and were ove parity. The burley rate, on the other hand, was raised to 6.1 cents because the farm price average for that type in the 1933 season was lower and the fair exchange value higher than in the 1932 season. Subsequently some of the rates were adjusted because of changes in the uses for which the tobacco was processed and changes in price relations. Leaf exports were not taxed, as tax payments on exported products were rebated.

Acreage control contracts were reinforced in June 1934 by passage of the Kerr-Smith Tobacco Marketing Control Act. That act provided for tax-free warrants to cover marketing allotments associated with the acreages that producers were permitted to grow under their contracts. Quantities offered for sale in excess of these allotments were taxed. The tax rate was set by the Secretary at one fourth the market price. It applied to all tobacco produced by noncontracting growers and was designed to prevent those growers from profiting without participating in the program.[8] It encouraged some growers to sign contracts and discouraged overplanting by contract signers.

The Kerr-Smith Act was applicable to all tobacco harvested in the 1934 season, except Maryland, Virginia sun-cured and cigar leaf tobaccos. In 1935, Maryland, Puerto Rican and cigar wrapper tobaccos were exempted. Thereafter, until 1939, the act was to apply to any type if growers representing three fourths of the land customarily used in its production voted in favor of operation under such a program. The general acceptability of the act among growers is indicated by the fact that in 1935 a high percentage of the growers of all types except Maryland voted to come under the act.[9] The strong sentiment of the growers in favor of the program is shown by the results of the referenda taken in June-July 1935. (See Table 8.) However, the Supreme Court decision of January 6, 1936 resulted in repeal of the act and the cancellation of the programs authorized by it.

8. There was in this act a significant difference from the provisions of the Bankhead Cotton Control Act in that the tax-free warrants were not transferable. Under the cotton program, after passage of the Bankhead Act, a grower who received warrants for more cotton than he grew, because of greater reductions in acreage or lower yields, could transfer to another grower the right to the excess in the warrant issued to him. In this respect tobacco control was more rigid than cotton control.

9. The reasons for the Maryland exceptions from the program in this period were that production had not been increased significantly even without controls and the demand for that type of tobacco was well established.

TABLE 8

TOBACCO: REFERENDA ON QUOTAS, JUNE–JULY 1935

Type of Tobacco	Total Number of Eligible Voters	Number of "Yes" Votes	Number of "No" Votes	Number of Eligible Voters Not Voting	Per Cent of Eligible Voters Voting	Per Cent of "Yes" Votes in Total Cast
All programs	521,508	360,804	16,467	144,237	72.3	95.6
Flue-cured	225,880	184,755	3,408	37,717	83.3	98.2
Burley	197,946	114,351	8,273	75,322	63.7	93.3
Fire-cured	52,124	30,359	2,638	19,127	63.3	92.0
Dark air-cured	18,307	12,285	956	5,066	72.3	92.8
Virginia sun-cured [a]	2,022	1,075	177	770	61.9	85.9
Cigar leaf [b]	27,251	19,054	1,192	7,005	74.3	94.1

Source: U.S. Agricultural Adjustment Administration, *Agricultural Adjustment, 1933–1935,* 1936, pp. 204, 207. Figures as given; not reconciled.

a. Virginia sun-cured is type 37, a dark air-cured type. Since it is the only dark air-cured type grown in Virginia, the Virginia state figures given under dark air-cured are assumed to be for Virginia sun-cured.

b. Includes cigar filler and binder tobaccos. Wrappers are grown only in the Connecticut Valley and in the Georgia-Florida area. In the AAA report, Georgia and Florida are not listed as producers of cigar leaf tobacco. In the Connecticut Valley, the adjustments in cigar wrapper tobacco were carried out by means of marketing agreements with handlers.

A formal referendum to determine whether growers desired a continuation in 1936 of the Maryland tobacco adjustment program was not carried out, as resolutions requesting such continuance were unanimously adopted at a growers' meeting held in Upper Marlboro, Maryland, on September 2, 1935.

Revenues Collected

Revenues collected from processing taxes from October 1, 1933 until the production control measures were declared unconstitutional amounted to about $61 million. The taxes derived from the penalties under the Kerr-Smith Act amounted to about $4 million. The total revenue obtained from these two sources exceeded the total expenditure on production and marketing control programs, which amounted to about $58 million.

The processing taxes provided funds for adjustment and rental payments. Flue-cured growers who sold their tobacco early in 1933 received payments to make up for the difference in price before and after the marketing agreement was put into effect. Payments were made to all contracting cigar tobacco growers at specified rates per acre on the acreage of the 1933 crop put under contract. Payments to these growers for compliance were continued in the 1934 and 1935 seasons. Both rental payments and payments on various accounts were made to other contracting growers for the 1934 and 1935 crops. These payments made substantial additions to income.

Effects on Production

Sizable reductions in acreage were required of the flue-cured and burley growers in 1934. Flue-cured growers were asked to reduce acreage by 30 per cent from that of the base period. The acreage harvested in 1934 was less than that allotted and 24 per cent below that of 1933. The burley acreage exceeded allotments but was 40 per cent less than the acreage harvested in 1932. No significant change in Maryland acreage was required. The harvested acreages of the other types of tobacco were not affected to any great extent by the control program. They had been reduced materially before the programs became effective and the controls served merely to hold them at these lower levels. The flue-cured acreage was permitted to increase to some extent in 1935 but the other types were held fairly close to the acreages grown in 1934. High yields per acre in 1934 and 1935 offset in part the acreage reductions made from the 1933 levels. New record yields produced a flue-cured crop in 1935 that exceeded the large crop of 1933.

In the meantime, the domestic demand for the flue-cured and burley tobaccos was increasing. The prices of cigarettes had been reduced and the increasing purchasing power of consumers was enlarging the demand for them. Burley stocks were reduced and prices were maintained for the 1934 and 1935 seasons at levels materially above those secured by agreement in the 1933 season. The large flue-cured crop of 1935 pushed prices down from the high level of 1934 but the crop was moved at prices well above those of 1933.

Reductions in the acreage and production of some of the dark tobaccos, and the holding of others down nearly to the low levels of 1933, did not result in significant price advances in the 1934 and 1935 seasons. The export takings of fire-cured declined and stocks continued heavy. The average price for the 1935 season was about the same as for the 1933 season. The position of dark air-cured tobacco improved to some extent because of a reduction in stocks brought about by holding down production while consumption and exports were maintained.

The position of the cigar tobaccos was substantially improved by reduced production and moderately strengthened demand. Consumption increased, stocks were reduced and prices rose about 50 per cent between the 1933 and 1935 seasons.

SOIL CONSERVATION AND DOMESTIC ALLOTMENTS

In 1936, tobacco was defined as a soil-depleting crop and goals or allotments were set for the several types. Growers were invited to enter into voluntary agreements by which they would continue to adjust production and would be compensated by means of soil conservation payments. In the 1936 season, plantings and production were held at about the 1935 levels. Payments amounting to about $15 million were made for diverting 393,000 acres. Prices and incomes received for the 1936 tobacco crop marked a complete recovery from the depression. Prices averaged somewhat higher than in 1928 and the dollar value of production was about the same while the prices farmers had to pay for goods and services were lower. Their purchasing power was therefore higher than in the predepression period.

The high returns for the 1936 crop caused tobacco growers and the Adjustment Administration to favor relaxation of controls. Since the price of burley was high, the goal set permitted a 20 to 30 per cent increase in acreage. The same mistake was being made in respect to cotton. The acreage goals set for flue-cured, dark air-cured and cigar types were about equal to or slightly above the acreages grown in 1936. Since fire-cured types had not shared in the recovery, the goals set were designed to reduce acreage by about 20 per cent, but some increase in the acreage of Maryland tobacco was considered desirable. The acreage goals for all types of tobacco totaled 1.6 million as compared with 1.4 million harvested in the previous year.

The growers of most types of tobacco planted more than the goals called for. They diverted only 292,000 acres and harvested 1,753,000. For burley, the increased acreage together with higher yields resulted in the production of more than 400 million pounds, an increase of 80 per cent over the amount produced in the previous year. As a consequence, the price dropped from 35.7 cents to 20.1 cents. The flue-cured growers, who were expected to hold to about the same level as in 1936, harvested some 15 per cent more acres and 25 per cent more tobacco. However, the market was strong enough to absorb the crop and even to permit a slight advance in prices. Maryland acreage and production were reduced moderately but the market weakened and prices were lower than in the previous year. The dark air-cured growers increased acreages in response to high prices and nearly doubled the crop. Prices declined about 50 per cent. The fire-cured growers harvested a moderately larger crop and prices adjusted downward from 12.3 cents to 10.7 cents. The cigar leaf growers also increased plantings and, for the most part, received somewhat lower prices. The over-all production of tobacco was increased about a third but the reductions in price averaged only about 10 per cent. Gross income from sales amounted to about $320 million, the highest since 1919.

Commodity Credit Corporation Operations

The first tobacco operation of the Commodity Credit Corporation was undertaken in 1936. On June 30 of that year the Corporation took over the outstanding balance of loans previously made to cooperatives by the RFC on fire-cured and dark air-cured tobaccos produced in the 1931–1935 seasons. These balances amounted to more than $7 million, secured by 66 million pounds of tobacco. The dark air-cured prices were high enough in the 1936 season to encourage producers to redeem some 24 million pounds of pledged tobacco for private sale. The prices for fire-cured remained relatively low and were not high enough to cover investment and carrying charges on accumulated stocks. The substitution of some salable 1936 tobacco for some of the lower-value stocks increased the investment of the Corporation to nearly $8.7 million. Flood damage and further deterioration greatly reduced the sale value of much of the stock. When this operation was fully liquidated, in 1941, the loss on it was put at more than $2 million.

The first tobacco price-support program that originated with CCC was a recourse loan to growers of dark fire-cured tobacco in the 1937 marketing season. The loan was made through the Eastern Dark Fired Tobacco Growers' Association at 15 cents a pound. That was a high rate and more than 6 million pounds valued at more than $900,000 were placed under loan. The loan was repaid in full by April 1940.

In addition, the Federal Surplus Relief Corporation used Section 32 funds to aid in the export of a small quantity of tobacco in the fiscal year 1937 and to divert a large quantity into nicotine insecticides. These payments were made to grower cooperatives to make up the difference between the amounts advanced to growers and the prices realized through sale to by-product manufacturers and to exporters. About 34 million pounds of fire-cured and dark air-cured tobacco of the 1931–1935 crops were diverted to nicotine at a cost of $2.8 million. Diversion payments by the Federal Surplus Relief Corporation from January 1937 to June 1938 amounted to some $3 million. (The over-all results of the program from 1933–34 to 1937–38 are shown in Tables 9 and 10.)

Effects of the Processing Tax

The diversity of products and the relatively small portion which the tax on the raw product constituted as compared with the price paid by the consumer make it very difficult to determine the incidence of the tax. It seems clear that the processors were in a position to pass the tax along to distributors or consumers. The margin between the wholesale price of cigarettes and the average price paid to tobacco producers increased in 1934 and 1935 by more than enough to cover the tax. For some products the margins did not advance sufficiently to cover the tax. However, since by far the largest part of tobacco is used in cigarette manufacture and since several of the large manufacturing companies produce a variety of products, including cigarettes, it is apparent that, for the most part, the increased margin on cigarettes would cover such losses as there might be on other products.[10] The increasing demand for

10. The marketing agreements of 1933 included a provision that the prices of the products should not be increased by more than the amount of the increase in the cost of tobacco. The average wholesale price of cigarettes was increased in 1934 by 0.8 cents but that was 1.7 cents below the 1932 average. The tax in 1935 amounted to only 0.3 cents per package. When it was eliminated in 1936 there was no change in price.

TABLE 9

TOBACCO: ESTIMATED FARM VALUE OF MAJOR TYPES WITH AND WITHOUT ADJUSTMENT PROGRAMS, INCLUDING BENEFIT PAYMENTS, 1933–34 TO 1937–38

Marketing Season	Without Program	With Program [a]	Income with Program as Per Cent of Income without Program
	(Thousands)		
Total	$875,209	$1,286,579	147.0
1933–34	131,439	176,898	134.6
1934–35	138,831	260,231	187.4
1935–36	145,171	246,278	169.6
1936–37	204,116	281,108	137.7
1937–38	255,652	322,064	126.0

Source: U.S. Agricultural Adjustment Administration, *Agricultural Adjustment, 1937–1938,* 1939, p. 153.

a. In addition to the payments included in this total, $360,000 accrued to producers of Maryland tobacco and $4,259,000 to Puerto Rican producers.

TABLE 10

TOBACCO: CROP VALUE ADDED BY ADJUSTMENT PROGRAMS, INCLUDING RENTAL AND BENEFIT PAYMENTS, FOR SPECIFIED TYPES, 1933–1937

(Thousands)

Type	Value Added by Program	Rental and Benefit Payments	Total
Total	$327,100	$84,270	$411,370
Flue-cured	226,000	37,071	263,071
Burley	70,000	26,825	96,825
Dark	23,000	7,958	30,958
Cigar	8,100	12,416	20,516

Source: U.S. Agricultural Adjustment Administration, *Agricultural Adjustment, 1937–1938,* 1939, p. 154.

cigarettes together with the relative inelasticity of that demand made it possible for processors and distributors to pass the tax along to consumers.

A CONTINUING PROGRAM FOR TOBACCO

The Soil Conservation and Domestic Allotment Act of 1936 and the Agricultural Adjustment Act of 1938 converted the emergency legislation of the early 1930s into basic legislation with more specific directives for a continuing program. Tobacco was recognized to be a soil-depleting crop and producers were to be paid for diverting acres from tobacco, in lieu of the rental and benefit payments available to them under the emergency program. Funds for these payments were to be provided by direct appropriation rather than through excise taxes collected from the processors and penalties for exceeding quotas. The act of 1938 provided marketing quotas for tobacco, in place of acreage allotments. CCC was authorized to make loans on tobacco, but the loan levels were not specified as they were for the other basic commodities. The rates were discretionary with the Secretary of Agriculture.

Specific provisions in the act of 1938 with reference to tobacco retained the base period August 1919 to July 1929 and designated the various kinds of tobacco—flue-cured, fire-cured, dark air-cured, burley, Maryland, and so on. Total supply of tobacco was so defined as to include the carry-over at the beginning of the marketing season, and the normal supply was to be a normal year's domestic consumption and exports plus 175 per cent of a normal year's domestic consumption and 65 per cent of a normal year's exports as an allowance for carry-over. The reserve supply level, for tobacco, was defined as the normal supply plus 5 per cent so as to insure a supply adequate to meet domestic consumption and export needs in years of adverse conditions as well as in years of plenty. This was an "ever-normal granary" provision.

Further, it was provided that whenever the Secretary should find that the total supply of tobacco exceeded the reserve supply, that fact should be proclaimed and a national marketing quota should be in effect for the next marketing season, unless more than a third of the producers voting in the referendum relating to the particular kind of tobacco to which the quota would apply had voted against the quota.

Another significant feature of the act was a clause that the Secretary of Agriculture should provide for the allotment of not more than 5 per cent of the national marketing quota for: (1) assignment to farms on which tobacco was to be produced for the first time in five years; and (2) increases in the allotments to small farms. The Secretary was given discretion in prescribing the manner and conditions for transferring farm marketing quotas.[11]

Experience under the 1938 Act

In the first round of experience with the new act, some growers accepted quotas but declined them in the next season. In accordance with the act, the Secretary proclaimed quotas for the 1938 season and they were approved by referendum for flue-cured, burley, fire-cured and

11. A concession was made to Pennsylvania in providing that marketing quotas would not be in effect with respect to the seedleaf filler of that state during the marketing seasons beginning in 1938 and 1939. This illustrates a tendency toward specific-area legislation with reference to tobacco. Apparently the exception was due to the fact that the prices for this type of tobacco had been rather stable and at a satisfactory level from 1934 on. The acreage had been greatly reduced, consumption had been maintained, and stocks had been reduced. Moreover, the higher prices of 1935 and 1936 and the greater freedom of 1937 had not resulted in a significant increase in acreage.

dark air-cured tobaccos.[12] Plantings were reduced moderately below the 1937 level. Yields were only slightly lower and the crop was reduced only about 15 per cent. Prices held close to the 1937 level in spite of some decline in business activity and national income. The new crops of flue-cured and burley were moved at satisfactory prices, but dark-tobacco prices remained low and were supported to some extent by a diversion program for converting considerable quantities into insecticides and fertilizer. Loans at about 95 per cent of parity were made available to the Wisconsin growers of cigar tobaccos. Dissatisfaction of some growers with the operation of the marketing quota system caused them to vote down the quotas announced for the 1939 season.

That season tested out both the reaction of growers when freed from controls and the need for supports in case of a marketing emergency. Freed from controls, flue-cured growers increased plantings by more than a third and harvested a crop 50 per cent larger than in 1938. Shortly after the marketing season opened, the outbreak of war in Europe caused British buyers to withdraw from the market. Growers were faced with an emergency similar to that of 1933 when a large crop was being harvested and buyers were already well stocked. Again the government program was adjusted to meet the emergency. When the British buyers withdrew, early in September, the market was closed to await the development of plans for dealing with the situation. A large part of the flue-cured was customarily exported, Great Britain taking about a third of the total crop. Moreover, the British market was an outlet for the better grades, which commanded the highest prices.

Within a short period, action was taken to prepare for reopening the markets. Marketing quotas were proclaimed for the 1940 crop and growers approved. CCC announced a loan and purchase program to support and stabilize prices for the remainder of the marketing season. The markets were reopened early in October. Prices were supported by CCC purchases at levels averaging about 15.4 cents per pound. The average market price before closing was 14.3 cents and prices for the entire season averaged 14.9 cents. The tobacco purchased by CCC was turned over to the domestic and British tobacco companies as agents, to be processed and stored for the account of the Corporation. These same companies were given options to purchase at cost plus a mark-up to cover interest and carrying charges.

About a tenth of the 1939 flue-cured crop was purchased for the British trade at prices averaging around 20 cents per pound. Most of it was sold to the Lend-Lease Administration for shipment to British Empire countries. The Corporation gained over a million dollars on the operation. This, however, was merely a bookkeeping gain as it resulted from a transfer to the Lend-Lease Administration, another government agency, at more than the cost of acquisition.

12. Except Virginia sun-cured.

The market for the dark tobaccos also was affected seriously by war conditions in Europe. Production of these tobaccos had been reduced greatly from 1933 on and there was only a moderate increase from 1938 to 1939. However, the export market had been absorbing about half the current production. The markets had not opened before the outbreak of war. Nonrecourse loans, varying from 59 per cent to 73 per cent of parity for the several types of dark tobacco, were offered through co-operative associations.[13] However, only one association participated in the loan program. Loans were made on about 4.8 million pounds, and nearly 3 million pounds were purchased. All of it was redeemed or was subsequently sold to the Lend-Lease Administration. Thus, the prices of the tobaccos immediately affected by the withdrawal of British buyers were supported at levels only moderately below those of the previous season.

The burley and Maryland tobaccos were not significantly affected by foreign market conditions. A large burley crop was harvested and the domestic demand kept prices at a level only moderately below that of the previous season. A crop that was 15 per cent larger brought prices that were only 10 per cent lower. Maryland harvested a larger crop and sold it at higher prices.

Acreage allotments had been made for the 1939 crop under authority provided in the act of 1936. With quotas out, there were no marketing penalties. The offer of conservation payments only to those who complied with allotments was not very effective in restraining production. For example, the national allotment for burley was 407,000 acres but growers harvested 425,000.

Since marketing quotas *only* as a means of control had proved rather unsatisfactory from an administrative standpoint, the act was amended in August 1939 to provide for acreage allotments and for marketing quotas related to those allotments. The objection to marketing quotas without acreage allotments was that yields could not be anticipated and the producer might find his crop larger or smaller than his quota with no provision for transfer of parts of quotas. The burley growers joined the flue-cured and the dark-tobacco growers in approving marketing quotas for the three years beginning with the 1940 crop.[14]

13. U.S. Production and Marketing Administration, Fiscal Branch, "Tobacco Price Support and Related Operations, June 30, 1936—June 30, 1949," p. 11, mimeo.

14. The results of the referendum were as follows:

	Number of Votes Cast				*Per Cent of Votes Cast*		
	For 3 Years	*For 1 Year Only*	*Against Quotas*	*Total Cast*	*For 3 Years*	*For 1 Year Only*	*Against Quotas*
Flue-cured	174,779	3,655	24,625	203,059	86.1	1.8	12.1
Burley	111,045	4,521	29,523	145,089	76.5	3.1	20.4
Dark air-cured	8,910	235	1,433	10,578	84.2	2.2	13.6
Fire-cured	20,109	490	2,697	23,296	86.3	2.1	11.6

(U.S. Department of Agriculture, *Report of the Agricultural Adjustment Administration, 1941,* p. 11.)

The 1940 season marked the beginning of a program of continuous price support by loans and purchases for several types of tobacco. It also marked the beginning of a series of advancing loan levels. Increasing demand for some kinds of tobacco, notably flue-cured, burley and Maryland, kept pace with advancing supports, but a declining demand for dark tobaccos provided no opportunity for maintaining production and moving supplies of that type into the ordinary channels of consumption.

ADJUSTING TO WAR CONDITIONS

The detailed legal specifications in the act of 1938 were soon found to be a handicap in adjusting the tobacco program to war conditions. To meet the problem, the Congress passed a number of amendments designed to insure tobacco growers prices and incomes that would be in line with the rising prices of other commodities and at the same time to protect them from overexpansion in response to rising prices. One argument for continuing to use allotments and quotas was that tobacco production would thus be prevented from encroaching on the production of other needed products. Some attention also was given to maintaining a balance among the growers of various types of tobacco.

The Situation of the Flue-Cured Tobaccos

As a result of war conditions and restricted market outlets, the production of flue-cured tobacco was cut back sharply in 1940, by allotments and quotas. The area harvested was reduced from 1,270,000 acres in 1939 to 741,000 in 1940. Production was curtailed nearly as much but stocks increased as a result of both the great reduction in exports and the unusually large 1939 crop. Prices were maintained moderately above the 1939 level by means of CCC loans at 75 per cent of parity and by substantial CCC purchases. Loans were advanced on 36 million pounds and purchases amounted to nearly 169 million pounds. Thus support operations were extended to more than 200 million pounds or about 28 per cent of the 1940 crop.

The 1941 season marked the turning point in the flue-cured tobacco situation. At the beginning of the season stocks were at a record high, but growers planted and harvested the smallest acreage since 1934—less than the allotment, in fact. Apparently, with the prices of alternative products advancing, the 16 cents per pound realized for the previous crop was not sufficient inducement to plant as much as the government program permitted. However, record domestic consumption and some increase in exports began to pull down stocks and the farm price advanced above the loan level, even above the higher parity level which had been provided by a shift in the base made in 1940.

The increasing demand for the flue-cured tobaccos which began in the 1941 season continued to advance prices against ceilings throughout the war period. The area harvested expanded in line with increased allotments. Quotas were continued as a result of special legislation. Production was increased both by higher yields and by increased acreages. Nevertheless, the strong demand caused stocks to be reduced. The pressure for tobacco of this type even led to the allocation of supplies to processors.

No Commodity Credit Corporation loans were required for flue-cured tobaccos through the remainder of the war period. However, the Corporation continued annual purchase operations for lend-lease and other wartime exports.

Demand for Burley Also Increasing

The demand for burley tobacco was not immediately affected by the outbreak of war in Europe since only small quantities were ordinarily exported. Increasing employment strengthened the domestic market and stimulated the demand for this type of tobacco. Since growers had approved quotas in 1939, the allotment for the 1940 crop reduced acreage about 15 per cent, but higher yields largely offset this reduction. Stocks were heavy. A loan rate of 75 per cent of parity (17 cents per pound) was offered and the price was stabilized at the loan level by placing 26 million pounds under loan. All the loans were later repaid, together with processing and carrying charges and interest.

Beginning with the 1941 season the domestic demand for burley increased enough to raise prices to more than the advancing loan rate level and even above the higher parity level. A small amount of burley, about 6 million pounds, was placed under loan in the 1941 season but all of it was redeemed during the season. During the remainder of the war period allotments were increased. The harvested acreage fell behind the allotments to a significant extent, an indication that reductions in the labor force and alternative enterprises were diverting resources to other products. However, the advance in average prices to growers from 16 cents per pound in 1940 to more than 45 cents in 1943 was sufficient to increase the harvested acreage and production. Prices pressed against ceilings and there was a relative scarcity, so stocks were reduced to some extent and allocations were imposed.

By 1944, increased plantings and higher yields had produced a crop large enough to cover current domestic requirements, add to stocks and bring a moderate reduction in prices. Another large crop harvested in 1945 made a further addition to stocks, reduced prices, and placed a small amount of burley tobacco under loan. The loan rate for the 1945 season was 30 cents, but the average price for the season did not drop to that level. However, the placing of some tobacco under loan was a signal that supply was overtaking demand.

The Dark Tobaccos

The demand for the dark tobaccos did not recover significantly until near the end of the war period. Allotments were imposed in 1941 for the purpose of cutting back acreage and production so as to make way for the movement of accumulated stocks. Exports declined to a low level through the 1943 season and domestic demand did not increase to any significant extent. Prices advanced, but only moderately. Crops fell short of allotments until allotments were abandoned for the 1944 and 1945 seasons.[15] The area harvested continued to be even below the level maintained in the seasons when quotas were in effect. Loans were offered at 75, 85 and 90 per cent of parity. Small quantities were placed under loan in each season but were redeemed within the war period. Some small amounts also were purchased and sold at a loss for making nicotine. However, in the last two seasons of the war, exports recovered to prewar levels and prices advanced sharply.

The demand for other types of tobacco was fairly well maintained throughout the war period. In the last season of that period, tobacco growers harvested a record crop of nearly 2 billion pounds and received more than 42 cents per pound for it. The result was a gross income of about $848 million, nearly double that received for the 1919 crop, which was the previous all-time high.

POSTWAR ADJUSTMENTS

The outlook for most types of tobacco at the end of the war seemed very favorable. Even the prospects for the dark tobaccos seemed brighter. The only significant exception was burley, stocks of which had begun to accumulate because of a high level of production. As a result, prices for some types were declining. Domestic consumption of all types of tobaccos had expanded through increases in population and in consumption per person. The export markets had been reopened and the volume of exports had returned to about prewar average. Prices generally had been pressing against ceilings, and they advanced when the ceilings were raised and finally removed. Stocks were at a high level but, with the exception of burley, not too high in relation to current consumption and exports.

Supports for the most important kinds of tobacco were to be provided at 90 per cent of parity for two years after the war. Burley allotments for the 1946 season were reduced moderately but the flue-cured allotments were increased and those on the dark tobaccos were reimposed at levels higher than those of 1943, the last which had been in effect. In total, a larger acreage with higher yields produced a record tobacco

15. Marketing quotas were terminated on August 14, 1943 and were not reinstated until 1946.

crop in the first postwar season. The crop amounted to 2,300 million pounds and was marketed at an average price of 45 cents per pound. It produced a record gross income of more than a billion dollars.

Shortly, the problems of readjustment began to appear. The domestic market expansion resulting from war conditions had run its course. In fact, there was a moderate decline in per capita consumption after the end of the war. Producers began to have more resources available and the tendency to overproduce reappeared. High supports, with reluctance to adjust allotments and quotas to changing conditions, resulted in heavy postwar investments even in the cigarette tobaccos.

Developments in the Flue-Cured Tobaccos

By the end of the war the importance of the cigarette use of tobacco had been greatly increased in both the foreign and domestic markets. Cigarettes absorbed about 75 per cent of the tobacco processed in the United States. This was the principal market for the flue-cured, burley and Maryland tobaccos. Production of the flue-cured types had increased to such an extent that they constituted about 60 per cent of the total crop. They supplied the bulk of the exports and about half the tobacco used in the domestic production of cigarettes. Allotments had been increased continuously from 1941 on and prices had advanced from 16 cents per pound to about 44 cents in 1945. Allotments were further increased in 1946 to produce a record crop. A substantial increase in exports made it possible to market that crop at higher prices.

Because of the subsequent decline in exports, the 1947 season marked a turning point for the flue-cured tobacco growers. Production was overextended. Stocks had begun to increase and exports declined. Prices fell rather sharply from the high level of the previous season, closing most of the gap between the current market and the support level. A large volume, nearly 20 per cent of the crop, was put under loan and some of it was carried over into the next season. Allotments were substantially reduced for the 1948 season, curtailing production to about the level of requirements for the reduced exports, offset in part by some increase in domestic consumption. The average price for the 1948 season returned to and went above the high average of 1946.

The Agricultural Acts of 1948 and 1949 continued the 90 per cent support levels for these tobaccos, provided producers approved marketing quotas. Allotments were increased moderately after 1948. Yields were maintained at high levels with crops exceeding a billion pounds per year. Domestic consumption continued high and exports were somewhat larger than in 1947 thus maintaining prices that were generally above the support levels. The outbreak of war in Korea again stimulated the market and contributed to the maintenance of high prices and incomes into the 1952 season. Moderate quantities were placed under loan annually without causing any large stocks to be accumulated and carried for long periods. In a referendum carried out in July 1952, about 98 per cent of those voting favored the continuance of marketing quotas for the next three crops, those of 1953, 1954 and 1955. (For a summary of these operations, see Table 11.)

TABLE 11

TOBACCO: PRICE-SUPPORT OPERATIONS FOR FLUE-CURED, 1946–1953

(*Farm-Sales-Weight Equivalent*)

Marketing Season	Placed under Government Loan		Remaining in Government Loan Stocks on August 31, 1954
	Amount	Per Cent of Total Crop	
	(*Million Pounds*)		(*Million Pounds*)
1946	66.5	4.9	none
1947	232.3	17.6	none
1948	106.1	9.7	none
1949	103.5	9.3	none
1950	77.6	6.2	none
1951	142.4	9.8	20.8
1952	165.0	12.1	66.1
1953	151.4	11.9	137.9

Source: U.S. Bureau of Agricultural Economics, *The Tobacco Situation,* 1955 Outlook Issue, September 27, 1954, p. 30.

The Situation in Burley

Burley tobacco shared with flue-cured in the increased demand for cigarettes. The export demand was not very significant in the market for burley but there was some increase in exports at the end of the war period. The annual domestic consumption is very stable with an upward trend. The first postwar crop was large enough to supply both the domestic and export requirements and increase stocks enough to reduce prices. A large part of the crop, about 24 per cent, was put under loan. That was a warning that, with high yields, the first reduction in burley allotments was not sufficient to hold production in line with market requirements. Allotments were reduced in the following year to bring supplies into line with requirements and restore prices. They were held at these lower levels until the outbreak of the Korean War.

High yields kept supplies large enough to meet requirements and cause some further accumulation of stocks. Fairly sizable amounts were put under loan in each season but were mostly moved into market channels during the two or three following seasons. Prices and incomes were maintained at relatively high levels. When the outbreak of the Korean

War again strengthened the demand for cigarette tobaccos, allotments were increased, but stocks accumulated and the government continued to take large amounts in supporting the market. (See Table 12.)

TABLE 12

TOBACCO: PRICE-SUPPORT OPERATIONS FOR BURLEY, 1946–1953

(Farm-Sales-Weight Equivalent)

Marketing Season	Placed under Government Loan		Remaining in Government Loan Stocks on August 31, 1954
	Amount	Per Cent of Total Crop	
	(Million Pounds)		*(Million Pounds)*
1946	147.8	24.1	none
1947	37.7	7.8	none
1948	96.7	16.0	none
1949	39.1	7.0	none
1950	44.2	8.9	2.4
1951	97.5	15.7	56.3
1952	103.9	16.0	68.4
1953	102.1	17.9	97.6

Source: U.S. Bureau of Agricultural Economics, *The Tobacco Situation,* 1955 Outlook Issue, September 27, 1954, p. 33.

Maryland tobacco also shared in the increased demand for cigarettes. Production of this type was not under control. A large crop was harvested in the first year after the war but stocks were relatively low. The acreage and production continued fairly stable with prices maintained at a relatively high level. Small quantities were put under loan annually, beginning with the 1948 season, and a large part of the loan stocks remained unsold at the end of the 1950 season. A vote was taken on marketing quotas for the 1951 crop but the proposal was not approved. Consequently, loans were not available on that crop. The total supply for the season was relatively large and the market weakened.

Developments in the Dark Tobaccos

The temporary increase in exports, with government aid, in the last years of the war period strengthened the market for the dark tobaccos. After the war, exports declined to some extent but remained at about the 1939 volume (a relatively low year) while domestic consumption continued to decline. Special legislation, approved in 1945, raised the support level by relating the supports on these tobaccos to the burley support level.[16] It was provided that, beginning with the 1945 crop, the

16. The farm prices of fire-cured tobaccos in the war period had averaged only about half the burley prices. The argument used for relating the prices of the dark tobaccos more closely to burley was to reduce the incentive for the dark-tobacco growers to shift to burley production.

fire-cured tobaccos would be supported at three fourths of the burley level while the dark air-cured and Virginia sun-cured types would be supported at two thirds of the burley level, if the growers of these types had not rejected marketing quotas. Quotas were approved in 1945 for the 1946, 1947 and 1948 crops. The support level on fire-cured tobaccos was raised from 13.5 cents in the 1944 season, when it was at 90 per cent of the parity for these tobaccos, to 21.8 cents in 1945. The increased exports of the 1944 and 1945 seasons had raised prices above support levels.

It was recognized that such an advance in prices would stimulate an increase in production. These conditions led to the restoration of acreage allotments and marketing quotas in the 1946 season. However, the allotments were considerably higher than in 1943 and provided ample opportunity for expanding production. The harvested acreage increased by a third and production nearly doubled in the first postwar year. Consumption and exports declined; stocks increased. More than a third of the total crop was put under loan. Prices declined to the support level.

The postwar demand did not justify restoring the prewar production of the dark tobaccos. Consumption of most of the products in which these types of tobacco are used continued to decline. It declined sharply for pipe smoking tobacco and more normally for chewing tobacco, the principal outlet for the dark air-cured type. However, the consumption of snuff, which is the main outlet for fire-cured, was maintained at about the prewar average. The large 1946 crop of fire-cured tobacco caused enough of it to be put under loan to more than suffice for a full year's domestic consumption of that kind of tobacco. It was therefore considered necessary to reduce sharply the acreage allotments and quotas for the fire-cured types in the years following 1947. By 1950 the allotments had been reduced by more than 50 per cent.

With the support level for dark air-cured tobaccos somewhat lower than for fire-cured and with a more favorable demand situation in the markets for that type, quotas were not applied to Virginia sun-cured until 1950 and the allotments of the other dark air-cured tobaccos were reduced only moderately.[17] However, production of the dark tobaccos had not yet been reduced sufficiently to clear accumulated supplies. At the beginning of the 1951 season, stocks were excessive in relation to annual domestic requirements, and the Commodity Credit Corporation carried a considerable volume of loan stocks. Stocks continued to accumulate and amounted to 37.5 million pounds as of August 31, 1954. (See Tables 13 and 14.)

The government agencies resorted to various measures for disposing of the surplus of dark tobaccos. In the 1947 season, exports to Germany

17. The demand for snuff declined less than the demand for chewing tobacco. However, exports are of much greater relative importance in snuff and the other fire-cured types and exports were declining.

TABLE 13

TOBACCO: PRICE-SUPPORT OPERATIONS FOR FIRE-CURED, 1946–1953

(*Farm-Sales-Weight Equivalent*)

Marketing Season	Placed under Government Loan		Remaining in Government Loan Stocks on August 31, 1954
	Amount	Per Cent of Total Crop	
	(*Million Pounds*)		(*Million Pounds*)
1946	40.7	37.5	2.5
1947	31.3	36.2	4.1
1948	27.3	37.3	6.8
1949	18.7	25.9	5.6
1950	12.2	20.9	9.0
1951	7.5	12.6	4.8
1952	10.9	18.7	8.4
1953	8.0	16.4	8.0

Source: U.S. Bureau of Agricultural Economics, *The Tobacco Situation*, 1955 Outlook Issue, September 27, 1954, p. 38.

TABLE 14

TOBACCO: PRICE-SUPPORT OPERATIONS FOR DARK AIR-CURED, 1946–1953

(*Farm-Sales-Weight Equivalent*)

Marketing Season	Placed under Government Loan		Remaining in Government Loan Stocks on August 31, 1954
	Amount	Per Cent of Total Crop	
	(*Million Pounds*)		(*Million Pounds*)
1946	15.7	31.7	none
1947	14.5	39.0	4.3
1948	8.9	25.6	4.6
1949	4.1	11.3	2.4
1950	4.1	14.3	3.5
1951	7.3	23.0	6.6
1952	10.0	29.6	8.9
1953	7.5	28.2	7.2

Source: U.S. Bureau of Agricultural Economics, *The Tobacco Situation*, 1955 Outlook Issue, September 27, 1954, p. 40.

and other countries were negotiated. Considerable quantities of dark tobacco and other types from the 1947 and earlier crops were shipped abroad in a move to re-establish foreign markets and dispose of accumulated surpluses. The exports were handled through domestic companies with one third of the sale price paid from Section 32 funds and the remaining two thirds paid by the purchasers. The export subsidies provided in that way amounted to some $9 million. A sale of tobacco to an Austrian tobacco monopoly also was negotiated through domestic companies, without any cost to the government. In 1949, losses were taken by the Commodity Credit Corporation on the sale of small quantities of dark tobaccos from previous crops. In addition, 5 million pounds of the 1946 crop of fire-cured were exported at reduced prices in the 1950 season.

Cigar Tobaccos in the Postwar Period

The postwar manufacture and consumption of cigars continued above prewar levels. Relatively high prices for the several types of cigar leaf tobaccos at the end of the war stimulated some increase in production. After stocks had been reduced to moderate amounts in 1946 and 1947, increasing production rebuilt them to prewar size and prices declined.

Loans were available for all cigar types of tobacco, but on some of the filler and binder types they were not used until 1950. The markets for some types weakened at the end of the war period. Loans were made on Wisconsin tobaccos in the 1946–1948 seasons and on Puerto Rican tobaccos in the 1946 and 1947 seasons. In the 1949 season, more Wisconsin and Puerto Rican tobaccos and a relatively large volume of Connecticut binder went under loan. Pennsylvania cigar filler tobacco became ineligible for loans in 1951 because producers did not approve marketing quotas. Producers of those types for which quotas were approved in the 1951 season refused approval on the 1952 crop by a narrow margin. Loans were continued on the Puerto Rican tobacco through the 1952 season.[18] By that time, the government had accumulated under loan and in inventory about 20 million pounds of various types of cigar tobaccos.

Acreage allotments for filler and binder tobaccos had been abandoned before the end of the 1943 season. The accumulation of some stocks of these tobaccos under loan led to the proclamation of quotas for the 1951 season. Quotas were approved on the cigar filler and binder types except on Pennsylvania cigar filler. However, the growers of these types of tobacco did not approve quotas for the 1952 season. Under the terms of the Agricultural Act of 1949, whenever tobacco producers had rejected marketing quotas they were not eligible for loans.

Acreage and production were substantially reduced in the 1951 season. The producers of the cigar types continued these smaller acreages in 1952 and in some areas reduced them further even though controls were not applied. Production was reduced enough to bring about a re-

18. There was no federal quota system for Puerto Rican tobacco. However, the Island government maintained an acreage control program of its own. The Puerto Rican growers were eligible for price-support loans but were not statistically in such a position that quotas would be applied under the terms of the act.

duction of stocks and to maintain prices at or above those of 1951, when controls were in effect.

Despite the relatively satisfactory situation in the 1952 season, which was partly due to the generally strong demand that grew out of the Korean War, quotas were reinstated for 1953 and 1954. All cigar types were supported at 90 per cent of parity in those years, as required by law if quotas had been approved. In 1955, quotas and 90 per cent of parity support were in effect for all cigar types except type 41 (Pennsylvania seedleaf), for which growers rejected quotas.

For types other than cigar filler and binder, supports and quotas were continued in the 1952–1955 seasons on about the same basis as in 1951. All of them, except fire-cured, dark air-cured and Virginia sun-cured, were supported at 90 per cent of parity. As provided by law, fire-cured was supported at 75 per cent of the rate for burley, and dark air-cured and Virginia sun-cured at 66⅔ per cent of the burley rate.

The acreage harvested, for all tobaccos, continued at about the 1950 level, but yields showed some upward trend. In 1954 and 1955, total production was some 2 million pounds higher than the 1944–1953 average but there was no large increase in stocks. A generally strong domestic market and a fairly strong export market absorbed the small increase in production without causing any serious problems of excess stocks. The CCC closing inventory as of June 30, 1955 was negligible ($92,000). However, there had been a loss of $435,000 on the 1954–55 loan operations.

Cost of Tobacco Programs Not High

The tobacco price-support program as a whole has not involved large government costs. In fact, CCC operations for the period 1933 through June 30, 1955 showed a small net gain of $188,000. That was due largely to the gains on inventories ($7 million) which occurred in the 1946–1951 period. There were losses of $2.1 million between 1933 and 1941 and of $1 million to $2 million in the fiscal years 1952, 1953 and 1954, plus about a half million dollars loss in fiscal 1955. Some other small gains and losses brought the over-all figure for the 22-year period to the $188,000 net gain.

There were other program costs, principally in the 1930s and early 1940s. These included some $85 million in allotment and conservation payments, $18 million spent on surplus removal and $6 million in parity payments.[19]

19. See U.S. Department of Agriculture, *Realized Cost of Agricultural and Related Programs, by Function or Purpose, Fiscal Years 1932–1953,* in U.S. Senate Committee on Agriculture and Forestry, *General Farm Program,* Hearings, 83d Cong., 2d sess., Part I, 1954, pp. 74–89 (reproduced in Appendix B in Murray R. Benedict, *Can We Solve the Farm Problem?,* Twentieth Century Fund, New York, 1955).

On the whole, the tobacco program, if its general objectives are accepted, has been one of the most manageable and successful of the farm programs. That has been due in large measure to the fact that acreage and production controls could be fairly well enforced and that the acreages taken out or kept out of tobacco were not large enough to be seriously disturbing to the over-all organization of the farms on which tobacco was grown.[20]

The relative success of the program was also greatly facilitated by the rapid increase in demand for the kinds of tobacco used in cigarette manufacture, which not only absorbed most of the increase in production but also helped to offset some decline in the consumption and exports of the dark tobaccos. A principal defect of the program was that it had possibly retarded unduly readjustments needed in the dark-tobacco areas.

Program Involved Rigorous Controls on Output

The price and production policies followed have required rigorous controls on production of a nature that probably could not be made equally effective or acceptable for crops grown on larger acreages. The acreage planted to tobacco amounts to less than one half of one per cent of the total crop acreage of the United States. Consequently, even very large percentage decreases or increases in tobacco acreage could not greatly affect the acreages available for other crops. That is not true for most of the other crops to which controls have been applied. For example, a sharp cutback of cotton acreage tends to increase peanut production, a decrease in wheat throws more acreage into coarse grains and forage, and so on. Hence, it cannot be expected that the procedures used in controlling tobacco production and distribution would work equally well for most of the other major crops.

SIGNIFICANCE AND EFFECTS OF THE PROGRAM

The first phase of the AAA program for tobacco, as for the other major crops, was to aid growers during an acute depression and to bring about a quick adjustment of production. That phase was completed by 1936 and tobacco growers were in a relatively favorable position in the

20. However, the Congress apparently considered the problem of enforcement sufficiently serious to strengthen the legislation relating to it in the spring of 1955. Public Law 21, approved on March 31, 1955, provided, among other things, that (1) the acreage of any kind of tobacco harvested in excess of the farm acreage allotment in 1955 and after could not be taken into account in establishing state and county allotments; (2) a reduction in the following year's allotment for any kind of tobacco would be made if the producer filed or aided or acquiesced in the filing of any false report with respect to the acreage of tobacco grown on his farm; and (3) the penalty for marketing tobacco in excess of the farm's marketing quota would be increased from 50 per cent to 75 per cent of the average market price of such tobacco in the preceding year. (See *The Tobacco Situation,* June 10, 1955, pp. 19–25.)

fourth year of the program. From 1938 on, the principal objective was to hold the gains achieved in the earlier period.

The relaxation of controls from 1936 on and the disruption of the foreign market that resulted from the outbreak of war would undoubtedly have caused severe depression and disturbance in the tobacco areas if the government had not stepped in to absorb excess supplies and carry them over until the foreign markets could be reopened. Conservation and parity payments made in that period (and up to 1943) also helped materially to maintain the incomes of tobacco growers.

During the war years and in the immediate postwar years government support as such was not important. However, lend-lease purchases, and later the purchases made under the various foreign-aid programs, did, of course, provide a good deal of indirect support for the tobacco market. Though CCC price-support loans were available in those years, they were not used widely enough to have much effect on the market. In later years, the support loan and purchase operations of CCC, and its ability to absorb considerable quantities of tobacco while production adjustments were being made, undoubtedly contributed to the stability of the tobacco industry. The effect on incomes varied considerably from one tobacco type to another. For some, the effect was largely to stabilize incomes. For others, notably the dark tobaccos, diversion payments and export subsidies served to raise income levels.

The Role of CCC

The Commodity Credit Corporation has come to be an important factor in the program for stabilization of the tobacco industry. It has operated effectively in that realm because of the protection it could be given through marketing quotas and acreage allotments. Such protection is essential to a lending agency of the CCC type in dealing with situations in which the demand for a particular type of tobacco may be declining or where the land and labor used for tobacco production tends to be continuously in excess of that needed to supply the demand. Controls on acreage and output are more easily applied to tobacco than to some of the more extensively grown crops. Acreages per farm, for the most part, are small; the tobacco-growing areas are rather sharply segregated; and the total acreage involved in cutbacks or expansions is not large enough to disturb seriously the over-all land-use pattern of the region.

CCC loans at support levels strengthen materially the bargaining position of the grower in an industry where the buyers are few and large and are in a position to stay out of the market for long periods if they choose to do so. An outlet such as an agency of the CCC type can provide is especially important in dealing with sharp ups and downs in export demand. Some operations of that kind may involve the holding of inactive stocks for longer periods than is practical for either private handlers and processors or cooperatives. The domestic demand for tobacco is relatively stable even in times of depression but export demand may vary widely from year to year or even over periods of several years.

The producer cooperatives are not strong enough financially to carry out holding operations on any large scale. They may also be too limited as to the areas in which they operate or too dependent on the processing companies to whom they sell. They have, however, performed important services in connection with the government program. They represent CCC in making and collecting loans and in some cases also serve as warehousers, selling agents and even, in part, as processors. Some of them have become well established and have independent assets. They could and would continue to function if CCC loans were discontinued. Others are primarily agents of the Corporation and could not operate effectively without its financial support.

CCC loans also are helpful in stabilizing prices and movement within the season. In some seasons large quantities of tobacco are put under loan for only a short period. Growers can thus obtain funds for current use without being forced to dispose of their holdings in temporarily weak or glutted markets. Credit of that kind should normally be available through ordinary private or cooperative credit agencies, but the opportunity afforded by the CCC loan for disposal at a known minimum price if the market should continue weak naturally appeals strongly to the grower.

Demand for Most Tobaccos Increasing

One of the most significant developments in the tobacco industry in the period here discussed has been the increase in demand. The per capita consumption of all tobacco rose from 8.93 pounds in 1928 to 11.22 pounds in 1944. This rise in per capita consumption together with a rapid increase in population caused an increase in the total domestic consumption of tobacco of more than 80 per cent between the late 1920s and the early 1950s. The most significant change was the large increase and upward trend in cigarette consumption, which is attributed largely to the great rise in cigarette consumption by women.[21] Per capita consumption was also affected by war conditions and by high levels of income.

Cigarette use not only accounted for all of the increase in tobacco consumption but offset some decrease in the amounts used for pipe and chewing tobaccos. The per capita consumption of snuff and of cigars also declined. (See Table 15.) However, the increase in population has about maintained the over-all consumption of these types in the years since the depression. The consumption of cigarettes is nearly four times

21. See, for example, Elmo L. Jackson, "Trends in the Consumption of Tobacco Products, United States, 1900–1950," *Journal of Farm Economics*, Proceedings Number, November 1950, pp. 881–93, and discussion by Arthur G. Conover, *ibid.*, pp. 923–24.

TABLE 15

TOBACCO: CHANGES IN USE, 1924–1928 TO 1946–1951

(*Unstemmed Processing Weight Equivalent*)

Use	Amount		Percentage Change
	1924–1928	1946–1951	
	(*Million Pounds*)		
Cigarettes	266	1,091	310
Cigars [a]	152	135	−11
Smoking and chewing [b]	275	123	−55
Snuff [b]	37	38	3

Source: U.S. Bureau of Agricultural Economics, *1953 Agricultural Outlook Charts,* October 1952, p. 69. Based on data from annual report of Commissioner of Internal Revenue.

a. Includes tobacco used in custom bonded manufacturing warehouses.
b. Estimated.

what it was in 1920; it represented 20 per cent of total tobacco consumption in 1920, 80 per cent in 1952.

Consumption in foreign countries is probably rather stable under normal conditions, but annual purchases from the United States have been very unstable. In the 1925–1929 period about 44 per cent of the total U.S. crop was exported, chiefly the flue-cured and fire-cured types. The shift to cigarettes has maintained the exports of flue-cured tobacco at a fairly high level but that shift, together with increasing production of foreign tobaccos, has greatly reduced the exports of U.S.-grown dark tobaccos. Total leaf exports have held about at the 1925–1929 average but with a significant shift to the cigarette types.

Under these conditions, the most important functions of CCC have been to serve as a shock absorber against the large fluctuations in foreign demand, to stabilize the domestic market in relation to variations in yield and short-run business cycles, and to merchandise accumulated surpluses.

The increase in demand for cigarette tobaccos has been an important factor in the increase of prices and incomes to growers and in the success of the Corporation's stabilization operations. A temporary surplus could be cleared in the market simply by waiting for the mounting demand to absorb it, provided production was held in check. The Corporation has also been helpful in maintaining prices and incomes on the tobaccos for which demand was not increasing or may even have been declining. For these, the principal problem was to minimize losses. There is a great reluctance to adjust production downward as demand decreases, but the maintenance of production is likely to lead to losses both to growers and CCC.

Adjustments in Production

Under free-market conditions, there was a strong tendency for the producers of tobaccos for which demand was increasing to overplant in response to rising prices over a period of two or three years. Thus, surplus stocks would develop and prices would be greatly depressed. Plantings would then be cut back sharply and some growers would go out of business, only to come back in again and produce surpluses when prices had recovered.

The government programs have reduced these swings, but administrators as well as growers respond to price pressures. They may become too optimistic and expand allotments too fast when the market is rising and thus may bring on another surplus problem. The 1934 and 1939 overplantings were departures from the program as a result of relaxing controls. The expansion of acreage in the last years of the war period was a response to unusual demand pressures and was carried somewhat too far in some of the postwar years.

Following each of these high points in production, controls have been used to cut back production and clear away excess stocks. Without controls, similar cutbacks would have been brought about by sharp price reductions, but they would have been much less orderly.

The producers of the dark tobaccos, having reduced acreages to low levels as a result of depression prices, were faced with declining rather than increasing demand. In that situation, controls were effective in reducing losses that were occurring as a result of accumulating surpluses. They contributed to stabilization at lower levels and to some increases in prices and incomes. Cigar leaf production was held down enough to permit the clearing away of excess stocks. (For data on acreage and production changes, see Table 16.)

The over-all effect of these adjustments was to reduce greatly the acreage and production of the dark tobaccos and maintain a reduced level of acreage and production of the cigar tobaccos while holding the acreage and production of cigarette tobaccos at levels that would supply the domestic and foreign markets without depressing prices unduly.

Yields Have Increased Markedly

As with most of the other farm crops, one of the most striking developments in tobacco production during the past two decades was the great increase in yield per acre. In the case of tobacco, this change was largely though not entirely a result of the control programs. Between 1924–1928 and the 1946–1951 period, the average yield for all tobaccos increased from 765 pounds per acre to 1,225 pounds. Yields continued at about that average in 1952 and 1953 and moved up even

TABLE 16

TOBACCO: CHANGES IN ACREAGE AND PRODUCTION, 1924–1928 TO 1946–1951

Type	Acreage			Production		
	1924–1928 Average	1946–1951 Average	Percentage Change	1924–1928 Average	1946–1951 Average	Percentage Change
	(*1,000 Acres*)			(*Million Pounds*)		
Flue-cured	894	1,040	16	606	1,264	109
Burley	322	443	37	261	563	115
Maryland	31	49	58	24	40	65
Fire-cured	224	67	−70	173	76	−56
Cigar	142	98	−31	165	141	−14
Dark air-cured	86	32	−63	69	36	−47

Sources: U.S. Bureau of Agricultural Economics, *Tobaccos of the United States, Acreage, Yield per Acre, Production, Price and Value, by States, 1866–1945 and by Types and Classes, 1919–1945,* July 1948; U.S. Production and Marketing Administration, *Annual Report on Tobacco Statistics, 1951,* Statistical Bulletin 103, December 1951; and U.S. Bureau of Agricultural Economics, *The Tobacco Situation,* August 1952.

further in 1954 and 1955, reaching 1,342 pounds in 1954 and 1,498 pounds in 1955.

A principal reason for the increase was, of course, that reducing acreage and maintaining prices caused growers to eliminate the poorer tobacco-growing lands and to hold in production the acres that were likely to produce the best yields. Also, since in the later years the marketing quotas established permitted producers to market the tobacco produced on the allotted acres, there was a strong incentive for more intensive culture. Moreover, the stabilization of prices and the prospect of maintaining rights to grow specific numbers of acres encouraged more intensive culture and greater investment of resources for the improvement of yields.

Here too, as in almost all types of agricultural production, financial incentives for higher yields were reinforced by improvements in cultural practices. The conservation program encouraged the use of cover crops, and closer planting for smaller leaves tended to result in the production of more pounds per acre. Producers also learned how to use more of the right kinds of fertilizer in such a way as to increase volume of output and quality. Better control of diseases, especially the development of strains resistant to root rot, made possible continuous growing of tobacco on the best-producing acres.[22]

The most continuously controlled types of tobacco have shown the largest increases in yields. The increased demand for cigarette tobaccos

22. For a statistical analysis of yields, see Glenn L. Johnson, *Burley Tobacco Control Programs,* Kentucky Agricultural Experiment Station, Bulletin 580, February 1952, pp. 45–46.

has been met primarily by increased yields and without much change in acreage. For the dark tobaccos, increased yields and decreasing demand have contributed to the need for further reductions in acreage. (For yield changes by types, see Table 17.)

TABLE 17

TOBACCO: CHANGES IN YIELD BY TYPE, 1924–1928 TO 1946–1951

Type	Yield per Acre 1924–1928 Average	Yield per Acre 1946–1951 Average	Percentage Change
	(Pounds)		
Flue-cured	676	1,219	80
Burley	807	1,272	58
Fire-cured	767	1,149	50
Dark air-cured	784	1,127	44
Cigar	1,212	1,367	13
Maryland	781	816	4

Source: Derived from data given in U.S. Bureau of Agricultural Economics, *The Tobacco Situation,* August 1952, p. 32.

Effect of Allotments

The use of continuing allotments for the same farms tended not only to hold production within established areas but also to freeze production patterns. Most areas have been held in production without significant change. The increasing demand for burley and flue-cured has made possible some relaxation of controls and some shifting of areas. The most significant shift was the expansion of flue-cured acreage in Florida. The relaxation of controls in 1937 and 1939 resulted in a rather marked expansion there, but since 1939 further increase has been held in check by effective quotas. There have also been some shifts within states as between burley and the dark tobaccos, but these have not been large enough to be very significant.[23] The legislative formulae governing allotments do not permit much administrative discretion in making allotments.

The increased demand and relatively high prices for the flue-cured and burley tobaccos have, of course, made it attractive for growers producing other tobaccos in the same areas to shift to these types. The production of the dark tobaccos would no doubt be reduced without allotments if these growers were free to shift to the other types. It was because of this that the appeal of the dark-tobacco growers for the maintenance of a higher support level in relation to burley was acceptable to the growers of flue-cured and burley. The higher supports were made available on condition that the dark-tobacco growers would agree to the imposition of marketing quotas. Naturally they accepted the

23. See Johnson, *Burley Tobacco Control Programs,* pp. 32–42.

quotas since that meant higher prices while without quotas they still would have been barred from producing flue-cured and burley so long as allotments on those types were continued.

The various legislative and administrative regulations put into effect resulted in some changes in the numbers and relative sizes of allotments in the period 1941–1951. For both burley and flue-cured, increasing demand made possible an increase in both the number of allotments and their average size. For fire-cured, the number of allotments and the average size of allotment were reduced because of declining demand. For dark air-cured, new producers came in in 1943–1946 when allotments were not in effect. When allotments were reimposed, these growers had to be taken into account. As a consequence, the number of allotments was considerably increased and the average size was sharply reduced. (See Table 18.)

TABLE 18

TOBACCO: ALLOTMENTS BY TYPE, 1941 AND 1951

	1941			1951		
		Acreage Allotted			Acreage Allotted	
Type	Number of Allotments	Total	Average	Number of Allotments	Total	Average
Flue-cured	191,857	761,591	4.0	210,735	1,119,309	5.3
Burley	244,736	381,586	1.5	300,638	472,383	1.6
Fire-cured	33,710	84,330	2.5	28,811	56,918	2.0
Dark air-cured	20,475	35,796	1.7	27,734	26,641	1.0

Sources: U.S. Production and Marketing Administration, *Annual Report on Tobacco Statistics,* November 1947, p. 33; and *ibid.,* 1951, p. 22.

Since the tobacco crop continued to be a dependable source of income, most farmers contrived to produce the acreages permitted under their allotments. The payments for diversion and conservation contributed to some reduction in soil-depleting crops and some increase in cover crops, pasture and hay crops. Livestock production also increased, stimulated by increased demand for meat animals.

Effect on Land Values

A survey of land values in relation to allotments which was made at the end of the war period showed that high values were placed on acres eligible for tobacco allotments in both the burley and flue-cured areas.[24] A more recent study by Hoover and Ratchford reports that in the principal flue-cured areas it has been accepted practice for several years to base the whole value of ordinary small tobacco farms on the size of the

24. See John E. Mason, "Acreage Allotments and Land Prices," *Journal of Land and Public Utility Economics,* May 1946, pp. 176–81.

tobacco allotment.[25] For many of these small farms, tobacco is almost the sole source of cash income. It is natural therefore that the value placed on the farm tends to be related to the established rights to grow tobacco on it when neighboring farms of similar type can get such allotments only with great difficulty if at all.

For tobacco growers whose farms were big enough to provide for grazing and feeding livestock, livestock products were relatively favorable alternative sources of income and some of these growers underplanted their quotas of dark tobacco during the war years. However, so long as allotments are continued or in prospect many growers will be careful to guard their allotment rights since, with a decline in the value of other products or an increase in the value of tobacco, they might be caught without rights to produce.

Parity and Loan Rates

The use of parity as a basis for determining loan rates developed after passage of the Agricultural Adjustment Act of 1938. While that act did not specify the loan-rate level for tobacco, it did authorize CCC to make loans on tobacco. The first loans, made available in 1939, were at conservative levels (60 per cent of parity on fire-cured, 66 per cent on dark air-cured and 75 per cent on flue-cured).[26]

The 1938 act also authorized government payments to bring returns to producers as nearly up to parity as the funds appropriated would permit. The Price Adjustment Act of 1938 (attached to the Work Relief and Public Works Act of 1938, approved in June of that year) made funds available for making such payments on a basis that would bring returns on tobacco up to 75 per cent of parity. Thereafter funds were provided in the agricultural appropriation acts until such payments were discontinued. The rate was raised to 100 per cent of parity in 1941 because of the low prices prevailing in the 1940 season and was continued in 1942 and 1943 because of the low prices of some types of tobacco. Payments for the three seasons amounted to some $6 million. During the remainder of the war period, returns in the market were high enough so that government payments were not required.

The exceptional treatment of tobacco in respect to the base period chosen in determining parity has been frequently criticized as a special

25. Calvin B. Hoover and B. U. Ratchford, *Economic Resources and Policies of the South,* Macmillan, New York, 1951, p. 357.

26. As pointed out earlier, the parity for tobacco was, by law, figured on a 1919–1929 base rather than the 1910–1914 base used for most other farm products. Had the 1910–1914 base been used, the 1939 rates would have been at or above parity. However, the tobacco areas had long been recognized as having some of the lowest average farm incomes in the United States and they still show the highest concentration of "low-income" farms of any major agricultural region. In part, this situation stems from the very small acreages of many of the tobacco farms and from other institutional influences of long standing.

legislative concession to strong political leadership.[27] Regardless of its motivation, in the light of later developments the adoption of a postwar base for computing the parity prices of tobacco can be looked on as a first step toward modernization of the parity formula. Significant changes in the supply and demand conditions relating to tobacco had occurred during and after World War I.[28]

A further change in the base period to be used in computing parity prices for burley and flue-cured tobaccos was made in 1940. This change, which shifted the base period for these types from 1919–1929 to 1934–1938, was a second step in recognizing the changing relative demands for the different types of tobaccos. However, to have been entirely consistent and logical it would have implied a need for some downward adjustment in the parity levels of those types for which demand was declining. That step was not taken and the 1919–1929 base was continued for the other types.

The 1940 change of base for flue-cured and burley tobacco raised their parity prices about 30 per cent, or 4 cents per pound. Later legislation established the support level for the 1941 crop at 85 per cent of parity and shortly thereafter at 90 per cent. Subsequently, the parity prices became ceilings. The loan rates for flue-cured and burley were continued at 90 per cent of parity in the postwar period. The modernization of parity in 1948 and the addition of wage rates to the parity index in 1949 increased the parity prices moderately. The parity for flue-cured in June 1952 was 55.8 cents per pound whereas it would have been 53.1 cents if computed on the 1934–1938 base. The new parity for burley was also about 3 cents higher than if the 1934–1938 base had been used.

For the other types of tobacco, the 1919–1929 base continued to be used until the "modernized" formula was put into effect. The new formula increased the parity prices of these types much more than it did those of flue-cured and burley, partly, of course, because much of the adjustment on flue-cured and burley had already been made. The higher parities established under the "modernized" formula were due mainly to the upward movement in the prices of all tobaccos as a result of war conditions.

Though price supports were an important factor in producing the relatively higher parity prices for the dark tobaccos when the new formula went into effect, the higher levels for the cigar types were almost wholly due to higher free-market prices. Without any supports, they

27. See, for example, Hoover and Ratchford, *Economic Resources and Policies of the South,* and Charles M. Hardin, "The Tobacco Program: Exception or Portent?," *Journal of Farm Economics,* November 1946, pp. 920–37.

28. The specifying of a 1919–1929 base for tobacco was not, in fact, dictated by a desire for development of a generally more flexible, "modernized" approach to the parity idea. Whatever its merits or demerits, the action taken was due largely to the strategic positions of some of the tobacco state legislators in the Congress at that time. Many of these same legislators opposed vigorously the general adoption of the "modernized" method of computing parity contained in the Agricultural Act of 1948.

brought much higher prices during the war and postwar years than in the prewar period. The result was a parity price that was twice what it would have been with the older basis of computation.

The action taken in 1945, whereby the loan rates for the dark tobaccos were related to those for burley, was the most questionable step taken from an economic standpoint. The support levels for these types were raised significantly above what they would have been on the 1919–1929 basis and these levels were continued in the postwar years. Since the loan rates were effective in raising prices, they also raised the modernized parity for these tobaccos when the new formula was put into effect. However, it should be noted that the support levels of the early 1950s were determined not by the computed parities but by a prescribed relationship to the support levels for burley. While it was possible to maintain prices at these levels, the actions taken tended to discourage readjustments in production that would have brought it into better balance with demand.

The Agricultural Act of 1949 provided that tobacco should be supported at 90 per cent of parity through 1950, if marketing quotas were in effect. Later legislation modified that requirement to some extent, retaining mandatory support at 90 per cent on some types and providing permissive support on others.

Effects on Manufacturers and Consumers

Tobacco controls have not reduced production enough at any time to cause scarcities in the channels of trade. Domestic manufacturers and exporters have been abundantly supplied except in the war years when demand was abnormal. The operations of CCC have to some extent contributed to the insurance of supplies when needed, though it is probable that the trade would at times have carried larger supplies had the CCC stocks not been available to it. Some measure of price-stabilizing influence provided by CCC probably was helpful to some of the smaller independent manufacturers in competing with the larger ones.

To some extent, manufacturers absorbed, without loss, the price advances to growers. They also have shared, along with the growers, in such gains from reduction of risk costs as have been made. Though the net profits of cigarette manufacturers did not increase as much as the average for all manufacturers, their profits continued to be substantial, mainly as a result of technological advances in cigarette manufacture and rapidly increasing consumer demand.

Consumers had abundant supplies and retail prices did not keep pace with the rise in consumer incomes. In spite of higher taxes, cigarettes continued to be cheap as compared with other commodities bought by consumers, the amount of increase in prices being substantially less than that for foods. (For a general summary of pertinent statistics on tobacco acreage, production, prices, consumption and income, see Tables 19 to 23.)

TABLE 19

ALL TOBACCO: ACREAGE, YIELD PER ACRE, PRODUCTION, PRICE AND VALUE, 1910–1953

Crop Year	Acres Harvested	Yield per Acre	Production	Price per Pound	Gross Income
	(Millions)	*(Pounds)*	*(Million Pounds)*	*(Cents)*	*(Millions)*
1910	1.3	817	1,142	9.3	$ 106
1911	1.1	830	941	9.3	88
1912	1.3	837	1,117	10.7	120
1913	1.2	772	992	12.8	127
1914	1.2	824	1,037	9.7	101
1915	1.4	816	1,157	9.0	104
1916	1.4	814	1,206	14.8	179
1917	1.6	820	1,325	24.0	318
1918	1.7	840	1,445	27.9	403
1919	1.9	737	1,444	31.2	451
1920	1.9	780	1,509	17.3	260
1921	1.3	750	1,005	19.5	196
1922	1.6	776	1,254	22.8	286
1923	1.8	818	1,517	19.0	288
1924	1.7	731	1,245	19.0	237
1925	1.7	786	1,376	16.8	231
1926	1.6	792	1,289	17.9	231
1927	1.5	778	1,211	20.7	250
1928	1.9	737	1,373	20.0	274
1929	2.0	774	1,533	18.3	281
1930	2.1	776	1,648	12.8	211
1931	2.0	787	1,565	8.2	129
1932	1.4	725	1,018	10.5	107
1933	1.7	789	1,372	13.0	178
1934 [a]	1.2	852	1,085	21.3	225
1935	1.4	905	1,302	18.4	239

TABLE 19 (*continued*)

Crop Year	Acres Harvested	Yield per Acre	Production	Price per Pound	Gross Income
	(*Millions*)	(*Pounds*)	(*Million Pounds*)	(*Cents*)	(*Millions*)
1936	1.4	807	1,163	23.6	$ 274
1937	1.7	895	1,569	20.4	320
1938 [b]	1.6	866	1,385	19.6	270
1939	2.0	940	1,881	15.4	289
1940	1.4	1,036	1,460	16.1	234
1941	1.3	966	1,262	26.4	333
1942	1.4	1,023	1,408	36.9	519
1943	1.5	964	1,406	40.5	570
1944	1.7	1,115	1,951	42.0	820
1945	1.8	1,094	1,991	42.5	848
1946	1.9	1,181	2,315	45.1	1,046
1947	1.8	1,138	2,107	43.5	919
1948	1.5	1,274	1,980	48.2	955
1949	1.6	1,213	1,969	45.9	905
1950	1.6	1,269	2,030	51.7	1,049
1951	1.8	1,310	2,332	51.1	1,191
1952	1.8	1,273	2,254	49.9	1,125
1953 [c]	1.6	1,259	2,057	52.2	1,073

Sources: U.S. Bureau of Agricultural Economics, *Tobaccos of the United States, Acreage, Yield per Acre, Production, Price and Value, by States, 1866–1945 and by Types and Classes, 1919–1945,* July 1948, pp. 6–7; and U.S. Department of Agriculture, *Agricultural Statistics, 1954,* p. 95.

a. Production includes 26,500 pounds that were not utilized owing to the AAA program.

b. Owing to hurricane, 5,955,000 pounds harvested and shown under production were lost. Value is shown only for the quantity that was saved.

c. Data for 1953 preliminary.

TABLE 20

All Tobacco: Consumption and Prices, 1910–1955

Year	Total Consumption per Capita	BLS Consumer Price Index	Average Farm Price of Tobacco	Retail Price of Cigarettes
	(Pounds)	*(1947–49=100)*	*(Cents)*	*(Cents)*
1910	6.5		9.3	
1911	6.3		9.3	
1912	6.5		10.7	
1913	6.6	80	12.8	
1914	6.4	82	9.7	
1915	6.4	81	9.0	
1916	6.9	91	14.8	
1917	7.3	117	24.0	
1918	6.9	134	27.9	
1919	6.8	150	31.2	
1920	8.67	85.7	17.3	
1921	8.21	76.4	19.5	
1922	8.58	71.6	22.8	
1923	8.98	72.9	19.0	
1924	8.81	73.1	19.0	
1925	8.98	75.0	16.8	
1926	9.03	75.6	17.9	14.6
1927	8.96	74.2	20.7	14.4
1928	8.93	73.3	20.0	13.7
1929	9.21	73.3	18.3	13.2
1930	8.85	71.4	12.8	13.6
1931	8.45	65.0	8.2	13.7
1932	7.64	58.4	10.5	14.2
1933	7.79	55.3	13.0	11.8
1934	8.34	57.2	21.3	13.1
1935	8.21	58.7	18.4	13.2
1936	8.82	59.3	23.6	13.2

TABLE 20 (*continued*)

Year	Total Consumption per Capita	BLS Consumer Price Index	Average Farm Price of Tobacco	Retail Price of Cigarettes
	(*Pounds*)	(*1947–49=100*)	(*Cents*)	(*Cents*)
1937	8.95	61.4	20.4	13.8
1938	8.75	60.3	19.6	13.8
1939	8.83	59.4	15.4	14.4
1940	9.12	59.9	16.1	14.9
1941	9.78	62.9	26.4	14.2
1942	10.69	69.7	36.9	15.8
1943	11.46	74.0	40.5	16.1
1944	11.22	75.2	42.0	16.5
1945	12.46	76.9	42.5	16.4
1946	12.20	83.4	45.1	17.7
1947	11.95	95.5	43.5	18.6
1948	12.12	102.8	48.2	19.7
1949	11.93	101.8	45.9	19.7
1950	11.96	102.8	51.7	20.5
1951	12.48	111.0	51.1	21.3
1952	12.92	113.5	49.9	22.2
1953	12.90	114.4	52.3	22.9
1954	12.20	115.0	51.1	23.0
1955	12.32 [a]	114.0	52.7 [a]	23.3

Sources: Consumption data from U.S. Agricultural Marketing Service, *The Tobacco Situation,* September 28, 1955, p. 9 (includes use by U.S. overseas forces from 1940 on); consumer price index from U.S. Agricultural Marketing Service, *The National Food Situation,* August 2, 1954, p. 41, and February 21, 1956, p. 35; farm price from U.S. Department of Agriculture, *Agricultural Statistics, 1954* and earlier volumes; U.S. Agricultural Marketing Service, *Season Average Prices and Value of Production, 1953 and 1954,* p. 14; *1954 and 1955,* p. 19; and retail price from *Agricultural Statistics, 1954,* p. 106, from 1939 on. (Retail prices 1953–1955 interpolated from index numbers related to 1952.)

a. Preliminary.

TABLE 21

TOBACCO: GOVERNMENT PAYMENTS AS CONTRIBUTION TO INCOME, 1933–1943

(*Thousands*)

Program Year	Conservation Payments	Parity Payments	Receipts from Marketings	Total Payments and Receipts	Government Payments as Per Cent of Total
1933	$ 2,059		$178,418	$180,477	1
1934	43,930		225,084	269,014	16
1935	16,020		238,966	254,986	6
1936	15,380		273,944	289,324	5
1937	11,471		320,111	331,582	3
1938	10,622		270,492	281,114	4
1939	7,476		288,889	296,365	3
1940	12,573		234,453	247,026	5
1941	11,687	$4,580	333,085	349,352	5
1942	8,365	593	519,503	528,461	2
1943 [a]	7,460	889 [b]	569,974	578,323	1

Sources: U.S. Department of Agriculture, *Agricultural Statistics, 1945,* p. 521; and U.S. Bureau of Agricultural Economics, *Tobaccos of the United States, Acreage, Yield per Acre, Production, Price and Value, by States, 1866–1945 and by Types and Classes, 1919–1945,* July 1948, pp. 6–7.

a. After 1943, payments were not made on a commodity basis.
b. 1942 crop parity payments.

TABLE 22

TOBACCO: PRICES,[a] BY TYPE, 1919–1951

(Cents per Pound)

Crop Year	Flue-Cured	Burley Type 31	Mary-land	Fire-Cured	Dark Air-Cured	Cigar Filler	Cigar Binder	Cigar Wrapper	All Tobaccos
1919	44	33	26	18	16	19	30	78	31
1920	22	13	18	10	8	14	25	75	17
1921	22	21	17	17	14	13	14	71	20
1922	27	27	24	16	14	15	21	71	23
1923	21	20	28	13	11	17	22	83	19
1924	22	20	23	15	12	15	16	73	19
1925	20	18	24	10	8	11	15	84	17
1926	25	13	20	8	7	10	20	83	18
1927	21	26	23	15	10	14	19	87	21
1928	17	31	27	14	12	15	18	76	20
1929	18	22	28	13	11	13	20	55	18
1930	12	15	27	9	8	8	15	69	13
1931	8	9	15	5	3	7	9	62	8
1932	12	12	17	6	4	5	7	51	11
1933	15	11	18	9	7	5	9	58	13
1934	27	17	18	11	8	9	12	75	21
1935	20	19	20	9	8	10	13	80	18
1936	22	36	25	12	15	11	15	83	24
1937	23	20	17	11	8	10	13	89	20
1938	22	20	19	8	8	12	10	65	20
1939	15	18	21	11	7	12	17	68	15
1940	16	16	33	10	8	12	15	78	16
1941	28	29	30	14	12	13	17	98	26
1942	38	42	57	17	15	13	20	132	37
1943	40	45	45	23	27	20	30	168	41
1944	42	44	56	25	23	19	31	196	42
1945	44	40	57	32	25	34	48	197	43
1946	48	40	45	26	23	33	53	234	45
1947	41	49	43	29	26	31	43	296	43
1948	50	46	54	32	29	26	41	274	48
1949	47	45	48	30	28	26	36	201	46
1950	55	49	48	31	25	25	36	203	52
1951	52	51	44	39	24	20	38	193	51

Sources: U.S. Bureau of Agricultural Economics, *Tobaccos of the United States, Acreage, Yield per Acre, Production, Price and Value, by States, 1866–1945 and by Types and Classes, 1919–1945,* July 1948, pp. 6, 8, 14, 23, 24, 25, 29, 33, 41; *The Tobacco Situation,* October 1951, February 1952; and U.S. Production and Marketing Administration, *Annual Report on Tobacco Statistics, 1951,* December 1951, Statistical Bulletin 103, pp. 25–43; *1954,* March 1955, Statistical Bulletin 157, p. 15.

a. Auction market average. Figures rounded to nearest cent.

TABLE 23

Tobacco: Gross Income,[a] by Type, 1919–1951

(Millions)

Year	Flue-Cured	Burley	Mary-land	Fire-Cured	Dark Air-Cured	Cigar Filler	Cigar Binder	Cigar Wrapper	All Tobaccos
1919	$212	$100	$ 5	$51	$21	$18	$33	$10	$ 451
1920	132	39	5	25	9	14	27	9	260
1921	79	38	3	29	9	11	16	10	196
1922	113	74	5	40	17	12	16	8	286
1923	121	68	6	33	13	13	21	13	288
1924	94	59	5	32	11	12	14	8	237
1925	115	50	6	21	7	10	15	6	231
1926	140	38	5	15	5	7	14	7	231
1927	147	46	6	17	4	8	13	9	250
1928	128	82	5	19	5	10	15	9	274
1929	135	73	7	25	7	9	17	8	281
1930	103	54	5	14	5	6	15	8	211
1931	56	36	4	9	2	6	8	5	129
1932	43	38	5	8	1	3	5	4	107
1933	112	40	4	12	2	2	3	3	178
1934	152	39	5	14	3	4	3	5	225
1935	162	42	6	11	2	5	4	6	239
1936	151	79	8	12	4	6	6	8	274
1937	199	81	4	13	4	5	10	8	320
1938	175	64	5	7	3	6	5	5	270
1939	174	69	7	10	3	7	11	8	289
1940	124	61	11	10	3	8	10	7	234
1941	182	98	9	10	4	9	10	10	333
1942	312	144	16	12	5	7	11	12	519
1943	317	179	9	15	8	9	15	17	570
1944	461	260	21	16	10	11	18	22	820
1945	511	227	10	18	11	17	30	22	848
1946	653	244	21	28	11	21	39	29	1,046
1947	543	235	16	25	9	19	30	40	919
1948	541	277	19	23	10	18	25	41	955
1949	525	253	20	21	10	18	22	35	905
1950	688	243	19	18	7	18	23	31	1,049
1951	761	336	18	24	11	12	18	29	1,190

Sources: U.S. Bureau of Agricultural Economics, *Tobaccos of the United States, Acreage, Yield per Acre, Production, Price and Value, by States, 1866–1945 and by Types and Classes, 1919–1945,* July 1948, p. 6 and later tables by types; and U.S. Production and Marketing Administration, *Annual Report on Tobacco Statistics, 1951,* December 1951, Statistical Bulletin 103.

a. Does not include government payments.

3

Wheat, Rye and Rice

WHEAT is a basic and essential foodstuff in nearly all western countries. Its storability, ease of transport and high nutritive content make it one of the most important and readily transferable foodstuffs in all major war periods. For that reason, wheat production tends to be thrown badly out of balance in the exporting countries whenever abnormal demands from abroad have to be met.

Much of the difficulty in the wheat areas of the United States, and of Canada and Australia as well, has arisen from influences of that kind. In both World War I and World War II, there was strong pressure from the government for increased wheat production. In the years following World War I that pressure slacked off quickly, leaving a lasting and difficult adjustment problem for the industry. After World War II, the high demand continued much longer, but the problem of readjustment has now reappeared in much the same form as in the post-World War I period, though with much more developed machinery for dealing with it.

A further complication in the industry arises from the very rapid mechanization that occurred between 1920 and 1950. That development reduced greatly the real costs of wheat production and thus threw wheat price and cost relationships out of line with those of many other farm products.[1] With broad, general policies involving price supports in terms of uniform percentages of parity, based on a much earlier period, the tendency has been to overprice and overstimulate wheat in comparison with the incentives provided for many other kinds of farm production.

The wheat problem is also complicated by the fact that a sizable portion of the crop has long found its outlet in world markets, in which prices are established by world-wide supply and demand except as modified by direct or indirect governmental controls. In the absence of government intervention, prices to U.S. wheat growers tend to be determined more by conditions outside the United States than by domestic supply and demand.

1. Wheat yields have also increased moderately, as compared with earlier periods. Probably more important has been the improvement and adaptation of varieties for the different producing areas, which has tended to stabilize yields and reduce losses from diseases and pests. However, weather conditions continue to be a dominant factor in wheat production. Weather has had more influence on output than acreage controls in most periods.

Domestic Demand Relatively Stable

The domestic demand for wheat in food uses is very stable. Price changes do not affect it significantly, for most families buy about as much bread and flour as they need regardless of price and income levels. During the past thirty years, the decline in per capita consumption of wheat has about offset the increase in population. Hence, there has not been much change in the total amount required for food use in the United States. The amounts grown in excess of domestic food needs have customarily been exported, fed to livestock or added to government-owned stocks.[2]

Seed requirements vary only in relation to changes in the acreages sown. The demand for wheat in secondary uses, principally for feeding livestock, is elastic but usually at prices considerably below those obtainable for wheat used in making flour for human consumption. The demand for wheat to be used as livestock feed depends ordinarily on the availability of other feed concentrates. However, very large amounts of wheat can be moved into livestock feeding if it can be sold at roughly the price of corn. Industrial uses, which provide some small outlet at low prices, are seldom important except in wartime.[3]

Normally, the annual domestic requirement for food use is about 490 million bushels; the seed requirement is around 80 million. The amount fed to livestock is usually in the order of 120 million bushels,[4] making a total domestic usage of around 690 million bushels. In recent years, production has been running close to or well above a billion bushels. From 1945 to 1949, the excess was almost all exported.[5] Since then much of it has been accumulated in the form of government stocks.

Acreage and Production Show Wide Variations

The acreages of wheat sown and harvested have varied widely over the period here under review, and also during and after World War I. Because of severe winterkills there are, in some years, large differences between the acreages sown and those harvested. Over the past twenty years the loss from winterkilling and other factors has ranged from about 4 million to around 25 million acres. Yields also have fluctuated widely, largely as a result of droughts.[6]

2. Some small amounts have also been used as industrial raw materials, chiefly in the manufacture of alcohol.

3. During the years 1942–1945, nearly a billion and a half bushels of wheat were used for feed, and more than a quarter of a billion for industrial purposes. (See U.S. Department of Agriculture, *Agricultural Statistics, 1951,* p. 18.) These were much larger amounts than are customarily used for such purposes in peacetime.

4. Mostly off-grades and types not suitable for flour production.

5. Sizable quantities were still being used as livestock feed in 1945 but most of this was from stocks held by the Commodity Credit Corporation and from supplies imported from Canada for that purpose, rather than from current U.S. production.

6. The yield per harvested acre was 11.2 bushels in 1933 and 19.5 in 1942.

The acreage harvested stood at 52 million in 1913. It was increased to 74 million in 1919.[7] Because of the greatly reduced export demand and low prices in the early postwar years, a severe readjustment in acreage and production was made in the years 1920–1925. By 1924, the harvested acreage was again down to about the 1913 level (52.5 million as compared with 52 million in 1913). Production was low during World War I (except in 1915), because of low yields. It was critically short in 1917 and 1918.[8] Severe restrictions had to be put on domestic consumption in order to provide even the inadequate volume of exports sent to Britain and France.

During the 1940s the acreage sown ranged from 53 million (in 1942) to 83.9 million (in 1949). In general, yields after 1939 were in the order of 50 per cent larger than those of the 1930s. Wheat production ranged from 552 million bushels in 1933—less than enough to supply domestic requirements—to 1,359 million in 1947—about twice the amount used in the United States for food, seed and normal feed use.[9]

World Production Tends to Be More Stable

In most periods, world wheat production is much more stable than that of the United States, or of any other individual wheat-exporting country. Adverse or extremely favorable weather conditions are seldom world-wide and variations in the acreages sown tend to average out. However, there was a pronounced upward trend in world wheat production during the 1920s. From an outturn of only 2.8 billion bushels in

7. *Agricultural Statistics, 1937,* pp. 9–10. Seeded acreages for spring wheat are not reported for the years prior to 1919. Those for winter wheat go back to 1909.

8. Acreages harvested, yields, production and prices for these years were as follows:

Year	*Acreage Harvested (Thousands)*	*Average Yield per Acre (Bushels)*	*Production (Million Bushels)*	*Season Average Price to Farmers (Cents per Bushel)*
1913	52,012	14.4	751	79.4
1914	55,613	16.1	897	97.4
1915	60,303	16.7	1,009	96.1
1916	53,510	11.9	635	143.4
1917	46,787	13.2	620	204.7
1918	61,068	14.8	904	205.0
1919	73,700	12.9	952	216.3
1920	62,358	13.5	843	182.6
1921	64,566	12.7	819	103.0
1922	61,397	13.8	847	96.6
1923	56,920	13.3	759	92.6
1924	52,463	16.0	842	124.7

(*Agricultural Statistics, 1937,* pp. 9, 10.)

It should be noted that "acres harvested" does not necessarily reflect farmers' intentions to produce. That would be shown more clearly by data on acreages sown. Prices were under government control and support during part or all of 1917, 1918 and 1919.

9. The 1933, 1934, 1935 and 1936 crops were below domestic requirements. The deficit in 1933 was made up from government-held stocks carried over from the period of Farm Board operations. The short crops of 1934–1936 were supplemented by rather sizable net imports, especially in 1935 and 1936.

1919–20 it moved up continuously to almost 4 billion in 1928–29.[10] This heavy excess of production on a world-wide basis was one of the causes of the difficulties experienced by the Federal Farm Board in its efforts to support the price of wheat.

First Government Program, 1917–1919

The first government program relating to wheat was undertaken in 1917, as a means of stimulating production with a view to meeting domestic requirements and providing supplies desperately needed by Britain and France. Poor yields in the years 1916–1919 kept production below the amounts desired in spite of large increases in acreage in 1918 and 1919. Exports in 1916 and 1917 were well below 200 million bushels despite strenuous efforts by the British, French and U.S. governments to increase them. The U.S. government guaranteed minimum prices for the 1918 crop and later took over control of the entire wheat supply, thus establishing maximum as well as minimum prices. This was done by setting up the Food Administration Grain Corporation with authority either to buy or to sell wheat at the specified price.[11]

The relatively simple device used was entirely feasible under the conditions then existing. There was an unlimited outlet for all the wheat that could be acquired, and its distribution to the various claimants was under the control of the U.S. government. No surplus problem arose. The operation was successful in terms of the limited objectives for which it was designed. Prices were stabilized and a significant start was made in getting the larger production desired. The 1918 acreage harvested was 61 million as compared with 47 million in 1917. The continued shortage was due to heavy demand, a short crop in the preceding year and a very moderate yield (14.8 bushels) in 1918. Production was up from 620 million bushels in 1917 to 904 million in 1918.

The apparent ease of handling the situation by means of this simple mechanism led later to proposals for handling the much more complex postwar situation in the same way. But the postwar conditions were quite different and no such easy solution was possible. The wartime stimulus came more fully into effect in 1919 and resulted in a harvested acreage of 74 million—more than was needed in view of the cessation of fighting and the sharp reduction in foreign demand and buying power that came soon after.

The Food Administration Grain Corporation was by then nonexistent and there was no longer an unlimited outlet for export wheat produced in the United States. A quick downward adjustment of acreage and production was needed, but it is difficult to adjust supply in such circum-

10. *Agricultural Statistics, 1937,* p. 18. The data given are for world production excluding the USSR and China.

11. For a fuller explanation of this operation, see Murray R. Benedict, *Farm Policies of the United States, 1790–1950,* Twentieth Century Fund, New York, 1953, pp. 165–66.

stances. By 1921, the price had dropped to less than half the 1919 price and the wheat areas were in deeper depression than any other part of the economy.[12]

No Further Government Action until 1929

The government discontinued intervention in the wheat market in 1919, and did not again undertake direct action until the Federal Farm Board was established in 1929. However, there was much pressure for government help in the intervening years and the campaign for adoption of the McNary-Haugen plan, or some other type of government aid, became the principal political issue of the decade. The earliest and, in the main, the most vigorous pressure for government action in behalf of the producers of export crops came from the wheat-producing areas. The depression became extremely severe there and in the corn areas during the early 1920s.[13]

The pressure for government aid became so strong by the latter part of the 1920s that the Administration was virtually forced to take some action to provide more direct and vigorous assistance to agriculture.[14] This took the form of a Federal Farm Board, authorized to aid farmers in developing stronger and more efficient selling agencies and to undertake stabilization loans and purchases for the purpose of ironing out the more violent ups and downs of prices. The Board was given a revolving fund of $500 million to use in making loans to cooperatives and for setting up and financing stabilization corporations.

Farm Board Operations in Wheat

The Farm Board program was, to a considerable extent, an intermediate step between the earlier policy of no direct intervention by government and the much more extensive, direct-action programs that were undertaken from 1933 on. It was not intended by the Congress and

12. In 1924, U.S. wheat prices were lifted from the depression levels of 1922 and 1923 as a result of relatively short crops in the other exporting countries and in Europe. In 1925 they rose still further, to about the parity level, owing to a short crop in the United States. Acreage, production and prices in the second half of the 1920s were as follows:

Year	*Acreage Harvested (Millions)*	*Production (Million Bushels)*	*Season Average Price to Farmers (Cents per Bushel)*
1924	52	842	124.7
1925	52	669	143.7
1926	57	832	121.7
1927	60	875	119.0
1928	59	914	99.8
1929	63	823	103.6

13. The conditions, events and developments of that period are more fully described in Benedict, *Farm Policies of the United States, 1790–1950,* Chapters 9 and 10.

14. The prices of farm products had recovered considerably during the 1920s. However, the farm groups had by then become well organized and were in a position to exert more pressure than they could in the early 1920s when conditions were much worse.

the Administration to be a transition program. It was, in fact, conceived with longer-term objectives than those underlying the emergency programs initiated in 1933.

However, the march of events, including the onset of a major and general depression, so changed the setting that a different approach was soon in the making. The Farm Board experiment did not have a large effect on the wheat programs of recent years. Since its over-all nature, significance and results are discussed in the companion volume, *Can We Solve the Farm Problem?: An Analysis of Federal Aid to Agriculture* (Chapter 4), it is not described or analyzed here.[15]

The transitional step in the development of policy which was taken in 1929 did, however, have a bearing on the kind of program adopted in 1933. At the time the Agricultural Marketing Act of 1929 [16] was passed, conditions and attitudes in the Congress and in the farm areas would not have warranted such sweeping innovations as were undertaken in 1933. The situation did not then appear acute or serious enough to warrant emergency types of action. It was hoped that the intensification and speeding up of more traditional types of aid would do the job. Adjustments were occurring fairly rapidly and the general level of economic activity was high.

The tremendous change in the economic outlook that came so soon after the Agricultural Marketing Act was passed quickly dispelled this optimistic view of the situation and demonstrated the inadequacy of the powers granted to the Board for dealing with the very different conditions in which it had to operate.

In brief, the steps taken by the Board, in respect to wheat, were: (1) the offer of price-supporting loans through the cooperative selling agencies (some of them sponsored or created by the Board); (2) the setting up of a wheat stabilization corporation to acquire and hold stocks that could not be sold at acceptable prices; [17] and (3) various attempts to facilitate exports, stabilize the flow of wheat onto the markets and improve the efficiency of the marketing agencies, particularly the cooperatives.

These efforts were not successful. It soon became evident that (1) mere improvements in market organization, however meritorious in themselves, could not affect greatly the returns to farmers under the conditions then existing; (2) price-supporting activities designed to remove wheat from the market would require far larger resources than were available to the Farm Board, and a longer period of stabilizing action than was contemplated in the legislation; and (3) sizable down-

15. See also the more general description of the Farm Board's part in the evolution of policy and the setting in which it operated in Benedict, *Farm Policies of the United States, 1790–1950,* Chapter 11.

16. The act which created the Federal Farm Board.

17. Similar steps were taken in the effort to support cotton and wool prices.

ward adjustments in production would be necessary if all of the output was to be moved into consumption at any acceptable level of prices.

Wheat production was overabundant throughout the world. The $500 million revolving fund available to the Board, for all commodities, enabled it to absorb only limited amounts of the large excess supplies available, and once the funds were committed no further aid could be given unless the stocks already held could be liquidated. These stocks were, in fact, an element of weakness in the price situation since they were a potential addition to the excess supplies that were still being produced.

The inevitable result, barring further action by the Congress, was that the program came to a virtual standstill in 1932, with most of the Board's funds frozen through ownership of inactive stocks or commitments already made, and heavy stocks on hand for which no market was in sight. The farm groups were ready to turn to some more far-reaching and less orthodox approach, and the newly elected, incoming Congress and Administration were sympathetic to their aspirations. The result was the much more interventionist program adopted in 1933.

Emergency Adjustment and Relief

The heaviest pressure for farm relief legislation had come from the specialized wheat-producing areas, but with later strong support from the corn, cotton and tobacco areas. The discussion here relates only to the wheat and other cereal grain programs, since the other commodity programs are described elsewhere in this report. The act passed (the Agricultural Adjustment Act of 1933) authorized activities of several kinds: acreage reduction, payments to producers, removal of surpluses, expansion of markets, marketing agreements and so on. Funds for carrying out these programs were to be derived from an excise tax levied at the stage of first processing, but only on wheat used for domestic consumption.[18]

Preparations were made early in 1933 for a program designed to reduce seedings for the 1934 crop. Seedings for the 1933 crop had been increased somewhat in the eastern winter wheat, spring wheat and Pacific Northwest areas. The acreage seeded was estimated at 69 million, the largest since 1928. However, it became apparent early in 1933 that

18. The wheat processing tax was fixed at 30 cents per bushel in July 1933 and was continued at that rate until the Supreme Court decision of January 1936 terminated the authorization for collecting taxes of that kind. Since the demand for wheat is very inelastic, the tax had no significant effect on the prices paid to farmers. Processors paid the tax and passed it on to consumers. An analysis of the effects of the wheat processing tax, made after the tax was abandoned, confirmed the expectation that the tax would be passed on to consumers. (See U.S. Bureau of Internal Revenue, *An Analysis of the Effects of Processing Taxes Levied under the Agricultural Adjustment Act,* 1937, pp. 21–27.) The tax also had no effect on wheat exports since wheat exported was not subject to the tax and, where flour made from wheat on which the tax had been paid was exported, the amount of the tax was refunded.

winterkill would reduce the acreage of wheat harvested. Production might not exceed domestic requirements.[19]

Consequently, plans for a plow-up program similar to that used for cotton were abandoned. Instead, a plan was developed for raising prices from the very low level prevailing in 1932 and for holding down the acreage seeded in 1934.[20] It was expected also that the revaluation of the dollar (also authorized in the Agricultural Adjustment Act) would raise prices, particularly those of the export crops.

The plan agreed on, after conferences with growers, handlers and processors, was for contracts with individual growers whereby they would limit seedings in 1934 and 1935 to 85 per cent of the acreages sown in 1930–1932. Growers were informed in June that those who would agree to these acreage reductions would receive benefit payments. The plan contemplated processing taxes and benefit payments for the three years 1933–1935, and acreage restrictions for two years, 1934 and 1935. A processing tax of 30 cents per bushel on wheat milled for domestic consumption was levied from July 1933 on.

The Pacific Northwest Situation

There was an acute problem in Pacific Northwest wheat because of the large stocks that had been accumulated and the very low prices prevailing. The wheats principally grown in that area are of a different type from those grown in most other parts of the United States and find their outlet mainly in specialized uses here and abroad; for example, the "soft white" wheats are used extensively in cracker, noodle and pastry flours. The white club varieties found their outlet mainly in the export markets and the soft red and hard red winter types were not considered good milling wheats.[21]

To relieve storage facilities and prepare for the new crop coming in, the Secretary of Agriculture entered into a marketing agreement with producers and handlers in that area under which export subsidies would be provided. An export association was set up to handle the operation. The Secretary set aside 2 cents per bushel out of the 30-cent processing tax on wheat as a fund to be used in financing that program.[22] Some 28 million bushels from the three Northwest Pacific states were exported under the agreement, at a cost of about $6.5 million.

19. The actual abandonment in that year brought the acreage harvested down to 49.4 million, one of the largest reductions in the history of the industry. Production was only 552 million bushels, which was less than the amount required for domestic use. However, there was no shortage and no net importation because of the stocks carried over from Farm Board operations and the heavy production of earlier years. (*Agricultural Statistics, 1951*, p. 7.)

20. The average price received by farmers in 1932 was only 38.2 cents. (*Loc. cit.*)

21. For a fuller description of these different types and their uses, see Joseph S. Davis, *Wheat and the AAA*, The Brookings Institution, Washington, 1935, pp. 265–66.

22. Davis, *Wheat and the AAA*, p. 269. As an inducement for China to buy Pacific Coast wheat under this arrangement, the Reconstruction Finance Corporation authorized a loan of up to $10 million to aid in financing the purchase.

The growers considered the operation successful though the gain to them was estimated at only about $3 million, approximately half the amount of the subsidy provided. The exporters were less well satisfied and felt that the program caused some net loss to them. However, it did help to relieve congestion at the terminals. Millers in the Southwest and in the Southeast felt that their interests were adversely affected. On balance, the results seem to have been of minor importance and not such as to warrant continuance of the program.[23]

The export subsidy approach was not highly regarded by Secretary Wallace, since he favored less rather than more government interference in international trade. Some small operations of a similar kind had been carried out by the Federal Farm Board but neither then nor in the AAA period were export subsidies looked upon as anything other than a temporary emergency arrangement for meeting an acute local problem. With the world wheat markets as depressed and glutted as they were, export subsidies could not be helpful except in very special situations.

Price and Income Situation Better Than in 1932

As a result of the short crop nationally and the minor export operation described above, and with some stimulus from the revival of the economy and devaluation of the dollar, the price of wheat rose during the year to about twice what it had been in 1932 (a season average of 74.4 cents as compared with 38.2 cents). The heavy winterkill and the prospect of greatly reduced production were probably the most important factors, but there was some revival of confidence in 1933 and a generally better tone in the market. Also, some of the excess stocks were beginning to be worked off. Even though the 1933 crop was much smaller than the 1932 crop, its farm value was about $122 million higher. In addition, the growers received about $100 million in rental and benefit payments.[24]

The 1934 Crop

More than three quarters of the 1934 acreage was under contract. Although only about a third of the growers signed contracts, that third was estimated to include about 80 per cent of the crop and more than 80 per cent of the wheat marketed. The reduction sought was not great, only 15 per cent of the 1930–1932 acreages, which were large as compared with those of the 1920s. However, an important objective of the program was to prevent an increase in plantings in response to the expected increase in prices, rather than to bring about a large reduction.

Many growers were not actually required to reduce acreage at all, from what they would have grown in the absence of a program. The national average for the base years was 66 million acres. A reduction

23. See *ibid.*, pp. 264–302.
24. *Agricultural Statistics, 1937*, p. 384, and *1951*, p. 7.

of 15 per cent would have called for a seeded acreage of 56 million. However, the reduction actually made was only to about 64 million acres. Though contract signers reduced their acreages by more than the required amount, many nonsigners and some new growers maintained or increased their acreages.[25] The eastern soft winter wheat growers increased their acreages by more than 10 per cent.

The program apparently did reduce output slightly. Nourse, Davis and Black estimate that, in the absence of the AAA contraction efforts, the 1934 crop would probably have been about as large as the 1933 crop. Actually it was 25 to 30 million bushels less.[26]

The big factor in the 1934 situation was not a reduction in acreage seeded but rather the very severe drought of that year. Of the 64 million acres sown, only 43.3 million were harvested and the yield on these was only 12.1 bushels. The resulting outturn was only 526 million bushels, as compared with 552 million in 1933 and a usual range, in the 1928–1932 period, of 800 to 900 million. As Nourse, Davis and Black put it: "Nature was primarily responsible for reducing the crop 337 million bushels below the 1928–1932 average." [27]

Both the 1933 and 1934 crops were below domestic requirements. Even with the heavy carry-overs from the Farm Board period, wheat imports began to exceed exports in 1934. That was the first time in the recorded history of the industry (back to 1866) that exports had not been larger than imports. The net export-import deficit was larger in 1935 (30.7 million bushels) and continued near that level in 1936. Wheat stocks were reduced by 100 million bushels during the 1933–34 season and by about 130 million in 1934–35, thus bringing them down about to the levels customarily carried by the trade.[28] The troublesome carry-over of stocks from the Farm Board period had been eliminated.

Plantings Up in 1935

With higher prices and sizable benefit payments, and with no very effective controls on production, the acreage seeded in 1935 was up again to 69.6 million, somewhat above the levels that had resulted in sizable surpluses in the 1928–1932 period.[29] However, the drought of 1934 was still having some effect on growth conditions in the wheat areas and there was a heavy winterkill in the winter wheat region. The acreage harvested was only 51.3 million and the yield on the acres harvested only 12.2 bushels. The crop of 628 million bushels, though larger

25. Edwin G. Nourse, Joseph S. Davis and John D. Black, *Three Years of the Agricultural Adjustment Administration,* The Brookings Institution, Washington, 1937, p. 125.
26. *Loc. cit.*
27. *Ibid.,* p. 126.
28. *Agricultural Statistics, 1937,* p. 24.
29. The acreage seeded to winter wheat was nearly 3 million (about 7 per cent) above the average acreage sown in the 1930–1932 period.

than that of 1934, was still not large enough to meet domestic requirements.

Contract signers were asked to hold down their 1935 acreages to 90 per cent of the acreages sown by them in the base period. However, the nonsigners, on the whole, increased their acreages by larger amounts than the signers reduced theirs. By late March 1935, prospects for the crop were very poor. The contract terms were therefore relaxed. Winter wheat growers were, in effect, permitted to harvest whatever acreage they had sown, without loss of benefits, provided they would agree to make a correspondingly larger reduction in 1936. Spring wheat growers could sow as much as they wanted to.

With wheat production running below domestic requirements and no carry-over to dispose of, there was little reason to continue efforts to hold down production, except as a safeguard against prospective future surpluses. Though the program was nominally still in effect, there was little attempt to restrain seedings in the fall of 1935 and acreage was expanded. The invalidation of the processing tax, and of production control contracts, as a result of the Hoosac Mills decision of January 1936, caused controls to be eliminated entirely for the 1936 spring wheat crop.

Large Acreage but Low Production in 1936

With little or nothing in the way of curbs on production, the acreage sown for 1936 harvesting (about 74 million) exceeded even the high level of 1928.[30] It was close to the previous record high of 77 million acres sown for harvest in 1919. However, very adverse weather conditions in the 1935–36 season cut the acreage harvested to 49 million, which was about the same as that of 1933 and only 5.8 million larger than the extremely low 1934 acreage. With a yield of only 12.8 bushels on the harvested acres, production was only 630 million bushels, which again was less than the amount required to meet domestic demand. Net imports for the year amounted to 26 million bushels. The prices received for the small crops of 1934 and 1935 were relatively favorable, a little more than double the very low 1931 and 1932 prices.[31]

30. There was significant expansion in acres sown for all types of wheat but by far the largest percentage increase was in the durum or macaroni wheats. These were expanded by more than a million acres (about 45 per cent). Other spring wheats were increased by only about 600,000 acres (around 3 per cent). Winter wheat acreage was expanded by about 2.5 million acres (roughly 5.5 per cent).

31. The season average price received by farmers in these years was as follows:

	(*Cents*)
1931	39.1
1932	38.2
1933	74.4
1934	84.8
1935	83.1

(*Agricultural Statistics, 1951,* p. 7.)

Over-All Results—1933–1936

The 1935–36 season marked the end of the first phase of the agricultural adjustment program. During this first three-year period, operations were largely on an emergency basis. A basic objective was to bring production into better balance with the very restricted demand and to work down the heavy stocks of cotton, wheat, tobacco and some other products.

For wheat, that had been accomplished to an even greater extent than the plans called for. Wheat supplies were well below planned levels in 1934, 1935 and 1936. This situation, however, was to only a very small extent a result of the agricultural adjustment program initiated in 1933. It was almost wholly due to the severe droughts of those years. Production averaged 567 million bushels for the years 1933–1935. Nourse, Davis and Black estimate that, in the absence of a control program, it might have averaged 585 million bushels but not much more.[32]

The same writers, though recognizing that such guesses are highly speculative, estimate that, under more normal conditions, AAA, with the procedures then available to it, might have reduced production by around 160 million bushels per year, as compared with the 30-million-bushel reductions actually achieved in 1934 and 1935, as an average.

The small change attributed to the program, even while a very troublesome surplus was being cleared up, does not, of course, mean that there was no need for adjustment at the time the program was first undertaken. The severe droughts of the succeeding three years could not then be foreseen and the wheat situation as a whole was obviously badly out of balance. Furthermore, there was clearly a tendency for wheat acreage to be expanded too rapidly and too much to accord with the best interests of the growers.

The industry was undergoing a technological change that was reducing real costs per acre. Large resources not easily shifted to other uses were available and customary outlets in the world markets were severely restricted. It was evident that an unhealthy situation had developed which would not quickly work itself out through ordinary types of market influence on supply and demand unless very severe cutbacks occurred through natural causes. That kind of adjustment did occur but it was unforeseeable and quite unexpected.

A more pertinent question is whether a suitable adjustment could have been achieved under more normal conditions without stronger and more coercive controls than were provided in the agricultural legislation of 1933. Nourse, Davis and Black, as a result of their extensive and detailed study made in that period, appear to be dubious. The fact that stronger controls (the marketing quota system) were provided in the

32. *Three Years of the Agricultural Adjustment Administration,* p. 127.

Agricultural Adjustment Act of 1938 indicates that the Congress and the Administration shared that view.

All in all, the wheat program of the 1933–1936 period seems not to have had any large effect on the wheat situation generally. It was, in fact, virtually inoperative during most of the period. Its most significant effect, as far as wheat growers were concerned, was the transfer to them of some $315 million in rental and benefit payments.[33] This transfer, though not large considering the size of the industry, was of great importance to the recipients in view of the extreme need for additional money income in those years and the fact that many had no crop at all in some of the years. However, no significant basic adjustment in agriculture in the wheat region had been achieved. The problem to be faced in later years was much the same as that of the early 1930s. The over-all cost of the wheat program through June 30, 1936 was $354.6 million.[34]

Transitional Program, 1936–1938

The Hoosac Mills decision ended the collection of processing taxes on wheat as on the other commodities to which they applied. Consequently, there was no further provision for benefit payments, except with funds appropriated for carrying out commitments already made. Allotments were continued but with no definite provision for enforcement and with little incentive for compliance.

The Soil Conservation and Domestic Allotment Act was passed at the end of February 1936 and efforts were made under it to encourage some shift out of wheat and into soil-conserving crops. However, that action, because of its timing, could not have much effect on the 1936 crop. The acreage sown for harvest in 1936 (74 million) was almost a record high.

The Soil Conservation and Domestic Allotment Act came into effect in time for efforts to be made to reduce the wheat acreage sown for harvest in 1937, but the incentives provided were not sufficient to hold acreage down. Because of the short 1936 crop, and other factors, prices advanced to more than a dollar for the 1936 season and resulted in a further large expansion of acreage. The indicated desirable harvested acreage was 56 million, which, with 1928–1932 average yields, would have resulted in a production of about 800 million bushels. It was estimated that this would meet all domestic requirements, provide some wheat for export and allow for an adequate carry-over. Soil-conserving

33. *Agricultural Statistics, 1937*, p. 384. For these three years, rental and benefit payments amounted to more than a fourth of what the growers received for wheat sold.

34. U.S. Department of Agriculture, *Realized Cost of Agricultural and Related Programs, by Function or Purpose, Fiscal Years 1932–1953*, in U.S. Senate Committee on Agriculture and Forestry, *General Farm Program*, Hearings, 83d Cong., 2d sess., Part I, 1954, pp. 74–89 (reproduced in Appendix B in Murray R. Benedict, *Can We Solve the Farm Problem?*, Twentieth Century Fund, New York, 1955).

and diversion payments to producers were offered in the 1937 program, but payments were not specifically related to wheat acreage compliance. The mere announcement of goals therefore had little effect since there was no way of forcing farmers to abide by them.

Growers expanded seedings to 81 million, a record high as of that time. Yields were somewhat higher than in 1936 and abandonment much smaller. The result was a moderate-sized crop of 874 million bushels, which, in view of the small carry-over, brought an average return to farmers of 96.2 cents.

The relatively high prices of 1936 and 1937 caused growers to maintain seedings at a high level for the 1938 harvest (79 million acres). With a smaller abandonment, and yields about the same as in 1937, the outturn was 920 million bushels. The 1937 crop had been large enough to restore the carry-over to about the normal free-market level. Consequently, the larger 1938 crop sold at a much reduced price (56.2 cents as compared with 96.2 cents for the preceding year).[35]

The demonstrated ineffectiveness of announced goals without provision for enforcement led to stronger control measures in the Agricultural Adjustment Act of 1938, principally the marketing quota phase of the act. The 1938 act did not, of course, apply to fall seedings for 1938 harvest and had no significant effect on spring wheat acreage in that year.[36] The sharp decline in price for the 1938 crop made it clear that a more direct and vigorous program would be needed if wheat prices were to be kept either at the levels established as a goal in the agricultural adjustment legislation or at any level that would not result in severe hardship and discontent in the wheat areas.

Stronger Controls Provided in the 1938 Act

The Agricultural Adjustment Act of 1938 included a number of new provisions that were important in the wheat program. The soil conservation and allotment features of the 1936 act were continued, but with more specific directives as to how allotments were to be administered. Authorization and directives for a marketing quota arrangement to limit marketings to specified levels were included. Also, the act provided for initiating a crop insurance program (beginning in 1939), for a system of parity payments to supplement prices received in the market and for price-support loans through the Commodity Credit Corporation.[37]

Wheat acreages were to be apportioned annually on the basis of acres seeded in the preceding ten years, with adjustments for abnormalities and

35. The business recession of 1938 no doubt also had some effect on the price received though the major influence appears to have been the increase in supply. The average farm price had reached $1.27 in April 1937 but was down to $.75 by April 1938.

36. The act was approved on February 16, 1938, too late to have much effect on farmers' production plans, even in the spring wheat areas.

37. Some of the other provisions of the act had a bearing on the wheat program but these are the most important features so far as that program is concerned.

trends. A small reserve of 3 per cent of each county allotment was available to farmers who had not grown wheat in the last three marketing seasons. The allotments were not transferable. The national acreage allotment of seedings for the following year was to be proclaimed not later than July 15.

The allotted acreage was to be that which, with average yields, would produce an amount, in addition to carry-over, that would make available a supply equal to a normal year's consumption and exports plus 30 per cent. The normal supply for any season, which had a bearing on the level of CCC loans, was defined as a normal year's domestic consumption and exports with an addition of 15 per cent of that amount as allowance for carry-over.

Marketing quotas were to be proclaimed by the Secretary of Agriculture not later than May 15 of each season after 1938, if he determined that the total supply as of the beginning of the marketing season would exceed a normal year's domestic consumption and exports by more than 35 per cent. The marketing quota, in bushels, for any given farmer was to be related to the acreage allotted to him for that year. In no case could the quota be less than the normal yield times half the acreage allotment of the farm. No quotas were to apply on farms where production from acreages planted in the current season would be less than 100 bushels. Marketing quotas were not transferable.

If a farmer marketed wheat in excess of his marketing quota, he was to be subject to a penalty of 15 cents per bushel. However, excess wheat from one season could be carried over and included in the quota for the following year.

Provision for Price-Support Loans

Until 1938, wheat had not been included in the loan operations of CCC. Under the new act, the Secretary was directed to make loans available to cooperators (that is, to farmers who complied with acreage allotments) if the farm price of wheat on June 15, or at any time thereafter during the marketing year, was below 52 per cent of parity or if the July estimate indicated a crop that would be in excess of a normal year's domestic consumption and exports. Loans were to be at not less than 52 per cent of parity as computed at the beginning of the marketing year.[38] If quotas had been proclaimed by the Secretary and had failed to receive an affirmative vote by two thirds of the growers voting, the quotas were not to go into effect. In that case, loans would not be available for the season to which the vote applied.

38. If marketing quotas were in effect, loans to noncooperators were to be at 60 per cent of the rates to cooperators and were to apply only on such portion of their crop as would be subject to penalty if marketed.

Parity Payments Authorized

In addition to such price enhancement as might result from acreage allotments and marketing quotas, the act provided for supplements to the prices received in the market. These were essentially the same as the benefit payments authorized under the original Agricultural Adjustment Act of 1933 but were to be made from appropriated funds rather than from processing taxes assigned to the Secretary of Agriculture, since processing taxes were no longer being collected. The idea was to make the total return to farmers as nearly equal to the parity price as available funds would permit. Thus, if the farmer received a price of 70 cents in the market and a parity payment of 12 cents, his over-all return would be 82 cents. Such payments were to be in addition to and not a substitution for any other payments authorized by law.[39]

An act of June 21, 1938 (Public Resolution 122, 75th Cong., 3d sess.) appropriated $212 million for parity payments on wheat, cotton, corn, rice and tobacco for the fiscal year ending June 30, 1939. Parity payments were not to exceed the amount by which the farm price of the commodity was below 75 per cent of parity. Thereafter, the amount of payment was to be controlled by the size of the annual appropriation made by the Congress.

Crop insurance, the other principal feature relating to wheat in the Agricultural Adjustment Act of 1938, is discussed elsewhere.[40] It has not had any significant effect on wheat prices and has not, thus far, been applied to any large part of the crop.

Operations Relating to the 1938 Crop

The allotment for the 1938 crop was put at 62.5 million acres, and was exceeded by some 16.5 million. Since production was obviously likely to run well above the amounts that could be sold at or near parity prices, there was fear that allotments might be cut too severely under the new act. The Congress therefore directed that the allotment for 1939 should not be less than 55 million acres.[41]

In marketing the 1938 crop, growers faced a situation similar to that of 1933. The 1937 U.S. crop had been large enough to re-establish normal or slightly larger than normal carry-overs. The production in Europe, outside Russia, exceeded all previous records. World supply was about 4 per cent larger than the previous record supply of 1933. Under these conditions, the opportunity for exporting wheat from the United States was limited. The price to farmers fell to levels that were only moderately above the very low levels of 1931 and 1932.

39. That is, payments authorized under the soil conservation and domestic allotment features of the act.

40. See Benedict, *Can We Solve the Farm Problem?*, pp. 418–30.

41. Public Resolution 118, 75th Cong., 3d sess. (June 20, 1938).

CCC price-support loans were made available on the 1938 crop at 52 per cent of parity, which worked out to 59 cents per bushel as a national average. Some 85.7 million bushels were put under loan, but the support price was apparently not much above what the price would have been in the absence of price supports. Only 15.7 million bushels were actually turned over to CCC. At year end, CCC owned 6 million bushels and had 21.5 million bushels under loan.[42] The loan provision probably strengthened the market moderately and helped to slow down marketings, which might otherwise have depressed prices more severely during the fall months.

Some Adjustment Made in 1939

The large 1938 crop resulted in an increase of about 100 million bushels in total stocks carried over. That increase was about the amount by which July 1, 1939 stocks exceeded what might be considered normal commercial carry-overs. However, no serious difficulties arose in connection with that year's crop. Nevertheless, with world production high and exports at low levels, it became apparent that an excess wheat problem might again be developing.

Only the severe droughts of the preceding years and heavy abandonment of acreage had kept it in abeyance up to that time. Normal yields and abandonment on the acreages sown from 1933 through 1938 would have resulted in crops that could not have been sold at any reasonable price in the weak markets of that period. Had volume increased and prices declined to the extent that these large seedings implied, it is likely, of course, that farmers would have cut back acreage and that the Agricultural Adjustment Administration would have taken steps to curtail wheat production. However, it is doubtful that the powers available to it in the years 1936 through 1938 would have been adequate to hold production down significantly.

Be that as it may, efforts were made to reduce acreage for the 1939 and 1940 harvests, though marketing quotas were not invoked until the 1941 season. The acreage goal for 1939 harvesting was put at 55 million, the minimum allowed by law. Acres sown were about 16 million less than in 1938 but were still some 8 million in excess of the goals announced. Yields were slightly higher than in 1938 and abandonment about the same. The result was a crop of 741 million bushels, about 180 million below that of 1938. (See Table 24.)

Exports were less than half the 1938 volume[43] and there was some

42. U.S. Agricultural Marketing Service, *Grain and Feed Statistics through 1954,* Statistical Bulletin 159, March 1955, p. 55.

43. Net exports were only 44 million bushels in 1939. This low level was due largely to the outbreak of war in Europe. However, wheat production in the major exporting countries was well above normal and world supplies were abundant. (See International Wheat Council, *World Wheat Statistics,* London, April 1955, p. 15.) It would have been difficult to export any large amount of wheat at advantageous prices even

TABLE 24

WHEAT: ACREAGE, YIELD PER ACRE, PRODUCTION AND PRICE, 1933–1953

Year	Acreage Seeded	Acreage Harvested	Yield per Harvested Acre	Production	Season Average Price to Farmers
	(Thousands)	*(Thousands)*	*(Bushels)*	*(Million Bushels)*	*(Cents per Bushel)*
1933	69,009	49,424	11.2	552	74.4
1934	64,064	43,347	12.1	526	84.8
1935	69,611	51,305	12.2	628	83.1
1936	73,970	49,125	12.8	630	102.5
1937	80,814	64,169	13.6	874	96.2
1938	78,981	69,197	13.3	920	56.2
1939	62,802	52,669	14.1	741	69.1
1940	61,820	53,273	15.3	815	68.2
1941	62,707	55,935	16.8	942	94.4
1942	53,000	49,773	19.5	969	110.0
1943	55,984	51,355	16.4	844	136.0
1944	66,190	59,749	17.7	1,060	141.0
1945	69,192	65,167	17.0	1,108	150.0
1946	71,578	67,105	17.2	1,152	191.0
1947	78,314	74,519	18.2	1,359	229.0
1948	78,345	72,418	17.9	1,295	199.0
1949	83,905	75,910	14.5	1,098	188.0
1950	71,287	61,610	16.5	1,019	200.0
1951	78,048	61,492	16.0	981	211.0
1952	78,337	70,926	18.3	1,299	209.0
1953 [a]	78,741	67,608	17.3	1,169	201.0

Source: U.S. Department of Agriculture, *Agricultural Statistics, 1951,* p. 7, and *1954,* p. 1.

a. Preliminary.

further build-up of carry-overs though stocks were not excessive in view of the emerging war situation. The price to farmers (69.1 cents) was moderately higher than in 1938 but still very low in terms of parity. CCC support loans were put at 55 per cent of parity, which worked out to 61 cents as a national average. About 168 million bushels were put under loan but only 7.7 million bushels were delivered to CCC. At year end, CCC owned 1.6 million bushels and had loan commitments on 10.3 million.[44]

if there had been no war. The total U.S. carry-over as of July 1, 1940 was 280 million bushels, about twice the normal commercial carry-over. That carry-over had developed in spite of the very low prices at which wheat could be bought for export in 1938 and 1939.

44. *Grain and Feed Statistics through 1954,* p. 55. It is apparent that, with a strong war demand in prospect, mills and elevators were holding much larger stocks. However, stocks held on farms were down. (See *Agricultural Statistics, 1945*, p. 19.)

Stocks Begin to Accumulate in 1940

The modest loan arrangements of 1938 and 1939 did not create any serious problems in the way of excessive CCC holdings. Neither did they have much effect on prices. However, they did undoubtedly help some in strengthening or maintaining prices, and served to promote orderly marketing since loans were made available to financially weak holders who might have been under heavy pressure to sell in the early part of the year.

The acreage sown for harvest in 1940 was about 62 million, only slightly less than in 1939. Abandonment was lower and yields higher. Total production amounted to 815 million bushels. Net exports fell off still more and amounted to only 30 million bushels. The season average price for wheat was slightly below that of 1939 (68.2 cents) and probably would have been considerably lower had it not been for the support provided by CCC.

CCC loans were made available at 57 per cent of parity, 64 cents as a national average. Some 278.5 million bushels of wheat were put under loan and nearly 174 million bushels were signed over to CCC. Thus, for the first time since 1932, the problem of excess government holdings began to emerge. Stocks owned by CCC at year end amounted to 169.2 million bushels and 31.4 million bushels were under loan. This brought the total of CCC stocks and loans to 207.8 million bushels.[45]

Conservation and Parity Payments

In addition to the assistance given by means of Commodity Credit Corporation loans, substantial contributions to the incomes of wheat growers were made in the form of conservation and parity payments in the 1938–1943 seasons. (See Table 25.) They added, on the average, about 20 per cent to the cash incomes from wheat. Thus, for purposes of comparison, the prices for wheat as given for these years can be thought of as representing about four fifths of the actual return to growers. This added return was high in 1933–1935 and again in 1939–1940 (mostly above 30 per cent). In the later years (1941–1943) it was 15 per cent and had been lower in the period 1936–1938 when only soil conservation payments were made.

Acreage and Production Still High in 1941

Though efforts were still being made in 1941 to reduce acreage by the allotment method, the results were no more successful than in earlier

45. Including loans on 7.2 million bushels carried over from earlier years. Special export aids were used in moving a small part of the 1940 crop, mostly white wheat from the Pacific Northwest.

TABLE 25

WHEAT: PAYMENTS TO WHEAT GROWERS UNDER AGRICULTURAL ADJUSTMENT, AGRICULTURAL CONSERVATION AND PARITY PAYMENT PROGRAMS, 1933–1943

(*Millions*)

Crop Year	Adjustment or Conservation Payments [a]	Parity Payments	Total Government Payments	Value of Sales	Government Payments as Per Cent of Sales
1933	$ 94	—	$ 94	$291	32
1934	106	—	106	303	35
1935	115	—	115	375	31
1936	43	—	43	464	9
1937	—	—	—	640	—
1938	50	—	50	399	13
1939	84	$54	138	397	35
1940	48	56	104	434	24
1941	49	58	107	733	15
1942	57	80	137	891	15
1943 [b]	60	81 [c]	140	928	15

Sources: U.S. Department of Agriculture, *Agricultural Statistics, 1945,* p. 521; and U.S. Bureau of Agricultural Economics, *Wheat Production, Farm Disposition and Value, by States, 1909–44,* March 1948, p. 2.

a. Wheat included in general soil-depleting acreage under 1936 and 1937 agricultural programs. The payments shown for 1933, 1934 and 1935 were made under the Agricultural Adjustment Act of 1933 and hence were in the form of acreage adjustment and benefit payments.

b. Conservation payments for specific commodities were discontinued when acreage allotments were discontinued.

c. 1942 crop parity payments.

years.[46] Growers planted about 63 million acres, roughly the same as in 1939. Abandonment was small as compared with earlier years and yields were high (16.8 bushels). The resulting crop, 942 million bushels, was much larger than could be sold in the weak market then existing. Exports were down to 20 million bushels and the domestic market could not absorb the surplus for food, seed and ordinary feed use.

In the meantime (May 1941) the Congress had raised the minimum support level for basic crops to 85 per cent of parity. This worked out to a national average support price of 98 cents, which established, approximately, the price received by growers for the crop as a whole (national average price received—94.4 cents).

46. The principal advantage to farmers in abiding by the allotments assigned was to make them eligible for CCC loans. If they chose to rely on ordinary types of loans and on the prices obtainable in the market, they could ignore the allotment restrictions with impunity.

The action was very similar to the price-pegging purchases and loans made by the Federal Farm Board and had much the same result. Three hundred sixty-six million bushels went under loan and approximately 270 million bushels were transferred to CCC because they could not be sold for enough to cover the loan. CCC ended the year with 419 million bushels either owned or under loan.[47] This was a substantially larger holding than that of the Federal Farm Board, which had caused so much concern in 1931 and 1932.[48] It would have been a serious threat to the stability of the industry and to the continuing usefulness of the program had it not been for the entrance of the United States into World War II. The advent of war quickly made heavy stocks of grains a strategic asset rather than a problem.

WHEAT IN WORLD WAR II

Wheat stocks at the beginning of World War II were ample to meet any foreseeable need for exports or to offset possible droughts. The immediate war needs for other products were more pressing than the need for wheat. Acreage allotments *and* quotas were therefore applied, for the first time, in an effort to control the size of the 1942 and 1943 crops. As war needs grew and stocks were worked down, both allotments and quotas were abandoned for the duration of the war.

1942 and 1943—Acreages Cut, Production Large

The allotments made in 1942 and 1943 were for the minimum acreages permitted by law, 55 million. Since marketing quotas had also been announced, there were strong incentives for growers to keep within the allotments. If they failed to do so, they would not only be ineligible for CCC loans but would also be subject to heavy taxes on wheat marketed in excess of the quotas assigned to them.

The 1942 acreage sown was below the allotment (53 million acres) and the 1943 acreage only slightly above (56 million). However, in 1942, a yield well above any previously recorded (19.5 bushels) resulted in the largest crop grown since 1915 (969 million bushels). The yield was also high in 1943 (16.4 bushels), though not so high as in 1942. The 1943 outturn was 844 million bushels, well above current needs for food and seed use and exports.[49]

47. Stocks owned amounted to 319.7 million bushels and loan commitments to 99.5 million. (*Grain and Feed Statistics through 1954*, p. 55.)

48. The Farm Board-owned stocks reached 257 million bushels in July 1931. However, there were additional commitments in the form of loans to cooperatives to enable them to hold wheat off the market.

49. Only 51 million bushels were exported in 1943. Imports were much larger and resulted in a record volume of net imports (96 million bushels). That was due, however, to heavy importations from Canada for feed use, not to any shortage of domestic food wheats.

CCC loans at 85 per cent of parity were offered in 1942 and 1943. The rates per bushel (national average) were $1.14 in 1942 and $1.23 in 1943.[50] A large part of the 1942 crop went under loan (408 million bushels—about 42 per cent). However, the Congress provided in a series of acts for the release of considerable amounts of government-owned wheat at feed prices (approximately the price of corn). Feed use rose from 114 million bushels in 1941, about a normal amount, to 301 million in 1943.[51]

The use of wheat for livestock feed was stepped up still further in 1943, to 507 million bushels, and was in the order of 300 million bushels in 1944 and 1945. In all, nearly 1.4 billion bushels went into livestock feeding in the years 1942–1945. That was roughly a billion bushels in excess of normal wheat-feeding operations. There was also an abnormal drain of about 260 million bushels for industrial use, chiefly for alcohol production. Most of the one and a quarter billion bushels channeled to abnormal outlets came from CCC reserves and the heavy crops of the war years, but some was imported from Canada.

1943–1945—Prices above Loan Rates

Average prices received by farmers were slightly above the loan rates in all of the last three years of the war.[52] Under these conditions, there was little reason for growers in most areas to rely on CCC loans, except as a convenience in financing during the crop year. About 130 million bushels of the 1943 crop were put under loan but all except 0.3 million were redeemed. There was more use of that procedure in 1944, with 180.4 million bushels put under loan and nearly 73 million turned over to CCC. The 1945 operation involved loans on only 59.7 million bushels, practically all of which were redeemed by the growers receiving the loans.

The year 1944 marked the beginning of a long series of billion-bushel crops. Only once before, in 1915, had production reached that level. The abandonment of allotments and quotas in 1944 and after, plus government encouragement for growers to increase acreage, resulted in a new expansion, to 66 million seeded acres in 1944 and to 69 million in 1945. Abandonment of acres seeded was light and yields were high, 17.7 bushels per harvested acre in 1944 and 17 bushels in 1945.

50. Parity prices were rising rapidly in this period. Consequently, 85 per cent of parity was a changing figure from year to year.

51. *Agricultural Statistics, 1951,* p. 18.

52. Loan rates (national average) and season average prices to farmers in these years were as follows:

Year	*Loan Rate*	*Season Average Price Received by Farmers*
1943	$1.23	$1.36
1944	1.35	1.41
1945	1.38	1.50

(*Grain and Feed Statistics through 1954,* p. 55, and *Agricultural Statistics, 1951,* p. 7.)

Despite these large outputs, CCC stocks declined rapidly and were down to only 32.5 million bushels by June 1945. This was due partly to heavy drains on supplies for livestock feeding and industrial use,[53] and partly to the very sharp increase of exports for relief feeding and for use in the liberated areas. Net exports rose to 305 million bushels in 1945.

CCC losses on the wheat programs of the late 1930s and early 1940s were nominal because of the opportunity afforded by the war to liquidate stocks that appeared seriously out of line with needs or possible sales outlets. Much of the wheat used for feed was sold at approximately the price of corn. In most periods that would have resulted in heavy losses. In a period of rapidly rising prices, such as the 1940s, sizable quantities acquired earlier could be diverted to lower uses with little if any loss.[54] CCC losses on wheat for that period amounted to only about $12 million.

THE WHEAT PROGRAM OF THE POSTWAR YEARS

The end of the war in Europe left many of the European peoples in need of very large bread grain supplies from the overseas exporting countries. Fortunately, U.S. production continued high. The use of wheat for livestock feeding and alcohol production was cut down or eliminated and the large surpluses produced were channeled almost exclusively into the export market. U.S. financing for these heavy exports was supplied on a very large scale, through loans, the Marshall Plan, relief contributions and so on.

Even though production was far above that of any previous period, supplies were soon so short as to result in a very rapid increase in prices, especially after price controls were discontinued and the postwar inflation got under way. The average price to farmers rose from $1.50 in 1945 to $1.91 in 1946. Wheat supplies became very short in 1947 because of the heavy demand for wheat in the foreign-aid programs.[55] Exports reached a record volume of 480 million bushels and the season average price to farmers a record high of $2.29.

53. Many in the various war agencies felt that this policy of reducing wheat supplies through diversion to livestock feed was being carried too far and that larger reserves should be held to meet possible postwar food needs. However, Department of Agriculture officials, long plagued by surpluses, were more sympathetic to the idea of using the opportunities afforded by the war to get rid of burdensome stocks and to avoid possible oversupplies in the postwar period when, it was expected, the farm product markets would be glutted and depressed as they were after World War I.

As it turned out, very large supplies of wheat were needed in the early postwar years and U.S. stocks became dangerously short. A tragic shortage in supplies for relief feeding abroad was avoided only by the fortunate circumstance of continuing high yields in the United States and by scraping the bottom of the bin so far as U.S. domestic supplies were concerned.

54. For example, wheat acquired under a 64-cent support loan in 1940 or a 98-cent loan in 1941 could be moved in a 1942 market in which the average price of wheat was $1.10 and that of corn $.917.

55. The shortages were accentuated by very severe droughts in almost all of Western Europe in these years, particularly in 1947.

Foreign demand was even larger in 1948 and exports rose to 501 million bushels. However, the record-breaking U.S. crop of 1947, 1,359 million bushels, eased the situation and prices receded moderately, to a season average for 1948 of $1.99. A 1948 crop that was almost as large (1,295 million bushels), and some easing off of the acute food shortage in Europe, marked the end of the severe pinch in wheat supplies. Prices fell off further, to an average of $1.88 for the 1949 season.

The 1949 crop was again a large one (1,098 million bushels) but not so large as the huge crops of 1947 and 1948. European agriculture was recovering and the need for wheat as a stopgap, lifesaving source of nutrients became less urgent. Exports fell off to 308 million bushels in 1949 and a new surplus problem began to take shape. Even with the very heavy exports of 1948, the stocks on hand at the end of the crop year were above normal commercial carry-overs for peacetime years.[56] Sizable additions were to be made from the 1949 crop and the situation again became similar to that of the early 1940s.

Price Supports, 1945–1949

In 1945 and the two years thereafter, price-support loans were available at 90 per cent of parity but little use was made of them. The loan levels were well below prices in the market and farmers as a whole were prosperous and not in need of any large amount of loans for current operations.[57] In those years, the wheat market was virtually on a free-market basis, except for the supporting influence afforded by heavy government purchases to supply allied and liberated peoples.

The 1948 support level of $2.00 was high enough to be effective. Prices would undoubtedly have gone lower in that year if loans had not been available. As it was, the estimated average price to farmers, $1.99, was almost identical with the national average support level. A quarter of the crop (366 million bushels) was put under loan and 291 million bushels were eventually delivered to CCC. More than 240 million bushels of wheat were in government-owned stocks at the end of the year and total carry-over in all ownerships was 307 million.[58]

The strong demand, high prices and high yields of the war and early postwar years provided powerful incentives for expansion of acreage.[59]

56. Total stocks, as of July 1, 1949, amounted to 307 million bushels. However, only 3.7 million bushels were held by CCC. (*Agricultural Statistics, 1954,* p. 10.)

57. The loan rates (national averages) were: 1945, $1.38; 1946, $1.49; 1947, $1.83. The amount put under loan in 1945 was about 60 million bushels, but practically all of it was reclaimed. In 1946, 22 million bushels were put under loan and in 1947, 31 million. Only a negligible part of the 1945 crop was turned over to CCC and none at all from the 1946 and 1947 crops. (*Grain and Feed Statistics through 1954,* p. 55.)

58. *Grain and Feed Statistics through 1954,* p. 55, and *Agricultural Statistics, 1953,* p. 12.

59. Also, producers were encouraged by the government to expand acreage in that period as a means of meeting the acute needs in war-devastated areas and elsewhere.

Acreage did expand quickly and substantially, thus setting the stage for the period of overexpanded wheat acreage that was to become the most difficult of the adjustment problems of the succeeding period. Acreages sown moved up from 53 million in 1942 to 69 million in 1945 and thereafter to 78 million in 1947 and 1948. A further increase (to 84 million acres) occurred in 1949, after the peak of abnormal demand had passed. Yields were high and abandonment moderate throughout that period. Production was above a billion bushels in each of the years 1944 through 1949, substantially above in 1947 and 1948. The 1949 acreage was the highest on record.

The sharp decline in wheat exports in 1949, without a corresponding drop in production, put both the government and the industry in a difficult position. CCC was supporting the price at 90 per cent of "old parity" as provided by law.[60] That worked out to a national average support level of $1.95, slightly below the 1948 level. With exports declining and the market weakening, about a third of the crop (381 million bushels) was put under loan. CCC took over approximately a fourth of the crop and, as of the end of the year (June 30, 1950), owned or had under loan 361 million bushels, much in excess of what was then considered desirable. Total carry-over in all ownerships at the beginning of the 1950 season was 425 million bushels.

Stronger Demand and Higher Prices in 1950 and 1951

The outbreak of war in Korea led to further price inflation in nearly all lines, and to increased demand for wheat. Net exports rose to 354 million bushels, about 60 million above those of 1949. The acreage sown for 1950 harvest had been reduced by nearly 13 million, but good yields resulted in a total output that was nearly as high as in 1949 (1,019 million bushels).[61]

The support level of $1.99 was about the same as the average season

60. Title II of the Agricultural Act of 1948 provided for using the "modernized" parity in computing all of the parity prices. However, the stopgap arrangement provided in Title I of that act deferred the adoption of the new formula, for the "basic" commodities, until 1950. The Agricultural Act of 1949, and later legislation, continued the arrangement whereby the computation of parities for the "basic" commodities would be by the "old" formula if that resulted in a higher parity price than under the "modernized" formula. Because of great reductions in cost, and a lower relative price for wheat in the preceding years, its parity price would have been lower if computed by the "modernized" formula. Consequently, the level of support at 90 per cent of parity would also have been lower. The unrealistically high level at which support prices on wheat were maintained was a factor in the problems later encountered by CCC, though there would have been a difficult problem of adjustment and large accumulations of inactive stocks even if support levels had been substantially lower. However, downward adjustments in acreage might have come sooner.

61. Acreage allotments were authorized for 73 million acres in 1950 (11 million less than the acreage sown in 1949). However, seedings were only 71 million. The acreage allotted in 1951 was again 73 million but seedings for 1951 harvest amounted to 78 million acres. (U.S. Production and Marketing Administration, *CCC Price Support Statistical Handbook,* April 1952, p. 11.)

price received by farmers and undoubtedly had a good deal to do with maintaining prices at that level. However, the amount put under loan (197 million bushels) was only about half that of 1949 and only 42 million bushels were turned over to CCC. Prices were rising and more of the surplus was being carried by interior mills and elevators and by terminal marketing agencies. CCC holdings were reduced from 361 million bushels in June 1950 to 208 million in June 1951. Total carry-over was down about 30 million bushels.

The correction continued in 1951 but not as a result of actions taken by farmers. The acreage seeded was up to 78 million, as compared with 71 million in 1950, but heavier abandonment resulted in almost identical acreages for harvest. A slightly lower yield brought the outturn below the billion-bushel mark for the first time since 1943, but only slightly below (981 million bushels).

The upsurge of prices generally caused a sharp increase in the computed parity price and the 90 per cent support level worked out to $2.18, which was 7 cents above the season average price to farmers. A fairly heavy volume was put under loan (213 million bushels). Nearly half of it (91 million) passed into CCC ownership. However, heavy net exports of 442 million bushels relieved CCC to some extent and its holdings were down to 155 million bushels by June 1952, a not unmanageable and probably not excessive amount. The total national carry-over was down about 170 million bushels from the high point reached in June 1950. The liquidation accomplished through larger exports in 1950 and 1951 was due partly to export subsidies provided under the International Wheat Agreement, to which the United States became a party in 1949.

Significance of the International Wheat Agreement

The International Wheat Agreement was put into effect in July 1949 and was scheduled to operate until 1953, under the terms agreed to in 1949. It could be renewed thereafter but the terms were subject to renegotiation at the time of renewal.[62] Much of the wheat exported from the United States from 1949 on was handled under the terms of the Agreement.[63] Since the prices specified under the Agreement were lower than the support levels maintained in the United States, these exports required heavy subsidies, which, for the first four years, averaged about

62. The Agreement was renewed in July 1953 for an additional three-year period, but with some changes in its provisions. The basic minimum price was increased to $1.55 per bushel (in terms of Canadian dollars) and the basic maximum price was raised to $2.05. The United Kingdom, a principal consuming country, and Argentina, which in the past had been an important supplier of export wheat, did not sign the renewal Agreement. Argentina was not a signatory to the 1949 Agreement.

63. Under the Agreement, as renewed in 1953, the United States guaranteed to sell 270,174,615 bushels annually at the prices specified.

62 cents per bushel and required a government input of some $546.5 million.[64]

The Agreement entered into in 1949 was an outgrowth of numerous attempts to control and stabilize the international market for wheat. An earlier agreement, initiated in 1933, broke down within a year.[65] Another agreement was negotiated in 1939 but was not put into effect because of the outbreak of war in Europe. Some informal arrangements for controlling wheat movements were used during the war but later negotiations failed to produce a working agreement until 1949. The principal interest of the exporting countries was in regulating the sale of surplus wheat. Since no burdensome surplus existed in the early postwar years, there was not much pressure for revival of the wheat agreement idea until the latter part of the decade.

The 1949 Agreement did not provide for restrictions on production or regulation of imports. Instead, it included a schedule of supplies to be furnished by the exporting countries at specified prices, which were lower than those supported in the United States, and a commitment on the part of the importing nations as to the amounts they would take at prices not exceeding the minima specified in the Agreement.

The maximum price was put at $1.80 per bushel and the minimum at $1.50 (for 1949).[66] The underlying idea was that the importing countries would be assured of an agreed quantity at not more than the specified maximum price, if world supplies were short as they had been in 1946 and 1947. The exporting countries would be assured of an outlet for an agreed quantity at not less than the specified minimum prices if supplies were overabundant. Since U.S. supplies were large from 1948 on, the principal significance of the Agreement, so far as the United States was concerned, was that it permitted the U.S. government to provide export subsidies without creating antagonisms on the part of competing export countries or disrupting the world market unduly.

During those years, the demand for export wheat exceeded the amounts the exporting countries had pledged themselves to supply under the Agreement. Consequently, the price for wheat outside the quotas was

64. *Realized Cost of Agricultural and Related Programs.*

65. The United States, Canada and Argentina had agreed to abide by export quotas but, in the course of the first season, Argentina overshipped her quota. Furthermore, the price effects were not as anticipated. The importing countries agreed to some reduction of restrictions on imports, on condition that the Liverpool price could be brought up to 63 cents. The price dropped to 40 cents, so the agreement was ineffective both in controlling exports and in obtaining relief from import restrictions.

66. Basis No. 1 Northern at Port Arthur, in Canadian money. The minimum price was to be reduced 10 cents each year, that is, to $1.20 in the fourth year of operation. When prices in the world markets were between the specified maxima and minima, both suppliers and purchasers were free to trade or not trade as they saw fit. Since the price in the United States, a principal exporter, was above the maximum set in the Agreement, the United States supplied wheat at the maximum, as called on to do (through purchase in the United States or from government stocks), thus providing an export subsidy of the amount by which its costs exceeded the price specified in the Agreement.

higher than the maximum price specified in the Agreement. There was thus an incentive for the importing countries to obtain as much wheat as possible under the provisions of the Agreement. There were few free international markets open for determining prices in the usual way and there was no large volume of wheat moving from uncontrolled producing areas. Consequently, the maximum price set in the Agreement tended to establish the international price for about two thirds of the wheat entering international trade channels in the first years of operation under the Agreement. Wheat sold outside the Agreement brought higher prices.[67] The situation, from the standpoint of exporters, became less favorable as production recovered in the importing countries and stocks accumulated in the exporting countries.[68]

67. The price situation noted above was due in part to the policy followed by the United States of not releasing stocks held by it at prices below those that would cover the cost of the wheat owned (or some specified percentage of the parity price). Had this wheat been allowed to move freely, the relation between prices under the Agreement and those on wheat not covered by it would have been different from what it was. From 1952 on there was undoubtedly enough wheat available to have brought world prices well below the IWA maximum if released for sale at whatever it would bring.

68. The advantages and disadvantages of the International Wheat Agreement have been much discussed. The literature dealing with that subject is too voluminous for summarization here. The text of the renewal agreement of 1953 is available in U.S. Department of State, *International Wheat Agreement,* Treaties and Other International Acts Series 2799 (Department of State Publications 5183), 1954. A brief description of the terms of the Agreement, and some of the arguments in favor of it, are presented in U.S. Department of Agriculture, Office of Foreign Agricultural Relations and Production and Marketing Administration, *How Is the Wheat Agreement Working?,* Agriculture Information Bulletin 74, January 1952.

Analytical treatments are numerous. Among them are such articles and studies as the following: Frank H. Golay, "The International Wheat Agreement of 1949," *Quarterly Journal of Economics,* August 1950, pp. 442–63; Food and Agriculture Organization of the United Nations, *A Reconsideration of the Economics of the International Wheat Agreement,* Commodity Policy Studies No. 1, Rome, September 1952; C. D. Harbury, "An Experiment in Commodity Control—The International Wheat Agreement," *Oxford Economic Papers* (New Series), February 1954, pp. 82–96; and an earlier study, *International Commodity Agreements: Hope, Illusion or Menace* by Joseph S. Davis, The Committee on International Economic Policy, Carnegie Endowment for International Peace, New York, 1947.

The Golay article is primarily a straight economic analysis of the effects on prices in the first year of operation. The FAO analysis looks mainly to problems to be considered in renegotiating the Agreement and concludes that, with suitable modifications, ". . . a new Wheat Agreement would secure considerable benefits in the form of greater security and stability to exporting and importing countries alike and would tend to improve the normal functioning of the world wheat market" (p. 2).

The Harbury article points out that the experience to date, though generally regarded as favorable, pertains only to a boom period and that results might be less satisfactory in a continuing period of heavy, excess production. The results in respect to foreign exchange stability are regarded as favorable but the incentives for production adjustment have been less than they would have been in the absence of an agreement. Nevertheless, the agreement is regarded as among the best of the various alternatives.

The Davis article, written before the 1949 Agreement was adopted, is guardedly critical of the whole idea of international commodity agreements but admits the possibility that, with proper safeguards and conditions, such agreements may be found helpful in some situations.

CCC Stocks Increase from 1952 On

The wheat acreage sown for 1952 harvest was about the same as in 1951 but, with low abandonment and high yields, it resulted in another bumper crop of 1,299 million bushels. The stock situation had come into moderately good balance as a result of the smaller crop of 1951 and increased exports. The carry-over in all ownerships was only 256 million bushels at the beginning of the 1952 marketing season. CCC stocks and commitments amounted to only 155 million bushels, which was not excessive in view of the disturbed world conditions. The over-all carry-over was, if anything, on the low side, as the outbreak of a more general war or a very short crop could have resulted quickly in a dangerously short supply situation.

However, the abnormal demand created by the Korean War was easing off and production continued high. Stocks began to build up again at a very rapid rate, chiefly in the form of CCC holdings. By the end of the 1952–53 crop year, CCC owned or controlled 492.5 million bushels.[69] Total stocks amounted to 559 million.[70]

The 1953 crop was again a large one. The acreage seeded, 79 million acres, was nearly up to the record highs of the years 1947–1952. The acreage harvested was about 68 million, which reflected a somewhat larger than average abandonment. However, a high yield on the acres harvested (17.3 bushels) resulted in an output of 1,169 million bushels, far above the requirements of the domestic and export markets for wheat in food and normal nonfood uses.[71]

The CCC loan rate in 1953, at 90 per cent of "old formula" parity, was $2.21, as a national average. As in 1952–53, it was high enough to cause about half the crop (558 million bushels) to be put under loan. The take-over in 1954, from 1953 production, was 461 million bushels. As a consequence, CCC holdings and loan commitments reached a record level of 850 million bushels as of June 30, 1954.[72] That was nearly twice the largest amount ever held by the government up to that time. As in previous years of heavy carry-over, nearly all of the stocks in excess of working requirements were held by the government. Total carry-over at the end of June 1954 amounted to 903 million bushels as compared with 562 million in June 1953.

Under these conditions, the CCC price-support loan program, though not fully effective, was, of course, the major and, in fact, almost the only

69. *Grain and Feed Statistics through 1954,* p. 55.

70. U.S. Department of Agriculture, *Stocks of Grains in All Positions,* Release of July 24, 1953, p. 1.

71. U.S. Bureau of Agricultural Economics, *Agricultural Outlook Charts, 1955,* p. 66, and U.S. Department of Agriculture, *Crop Production, 1954 Annual Summary,* December 1954, p. 1. For the years after 1952, some of the data presented are preliminary and subject to change.

72. The loan rate in 1954 (national average) was $2.24.

determinant of prices received by farmers. The average price, to farmers, as of June 15, 1954, was $1.91, which was 4 cents above that of a year earlier. The price to growers in both periods was about 77 per cent of parity as computed by the "old" formula, which, as already noted, resulted in overpricing wheat as compared with most other farm products.[73]

Acreage Controls Instituted in 1954

The build-up of stocks noted above made it evident that production could not be continued at levels well above the billion-bushel mark without creating an unmanageable storage and cost problem unless abnormal outlets could be developed quickly and on a large scale. Consequently, steps were taken in the summer of 1953 to restrict acreage and marketing of wheat in accordance with the provisions of the Agricultural Act of 1938 and its various amendments, particularly those of 1948 and 1949.

As a result of the limitations thus announced, and later approved in a grower referendum, the acreage seeded for 1954 harvest was reduced to about 62 million from the 79 million of 1952–53. The harvested acreage was only 53.7 million but yields were high (about 18 bushels). The resulting 1954 crop of 970 million bushels[74] was considerably smaller than that of 1953 but still close to the billion-bushel level and well above the amount needed to supply usual types of demand.

The Agricultural Act of 1954 relaxed somewhat the requirement that the price be supported through loans at 90 per cent of parity. The rate could be reduced to 82½ per cent of parity for the 1955 crop and thereafter could be as low as 75 per cent. This was still, however, in relation to parity as computed by the "old" formula since the law did not provide for beginning a transition to computation by the "modernized" formula until 1955.

The national average support loan authorized for the crop to be harvested in 1955 was $2.06,[75] as compared with $2.24 a year earlier. The seeded acreage was cut again, to 57.5 million, and harvested acreage to 47.4 million. The yield (18.1 bushels) was high. Total production, as estimated in September 1955, was 917 million bushels, only about 6 per cent smaller than the 1954 crop.[76] The acreage harvested in 1955

73. U.S. Department of Agriculture, *Agricultural Prices,* July 30, 1954, pp. 4–5. The prices given here are June 15 prices, not "season average" prices.

74. *Crop Production, 1954 Annual Summary,* December 1954, pp. 1, 2, 10.

75. The rate was increased on July 5, 1955, to $2.08, as a result of an increase in parity prices. However, the $2.06 rate was the one presumably contemplated by growers at the time the winter wheat crop was sown in the fall of 1954.

A total of 430.6 million bushels from the 1954 crop had been put under loan. As of June 15, 1955, 345.6 million bushels had been delivered to CCC. (U.S. Agricultural Marketing Service, *The Wheat Situation,* July 19, 1955, p. 23.) CCC stocks as of May 31, 1955 amounted to 961.1 million bushels.

76. U.S. Agricultural Marketing Service, *Crop Production,* September 9, 1955, pp. 2–4.

was 12 per cent less than that of 1954 and 30 per cent below average. It was the smallest acreage harvested since 1934.[77] Seeded acreage was down about 7 per cent from that of 1954 and was around 25 per cent smaller than the 10-year average.

The total wheat supply for the 1955–56 season was estimated (as of August 15, 1955) at about 1,935 million bushels, about 59 million larger than the record 1,876 million bushels of a year earlier. Total carry-over, mostly in CCC ownership, amounted to about 1,020 million bushels, an increase of about 118 million bushels over that of July 1, 1954.[78]

Production and Disappearance as of 1955

As of 1955, production and disappearance had come more nearly into balance than in the years immediately preceding, but stocks still were much above the amounts needed as strategic reserves and some additions still were being made. There was some question, too, whether exports could be maintained at the levels of 1953–54 and 1954–55 unless heavily subsidized or supplemented by more aggressive disposal programs.[79] The major problem facing the industry, assuming that production could be kept at or near the 1955 level, was the disposal of several hundred million bushels of excess stocks without depressing domestic and foreign markets unduly.

If acreage was held down to around 55 million (seeded acres), severe droughts could reduce output below market requirements and draw down the stocks held. However, the acreage sown for 1955 harvest was apparently large enough to result in some excess over normal consumption and exports if abandonment had been average or below average.

A sudden upsurge in demand such as could result from the outbreak of war likewise could make some part of the stocks held very useful as a strategic reserve. It does not appear to be either desirable or wise in circumstances like those of the early and middle 1950s to reduce reserve stocks to the very low levels the trade would carry commercially. However, a strategic reserve of 400 million to 500 million bushels could apparently provide ample safeguards against foreseeable contingencies. This meant that at least 500 to 600 million bushels of excess wheat should be liquidated as soon as practicable. Part of it could be used as

77. *The Wheat Situation,* July 19, 1955, p. 5.

78. *Ibid.,* August 19, 1955, pp. 3, 28. CCC stocks and loan commitments amounted to 990 million bushels as of June 30, 1955. Of this, 976 million consisted of CCC-owned stocks.

79. The possibility of developing more diverse and effective disposal programs was under consideration by the Administration but had not yet been fully worked out. If yields should drop below the high levels of the preceding years that would, of course, make it easier to bring wheat supplies and disposals into better balance. However, severe acreage restrictions have a tendency to keep yields high except in years of very severe drought, because of the incentives provided for use of the better grades of land and of superior methods of production.

livestock feed if priced in such a way as to be competitive with the coarse grains. However, the stocks of feed grains as a whole were high and plans for disposing of large amounts of surplus wheat in that way were sure to be resisted by farmers in the corn and other coarse-grain areas.

Nevertheless, it appeared likely that sizable quantities of surplus wheat would eventually have to be diverted to livestock feeding, as was done in the early years of World War II. Such a solution almost certainly would result in heavy losses to CCC, but such losses had already been incurred though they did not yet appear as realized costs. Drought, war or further large-scale inflation could, of course, change that outlook.

The possibility of using more wheat in foreign-aid programs was also being explored, but liquidation by that means of such large excesses was almost certain to require considerable time and either heavy losses to CCC or further inputs of specially appropriated funds. The possibility that holdings might be further increased also could not be entirely ruled out [80] though considerable progress had been made in bringing the industry into balance.

Set-Aside and Foreign-Currency Provisions

The Agricultural Act of 1954 provided for setting aside for disposal through abnormal outlets of up to $2.5 billion worth of the commodities held by CCC. The act specified that a minimum of 400 million and a maximum of 500 million bushels of wheat were to be included in the set-aside. These quantities were to be reduced through (1) donation, sale or other disposition for disaster or other relief purposes outside the United States; [81] (2) sale or barter (including barter for strategic commodities) to develop new or expanded markets for American agricultural commodities; (3) donation to school lunch programs; (4) transfer to the national stockpile established pursuant to the Act of June 7, 1939 (50 U.S.C. 98–98 h), as amended, without reimbursement from funds appropriated for the purposes of that act; (5) donation, sale or other disposition for research, experimental or educational purposes; (6) donation, sale or other disposition for disaster relief in the United States or to meet national emergencies; and (7) sale for unrestricted use, to

80. For example, an adverse vote by the growers on the continuance of allotments and quotas, or even very high yields and low abandonment, could create a new crisis in the stock situation. Further action by the Congress to restore earlier levels of price support could also make it much more difficult to hold production down. Until new patterns of production and use of wheat were more definitely worked out and adopted, the situation was likely to remain unstable, with restraints on output maintained largely through government action rather than through individual grower decisions.

81. Subject to the limitations of Title II of the Agricultural Trade Development and Assistance Act of 1954. A principal provision of that Title was that the President take reasonable precautions to assure that such transfers not displace or interfere with sales that might be made through regular channels.

meet a need for increased supplies, at not less than 105 per cent of the parity price.[82]

The set-aside was designed in part as a means of reducing the size of the "supply" as officially defined in the agricultural acts of 1948 and 1949, and thus of modifying the level at which price-support loans could be made. Under the Agricultural Act of 1949, the support level was to be 90 per cent of parity if supply was not more than 102 per cent of normal and would be reduced as the supply increased. With a supply amounting to 130 per cent of normal or more, the support level would be 75 per cent of parity. Normal supply as defined in the Agricultural Act of 1948 [83] was the estimated domestic consumption in the immediately preceding marketing season, adjusted for trends and unusual conditions, plus estimated exports for the next season, plus 15 per cent of the consumption and exports as an allowance for carry-over.

With this definition of "normal supply" it was likely that, with the large stocks held in these years, total supply would be continuously in excess of 130 per cent of normal and the loan levels under the formula would necessarily be at the minimum, 75 per cent of parity (82.5 per cent in 1955), whether the current crop was large or small.[84]

OVER-ALL RESULTS OF THE WHEAT PROGRAMS

Though wheat control programs were nominally in effect from 1933 to 1943, they had very little effect on production in those years. The

82. The act authorized appropriations to reimburse the Commodity Credit Corporation for the value of commodities transferred to the set-aside, at market price or the amount of CCC's investment therein, whichever was less.

The Trade Development Act (July 10, 1954) had authorized the Commodity Credit Corporation to accept payment in foreign currencies, for commodities sold abroad, to the extent of $700 million. The foreign-currency balances so acquired were to be held for the account of the United States and the ways in which they might be used were spelled out in the act. Provision was made for reimbursing the Commodity Credit Corporation in U.S. dollars. The maximum amount of reimbursement that might be accepted in foreign currencies was increased, in 1955, to $1.5 billion.

83. This was essentially the same as the definition contained in the Agricultural Adjustment Act of 1938. In the 1949 act, the specification in regard to amount of carry-over to be included as normal supply was changed to "the average . . . for the five marketing years preceding the marketing year in which such normal supply is determined" with adjustments for abnormal conditions.

84. The Agricultural Act of 1954 was in essence a reversion to the provisions of the 1948 and 1949 acts, which were due to come into effect in 1955 and 1956 if no new legislation was enacted. The 1954 act provided that the minimum support level for basic commodities could not be less than 82.5 per cent of parity for 1955 but left the way open for the 75-to-90 per cent range provided in the 1949 act to come into effect thereafter. The 1954 act also provided for beginning the transition to the "modernized" parity formula for wheat and other basics in 1955. This would result in lower computed parity prices for wheat and thus in lower price-support loans at any given percentage of parity.

The set-aside of up to 500 million bushels, thus taking that much out of the computed total supply, might be expected to reduce expected production plus carry-over to a level at which, if the crop was small, total supply would be less than 130 per cent of normal supply and support levels might be higher than 75 per cent of parity.

very small outputs of 1933–1935 were due almost wholly to drought. No serious effort was made either to reduce production or to hold it down. The principal significance of the program was the transfer to wheat growers of funds collected as processing taxes and distributed in the form of rental and benefit payments. These transfers, though relatively small per grower affected, were very helpful in an industry as severely depressed and harassed by drought as the wheat industry was in those years. The total amount involved for the three-year period was about $355 million.[85]

The conservation payments made in the period 1936–1943 were also mainly direct transfers of funds from the general public to the wheat growers. Though acreage allotments were nominally in effect, they do not appear to have been important as checks on the over-all volume of output.[86] The addition of marketing quotas for the 1942 and 1943 crops appears to have been the principal factor in bringing about the reductions made in those years. However, the low prices of 1938, 1939 and 1940 would apparently have caused some reduction in acreages seeded, even if controls had not been imposed.

There was a sharp downward trend in seeded acreages from 1938 on even without quotas. It was good yields and low abandonment that kept production up, not large acreages. (See Table 24.) The high yields of 1941–1945, together with prices that were about double those of the late 1930s, brought over-all returns to wheat growers to higher levels than they had received since 1920. Returns were to go even higher in succeeding years.

No Controls from 1943 On

In the years 1944–1948, the amount of wheat grown was almost wholly a response to prices and incomes. Prices were high and yields were good. The result was a gross value that reached an all-time high of $3.1 billion in 1947. Until the World War II period, the $2 billion crop of 1919 had been the largest on record. Values in the 1930s had ranged generally from $400 million to $800 million and had been as low as $289 million in 1932.

By 1949, the acreage seeded was at an all-time high of 84 million. Quotas were announced for the 1949 and 1950 crops and probably had some effect, though not a large one. The average price to growers had dropped back from $2.29 in 1947 to $1.99 in 1948 and to $1.88 in 1949. The continuance of high price-support legislation was in contro-

85. Including some small amounts used in providing export subsidies and in other ways.

86. The acreage reduction from the very high level of 1937 (81 million) to 63 million in 1939 was large. But the price had declined from $1.025 in 1937 to $.562 in 1938. The acreages sown for harvest in 1939–1941, around 62 million, were only about 4 million smaller than the high acreages of the 1929–1932 period. They were well above the levels of the middle 1920s.

versy and the outlook for wheat was less favorable than in the preceding four years. Seeded acreage was cut back to 71 million in 1950 but was re-expanded as a result of high support levels and the strong demand that grew out of the Korean War.

No important readjustments in acreage were made until both allotments and quotas were established in 1954 and 1955. Seeded acreage was then cut back substantially as a result of allotments and quotas.[87] Part of the adjustment came about as a result of somewhat lower yields than in the late 1940s.[88]

Wheat Adjustment—A Recurring Problem

The experience of the past half century does not indicate that the wheat problem will be quickly or easily solved. It does not, in fact, remain the same from period to period. Twice in the past forty years there has been great need for a quick expansion of wheat output. In at least four periods the problem has been to find ways to cut back production and to absorb the surplus until adjustments could be made or markets broadened.

Contraction of wheat acreage is apparently more difficult than expansion. Several methods have been tried. Some have been moderately successful; others have had little effect on the industry. The attempt to expand wheat production in World War I was not notably successful, not because of failure to expand acreage but because of low yields. Also, there was not enough time for the efforts to become fully effective. The expansion that did occur, mainly in 1919, merely accentuated the postwar adjustment problem.

The post-World War I adjustment was made in the most difficult and painful way, that is, through a disastrous drop in prices. However, it was carried through rather quickly. Seeded acreage declined from 77 million in 1919 to 56 million in 1924. At the end of this five-year period, wheat production and market demand were in moderately good balance, but that had come about only through much hardship in the wheat regions, including a great many farm bankruptcies and the loss of a good part of the banking structure of the wheat-growing areas.

Wheat acreage and production were again getting badly out of balance in the late 1920s, largely as a result of too rapid expansion in other parts

87. The acreage sown for 1954 harvest was 62.6 million, about in line with allotments (*The Wheat Situation,* December 2, 1954, p. 5). The acreage allotted for 1955 harvest was 55 million (*Agricultural Outlook Charts, 1955,* p. 66). The acreage sown was estimated at 57.5 million (*The Wheat Situation,* August 19, 1955, p. 27). The establishment of marketing quotas does not result in a specified level of marketings. Wheat grown on acreages allotted can be marketed without penalty. Thus the limitation on marketings applies only to acres seeded in excess of allotments. The controls are thus less rigorous than those applied to cotton in the early AAA period.

88. The average yield per *seeded* acre in 1950–1954 was 14.8 bushels as compared with 16.4 bushels in the years 1944–1948. (*The Wheat Situation,* August 30, 1954, p. 32.)

of the world rather than from any large expansion of U.S. output. The effort to relieve the situation by market improvement and price-pegging was not successful. The difficulties were greatly intensified by the severe national and international economic depression. For the first time, burdensome carry-overs in government ownership became an important problem. With normal yields the problem would undoubtedly have persisted for some years longer. Actually, it was cleared up rather quickly by a natural disaster of unprecedented severity. Government stocks were liquidated, but again the main brunt of the adjustment fell on the wheat growers rather than on the government.

1933–1941 Results Not Encouraging

During the early years of the AAA period, nature was doing such an effective job of controlling production that the government neither needed nor sought to do much about holding down wheat output. Related programs were needed and were carried out on a massive scale, but they had little to do directly with the production, consumption or export of wheat.

They included not only the rental and benefit-payment features of the wheat program itself but the far-reaching actions to refinance farm indebtedness and a very extensive relief program. While not sufficient to restore prosperity in the wheat areas, the aid given to wheat producers probably was as generous as could be justified at that time, in comparison with the help given to other parts of a severely depressed national economy.

The program of the late 1930s made clearer the possibilities and limitations of the types of program then emerging. It became evident that the use of acreage allotments with only mild incentives for compliance would not keep wheat production in balance, once weather conditions became favorable for large production, if export markets continued to be weak and limited in scope.

It was found, however, that the market could be stabilized, temporarily at least, by nonrecourse loans, even though these might be low in relation to parity. Prices would undoubtedly have gone lower in 1938–1940 if the government had not stood ready to absorb the surplus and hold it off the market. But the problem was not solved. It was only postponed. The emergence of war demand was as unplanned and unpredictable as the droughts which had solved the problem of excess stocks in 1934–1936.

Had the war not occurred, the problem of excess U.S. wheat supplies would almost certainly have proved perplexing throughout the 1940s unless very drastic controls were instituted. Technological advance, mostly of the laborsaving, cost-reducing type, was going on at such a rapid rate that it is unlikely that price influences emanating directly from the market would have kept wheat production and consumption in balance at prices growers would have considered acceptable. The government would almost certainly have felt compelled to step in vigorously with production controls and price-support loans, and an acute problem of excess stocks would no doubt have arisen much sooner than it did.

World War II and After

The World War II situation, and the early postwar years, added relatively little knowledge about the handling of surpluses. However, the war and postwar periods did provide a useful body of experience with respect to some other aspects of the problem. They demonstrated that, with reasonably good weather, production could be expanded substantially and rather quickly, and without a prohibitive price increase. They also showed that with rather modest adjustments in the price, very substantial amounts of wheat could and would be used as livestock feed, thus pointing the way to at least one important method of reducing excess stocks. The postwar years also demonstrated the size and costliness of the kinds of diversion programs that would be required if enough wheat were to be taken off the market to keep prices at levels regarded as equitable by the wheat growers. The 400- to 500-million-bushel exports of 1947 and 1948 were far in excess of any previously recorded. They obviously could not be maintained in peacetime without major dislocations and readjustments in the international wheat markets, and the cost, even of a more modest program, would be heavy.

CCC Most Important in Later Years

From 1948 on, CCC price-support loans were shown to be effective temporarily in stabilizing prices, but in much the same way as the much smaller program of the Federal Farm Board held prices above the market for a time in 1929–1931. The stocks acquired were not disposed of and their potential impact on the supply situation was as great as, or greater than, if they had been disposed of as they came into being.

This does not mean that these supports were either useless or necessarily inappropriate as a stopgap arrangement. It does mean that such a procedure, unless accompanied by very drastic controls on production, cannot provide a real solution to the problem. It only postpones it. It is apparent, too, that the level of support provided from 1949 on was high enough to make wheat production unnecessarily and undesirably attractive, as compared with alternative types of agricultural production that might be carried on in the wheat areas. It thus increased and prolonged the problem of adjustment.[89]

89. The levels of support have also been out of line in terms of equity. Costs of wheat production had been reduced much more between 1910–1914 and the early 1950s than production costs of many other farm products. Consequently, if wheat prices were held at the same relationship with other farm prices as in 1910–1914, wheat production was bound to be overencouraged. The adoption of the "modernized" parity formula for computing parity prices could correct this to some extent, but only very slowly

On the positive side, the holdings acquired as a result of CCC operations in the late 1930s proved an unexpectedly desirable asset when the war came on. This fact, together with the possibility of severe and prolonged droughts, either here or abroad, points to the desirability of maintaining a sizable strategic reserve, which can best be handled by means of an agency of the CCC type. Needed additions to such a reserve can well be acquired in a way that will strengthen prices at times when the market is weak, and loans of the CCC type may well be appropriate in dealing with very large crops resulting from high yields. They also have a place in facilitating orderly release of the crop within the year, provided they are at levels that will encourage orderly selling rather than transfer to government holdings.

However, stocks held against unforeseeable eventualities such as drought or war do not need to be extremely large. Probably a range of 300 to 500 million bushels would be ample in most periods and would allow for some expansion and contraction to offset yield variations. Accumulations beyond the upper limits of an adequate reserve constitute an unwarranted drain on public funds and do not benefit the industry in the long run. Maintaining a large inactive and unneeded reserve is expensive in terms of interest on the funds tied up, storage costs, deterioration and, possibly, as a weakening influence in the market.

A substantial part of the excess stocks held, as of this writing, probably will be used for feed, foreign aid or drought relief in the United States. Though liquidation in these ways will take time and cautious handling, or more carefully worked out plans for constructive use in other parts of the world, there appears to be no advantage to either wheat growers or the government in delaying these steps, or in further heavy additions to the stocks held by the government. If losses must be taken in carrying out liquidation, they are not reduced by delay. If continuing aid to wheat growers is considered warranted, it obviously should not be in a form that creates more problems than it solves and it should encourage adjustments that will make such aid less needed.[90]

---

because of the transition steps provided in the law, which required several years, and because of the distortions in the price structure which resulted from the abnormal war and postwar demand and affected the ten-year moving averages used as bases in the "modernized" formula.

90. The wheat problem is not the same in all areas and wheat itself is not a single commodity. Different types are used for different purposes and reach different markets. There is not much excess production in the spring wheat areas and little export or import of these types of wheat. The big accumulations and excess capacity, for direct human consumption, are in the winter wheat areas and in the Pacific Northwest. Here the eventual solutions almost inevitably must be in more use for livestock feeding, at feed prices, or in very rigorous controls on output.

It is clearly not to the advantage of the growers of spring wheat to have uniform nationwide percentage reductions in output if they are to be cut back by the same percentages as the growers in the areas that produce heavy surpluses. They can apparently produce about as much wheat as they want to and still get prices comparable to those of recent years. (For a fuller discussion of this point, see *Can We Solve the Farm Problem?*, pp. 495–506.)

COST OF THE WHEAT PROGRAMS

The costs incurred in the wheat operations of the federal government, since 1930, are sizable but they have not all been for the benefit of the wheat growers. Some were undertaken for other purposes but did at the same time affect significantly the returns to farmers. For example, the very large grants and loans to other countries in the early postwar years were designed primarily to aid the people of those countries. However, they also helped to provide an unprecedented export market for wheat at high prices. Some of the more recent contributions for famine relief in Asia and the flour subsidies in the United States during World War II also were mainly for purposes other than the enhancement of returns to wheat producers.

The cost of the CCC loan program for wheat is indeterminate. As of this writing, CCC holds approximately a billion bushels of wheat, which is carried on its books at the amounts invested in it. Except in the event of a pronounced additional inflation, it will not be sold on a basis that will cover costs. How large the eventual loss will be cannot be estimated at this time. Some wheat will undoubtedly be given away as disaster relief or in aid programs here or abroad. Some will probably be sold for foreign currencies of uncertain value. Sizable amounts almost certainly will be sold eventually as livestock feed at prices well below the accrued costs on them.

The most comprehensive cost analysis available is the U.S. Department of Agriculture compilation, which carries to June 30, 1953. That compilation is on a realized cost basis and hence does not include probable future losses such as those mentioned above. Recognizing these qualifications, and the inherent limitations in using realized costs for continuing programs in which sizable outlays are inevitably deferred, the data now available are presented in Table 26.

Other Programs Helped Strengthen Wheat Prices

The data shown in Table 26 are those listed as primarily for stabilization of prices and incomes. There were, in addition, other expenditures that had some bearing on the wheat situation, though it is difficult if not impossible to determine the beneficiaries. The largest item was the foreign-aid program, which contributed greatly to the strength of the wheat market in the years 1945 through 1948. A good part of the 1.6 billion bushels of wheat exported in those years was paid for with U.S. government funds.

The primary purpose was not to aid wheat growers. Their prices would no doubt have been maintained at about the support level (90 per cent of parity) in any event, though acreage restrictions and marketing quotas would almost certainly have been imposed much sooner than

TABLE 26

WHEAT: REALIZED COST OF PROGRAMS RELATING TO WHEAT, 1932–1953

(*Millions*)

Commodity Credit Corporation	$ 96.3
International Wheat Agreement	546.5
Removal of surpluses	133.2
Federal crop insurance	1.8
Acreage allotment payments under Agricultural Conservation Program	351.2
Agricultural Production Programs (principally acreage allotments and marketing quotas)	22.0
Parity payments	328.2
Agricultural Adjustment Act of 1933 and related acts (rental and benefit payments, export subsidies, etc.)	354.6
Agricultural Marketing Act Revolving Fund and payments to stabilization corporations for losses incurred	148.1
Total	$1,981.9
Miscellaneous receipts	15.4
Net amount	$1,966.5 [a]

Source: Derived from U.S. Department of Agriculture, *Realized Cost of Agricultural and Related Programs, by Function or Purpose, Fiscal Years 1932–1953,* reproduced in Appendix B in Murray R. Benedict, *Can We Solve the Farm Problem?,* Twentieth Century Fund, New York, 1955.

a. The Department of Agriculture shows a credit against this of $244.9 million collected as processing taxes. However, since these were public funds collected through taxes, they are not deducted here.

they were. The amount by which the 1946 and 1947 prices exceeded support levels can probably be attributed to contributions made by the U.S. government, and the quantities produced and sold would no doubt have been smaller if there had been no foreign-aid program. However, the receiving countries would almost certainly have found ways of financing sizable imports, even in the absence of U.S. aid.[91]

More specifically related to the maintenance of wheat prices were the $238 million subsidy on wheat used for feed during the war and the $23 million subsidy on wheat released for alcohol production. These were partly for liquidation of wheat stocks built up under price-support operations and partly for the purpose of stimulating livestock and alcohol production as part of the war program. The government also paid sub-

91. Total deliveries under export programs from March 1941 to June 30, 1952 were valued at $4,395 million. The average price to farmers, in the United States, exceeded the average support level by 42 cents in 1946 and by 46 cents in 1947. By 1948 the two were about equal, indicating that by then the support-price loan level had become the principal factor in establishing the price.

sidies of $348 million to flour millers during the war years, to enable them to buy wheat at the support level and to sell flour at ceiling prices. This seems more clearly a part of the cost of price supports though not included as such in the compilation given above. It is clear that government aid to wheat growers in the period 1932–1953 was in excess of $2 billion; how much in excess depends on whether or not the items mentioned above are interpreted as including sizable elements of subsidy to wheat growers.[92]

SOME AID GIVEN TO PRODUCERS OF RYE

Rye is important as a cash crop in a few states and also has some relation to wheat as a supplemental bread grain.[93] It was not listed as a basic crop in the Agricultural Adjustment Act of 1933 but was added to the list in an amendment passed in 1935. It was not included as a basic crop in the act of 1938. However, CCC loans were made available in most seasons from 1939 on.

Rye does not bulk large in the over-all crop program. The total acreage grown has usually been no more than 5 to 10 per cent of the area sown to wheat. During World War I, rye became more important and the acreage was doubled between 1914 and 1918. The war provided an opportunity for exports and rye prices were not fixed as were those of wheat. Exports continued to be relatively high until 1928. By that time, recovery in Europe had virtually eliminated the possibility of exporting rye from the United States. The situation changed to one in which imports exceeded exports for most of the years between 1933 and 1946.[94] The acreage harvested has been declining since before World War II. It fell from 4 million in 1938 to 1.6 million in 1949 but increased slightly thereafter, to 1.7 million in 1954.

Rye became eligible for aid by way of processing taxes and benefit payments as a result of the amendments to the Agricultural Adjustment Act in 1935. A processing tax was imposed in September 1935 but was eliminated by the invalidation of such taxes in January 1936. Only about $146,000 in processing taxes was collected and the program relating to rye was abandoned before getting into full operation. Rental and benefit payments amounting to some $200,000 were paid later in closing out the commitments made before the Agricultural Adjustment Act was invalidated.

In 1939, CCC loans were offered at about 40 per cent of parity (38

92. The losses yet to be realized on CCC stocks are, of course, not included. They may be sizable.

93. The most important rye states are the Dakotas, Minnesota, Wisconsin and Michigan. Rye is grown in many other states but mainly as a cover crop or for feed use. It is a hardy crop for which yields are relatively stable and it does well on rather poor soils.

94. Except for the large crop of 1937 and some accumulation during the latter part of World War II, which was exported in 1945.

cents) and were made available thereafter until the end of the war at rates ranging from about 40 to 63 per cent of parity (38 cents to 75 cents per bushel). No large quantities were put under loan.[95]

Supports were reinstated in 1948 because of the great decline in prices from the high levels of 1947. Stocks accumulated in the 1948 and 1949 seasons, and the loss taken by CCC in 1950 ($223,000) was larger than the total losses of the 1938–1947 seasons. Assistance to rye growers has been limited almost wholly to CCC loans and the operations have not been important either in amounts spent or in effects on the industry.

THE RICE PROGRAMS

Rice was defined as a basic crop in the agricultural legislation of 1933 and has been continued in that status in the years since. Though a minor crop in comparison with wheat, cotton and corn, it is important in some states, principally Louisiana, Arkansas, Texas and California. It is a basic food crop in some of the southern parts of the United States and in many foreign areas.

The demand for rice is more elastic than the demand for wheat and the farm price has usually been more directly related to the size of the domestic supply. To some extent rice is competitive with potatoes and with other cereal grains. Consumption on the U.S. mainland varies rather widely from year to year but is more stable than that of some other farm commodities. In Hawaii and Puerto Rico, consumption is high and comparatively stable. The large variations in demand have been in the export market, which has been greatly affected in recent years by changing production and trade conditions in the important rice producing and consuming areas of Asia.

California rice competes with oriental rice in Japan. Rice from the southern states competes, mainly in Cuba and in the European markets, with rice grown in other parts of the world. During recent years, foreign takings have been much larger than in earlier times, largely because of severe disturbances in world rice trade which have resulted from World War II and the unsettled postwar conditions.

The Rice Situation in Earlier Periods

Until World War I, rice production about equaled domestic consumption but some rice was imported in most years. Prices rose sharply between 1914 and 1919, from about $2.00 a bag to more than $5.00. California came in as a heavy producer and production more than doubled.[96]

95. The computation of parity prices for rye has recently been shifted from the "old" to the "modernized" formula. This has resulted in a reduction of about 30 cents per bushel in the parity price as computed in the years since about 1950.

96. See *Agricultural Statistics, 1937*, p. 79.

The United States continued on an export basis after the war in spite of the downward drift of prices in the 1920s. The severe price break of the early 1930s (to less than $1.00 a bag in 1932) resulted in an 18 per cent reduction in acreage and caused much concern in the rice-growing areas. However, the Federal Farm Board did not become involved in stabilization operations relating to rice. Grower cooperatives had already been developed in the two important rice-growing areas and some loans were made to them, but the Farm Board operations relating to rice were not very important.

The very low price of 1932, and some accumulation of stocks, led to the inclusion of rice as a basic commodity in the Agricultural Adjustment Act of 1933. It thus was one of the commodities that could be handled under a processing tax and benefit payment program. However, a sharp advance brought the price up closer to the parity level in 1933, thus reducing the amount of processing tax that could legally be levied on it.[97]

The Administration decided, therefore, to use a marketing agreement approach designed mainly to keep production down and prices up, rather than to reduce production. Since the California industry was already being served by a well-established rice cooperative, the cooperative was one of the participants in the marketing agreement for that area. The agreement provided for minimum prices to be paid by the millers and for restrictions on acreage to act as a check on producer response to the higher prices.

Another marketing agreement was developed for the southern rice areas. There, since the growers were not so well organized, it was considered necessary to issue licenses as a means of bringing all producers, processors and handlers into the program. In both areas, the agreement raised prices but also increased carry-overs. The higher prices also resulted in some imports from the Philippines and reduced exports.[98] The area harvested in 1934 was up slightly but was still much below the levels of the 1920s and early 1930s. It probably was lower than it would have been without an agreement.[99]

The California agreement was regarded as reasonably successful, but that in the southern areas worked so unsatisfactorily that the agreement

97. The season average price to growers rose from 41.8 cents per bushel in 1932 to 77.7 cents in 1933. (*Loc. cit.*)

98. Net exports fell off from 8 to 9 million bushels per year in the 1929–1931 period to 1.5 million in 1934 and to less than a million in 1935. They had been as high as 18.8 million in 1921 and 13.3 million in 1928 but varied widely in the intervening years. Imports rose from 780,000 bushels in 1932 to 2.9 million in 1934. (*Loc. cit.*)

99. Harvested acreage in 1934 was 812,000. The 798,000-acre crop harvested in 1933 was the smallest for any year from 1915 on. During the preceding decade, acreages had been ranging mostly from 900,000 to 1,000,000. The very sharp price increase of 1933 might have been expected to increase acreage significantly if there had been no restriction on the acreages grown. However, acreage did not increase significantly until 1936.

and license were abandoned.[100] The analyses that have been made do not indicate that the agreement had any significant effect on prices or grower incomes.

The difficulties encountered in the 1934 season led to special legislation for levying processing taxes on rice and making benefit payments to growers (Public Resolution 20, 74th Cong., March 18, 1935). A processing tax of one cent per pound was put into effect in April 1935. This apparently resulted in a lower price paid by millers rather than in a higher price to consumers. However, a considerable part of the carryover was moved into consumption, and grower returns, including government payments, were higher for the 1935 crop than for the preceding year.[101]

Rice Programs in the 1936–1941 Period

Rice was included in the 1936 and 1937 conservation programs, but without other forms of control since processing taxes and grower contracts had been eliminated by the Hoosac Mills decision. Acreage was increased to about predepression levels. With higher yields, production was up some 5 to 6 million bags above the low levels of 1933–1936 (about 25 to 30 per cent) and was 10 per cent or more above the 1930 level. Both the season average price and total farm value declined.[102] However, rice growers received about $5 million in conservation payments for the years 1936 and 1937. The price of the 1937 crop was supported by rather substantial purchases from Section 32 funds.

Since rice was included as a basic commodity in the Agricultural Adjustment Act of 1938, both acreage allotments and quotas could be applied. However, only the allotment procedure was used.[103] Acreage and production remained at about the 1937 level until 1941 when they began to increase. Prices remained low until 1940 but rose sharply thereafter.

Substantial conservation and parity payments were made during the

100. The amount produced in California was about the amount set as a goal, but in the southern areas production exceeded the goal by about 4.2 million bushels. Most of the excess was taken over by the Federal Surplus Relief Corporation. (See *Three Years of the Agricultural Adjustment Administration,* p. 112.)

101. *Ibid.,* p. 320. The government acted in a number of ways to strengthen the market for rice. Imports were checked by imposing a compensating tax, exports were facilitated by refunding the processing tax on exports and about 50 million pounds of rice were bought for relief distribution. The gain to growers from the 1934 and 1935 programs was estimated at about $10 million though the farm value of the crop was about the same in 1933, 1934 and 1935, approximately $30 million. (*Agricultural Statistics, 1937,* p. 79.)

102. The average price per bag declined from $1.85 in 1936 to $1.46 in 1937 and to $1.42 in 1938. (In current reporting, rice is given in terms of 100-pound bags rather than in bushels, which, for rough rice, weigh 45 pounds.) The farm value of rice declined from $41.6 million in 1936 to $35.2 million in 1937 and to $33.6 million in 1938. (*Agricultural Statistics, 1951,* p. 28.)

103. The acreages grown exceeded the allotments assigned.

late 1930s and early 1940s.[104] The price of rice was also supported to some extent through purchases for use in the food stamp program and for direct distribution. CCC loans were available but were not used. The loan rates were later adjusted upward, to 85 per cent of parity for the 1941 season, and to 90 per cent for 1943 and after, but market prices had risen even more, so growers still did not put rice under loan.

Rice in the War Years

During the war years, rice acreage moved up from around 1 million to nearly 1.5 million and remained fairly constant at about that level until 1946. Production increased in about a proportionate amount. Demand was strong and prices were held down to some extent by price ceilings. The price in the later war years was just under $4.00 per hundredweight, as compared with $1.80 in 1940. The farm value of the crop rose to record levels—about three times those of the 1930s.

During the postwar years, with price ceilings off, the price of rice rose sharply, reaching $5.97 as a season average in 1947.[105] The large 1947 crop had a record farm value of $210 million, more than five times that of 1939.

Prices declined in 1948 and 1949, and in the 1948 season growers, for the first time, pledged rice for CCC loans.[106] Exports continued at high levels but the downward adjustment in prices resulted in considerable quantities being put under loan. By August 1, 1950, CCC had acquired 459,000 bags, or more than an eighth of a year's production. A serious oversupply appeared to be in the making.

However, the situation changed quickly with the outbreak of war in Korea. Prices moved up again to new record highs but the gains were temporary and the price soon fell again. Large quantities were put under loan in the 1954 and 1955 seasons and more than 3 million bags were turned over to CCC out of the 1953 crop. By August 1, 1955, CCC owned nearly 25 million bags.[107] The rice industry thus found itself facing a situation somewhat similar to that of wheat. Recognizing that there

104. Such payments amounted to about $11 million for the years 1938–1943. (See *Agricultural Statistics, 1946,* p. 655.) Parity payments were discontinued after the 1941 season and conservation payments after the 1943 season. By 1941, the price was above parity and rice was therefore not eligible for parity payments.

105. The season average price stood at $3.98 per bag in 1945, which was about two and a half times that of the late 1930s. Prices in the years 1946–1952 were as follows:

1946	$5.00	1950	$5.09
1947	5.97	1951	4.82
1948	4.88	1952	5.87
1949	4.10		

(*Agricultural Statistics, 1953,* p. 22.)

106. Until then, prices had exceeded loan levels in every year from the time the support programs were started in 1941. Even in 1948, 1949 and 1950, the season average price received by farmers was above the loan rate, but it dropped below in 1951, 1954 and 1955.

107. *The Wheat Situation,* February 28, 1956, p. 35.

were difficult problems ahead, grower groups and the government initiated discussion and study of the rice situation in 1953 and 1954.

As a result of these efforts, several studies were made of the rice market and of ways to deal with industry problems relating to it.[108] As of this writing, new approaches, though extensively discussed and studied, have not been adopted. Rice, like the other basic crops (under the Agricultural Act of 1954), is eligible for CCC price-support loans at 82.5 to 90 per cent of parity for the 1955 crop and at 75 to 90 per cent thereafter.

Realized Costs of the Rice Program to 1953

As of June 30, 1953, the rice programs had involved realized costs to the government of approximately $36 million, mostly in the 1930s and early 1940s. This, however, does not take account of potential losses on CCC operations from 1953 on. The costs to 1953 were roughly equivalent to the current value of one full year's crop. The breakdown by categories is as follows (in millions): [109]

Under Agricultural Adjustment Act of 1933	$10.1
Acreage allotments under Agricultural Conservation Program	11.7
Parity payments	5.6
Agricultural production programs	.4
CCC price-support programs	1.5
Removal of surplus	6.6
Total	$35.9

Program Effects Not Large in Most Years before 1953

For the 1930–1953 period as a whole the government programs relating to rice did not have an important effect on the industry. The experiment with marketing agreements, in 1934, was not successful. It may have had some influence in holding production down in that year, but production control was not an important feature of the program until 1955. However, the over-all assistance given to rice growers during the 1930s, mainly in the form of direct payments, was substantial considering the size of the industry.

Export subsidies were not used to any significant extent but government purchases made prior to World War II did give some support in times when the market was weak. From 1941 through 1951, market

108. Among them, a series of studies by G. L. Mehren and Nicholas Thuroczy of the University of California (*The Market for United States Rice: Domestic* and *The Market for United States Rice: Foreign,* California Agricultural Experiment Station, Giannini Foundation, Mimeographed Reports 162 and 163, March 1954, and *Multiple Price Plans for Rice* by G. L. Mehren, Report No. 175, April 1955). These and other discussions and studies are too lengthy for summarization here.

109. *Realized Cost of Agricultural and Related Programs.*

prices were mostly above support levels and little use was made of CCC loans until 1949. Deliveries to CCC from the 1949 crop were large, but these holdings were liquidated during the succeeding two years without much loss.

It is probable that from 1941 to 1952 the price situation would not have been much different if there had been no price-support program. Price supports first became an important element in the situation in the 1953–54 and 1954–55 seasons. Large quantities passed into CCC ownership in those years and seemed likely to result in heavy losses to the government.

The Situation as of 1955

In the period 1935–1954, rice production increased rapidly, from 17.8 million hundredweight in 1935 to 64.5 million in 1954. Until just prior to World War II, it was still less than 25 million hundredweight. Though U.S. production still constituted less than 2 per cent of the world total, by 1951 the United States had become, at least temporarily, the third largest exporter. It accounted for about 13 per cent of the total international trade in rice in 1954.[110] From 1950 to 1954 about 45 per cent of the rice grown in the United States was exported.

Various factors have had a bearing on the situation. In 1953, the Japanese crop was poor. But several of the Asiatic countries were endeavoring to increase their output of rice. Surplus stocks of low quality were beginning to accumulate in parts of Asia, and tended to depress prices but there was no surplus of good-quality rice and some types were in short supply.[111]

In the United States, market prices fell below loan rates in 1951 and some 5.8 million bags were put under CCC loan and purchase agreements. However, most of it was later redeemed. Prices recovered as a result of strong demand in the Asiatic areas but receded thereafter. About 4.5 million bags of the 1953 crop were put under loan and purchase agreements and more than 3 million were delivered to CCC. (See Table 27.)[112]

With a large carry-over from the 1953 crop, and prospect of a larger one from the 1954 crop, acreage allotments and marketing quotas were

110. Burma ranked first, with 30 per cent of world exports. Thailand was second with 26 per cent of the total. Until World War II, Cuba was the largest foreign buyer of U.S. rice, purchasing more than two thirds of the amount exported. In the early 1950s, Cuba was absorbing more U.S. rice than in the prewar years but its takings amounted to less than a third of total U.S. shipments to other countries. Japan had become about as large a purchaser as Cuba. However, the large Asiatic takings could not be regarded as normal or dependable since they were due largely to war disturbances. World production began to increase gradually in 1952 and by 1955 supplies had become more abundant.

111. *The Wheat Situation*, February 28, 1955, p. 14.

112. About the same amount had been turned over to CCC in 1949 but the increased demand that developed shortly thereafter made it possible to liquidate the bulk of the CCC holdings.

TABLE 27

RICE, ROUGH: PRICE-SUPPORT OPERATIONS AND PRICE ANALYSIS ITEMS, 1940–1955

Year Beg. Aug.	Production	Owned by CCC on August 1	Under Price Support: Loans	Under Price Support: Purchase Agreements	Under Price Support: Total	Deliveries to CCC	Support Rate per Cwt.	Season Average Price Received by Farmers [a]
	(1,000 Cwt.)	(1,000 Cwt.)		(1,000 Cwt.)		(1,000 Cwt.)		
1940	24,495							$1.80
1941	23,095						$2.04	3.01
1942	29,082						2.33	3.61
1943	29,264						[b]	3.96
1944	30,974						[b]	3.93
1945	30,718 [c]						2.82	3.98
1946	32,535 [c]						[b]	5.00
1947	35,253 [c]						3.76	5.97
1948	38,320 [c]		153	3,565	3,718	611	4.08	4.88
1949	40,784 [c]	11	1,865	6,282	8,147	3,043	3.96	4.10
1950	38,757 [c]	459	217	575	792	26	4.56	5.09
1951	45,853 [c]	369	4,008	1,843	5,851	518	5.00	4.82
1952	48,260 [c]	226	209	—	209	—	5.04	5.87
1953	52,761 [c]	1	1,808	2,666	4,474	3,168	4.84	5.19
1954	64,514 [c]	3,168	17,554	12,923	30,477	25,184 [d]	4.92	4.57
1955 [d]	53,647 [c]	24,909	14,267 [e]	658 [e]	14,925 [e]		4.66	4.53

Source: U.S. Agricultural Marketing Service, *The Wheat Situation,* February 28, 1956, p. 35.

a. Season average prices received by farmers weighted by sales.
b. Price support was mandatory at 90 per cent of parity but since prices were so far above support levels, support rates were not announced.
c. Includes production in minor rice-producing states (Missouri, South Carolina, Arizona and Florida), which are not included in the estimates of production of the Crop Reporting Board.
d. Preliminary.
e. Through January 15, 1956.

proclaimed for the 1955 crop, as required by law. Some 90 per cent of the growers voted approval of marketing quotas in the referendum of January 28, 1955 and quotas were therefore put into effect for the 1955 crop.[113] The national acreage allotment proclaimed was 1,859,099 acres, 24.7 per cent less than the acreage grown in 1954 and 11 per cent less than the 1950–1954 average. This gave promise of some easing of the situation but it seemed apparent that some further adjustments in U.S. production would be necessary. The amount of adjustment needed would depend in considerable measure on what happened in other parts of the world.

113. With a marketing quota in effect, growers who exceed their farm acreage allotments are subject to a penalty on rice grown on excess acres in the amount of 50 per cent of the June 15 parity price. Under the law, acreage allotments and marketing quotas must be proclaimed by the Secretary of Agriculture, except under emergency conditions, if supply exceeds normal by more than 10 per cent. If more than two thirds of the growers vote in favor of marketing quotas they are put into effect.

4

Oilseed Crops

THE OILSEED CROPS have had a prominent place in the farm program for two reasons: first, they are an important source of farm income in some regions and, second, vegetable oils became important strategically in World War II. The outbreak of war in the Pacific cut off, very suddenly, a large volume of U.S. vegetable oil imports previously derived from that area. Since Western Europe also relied heavily on Eastern Hemisphere sources for vegetable oils of various kinds, its supplies too were severely curtailed. Fats and oils were therefore in short supply throughout the war and, in Western Europe, for some time thereafter.[1]

Oil Crops Closely Interrelated

The fats and oils economy is more complex than those of many other farm commodities because of the close technical and economic relationships between the various kinds of fats and oils. The markets for all of them are interrelated and many of them can be used interchangeably for various purposes.[2] The vegetable oils compete with animal fats (butter, lard and tallow), and the domestically produced oils are in competition with imported oils such as coconut, palm, olive, sesame, perilla and tung.

Fats and oils are commonly classified into four major groupings: food, soap, drying (for paints and varnishes) and industrial. The most important domestically produced food fats are butter, lard and the oils from cottonseed, soybeans, corn and peanuts. The drying oils include linseed, tung and castor oil. Soybean oil has drying properties of lower quality but can be used to supplement other drying oils. The fats and

1. Special programs were undertaken by nearly all of the nations allied against the Axis in an effort to make up for the loss of Pacific area supplies and to meet the increased demand for fats needed in carrying on the war. Britain undertook to enlarge the supply of whale oil and to increase the output of ground nuts in Africa. The United States sought to expand the production of peanuts, soybeans, flaxseed and so on. Rationing and allocation of supplies were resorted to in nearly all of the war-involved nations, and in some others as well. The use of fats in the production of soap was severely restricted, and, for some time after the close of the war, the prices of fats and oils were much higher in the sterling area than in the hard-currency countries.

2. For example, in the war years, Russia used considerable quantities of linseed oil in the manufacture of margarine though linseed oil is not ordinarily considered suitable for food use.

oils most commonly used in making soap are tallow, grease and imported palm and coconut oils. Surpluses of low-priced lard and cottonseed oil are also used in the production of soap. Smaller quantities of several of the oils, such as palm, castor, neat's foot and fish oils, are used for industrial purposes. However these various fats may be classified, they are so interrelated in chemical structure and characteristics that they can, to a considerable extent, be shifted from one use to another.[3]

The Pre-1933 Fats and Oils Situation

At the beginning of the century, most of the food fats used in the United States, and those used in making soap, were of animal origin (butter, lard and tallow). Production exceeded domestic needs and large quantities were exported. The chief oilseed crop was flaxseed, which at first was produced in sufficient quantity to supply domestic needs but later declined so that sizable imports were common.[4] The heavy demand for food fats and oils during World War I led to an increase in peanut production and a shift to emphasis on peanuts for oil, but flaxseed production was smaller than in the prewar years.

Following World War I, the demand for food fats declined and imports of some types of edible oil increased. However, the major impact of the expansion of vegetable oil production in foreign areas was on the export markets for U.S.-produced lard and cottonseed oil. Technological developments in the processing of vegetable oils brought them into competition with beef fat and butter through their use in making margarine.

Before the depression of the 1930s, considerable amounts of vegetable oil, in the form of oil-producing materials, were imported free of duty, or virtually so. Such tariffs as existed tended to be ineffective, partly because the United States was a heavy exporter of animal fats and partly because much of the copra and other oil-producing material came from the Philippines, which were within the U.S. free-trade area. Only flaxseed and peanuts used as nuts could be protected effectively in most periods.

3. The superiority of some of the fats and oils for particular uses results in special demands that are reflected in price relationships. For example, the drying oils, such as linseed and tung, are not commonly used as food. Their prices are primarily determined by the demand for paints and varnishes. The demand for food fats is affected mostly by levels of income and the relative supplies of the different types. Normally, there are fairly well-established relationships between the prices for the different kinds of oils and fats, but variations in relative supplies may affect price relationships significantly.

4. Production reached a high of 36 million bushels in 1902 (but was more commonly around 25 million). By the beginning of World War I, it was down to about 12 million, and net imports were at a rate of 10 to 14 million bushels per year. (See U.S. Department of Agriculture, *Agricultural Statistics, 1937,* p. 70.)

Though the dairy interests complained of the growing competition from imported vegetable oils and the flax growers sought increased tariffs on flaxseed and linseed oil, there was no specific plan for supporting prices of the oilseed crops until 1933.[5]

THE PROGRAMS RELATING TO PEANUTS

The only oilseed crop included in the pre-World War II farm program was peanuts. The peanut growers asked for help with their problems in 1933 and were given various types of assistance in the years 1933–1941. With the outbreak of war and the resulting acute shortage of vegetable oils throughout the western world, the peanut program was merged with others in the general effort to increase oilseed production. Thereafter it ceased to stand by itself though it continued to have some special features because of differences in the basic legislation relating to it.

The peanut crop is an important source of farm income in the southern states. It is second to tobacco in Virginia and to cotton in Alabama. It is third, after cotton and tobacco, in Georgia and North Carolina. In some southeastern areas, the peanut crop has to some extent replaced cotton, as a result of boll weevil damage to the cotton crop. In recent years it has become an important cash crop in Oklahoma and Texas.

Until World War I, the total production of peanuts went to the "edible" trade and imports exceeded exports. In the prewar period 1909–1914 production was stable and the price to farmers averaged about 4.8 cents per pound. The outbreak of war in 1914 stepped up the demand for fats and oils and encouraged a marked increase in peanut production for oil. Production more than doubled and crushing for oil became an important industry. The average farm price advanced from 4.8 cents in 1916 to 9.3 cents in 1919.[6]

During the 1920 and 1921 seasons, prices dropped back to about the prewar level. Production was cut back but not to the low prewar level.[7] Oil crushing became merely a way of using the discards from the "edible" trade. After the postwar depression, prices made some recovery, and acreage, production and consumption increased. With imports exceeding exports, the tariff was effective to some extent in maintaining prices in the "edible" trade, but the price of oil was not affected as there was an export surplus of competing fats and oils.

In the late 1920s and early 1930s, the acreages grown were some two

5. The flaxseed growers and processors did succeed in getting a higher tariff on their products and the dairymen were able to retain a high domestic excise tax on colored margarine, which held it in check as a competitor of butter.

6. See Antoine Banna, Sidney J. Armore and Richard J. Foote, *Peanuts and Their Uses for Food,* U.S. Bureau of Agricultural Economics, Marketing Research Report No. 16, 1952, pp. 42, 66, 74.

7. *Ibid.,* pp. 66, 74.

to three times as large as in the prewar years and the trend was upward.[8] However, prices were declining from 1927 on and were very low in 1931 and 1932. The large crops of 1931 and 1932 had to be absorbed in the domestic market as conditions abroad were unfavorable for export even at the low prices then prevailing.[9]

Emergency Relief Sought in 1933

The low price of peanuts in 1932 led to reduced plantings in 1933. The farm price rose from 1.5 cents in April 1933 to 2.6 cents in August, because of the prospect of a smaller crop and the general advance in farm prices. However, the price was still very low and grower representatives appealed to the Secretary of Agriculture for help in supporting prices for the new crop.

Early in October, the Administrator of the Agricultural Adjustment Administration asked the cooperation of shellers and cleaners in putting into effect immediately an arrangement for paying an agreed minimum price and recommended that they submit as soon as possible a formal marketing agreement. The Administrator's request is thought to have helped somewhat in maintaining prices near the August level during the early months of the marketing season.[10]

A marketing agreement, approved by a majority of the processors, was put into effect in January 1934. It was extended to nonsigners by means of licenses. The minimum price to be paid to producers ranged from $55 per ton for Runners to $65 for Virginias (2.75 cents per pound to 3.25 cents). However, the agreement did not specify the amount to be purchased, as was the case in the tobacco agreement. When the processors found that they could not sell the products at prices that

8. Acreages, production and prices for these years were as follows:

Year	*Acreage Planted (Thousands)*	*Acreage Picked and Threshed (Thousands)*	*Production (1,000 Pounds)*	*Price (Cents per Pound)*
1926	1,520	860	662,190	5.04
1927	1,859	1,086	844,220	5.15
1928	2,039	1,213	843,505	4.88
1929	2,064	1,262	898,197	3.73
1930	1,881	1,073	697,350	3.51
1931	2,299	1,440	1,055,815	1.62
1932	2,649	1,501	941,195	1.55
1933	2,350	1,217	819,620	2.85

(*Agricultural Statistics, 1952,* p. 152.) A considerable part of the acreage grown is for hay and other uses.

9. In the late 1920s, the volume of imports was from five to fifteen or more times the volume of exports, so the adjustment came about mainly through a reduction in imports, almost to the vanishing point. Exports dropped from around 4 to 5 million pounds in the late 1920s to 300,000 in 1934. Imports were down from as much as 95 million pounds in 1927 to less than 400,000 in 1934. (*Loc. cit.*)

10. For a more detailed description of these developments, see Edwin G. Nourse, *Marketing Agreements under the AAA,* The Brookings Institution, Washington, 1935, pp. 76–78, 88–95, 306.

would cover their costs, if they paid the minimum prices to growers, they refused to buy. They were willing to custom process, letting the producer sell at market prices. That undercut the market and the agreement was terminated in September 1934.

The price held above 3 cents per pound for the remainder of the season and the season average was 2.85 cents, which was 1.3 cents above that of the preceding year. A reduction of about 12 per cent in the size of the crop and some general improvement in market conditions were largely responsible for the higher prices. However, the request made by the AAA Administrator, and the subsequent actions taken, may have increased the season average price by as much as half a cent.

Production Control and Diversion

In April 1934, an amendment to the Agricultural Adjustment Act added peanuts to the list of basic commodities (Public Law 142, 73d Cong.). That opened the way for the levying of processing taxes to finance production control and other programs relating to peanuts. A program for diverting some of the 1934 crop to livestock feed and oil production, and for limiting the acreage planted in 1935, was announced in September 1934.

A processing tax was put into effect for the 1934 crop but at a rather low rate so as not to cut down consumption.[11] The tax apparently was passed on to consumers.[12] Nearly 24 per cent of the 1934 crop was diverted to oil. Consumption, in "edible" uses, was reduced to some extent by higher prices and diversion to oil. The amount of tax collected for the period October 1934 to January 1936 was $3.7 million. The farm value of the 1934 crop was about $10 million (40 per cent) higher than the 1933 value and that of 1935 about $3 million above the 1934 value.[13] The increase was due in part to a 25 to 40 per cent increase in production in those years, but the higher price of oil and some improvement in economic conditions also helped to strengthen prices received

11. The law permitted a rate of 2.9 cents per pound, the difference between the current price and "fair exchange value." In the hearings, the processors argued that such a rate would reduce consumption for peanut butter, confections and so on. Consequently, the rate was put at 1 cent per pound, and peanuts processed for oil were exempted. The tax was continued at that rate until January 1936.

12. See U.S. Treasury Department, Bureau of Internal Revenue, *An Analysis of the Effects of the Processing Taxes Levied under the Agricultural Adjustment Act,* 1937, pp. 60–65.

13. *Agricultural Statistics, 1952,* p. 152. A sharp reduction in the cotton crop caused an increase in the demand for peanut oil. The price of cottonseed oil advanced from an average of 4 cents in 1933 to 8.5 cents in 1934. A similar advance in the price of peanut oil reduced the cost of diverting peanuts to crushers. The peanut oil diversion amounted to such a small part of the total oil supply (less than 1 per cent) that it had no significant effect on the price of oil. The cotton program was the principal factor in improving the situation with respect to peanut oil.

by growers. The growers received in addition (for the two years) $3.7 million in payments derived from processing taxes.[14]

Nearly 80 per cent of the commercial peanut growers signed contracts agreeing to reduce acreage in 1935, but other growers increased plantings. The acreage harvested was cut back only about 3 per cent (17,000 acres) from that of 1934. Production of nuts was up about 140 million pounds (approximately 13 per cent). Direct consumption increased to some extent and about 15 per cent of the crop was diverted to oil.[15]

The principal result of the emergency programs was to raise prices and incomes to growers and to check, to some extent, an anticipated expansion of production in 1935. The season average price to farmers rose from 1.55 cents in 1932 to 3.28 cents in 1934 and held at 3.14 cents in 1935. Receipts from marketings increased from $14.5 million in 1932 to $36 million in 1935.[16] The peanut programs may have contributed about 30 per cent to the increase in returns to growers. For the 1935 season, income from sales, plus adjustment payments, gave growers a return nearly as large as that of 1928.[17] However, the 1935 crop was about 37 per cent larger than that of 1928.

Allotments and Payments, 1936–1940

After the invalidation of processing taxes and control contracts, in January 1936, incentive payments under the Soil Conservation and Domestic Allotment program became the principal mechanism for holding peanut acreage in check. Peanuts were classified as a soil-depleting crop but were not designated as a "basic" commodity. Payments were offered for complying with approved conservation practices, for diverting peanut acreage to soil-conserving crops and for keeping acreages within the allotments.[18]

The recovery of peanut prices and incomes in 1934 and 1935 provided a strong incentive for increased production in 1936. To guard against too rapid expansion, a base acreage was established for each farm, and growers were offered a payment of $25 per ton on the normal

14. There were also payments of some $397,000 to processors for diverting peanuts to oil, most of it derived from Section 32 funds.

15. *Peanuts and Their Uses for Food,* p. 49. Payments of 0.5 to 1.0 cent per pound were offered to growers on peanuts sold for crushing, up to 20 per cent of their production. Not many took advantage of the offer. Processors were paid a subsidy of $9.82 per ton on peanuts bought for crushing. An adjustment payment of $8 per ton on peanuts grown in 1934 was made to growers who agreed to limit their 1935 acreages to the average of the amounts grown in 1933 and 1934.

16. Approximately 6 per cent of the 1935 crop was diverted to crushers. (*Ibid.,* p. 50.) In the 1934 and 1935 seasons about 80 per cent of the peanuts diverted were from the southeastern area. They were mostly of the Spanish and Runner types.

17. The 1928 farm value was $41 million, that of 1935, $36 million (not including adjustment payments).

18. The Agricultural Adjustment Act of 1938 did not include authorization for marketing quotas on peanuts until it was amended early in 1941 to provide controls similar to those authorized for cotton and tobacco.

yields of acres diverted to soil-conserving crops, up to 20 per cent of the base acreages assigned. Many growers complied and received diversion payments. Others increased their acreages. The net result was an increase of about 11 per cent in the acreage harvested for nuts and a crop of record size. Fortunately, a strong demand maintained prices above the 1935 levels without price-support operations.

The relaxation of controls on competing crops in 1937 resulted in expansion of some of them, especially cotton and tobacco. This helped to keep peanut acreage in check. Conservation payments on peanuts were continued at the same rate as in 1936 but fewer applications were made, apparently because the crops growers wished to shift to were not classed as "soil-conserving." The 1937 acreage was about 100,000 less than that of 1936 but production was about the same. Demand was weaker and sizable amounts of peanuts were purchased for diversion to crushers at considerable loss to the government.[19]

Acreage allotments were continued as the only means of control for the 1938–1940 seasons but, in addition to the provisions previously in effect, penalties were assessed for exceeding the allotments assigned. Apparently the change had no significant effect. However, the more effective controls applied to cotton in 1938 probably encouraged some shift to peanuts.

Harvested acreage increased in the late 1930s and by 1940 was up to 2,052,000, about 30 per cent above the 1937 acreage. The 1940 acreage was about a third larger than the allotments called for and production was up about 40 per cent from the level of the late 1930s. Nearly a third of the crop was purchased in price-support operations.

Prices and Program Costs, 1938–1940

Through various methods of support, the price to farmers was kept at approximately 3.3 cents per pound (about 55 per cent of parity) in the 1938–1940 seasons. Considerable quantities were pledged for loans in 1937 and 1938 but only small amounts in 1939 and 1940.[20] Large quantities were purchased, except in the 1939 season, and for the most part were diverted to oil. In the first season after the outbreak of war in Europe, the market for "edible" nuts strengthened and only 10 per cent of the crop was diverted for crushing. In the 1940 season, the "edible" market was strong, but the crop was so large that about 34 per cent of it was crushed for oil.

Government expenditures for conservation, acreage control and diversion in the five seasons 1936–1940 amounted to about $18.7 million. Of this, about $4.5 million was for conservation payments designed

19. Crushings totaled 228 million pounds and the cost of diversion, from Section 32 funds, was $2.3 million.

20. Price support through CCC loans and purchases had been offered to growers beginning with the 1937 season.

mainly to provide incentives for keeping acreage down. These government expenditures were, in effect, income supplements to the growers.[21] Most of the $3.3 million used in purchases for diversion tended to protect the relatively inelastic market for peanuts in nut form and thus maintained prices at somewhat higher levels than would have been obtainable without diversion purchases. The receipts from marketings probably were increased by more than the expenditure for diversion purchases.[22]

However, the large expansion of acreage in the 1938–1940 period made it evident that with prices maintained at the levels of those years, stronger measures would be needed if peanut acreage was to be kept down. The mounting cost of the program led to the passage of special control legislation early in 1941.[23]

THE PEANUT PROGRAM IN THE WAR YEARS

The Peanut Control Act of 1941 (Public Law 27, 77th Cong., 1st sess., approved on April 3) amended the Agricultural Adjustment Act of 1938 so as to provide marketing quotas for peanuts similar to those already authorized for cotton, tobacco, wheat, corn and rice. This action re-established peanuts as a "basic" crop so far as legislation was concerned. The penalty for marketing peanuts from excess (nonquota) acreage was to be 3 cents per pound.

However, such peanuts could be delivered for crushing to an agent designated by the Secretary of Agriculture. The proceeds, at the price for oil less cost of handling, would be paid to the grower. This meant, in effect, the marketing of excess peanuts for oil without the government taking the loss. It left the way open for unlimited production of peanuts for oil. An advancing market for oil and meal could thus encourage production in excess of the marketing quotas.

Quotas Applied in 1941

The allotments for the 1941 crop were the same as the conservation allotments already announced for the season, but, in addition, the Secre-

21. Diversion and conservation payments in these years were as follows (in thousands):

Fiscal Year	*Diversion Payments*	*Conservation Payments*
1936	$ 306	$1,251
1937	—	871
1938	2,302	1,217
1939	—	652
1940	699	464

(U.S. Production and Marketing Administration, *Section 32 Handbook,* March 1953, p. 30, and *Agricultural Statistics, 1946,* p. 655.)

22. Because of the inelastic demand for nuts and the fact that the bulk of the crop moved into the "edible nut" market.

23. Diversion costs for fiscal 1941, which were those incurred in respect to the 1940 crop, amounted to $8.1 million. (*Section 32 Handbook,* p. 30.)

tary of Agriculture announced marketing quotas subject to grower approval.[24] Growers approved quotas for the 1941, 1942 and 1943 seasons. Hence, the 1941 marketings were under marketing quota control.

In the meantime, developments in Europe were strengthening the demand for fats and oils. The first effect of the war had been to reduce European imports of these commodities. However, after the passage of the Lend-Lease Act (March 1941), the United Kingdom began to take considerable quantities of lard. That strengthened the whole fats and oils market and improved the outlook for producers of peanuts for oil.

Again the cotton situation affected the peanut program. Since there was a large accumulation of cotton, it seemed desirable to divert some of the cotton acreage to food and feed crops. In April 1941, the Secretary of Agriculture moved to cut cotton acreage by authorizing, without penalty, increased plantings of peanuts for oil within the cotton acreage allotments.[25]

The incentives for overplanting led to a 1941 acreage for harvest as nuts of 1.9 million, about 18 per cent above the national allotment and only 5 per cent less than the acreage harvested in 1940. However, lower yields reduced the crop by about 16 per cent. Nearly 40 per cent of the crop was purchased under support operations but was resold without significant loss to the government.

The outbreak of war in the Pacific, with the United States as an active participant, changed the situation markedly. Before the end of the 1941 marketing season, plans were made for increasing oil production in 1942. In February, the Secretary of Agriculture announced a program for that purpose. It set up a goal of 5 million acres for peanuts and promised price support at 85 per cent of "comparable" parity price on peanuts for oil. Subsequently, the support level was raised to 90 per cent.

The acreage for harvest as nuts increased about 76 per cent (to 3.4 million) and production was up about 50 per cent.[26] However, the increase in demand for use in nut form was so large that it absorbed about all of the crop that was suitable for such uses, thus reducing the supply available for crushing. More than half the supply purchased in price-support operations was sold in the "edible nut" market.

24. The allotment proclaimed for the 1941 season was 1.6 million acres, which was a little larger than the 1940 allotment but about 20 per cent less than the 1940 harvested acreage. The amendment had provided that allotments made in succeeding years could not be less than 95 per cent of the acreage allotted in 1941.

The marketing quota legislation was intended primarily as a means of maintaining the prices of peanuts used as nuts. The national acreage allotments would normally produce more than enough nuts to supply the "edible" market, but the surplus would be mostly low-grade and broken kernels, which would be sold to crushers without cost to the government.

25. See Robert M. Walsh, *Fats and Oils in World War II: Production and Price-Supporting Programs,* U.S. Bureau of Agricultural Economics, War Records Monographs No. 6, October 1947, p. 3.

26. *Agricultural Statistics, 1952,* p. 152, and *Peanuts and Their Uses for Food,* p. 66. See also Table 28.

Further Efforts to Expand Production

Marketing quotas and allotments were suspended for the 1943 season and production control was abandoned for the duration of the war. Price supports were continued, but without distinction as between peanuts for nuts and peanuts for oil. The only restraining influences were the availability of resources and price ceilings. There was a small increase in harvested acreage (to 3.5 million) in 1943 but thereafter the acreage grown stabilized at about 3 million for the remainder of the war and through 1946.[27]

The increased demand for peanuts as nuts overrode the increased demand for oil throughout the war years. The large 1940 crop had provided record supplies for both oil and nut use, but consumption in nut form expanded from 4.9 pounds per capita in 1940 to 6.1 pounds in 1942 and remained high throughout the war. The result was a smaller volume for crushing though the crops were up about two thirds from the average of the late 1930s.

The price to farmers rose from 3.3 cents per pound in 1940 to 6.0 cents in 1942 and continued to advance at a slower rate thereafter, reaching 8.3 cents in 1945 and moving on up to 9.1 cents in 1946. The drive for increased oil production during the war years was thwarted by the large increase in demand for peanuts for use in nut form and by the restraints that resulted from the maintenance of price ceilings.

Wartime Support Operations

War needs resulted in a significant change in government support operations. The support programs for 1941 and 1942 were, in effect, a two-price system. In the first season, only quota peanuts were supported. The excess, and nonquota marketings, were accepted for crushing and farmers were paid whatever price they would bring for oil use. In the second season, the emphasis was shifted to oil production by providing, under the Steagall Amendment, for support of the prices of peanuts crushed for oil as well as of those used as nuts.

The support offered in the 1942 season (85 per cent of parity) was 6.2 cents per pound for quota peanuts for direct consumption and 3.94 cents for excess and nonquota peanuts used for oil.[28] These operations caused no loss to the government but the support level on peanuts for oil obviously was not high enough to bring about the desired expansion of output.

27. The acreage grown in the war years was continuously below the goals announced by the Department of Agriculture. It averaged only 64 per cent of the goal in 1942, 1943 and 1944, but was 98 per cent of a much reduced goal in 1945. (See *Fats and Oils in World War II,* p. 23.)

28. The support level on all of the Steagall and "basic" commodities was later raised to 90 per cent of parity.

The method of support was changed in 1943 to a single schedule of support prices for all peanuts. The Commodity Credit Corporation became the sole purchaser. The mills and the cooperatives became agents of the Corporation to buy and dispose of the peanuts acquired. Purchases were made on the basis of the guaranteed minimum prices and sales were at prices related to the ceiling prices of the products.

The Commodity Credit Corporation made a net gain on the 1943 operations. In 1944 and 1945, the receipts from sales did not cover the cost of purchases. Supports were continued at 90 per cent of parity but returns to growers were a little above the support level. There was no net loss or gain to CCC on the peanut program for the war years as a whole (July 1, 1941 through June 30, 1946). However, the government subsidized the consumption of peanut butter to the extent of some $20 million.[29] That did not add to the returns to growers but probably did cause a larger part of the crop to go to nut uses rather than for oil.

During 1941 and 1942, conservation payments added about $1.75 million to grower incomes. Thereafter incomes were derived wholly from sales. The government loan and purchase operations apparently had no significant effect on the average level of prices from 1941 on. Without price ceilings and controlled distribution, demand would probably have pushed prices and production to higher levels. Prices advanced after decontrol and there was some increase in production in 1947 and 1948.

THE SITUATION IN THE POSTWAR YEARS

The postwar price guarantees afforded protection to the growers in the years 1946 and 1947 and gave opportunity for testing postwar requirements and making adjustments. It was expected that the demand for peanuts would decline and that some readjustments in production and in the prewar control and support legislation would be needed.

The first postwar crop was planted while marketings were still subject to control but was harvested after decontrol. The acreage harvested was about the same as in 1945. Price ceilings on peanut oil were terminated as of October 16, 1946. The exclusive authority of CCC to buy and sell peanuts also was terminated. The cooperative growers' associations were designated, as in the prewar period, to act as agents of CCC in supporting the price of peanuts by means of purchases.

The demand for the 1946 crop was strong enough to raise prices above support levels. All peanuts were to be supported at prices that would yield farmers an average return of 8.6 cents per pound (90 per cent of parity). A new feature designed to encourage diversion of No. 2 shelled peanuts to oil was added in September. Crushers were offered subsidies for diverting such peanuts. Food use declined but this was

29. *Peanuts and Their Uses for Food,* p. 54.

offset by increased exports and a sharp advance in oil prices.[30] Prices averaged 9.1 cents for the season, without subsidies except those to crushers, which were noted above.

Return to Production Controls

A slightly larger crop in 1947 and the prospect of less active demand led the Secretary of Agriculture to proclaim marketing quotas for the 1948 season and to submit the program in a referendum which was held on October 9, 1947. The growers registered a strong vote in favor of marketing quotas for the 1948, 1949 and 1950 crops. However, the Secretary suspended quotas in January 1948, for the 1948 crop, because of the current high price and evidence of a world shortage of fats and oils.

Growers reduced harvested acreage slightly but higher yields resulted in a record crop of 2.3 billion pounds. The large crop together with very strong foreign demand contributed to a volume of exports that was far above any level previously attained. Exports amounted to 739 million pounds, nearly 50 per cent above the previous year's record high of 531 million.[31]

Substantial amounts were exported under the Foreign Assistance Act of 1948 and about $10 million of Section 32 funds were used to finance exports. In all, about a third of the crop was exported. With oil prices declining, sizable subsidies were required in diverting peanuts to oil outlets. The losses taken by the Commodity Credit Corporation amounted to nearly $24 million.[32]

The first postwar quotas and allotments were put into effect in 1949. This was the beginning of a major effort to adjust production to a shrinking demand. "Edible" use, on a per capita basis, had declined to about the prewar level. The supply of vegetable oils was increasing and prices were declining. The export outlet was expected to shrink and the question to be faced was how much adjustment to make and how fast it should be.

30. For some time after the war, Western Europe was very short of fats and oils and there was a wide differential between U.S. and European prices because of exchange restrictions and shortage of buying power in the European countries. This situation led to Britain's extensive and costly effort to produce large quantities of ground nuts in some of the African areas under her control.

31. Even in the war years, exports had ranged only from 21 to 63 million pounds. They rose to about 250 million in 1946 but had never, before 1942, been above the 22-million level reached in 1916. Until 1947, imports nearly always exceeded exports though there were small net exports in 1931–1933 and in 1941, 1943 and 1945.

32. U.S. Production and Marketing Administration, *Review of Operations—Commodity Credit Corporation—Fiscal Year 1949,* p. 11. (These reports are hereafter referred to as Commodity Credit Corporation, *Review of Operations,* with appropriate fiscal-year designations.)

The national marketing quota for the 1949 season was put at 1.7 billion pounds, a reduction of more than 20 per cent. The acreage allotment was 2.6 million, a reduction of about 22 per cent from the acreage harvested in 1948. Notwithstanding the continuance of support at 90 per cent of parity, growers reduced harvested acreage to 2.3 million, which was well below the allotment. Cotton was not then being controlled, and prices and demand were good. Consequently there was opportunity for some shift of peanut land to cotton.

Exports continued high, though at only about a third of the 1948 rate. The price was approximately at the support level of 10.5 cents, indicating that, as in 1947 and 1948, price supports were a principal factor in establishing the price.[33] CCC losses were the largest incurred in any year up to that time, $40.6 million, and expenditures of Section 32 funds, mainly for export subsidies, amounted to $4.6 million.[34]

Marketing Quotas Continued from 1949 On

Marketing quotas and allotments were continued in the years following 1949. However, the allotments were reduced gradually, to 1,673,000 acres in 1952, which was near the minimum established in the amendment of 1941 (1,610,000). Several congressional acts changed the rules governing allotments and slowed up the adjustment in 1950 and 1951.[35] The acreages harvested were reduced more rapidly than the allotments. By 1952, harvested acreage was down to 1,459,000, which was less than half the 1948 acreage and about at the 1935 level.[36] However,

33. Prices and support levels for the years 1946–1952 were as follows:

Crop Year	*Support Level (Cents per Pound)*	*Per Cent of Parity*	*Season Average Price (Cents per Pound)*
1946	8.6	90	9.1
1947	10.0	90	10.1
1948	10.8	90	10.5
1949	10.5	90	10.4
1950	10.8	90	10.9
1951	11.5	88	10.4
1952	12.0	90	10.9

(U.S. Production and Marketing Administration, *CCC Price Support Statistical Handbook,* April 1952, p. 23; U.S. Department of Agriculture, *Agricultural Statistics, 1954,* p. 118.)

34. Commodity Credit Corporation, *Review of Operations,* fiscal 1950, p. 11, and earlier and later issues. For Section 32 fund expenditures, see *Section 32 Handbook,* p. 30. The years 1948, 1949 and 1950 were the ones in which the heaviest CCC losses occurred. They amounted to $23.8 million on the 1948 operations, $14.6 million on the 1950 crop, and $8.7 million on the 1951 crop. Export subsidies from Section 32 funds amounted to $10.2 million on the 1948 crop and to $4.6 million on that of 1949. (The fiscal years for which these items are reported are the ones immediately succeeding the crop year to which the operation pertained.)

35. In a 1950 referendum, growers approved quotas for the following three years.

36. The phenomenally high price of cotton in these years made cotton growing more attractive than peanut production, in the areas suited to cotton.

the reductions in acreage were offset to some extent by higher yields.[37]

The consumption of peanuts for food use had stabilized at about 4.3 pounds per capita, about the same as the 1935–1939 average. The growth of population had increased total consumption in food uses to about 900 million pounds of farmers' stock. Exports had dropped off to negligible amounts.[38] The weakness in the oil market was reflected in the decline of about 50 per cent in oil prices between 1947 and 1949. The outbreak of war in Korea strengthened prices temporarily but they soon dropped back to about support levels. CCC losses were moderate on the 1951 and 1952 crops (fiscal years ending in June 1952 and 1953) but were very heavy on the 1953 crop ($23.4 million).[39]

Program Costs, 1932–1953

For the period 1932 through June 30, 1953, expenditures on the various farm programs have been brought together and consolidated in a comprehensive review prepared by the U.S. Department of Agriculture.[40]

37. Acreages, yields and production for the years 1946–1955 were as follows:

Year	*Acreage Harvested for Nuts (Thousands)*	*Production (1,000 Pounds)*
1946	3,141	2,038,005
1947	3,377	2,181,695
1948	3,296	2,335,840
1949	2,308	1,864,780
1950	2,268	2,036,670
1951	2,009	1,675,955
1952	1,459	1,354,010
1953	1,541	1,588,415
1954	1,388	1,023,070
1955	1,656	1,689,325

(*Agricultural Statistics, 1953,* p. 128, and later U.S. Department of Agriculture reports.) The 1955 increase in acreage reflected a 7.5 per cent increase in allotments and the picking and threshing of the crop from a larger percentage of the allotted acres. The 1955 crop was expected to result in available supplies for crushing, export and addition to stocks of about 450 million pounds, and a price approximating the support level of 12.2 cents per pound (less costs of about one-half cent). (U.S. Agricultural Marketing Service, *The Fats and Oils Situation,* September 26, 1955, pp. 6–7.) This implies a continuing problem of adjustment in peanut production and use.

38. The peanut market had been adjusting to a domestic basis. Exports had virtually ceased and were not likely to be revived except through government aid. Prices were held too high for exporters to compete even in the "edible" market of Canada. The domestic market was protected by means of duties and quotas. In June 1953, under the provisions of Section 22 of the Agricultural Adjustment Act of 1933 as amended, peanut importations were limited to 1,709,000 pounds (shelled). The oil market cannot be effectively protected in that way so long as there is an abundant supply of fats and oils.

39. Commodity Credit Corporation, *Report of Financial Condition and Operations as of June 30, 1955,* p. 31. The losses for fiscal 1955 (on the 1954 crop) were $2.1 million. Those on the 1951 and 1952 crops amounted to $8.7 million and $3.0 million, respectively.

40. *Realized Cost of Agricultural and Related Programs, by Function or Purpose, Fiscal Years 1932–1953,* in U.S. Senate Committee on Agriculture and Forestry, *General Farm Program,* Hearings, 83d Cong., 2d sess., Part I, 1954, pp. 74–89 (reproduced in Appendix B in Murray R. Benedict, *Can We Solve the Farm Problem?,* Twentieth Century Fund, New York, 1955).

For peanuts, the costs shown are as follows (in millions):

Under Agricultural Adjustment Act of 1933	$3.7
Acreage allotment payments under Agricultural Conservation Program	6.2
Agricultural production programs (principally acreage allotments and marketing quotas)	13.6
Removal of surplus agricultural commodities	26.8
Price-support programs	92.6
Total	$142.9
Less miscellaneous receipts	1.3 [a]
Net to June 30, 1953	$141.6

a. The U.S. Department of Agriculture summary also deducts $3.7 million received as processing taxes. However, since this was a public expense, it is included here as a debit rather than as a credit.

In addition to the costs listed above, CCC showed realized costs on peanuts for the fiscal years 1954 and 1955 of $23.4 million and $2.1 million respectively.[41] The total cost to the middle of 1955 (that is, through the 1954 season) was therefore approximately $167 million. Of this total, about $118 million was incurred through the Commodity Credit Corporation, the remainder being made up from Section 32 and other funds.

EXPERIENCE UNDER DIFFERENT METHODS OF SUPPORT

Nearly all of the various price-support measures have been used or tried in the programs relating to peanuts. The experience with that crop covers a longer period and a more diverse array of activities than for any of the other oilseeds.[42] Purchase and resale for diversion to oil has been the method most widely used. In the main, it has been effective, but very expensive to the government in view of the small part of the national farm income that is derived from peanuts.[43] The apparent success of that procedure has been due in considerable measure to the special characteristics of the crop and to the abnormal demand for oil during and after World War II.

Almost any expectable amount of peanut oil can be fed into the large fats and oils market without disturbing it greatly, if the govern-

41. Commodity Credit Corporation, *Report of Financial Condition and Operations as of June 30, 1955,* p. 31.

42. They have included rental and benefit payments, acreage allotments, conservation subsidies, marketing quotas, CCC loans, direct government purchases, export subsidies and two-price plans.

43. The value of the peanut crop (picked and threshed) was only seven tenths of one per cent of the value of all crops grown in 1952. (See *Agricultural Statistics, 1953,* pp. 573–75.) If livestock products are included, the relative importance of peanuts is, of course, much smaller. Subsidies of comparable size, if applied to the major crops, would involve prohibitive costs, or even if all the minor crops were to be subsidized in a comparable way.

ment is willing to absorb the loss on the amounts so diverted. The sudden increase in the demand for oil which for a time made the oil outlet nearly as favorable as that for "edible" nuts tended to obscure some of the problems that became more prominent as oil and nut prices settled back to more usual relationships.

Purchases were made annually in the 1937–1942 period, mostly with Section 32 funds. Beginning with 1943, CCC became the sole purchaser of all peanuts, at prices established by a schedule related to parity. More normal methods of trade were resumed after the war but substantial purchases by CCC were made as well. Though much the largest part of the volume purchased by the government, except when CCC was the sole purchaser, was diverted to oil, sizable quantities were sold for "edible" use in some years. That was true in 1940–1942 and again in 1950.[44] After the war, the cost of diversion to oil was borne by CCC but there was some use of Section 32 funds in providing subsidies on exports.

In the early 1950s, loans were available but growers did not make much use of them. They chose instead to deliver peanuts to their cooperatives or to other buyers, at support prices, rather than to warehouse them or to obtain loans on their own account. Loans were made or guaranteed to cooperatives, shellers and crushers on the basis of agreements to pay growers not less than support prices. Such loans were recourse loans and were usually repaid without loss to the government. Beginning with the 1952 season, this type of purchase agreement was replaced by nonrecourse loans and purchase agreements to growers, through their cooperatives.[45]

Grower Cooperatives Used Extensively

Grower cooperatives have played a significant role in the peanut program. A grower cooperative participated in negotiating the marketing agreement of 1933. In 1937, four regional cooperatives were organized to assist in carrying out the program.[46] They were authorized to buy from growers, up to a maximum quantity, at scheduled prices established by the Department of Agriculture. They also disposed of peanuts in accordance with directives from the Department. The cooperatives were paid for the services rendered and the government took any losses involved from selling below cost.

44. Some peanuts were assigned to the food stamp program, as peanut butter, in the 1941 and 1942 seasons.

45. The "excess oil" provision of the Agricultural Adjustment Act of 1938, as amended, was repealed on March 28, 1952. Thereafter, growers who harvested and marketed peanuts from excess acres (if marketing quotas and acreage allotments were in effect) were not to be eligible for price support and were to be subject to marketing quota penalties. (See U.S. Agricultural Adjustment Administration, *Report of the Administrator of the Production and Marketing Administration, 1952,* p. 34.)

46. The number was reduced to three in 1940, one each for the major producing regions, Virginia–North Carolina and the southeast and southwest areas.

When CCC was the sole purchaser, the cooperatives were included in the list of designated purchasers. After the war, they resumed the role of agent for support purchases and later, in 1952, became loan and service agencies for the government in dealing with the growers.[47] When marketing quotas were in effect, they were designated by the Secretary of Agriculture as agents to receive nonquota peanuts and convert them into oil, returning the net to growers.

Efforts to Maintain Differential Prices

Several methods have been tried in the effort to maintain higher prices for "edible" nuts than on those crushed for oil. The first experiment was with the processing tax of 1934 and 1935. Nuts to be crushed for oil were left free of tax so as to encourage crushing and reduce the supply available for the "edible" market. There was only one price to the grower but it was a composite of the two prices to consumers. It was probably a little higher than it would have been without the tax, because of the greater inelasticity of the demand in the higher use.

In the 1941 season, a two-price system was introduced. Marketing quotas were established in an effort to limit production to about the amounts that would be taken by the "edible" trade at support prices. The excess was to be sold as oil at whatever it would bring. That procedure was modified in the 1942 season by the introduction of a "comparable" support level on peanuts for oil, which was lower than that applied to "edible" nuts. As the demand for oil increased, the degree of discrimination was reduced.

The system of paying two prices to growers was abandoned in 1943 when CCC became the sole purchaser. During the remainder of the war, losses on distribution, after paying growers at the support price, were made up by subsidies in order to hold the prices of the products at ceiling levels.

After the war, CCC attempted to encourage diversion by subsidizing the crushing of No. 2 nuts. No subsidy was required in 1946, as the demand for oil was sufficient to result in support prices for the peanuts crushed. But in 1947 the situation changed. The demand for No. 2's for domestic crushing and export was not sufficient to absorb all of them at support prices. A larger volume had to be diverted at a loss. That experience was repeated in the 1948 season.

Purchases and costs mounted as the size of the crop increased, and per capita demand for "edible" nuts shrank back to about the prewar

47. Peanuts are more perishable than cotton or the grains. Under usual farm storage conditions, the farmer would be likely to incur heavy losses if he attempted to store peanuts himself, and therefore could not get a loan on them. The cooperatives provided approved storage facilities; graded, purchased or pooled the nuts; and, if the grower so desired, put them under loan. If the nuts were put under loan, the grower was paid the support price, less service charges, and if any net profits accrued from sales he got his pro rata share of them.

level. With the return to quotas and allotments in 1949, the effort to handle the situation by diverting No. 2's was abandoned. The prewar two-price system, with modifications, was reinstated in 1950. The government had taken a heavy loss on purchases in the 1949 season, in spite of the heavy cut in production brought about by reimposing allotments and quotas. In the 1950 season, the grower of excess peanuts could market them without penalty up to the amount produced for sale in 1947, provided the excess peanuts were delivered to a designated agent for crushing.

The 1950 crop was larger than the 1949 crop and more oil was produced, but in the meantime the demand for oil had increased. The cost of supports was not eliminated but was much smaller than in 1949. The same procedure was continued in 1951 and 1952. However, those provisions of the legislation which permitted growers to market peanuts from acreages in excess of allotments were cancelled in March 1953.

Effects of Two-Price Plan

It is difficult to appraise the effects of the two-price operations of the 1950 and 1951 seasons. Developments in 1950 were in line with expectations; developments in 1951 were not. The sizable reduction in the 1951 crop, and in price-support losses, must be attributed to other factors than the peanut price and control program. It was due principally to the cotton situation and the conditions associated with the outbreak of war in Korea.

There was general dissatisfaction with the program. Government administrators complained that it was too hard to administer. Their most difficult problem was that of keeping "excess" peanuts out of the higher-priced "edible" market. Many growers complained that they could not afford to grow peanuts for oil and that surplus production was weakening the market for "edible" nuts. Shellers objected on the ground that the program disturbed established channels of trade. The two-price system was therefore abandoned. It was replaced by the simpler procedure of more rigid controls on acreage and continuing high support prices on peanuts for the "edible" market. Realized losses were much smaller on the 1952 crop (about $3 million) but were heavy on the crop grown in 1953 ($23 million).

Both acreage and production were reduced markedly in 1952 and remained low in 1953 and 1954. (See Table 28.) In 1953, 17 per cent of the crop (269 million pounds) was taken over by the government, thus accounting for the heavy loss incurred by CCC in fiscal 1954, the year in which losses on the 1953 crop were reported. In 1954, droughts in two of the three major producing areas reduced average yields markedly and prices were above support levels. Few peanuts were put under the support program.

As of 1955, the situation had reverted to one more like that of the

TABLE 28

PEANUTS: PRICE, ACREAGE, YIELD, SUPPLY AND DISPOSITION (FARMERS' STOCK BASIS), AVERAGE 1937–1941, ANNUAL 1942–1954

Year Beg. Sept.	Season Average Price per Pound Received by Farmers [a]	Picked and Threshed: Acreage	Picked and Threshed: Production [a]	Total Supply [b]	Exports and Shipments	Crushed for Oil	Domestic Food Use: Military	Domestic Food Use: Civilian	Domestic Food Use: Civilian per Capita
	(Cents)	*(1,000 Acres)*	*(Million Pounds)*	*(Million Pounds)*	*(Million Pounds)*	*(Million Pounds)*	*(Million Pounds)*	*(Million Pounds)*	*(Pounds)*
Average 1937–1941	3.6	1,818	1,395	1,522	3	302	15	891	6.7
1942	6.1	3,355	2,193	2,312	4	448	146	1,170	8.9
1943	7.1	3,528	2,176	2,393	36	478	223	1,092	8.4
1944	8.0	3,068	2,081	2,412	29	431	288	1,140	8.7
1945	8.3	3,160	2,042	2,283	63	378	14	1,243	9.1
1946	9.1	3,141	2,038	2,319	252	534	—	1,036	7.2
1947	10.1	3,377	2,182	2,383	483	478	3	951	6.5
1948	10.5	3,296	2,336	2,511	762	483	6	914	6.2
1949	10.4	2,308	1,865	1,984	131	612	7	887	5.9
1950	10.9	2,268	2,037	2,155	72	642	14	947	6.2
1951	10.4	2,009	1,676	1,929	4	415	10	991	6.4
1952	10.9	1,460	1,366	1,698	3	198	10	1,008	6.4
1953	11.1	1,541	1,589	1,930	227	305	10	1,034	6.5
1954	12.3	1,394 [c]	1,025	1,421 [d]	9 [d]	94 [d]	9 [d]	986 [d]	6.0 [d]

Sources: Exports from U.S. Bureau of the Census; other data from U.S. Agricultural Marketing Service, *The Fats and Oils Situation,* January 31, 1955, p. 14; January 31, 1956, p. 15.

a. Year beginning August 1 in the Southwestern area; September 1 in the Southeastern area; and November 1 in the Virginia-Carolina area.
b. Includes imports (except in 1954–55), which were negligible in every year except 1944, when 85 million pounds were imported from Argentina for crushing.
c. U.S. Agricultural Marketing Service, *Annual Summary, Acreage, Yield and Production of Principal Crops, 1955,* p. 78.
d. Preliminary.

pre-World War II period, with peanuts grown mostly for the "edible" nut trade, but with acreages held in check by allotments and quotas and with prices supported at high levels.[48] However, the high price for the short crop of 1954 led to increased acreage and production in 1955.

OBJECTIVES AND POLICY CONSIDERATIONS

In the period 1933–1941, the program was designed specifically for aid to growers rather than as a means of meeting national needs. Since

48. The support level for the 1955 crop was put at 90 per cent of parity, which was the same as for 1954. (*The Fats and Oils Situation,* May 31, 1955, p. 9.) This was the first year that 90 per cent support was not mandatory (if farmers had approved marketing quotas). On the basis of supply and demand, support could be anywhere between 82.5 and 90 per cent of parity. On the basis of the then current supply-demand situation, it was put at 90 per cent.

the peanut crop is of minor importance nationally, and since the secondary product, peanut oil, is not a dominant factor in the fats and oils economy, the crop can be manipulated in ways that are impractical or too expensive in dealing with the major crops. On the other hand, the perishability of the crop makes the usual type of loan and storage program unsuitable.

There does not appear to be, in peacetime, a social advantage in subsidizing heavy production of peanuts for oil, except in dealing with chance variations in output or demand. A more desirable long-run program would seem therefore to suggest the following alternatives: one, the maintenance of acreage controls designed to hold production to about the amount that can be sold at prices the Congress chooses to support;[49] two, reversion to a two-price plan in which sales in the "edible nut" market would be restricted and the surplus diverted to oil at whatever price the oil market would yield; or, three, letting peanuts find their relative level of prices in competition with other crops, particularly cotton.[50]

Revised Parity Formula May Ease Problem

Peanut price supports from 1941 on were related to a parity price that was based on the returns for "edible" nuts in an earlier period when there was no significant output of peanut oil. Consequently, prices were maintained at high levels during the postwar years when the demand for peanuts was declining. This contributed to the high cost of supports and to heavy pressure for reduced production.

Use of the "modernized" parity formula, which was designed to adjust parities more realistically to present-day relationships between prices for the various farm products, would lessen the stimulus to peanut production, at any given level of support in terms of percentage of parity.[51] Peanut prices did not advance as much in the 1940s and early 1950s as did the average for all farm products. Use of the "modernized" parity formula would therefore have reduced the parity price for the 1949 crop, from 11.6 cents per pound to 9.5 cents. The support level, at 90

49. This would imply production mainly for the "edible nut" trade and very minor reliance on the oil outlet.

50. This third approach might be more adverse to peanut producers than a completely free market for all crops in that there is clearly a relationship between the acreage of cotton grown and that of peanuts. If cotton acreage is restricted while peanut acreage is left uncontrolled, there is a tendency for more land to be put into peanuts than if no crop control programs at all are in effect. However, many cotton growers also grow peanuts and vice versa, so in many areas the primary concern is the joint return from the two crops.

51. Retention of the "old" formula in computing parity prices for peanuts kept the official parity from 1949 on about 20 per cent above what it would have been if shifted to the "modernized" formula as provided in Title II of the Agricultural Act of 1948.

per cent of parity, would then have been 8.6 cents instead of 10.5 cents.[52]

By 1952, the support level, at 90 per cent of "modernized" parity, would have been about 10 cents instead of 12 cents and probably could have been maintained without much expenditure of government funds or the use of marketing quotas.[53] Also, adjusting the support rates for the relation of current supply to "normal" supply, as provided in the Agricultural Act of 1949, would have reduced costs to a moderate level and encouraged readjustment without resort to marketing quotas.

THE COTTONSEED PROGRAMS

Cottonseed is one of the most important oil crops of the United States. Before World War II, and during the war, it was a principal source of vegetable oils. Since the war, oil production from soybeans has increased to a point where it supplies a larger part of the market than cottonseed oil. In 1954, the two together accounted for about 90 per cent of the food fats and oils other than butter and lard. The supply of these oils is therefore a dominant factor in determining the price of vegetable oils for food.

Cottonseed is also an important source of income to cotton producers. In recent years, it has provided returns amounting to about 15 per cent of those from cotton lint and its value is more than twice that of the peanut crop. Though cottonseed is more important than peanuts as a source of oil, it did not come into prominence in the farm price-support program until World War II, since cottonseed is a by-product rather than a primary source of income.

In the situation brought about by U.S. entry into World War II, there was need for more food fats and oils but not for more cotton. Since not all of the cottonseed produced was being crushed for oil, it was considered desirable to provide incentives for crushing a larger portion of it than had been customary in the past. As food oils became more plentiful in the postwar years, the problem was to stabilize the vegetable oil industry rather than to induce larger production.

The Nature of the War Program

During the war, the policy relating to cottonseed was subordinate to that of restricting the output of cotton lint and the two were somewhat

52. Title II of the Agricultural Act of 1948 provided for a shift to the "modernized" formula beginning in 1949. That provision, so far as the "basic" crops were concerned, was deferred by congressional action until 1956. (See *Can We Solve the Farm Problem?*, Appendix A.)

53. That procedure would probably have resulted in a somewhat larger volume of marketings and might have resulted in total returns to farmers that would have been as much as or possibly more than they were with heavy pressure for reduced production. The receipts from marketings in 1949 would have been smaller but the adjustment would probably have been made at less cost to the government and it is likely that a larger market for peanuts would have been retained.

in conflict.[54] Cotton growers were being encouraged to shift to food crops, especially to peanuts for oil and for "edible" uses. The plan adopted was also intended to induce cotton growers to sell to the mills for crushing a larger portion of the seed grown. CCC contracted to pay minimum prices to the crushers for their products provided they paid growers not less than the specified minimum prices, $49–$50 per ton.

The 1942 cotton crop was 2 million bales larger than that of 1941. The price received by farmers for cottonseed declined to $45.60 per ton as compared with $47.65 in 1941. However, deliveries to mills, which had amounted to about 3.75 million tons in 1941, increased to about 4.15 million in 1942.[55] Though there was an increase in deliveries, the percentage increase in deliveries to crushers was slightly smaller than the percentage increase in production. Thus the 1942 program did not maintain either prices or the proportion of the total seed crop delivered to the mills.

However, the program was continued, chiefly as a means of keeping returns to cottonseed producers on an equitable basis with those to the growers of other oilseed crops. It was somewhat more effective in the later war years but not in such a way as to make it an important factor in the situation. The proportion of the seed crop delivered to mills was not increased significantly but prices were stabilized at a somewhat higher level than in 1942.[56] The behavior of prices after the close of the war indicates that two factors were primarily responsible: one, the discontinuance of price controls; the other, and probably the more important, the severe fat shortage of the early postwar years. War was again a major factor in 1950.

Price Support in the Postwar Years

Cottonseed supports were discontinued after the war, as prices were much above parity. A large crop harvested in 1948, and a general decline in the prices of cottonseed oil and meal, led to the offering of price supports at 90 per cent of parity ($49.50) on the 1949 crop. However, another large crop and continuing deflation reduced the price to $43.40, the lowest since 1940.

54. Cotton stocks in government hands were very large when the war began and continued high until 1946.

55. *Agricultural Statistics, 1951,* p. 122.

56. The price was $52.10 in 1943 and remained at about that level until 1946, when it jumped to $71.90. Cottonseed prices for the years 1940–1954 were as follows:

Year	Price	Year	Price	Year	Price
1940	$21.72	1945	$51.10	1950	$86.60
1941	47.65	1946	71.90	1951	69.30
1942	45.60	1947	85.90	1952	69.60
1943	52.10	1948	67.20	1953	52.70
1944	52.70	1949	43.40	1954	60.30

(*Loc. cit.,* and *The Fats and Oils Situation,* September 26, 1955, p. 8.)

A rollback of one-half cent per pound on refined cottonseed oil was put into effect in 1942. Its cost for the duration of the war was about $7 million.

This first postwar cottonseed price-support program was not very successful. Loans were offered to growers on clean, safely stored cottonseed, but only about 7,000 tons were put under loan (out of a total of 6.6 million tons). As a means of checking the decline in prices, a purchase program was announced in October. Purchases were made through ginners, acting as agents for CCC. The purchase price was put at $46.50, $3.00 per ton less than the support offered to farmers. The $3 differential was to cover transportation, storage and other handling charges that the grower would have to pay if he put his seed under loan.

Total purchases amounted to 800,000 tons, about 14 per cent of the amount delivered to mills. The purchase program probably contributed some strength to the market in the latter part of the season but the season average price, $43.40, was about 36 per cent below that of the preceding season and about $6.00 below the announced support price.

New Upsurge of Prices in 1950

Loans, purchases and purchase agreements were again offered in 1950 at about the same level as in 1949 ($47 per ton as compared with $49.50). However, a short crop and the outbreak of war in Korea raised prices far above the support level ($86.60 as a season average).[57] There were no additions to CCC stocks as a result of the 1950 program.

Prices turned down again in 1951 and had fallen to support levels in some areas by the end of the season. The Administration had announced before planting a high support level for the 1951 crop. This was for the purpose of encouraging an increase in the cotton crop, since cotton supplies had been very short in 1950 and prices at all-time highs. The announced support rate on cottonseed, $61.50 per ton,[58] was at about 90 per cent of the January 15, 1951 parity price of $71.00.

Cotton acreage was increased to the highest level reached since the big crop of 1937. The volume of seed crushed was nearly equal to that of 1949. Though the season average price was above the support level, CCC purchases resulted in the beginning of an accumulation of surplus stocks in government hands. The volume purchased was probably not large enough to have much effect on the prices paid to growers. The Corporation bought from cotton producers only 114 tons of seed and disposed of it at very small loss. However, the purchases of cottonseed products from processors did have a significant effect on the prices of some of them.

The purchases of meal, oil and linters, from processors, were condi-

57. Controls on cotton production were imposed in 1950 and acreage was reduced from about 27.5 million to less than 18 million. Cottonseed production was down by more than a third from the high level of 1949.

58. The stated levels of price support vary somewhat in different sources. Some relate to specified grades, qualities and locations. Others are reported as national season averages. The rates used here are as shown in *The Fats and Oils Situation,* September 26, 1955, p. 8.

tioned on certification by the processors that they had paid not less than the specified support prices to growers. The Corporation bought 54 million pounds of linters, 79 million pounds of oil and 350 million pounds of meal. These purchases constituted about 4.8 per cent of the oil, 7 per cent of the meal and 6 per cent of the linters produced in processing. They were the product of some 425,000 tons of cottonseed, roughly 6.5 per cent of the quantity crushed.[59] The meal was sold back at a profit, but nearly all of the oil and linters were carried over into government inventories at the end of the season.

High-Level Supports Continued in 1952

The support level for the 1952 crop ($62.50) was a dollar higher than the high support of 1951. It was announced in advance of the planting season. By that time, the possibility of more extensive involvement in war was no doubt a factor in the decision to continue supports at a relatively high level. However, the support price proved to be high enough to cause nearly half the crop to pass into the hands of CCC (2.66 million tons out of a crop of 6.2 million tons)—notwithstanding the fact that the season average price was well above the support level. Prices to growers were reported as $69.60 per ton (crop year average).

Production was about the same as in 1951 and nearly up to the high volume of 1949. The amount of seed crushed was also about equal to that of 1951. CCC purchases were substantial and undoubtedly an important factor in holding the price high.[60] Most of the meal was sold at a profit, but most of the oil and linters accumulated in CCC inventories.

The 1952 support operation resulted in the first really burdensome increase of CCC holdings. At year end, CCC held 77 per cent of the 1,016-million-pound stock of cottonseed oil[61] and 85 per cent of the million-bale stock of linters. Moreover, these had been acquired at prices that were substantially in excess of the then current values.

Supports Lowered in 1953

The support level was reduced sharply in 1953, to $50.50 per ton. However, seed production increased to a record postwar high of 6.7 million tons.[62] Cotton production was up moderately from that of 1952 and well above the 1943–1952 average. The season average price of cottonseed was above the support level[63] but CCC again added sub-

59. *The Fats and Oils Situation,* January 31, 1955, p. 12.

60. CCC purchased 2,184 million pounds of meal (42 per cent of the output), 678 million pounds of oil (37 per cent of the amount produced) and 481 million pounds of linters (57 per cent of total production).

61. Commodity Credit Corporation, *Review of Operations,* fiscal 1953, p. 7.

62. Preliminary estimate as reported in *The Fats and Oils Situation,* January 31, 1955, p. 12.

63. $52.70 as compared with $50.50 (*loc. cit.*).

stantially to its holdings. It acquired (in seed equivalent) more than a million tons of seed, about one sixth of the crop. Its holdings as of the end of the crop year amounted to 884 million pounds of cottonseed oil, 637 million pounds of cotton linters and 186 million pounds of cottonseed meal.[64]

There was a further slight reduction in the support level in 1954, to $50 per ton. More important was the sharp reduction in the cotton crop as a result of the reimposition of cotton controls. Cottonseed production was down from 6.7 million pounds to 5.6 million. Cottonseed prices were much stronger than in 1953, averaging $60.30 for the season, which was much above the support level. The support level was further reduced, to $42, in 1955 and cotton acreage controls were continued.

Cost of the Cottonseed Support Program

The cottonseed and cottonseed products program did not involve heavy losses to the government until 1954 and 1955, though the situation that was to result in heavy realized losses in those years was beginning to build up before that time. No realized losses or gains were recorded in the period prior to 1946. Between 1946 and 1951,[65] the cottonseed operations showed a net gain of $4.9 million, mainly because prices and demand were increasing.

The fiscal years 1952 and 1953 also showed gains, of $2.7 million and $7.7 million, respectively. Fiscal 1954 brought the first heavy realized loss ($20.3 million), on stocks acquired in the 1953 crop season and earlier. Fiscal 1955 showed a much larger loss ($58.7 million), making the net loss for the entire period 1946–1954, $63.7 million.[66]

THE SUPPORT PROGRAM FOR SOYBEANS

The soybean crop has become in recent years the most important vegetable oil crop and one of the most important cash crops of the United States. In 1951 and 1952, it supplied more than half the fats and oils, other than lard and butter, used in food products. It has industrial uses as well. As a source of cash farm income it equals peanuts and cottonseed combined.

First Price Program in 1941

The first government price program for soybeans was inaugurated in 1941, as a means of expanding production to replace imports of

64. Commodity Credit Corporation, *Report of Financial Condition and Operations as of June 30, 1955,* p. 41.

65. Data are for fiscal years ending in June of the years given and consequently relate to operations in the preceding crop season or seasons.

66. Commodity Credit Corporation, *Report of Financial Condition and Operations as of June 30, 1955,* p. 31.

vegetable oils that might be cut off by war. It was continued after the war, as required under the price guarantees enacted during the war and extended by subsequent legislation.

Acreage and production had been increasing from 1936 on, without government price support, though soybeans had been classified as a soil-depleting crop if harvested for beans and hence were presumably subject to some restraining influence. Though there were penalties for overplanting, the acreage harvested increased from 2.4 million in 1936 to 4.8 million in 1940. Soybean oil production increased from 184 million pounds to 564 million.

The restrictions were partially relaxed in 1941 and growers were encouraged to increase the acreage harvested for beans. Loans were offered in October at about $1.00 per bushel. The price was then above the loan level but a crop of record size was in prospect, and there was thought to be some possibility that the price would go below the level that the loan was designed to maintain. The 1941 harvested acreage (5.9 million) was more than a million acres larger than that of 1940. Oil production increased to 707 million pounds, but prices remained above support levels.[67] (For data on acreage, production, disposition and prices in the years 1939–1955, see Tables 29 and 30.)

In January 1942, the Secretary of Agriculture announced that it was necessary to encourage further expansion of soybeans for oil. As provided in the Steagall Amendment, this meant that the prices of soybeans would be supported throughout the war and for two years thereafter. The high prices received for the 1941 crop and the abandonment of all restrictions on production resulted in a 1942 crop about 75 per cent larger than that of 1941. Oil production was up by a corresponding amount. The support level had been raised to $1.60 per bushel, which was 111 per cent of comparable parity.[68]

The 1942 production was high enough to require government support if the announced price was to be maintained. Some 3.6 million bushels were put under loan. In addition, CCC contracted with processors to purchase soybeans at not less than $1.60 per bushel. Because of the inadequacy of crushing facilities in the producing areas, it also bought substantial quantities for shipment, at government expense, to oil-processing plants in other areas. Farm prices were held slightly above support levels ($1.61 per bushel).

Price ceilings were placed on soybean products in December 1941 and were continued until the end of the war. However, they did not prevent further increases in returns to growers. From 1943 on, subsidies protected the returns to processors and the costs to consumers,

67. The price received for beans averaged $1.55 per bushel and such amounts as were put under loan were redeemed before the end of the season.

68. The comparable price was determined from the average of the farm prices for soybeans from August 1934 to July 1939 adjusted by the factor 0.79 for the relationship of the six basic commodities to parity in that period.

TABLE 29

SOYBEANS: ACREAGE, YIELD, PRODUCTION, CRUSHING FOR OIL, AND EXPORTS, AVERAGE 1937–1941, ANNUAL 1939–1955

Crop Year	Acreage Harvested for Beans	Yield per Acre	Production	Crushed as Per Cent of Production	Oil Production	Exports: Beans	Exports: Oil
	(*Million Acres*)	(*Bushels*)	(*Million Bushels*)		(*Million Pounds*)	(*Million Bushels*)	(*Million Pounds*)
Average 1937–1941	4.1	18.7	77	71	500	3	11
1939	4.3	20.9	90	63	533	12.0	13
1940	4.8	16.2	78	82	564	[a]	13
1941	5.9	18.2	107	72	707	.5	21
1942	9.9	19.0	188	71	1,206	.7	44
1943	10.4	18.3	190	75	1,219	1.0	59
1944	10.2	18.8	192	80	1,347	[a]	67
1945	10.7	18.0	193	83	1,415	5.0	74
1946	9.9	20.5	203	85	1,531	3.8	91
1947	11.4	16.3	187	88	1,534	3.0	112
1948	10.7	21.3	227	81	1,807	23.0	300
1949	10.5	22.3	234	85	1,937	13.1	291
1950	13.8	21.7	299	84	2,454	28.0	490
1951	13.6	20.8	284	86	2,444	17.0	271
1952	14.4	20.7	299	81	2,536	31.9	93
1953	14.8	18.2	269	80 [b]	2,350	39.7	71
1954	17.0	20.0	341	72 [b]	2,711	60.5	54
1955	18.7	19.9	371		3,030	65	

Sources: U.S. Foreign Agricultural Service, *United States Farm Products in Foreign Trade,* Statistical Bulletin 112, 1953, pp. 69, 70 (as modified by later revisions); U.S. Department of Agriculture, *Agricultural Statistics, 1954,* pp. 124, 130; U.S. Agricultural Marketing Service, *The Fats and Oils Situation,* November 30, 1955, pp. 24–26, and July 24, 1956, p. 6; and *Acreage, Yield and Production of Principal Crops, 1955,* pp. 36, 39, 41.

a. Less than 500,000 pounds.
b. Computed from data given.

even though the prices paid to growers were being increased. By 1943, support prices were above what the processors could pay and still sell the products at ceiling prices. The government paid the difference by contracting with the processors to buy the beans for the government, at support prices, and thereafter selling them back to the processors at prices that would enable them to sell the products at ceiling prices.[69]

69. The first ceiling on soybeans at the farm level was applied on February 27, 1942, at $1.66 per bushel for top grades. It was subsequently raised to $1.92 in 1943 and to $2.10 in 1944.

TABLE 30

SOYBEANS: SUPPORT LEVEL, FARM PRICE, FARM VALUE AND PRICE-SUPPORT OPERATIONS, 1939–1955

Crop Year	Support Level: Average	Support Level: Per Cent of Parity	Season Average Farm Price	Farm Value	Price-Support Operations: Total under Price Support	Price-Support Operations: Per Cent of Crop
				(*Millions*)	(*1,000 Bushels*)	
1939			$ .81	$ 73		
1940			.90	70		
1941	$1.05	81	1.55	166	149	.1
1942	1.60	111	1.61	301	3,641	1.9
1943	1.80	114	1.81	345	261	.1
1944	2.04	125	2.05	394	79	.0
1945	2.04	123	2.08	402	32	.0
1946	2.04	104	2.57	522	6,456	3.2
1947	2.04	90	3.33	621	3,536	1.9
1948	2.18	90	2.27	516	10,993	4.8
1949	2.11	90	2.16	506	16,061	6.9
1950	2.06	80	2.47	738	14,954	5.0
1951	2.45	90	2.73	770	11,133	3.9
1952	2.56	90	2.72	809	14,455	5.0
1953	2.56	90	2.72	732		
1954	2.22	80	2.46	842		
1955	2.04	70	2.10	779		

Sources: U.S. Production and Marketing Administration, Grain Branch, *Grain Market News and Statistical Report,* September 18, 1953, p. 16; U.S. Department of Agriculture, *Agricultural Statistics, 1954,* p. 124; and U.S. Agricultural Marketing Service, *Season Average Prices and Value of Production, 1952 and 1953,* p. 13; *1953 and 1954,* p. 11; *1954 and 1955,* p. 16.

Support Prices Increased in 1943

The soybean support price was raised to $1.80 for the 1943 crop and to $2.04 for the 1944 and 1945 crops. Only small quantities were put under loan. The principal method of support was through purchase at support levels. Prices to growers were kept close to the announced support prices. Both acreage and production continued at about the levels reached in 1942 though there was a slight upward trend, particularly in oil production. The government announced higher acreage and production goals in 1943 and 1944, but they were not achieved.

Taken as a whole, the wartime soybean program can be considered successful. Production was increased and prices were stabilized, but at relatively high cost to the government. Oil production was doubled between 1941 and 1945. The prices of soybean products were stabilized under ceilings. The season average price to growers advanced from $1.55

to $2.08. The cost to the government, including transportation subsidies, was about $66 million.[70]

However, that expenditure must be regarded as largely a war expense and a subsidy to consumers rather than as a subsidy to farmers. Apparently it was necessary to advance prices by about the amounts specified in order to make soybean production sufficiently attractive to induce farmers to make the expansion needed. Soybean prices did not, in fact, advance as much as those of many other farm products and the incentives provided were not sufficient to induce the increases sought in 1943 and 1944.

High Demand in Postwar Years

Soybean prices advanced after decontrol in October 1946 and continued above support levels during the first two years following the war. The first postwar crop was harvested from a reduced acreage, but high yields resulted in a crop of record size (203 million bushels). The level of support was continued at $2.04, but prices were much above those guaranteed ($2.57 in 1946 and $3.33 in 1947).

The advance in prices during the 1946 season enabled CCC to dispose of stocks on hand from earlier purchases at a profit. The higher prices also encouraged increased plantings. A record acreage was harvested in 1947 but the increase was more than offset by lower yields. The crop totaled only 187 million bushels. The small crop, together with the clearing up of CCC stocks and the strong foreign demand, contributed to the phenomenally high price of that year.

The acreage harvested in 1948 was smaller but about at the 1943–1946 level. A high yield of 21.3 bushels resulted in a crop 10 per cent larger than the record outturn of 1946. The season average price dropped to $2.27, which still was above the 90 per cent support level of $2.18. However, supplies were becoming more abundant and prices were easing off generally.

As directed in Title I of the Agricultural Act of 1948, CCC continued price supports at 90 per cent of parity for the 1948 and 1949 seasons ($2.18 in 1948 and $2.11 in 1949). Substantial quantities of beans were put under loan and the supports provided undoubtedly checked the decline and helped to stabilize prices. The 1949 season average price ($2.16), though lower than that of 1948, was still somewhat above the

70. U.S. General Accounting Office, Corporation Audits Division, *Report on Audit of the Commodity Credit Corporation,* House Doc. No. 632, 81st Cong., 2d sess., p. 75. ". . . only the dairy production program and the wheat-for-feed program were of greater magnitude. . . . The subsidy aspect under soybean processor contracts terminated after May 13, 1946, when the OPA ceiling price on soybean meal was raised."

Ceiling prices were re-established on August 23, 1946, under the Price Control Extension Act of 1946, but all price ceilings on soybeans and soybean products were terminated on October 17, 1946. (*Ibid.,* p. 78.)

support level. The 1949 crop, which set a new record of 234 million bushels, was about 3 per cent larger than the large crop of 1948.

A record volume of exports in 1948 and 1949, and a comparatively strong market, enabled CCC to dispose, at some profit, of the quantities delivered to it. The returns to growers were sufficiently favorable to induce them to make a 30 per cent increase in harvested acreage in 1950. Production was well above even the large crops of 1948 and 1949. These plantings were made before the outbreak of war in Korea and the new wave of inflation that accompanied it.

Price supports were no longer required by law but were extended by administrative decision. The rate was reduced to $2.06, but was not important as the season average price of $2.47 was above the support level.[71] Production was again increased, to almost 300 million bushels, but only about 5 per cent of the crop was put under loan. The amounts pledged were redeemed without significant loss to the government.

Higher Supports and Large Crops, 1951–1953

The support level for 1951, at 90 per cent of parity, was $2.45. The general increase in prices and continuance of the 90 per cent rate put it at $2.56 for the 1952 and 1953 seasons. Production was maintained at about the 1950 level, though it was down 10 per cent in 1953. Prices continued to exceed support levels by fairly substantial margins. The season average price in 1951 was $2.73 and in 1952 and 1953 it was $2.72.[72] Support operations did not result in significant loss to the government in those years. However, October 1 stocks were showing a rather substantial increase by 1954.

The cottonseed program probably contributed more to the results shown in this period than did the soybean program. It resulted in the accumulation of large quantities of cottonseed oil, as a means of supporting the price of cottonseed. Accumulations as of June 30, 1953 amounted to about 15.6 per cent of the total production of edible vegetable oils.[73]

71. In 1950, the "modernized" parity formula provided in the Agricultural Acts of 1948 and 1949 replaced the "comparable" parity used previously. It raised the parity price for soybeans by about 10 per cent. However, the shift to the higher parity basis was partly offset by reducing the support level from 90 per cent to 80 per cent. Thereafter, the 90 per cent rate was restored for the 1951, 1952 and 1953 seasons. It was reduced to 80 per cent for 1954 ($2.22) and to 70 per cent for 1955 ($2.04). (*CCC Price Support Statistical Handbook*, p. 44, and *The Fats and Oils Situation*, March 30, 1955, p. 8.)

72. *The Fats and Oils Situation*, September 26, 1953, p. 9. The stability of the price in relation to support level in this period would seem to indicate that the level of support was an important factor in establishing the price even though it was lower than the average price actually received and the amounts placed under loan were not large. Putting 4 or 5 per cent of the crop under loan serves mainly as an aid to some producers in marketing the crop. A nonrecourse loan or a purchase agreement relieves the producer of the risk of a price decline and probably tends to steady the flow onto the market.

73. Statistical analyses indicate that allowing that amount of cottonseed oil to go onto the market would have reduced the price of soybean oil by about 25 per cent, that is, from 12.1 cents to about 9 cents in 1952. The price of soybean meal probably

However, a number of other factors were important. The period as a whole cannot be considered a normal one. The outbreak of war in 1950 increased the price of soybean oil by about 50 per cent for that year. It dropped back to about the 1949 level in 1951 and remained at that level through 1954.[74] The price of soybean meal was up about 30 per cent in 1951, nearly offsetting the decline in the price of oil. It was again high in 1953.[75]

There was also a marked shift from cottonseed oil to soybean oil in the manufacture of margarine. In 1949, cottonseed provided about 60 per cent of the fats and oils used in margarine production. By 1953, it was down to less than 30 per cent and was still declining at a rapid rate. Nearly all of the difference was made up by an increase in the amount of soybean oil used.[76]

Program Costs

There has been very little cost to the government on price-support operations for soybeans as such. If we ignore the wartime consumer and transportation subsidies on soybean products (about $66 million), the soybean program showed a profit of some $4.4 million for the period 1941 through fiscal 1952. There were small losses in fiscal 1953, 1954 and 1955 (on the crops of 1952, 1953 and 1954), but even the largest of them, in fiscal 1954, was less than a million dollars. For the entire period 1941–1955 the program showed a gain of $3.7 million.

That was due in part, of course, to the upward trend of prices, which made it possible usually to sell amounts acquired by CCC at more than the cost of acquisition. There was, however, a significant indirect subsidy in that pressure on the vegetable oil market as a whole was met, for the most part, through heavy acquisitions of cottonseed, peanuts and flaxseed, and their products. Losses on the other major oil crops (particu-

---

was not affected significantly as only small amounts of cottonseed meal were withheld from the market. If cottonseed oil had not been held off the market, the price of soybeans probably would have been reduced about 10 per cent, from $2.72 to the support level of $2.56 or, without supports, to $2.46. (See Martin S. Simon, *Soybeans,* U.S. Bureau of Agricultural Economics, Marketing Research Report No. 35, May 1953.)

74. U.S. Agricultural Marketing Service, *Oilseeds, Fats and Oils, 1909–53,* Statistical Bulletin 147, p. 210.

75. The prices of meal per ton and oil per pound and their combined values in these years were as follows:

	1949	*1950*	*1951*	*1952*	*1953*	*1954*
Meal per ton (dollars)	64.30	64.44	83.33	67.57	78.63	60.50
Oil per pound (cents)	12.3	17.8	11.3	12.1	13.5	12.0
Combined value per bushel crushed (dollars)	2.77	3.26	3.12	2.95	3.38	2.69

(*The Fats and Oils Situation,* September 26, 1955, p. 9.)

76. From chart published by the National Cottonseed Products Association (based on Bureau of Census data), undated.

larly on the 1953 and 1954 crops) were heavy (nearly $180 million). The supports provided in that way had, of course, an important bearing on the strength of the market for soybeans and their products. Taken as a whole, the oilseed crops showed losses for fiscal 1954 and 1955 that were among the heaviest recorded for the various groups of farm commodities. They were exceeded only by corn, wheat and manufactured dairy products.[77]

Taken as a whole, the losses and costs on the oilseed crop programs, not counting consumer subsidies, amounted to nearly $320 million, through June 1955. Though much smaller in absolute amount than the expenditures on the corn, cotton and wheat programs, the costs in relation to the values of the crops concerned make the oilseed crop subsidies probably the heaviest for any crop except potatoes.

Not much of this cost can be properly considered as a war expense. A good part of the peanut expense was incurred prior to World War II and all the rest of it in the postwar years. The oilseed crop programs (except for consumer subsidies) were virtually costless in the war years themselves but heavy expenses were incurred on peanuts and flaxseed in 1946–1951. The heavy costs on the 1953 and 1954 crops of cottonseed, peanuts and flaxseed were a result of continuing unbalance in production and high price supports rather than of war needs or efforts to expand production.[78]

THE FLAXSEED PROGRAM

Linseed oil is the principal drying oil used in paints and varnishes. From 1931 to 1940, it constituted 70 per cent of the oil used in the paint

77. While this generalization is substantially correct, even in a longer-term setting, it does not present an entirely true picture of relative costs. The realization of costs on the storables, such as wheat, cotton and corn, could be and was deferred. Potentially these losses were much larger than the ones actually shown. The oils and manufactured dairy products, though storable for moderate periods of time, must be moved fairly promptly. Consequently, losses that must be taken usually show up within a relatively short time after the products are acquired. Stocks of cotton, corn, wheat and tobacco may be held for considerable periods without serious depreciation.

Heavy realized costs were also recorded for the grain sorghums in fiscal 1954 and 1955, but not so heavy as for the oilseed and other crops mentioned above.

78. Realized costs to CCC can be summarized as follows (in millions):

Period	*Peanuts*	*Cottonseed and Products*	*Flaxseed and Linseed Oil*	*Soybeans*
July 1, 1946— June 30, 1951	$ 81.0	$ 4.9 (gain)	$ 60.0	$4.4 (gain)
Fiscal 1952	8.7	2.7 (gain)	4.7	*
Fiscal 1953	3.0	7.7 (gain)	1.4	*
Fiscal 1954	23.4	20.3	51.3	.6
Fiscal 1955	2.1	58.7	22.8	*
October 17, 1933— June 30, 1955	118.1	63.7	140.3	3.7 (gain)

* Gain or loss of less than $100,000.

(From Commodity Credit Corporation, *Report of Financial Condition and Operations as of June 30, 1955*, p. 31. The costs and gains shown are only those of the Commodity Credit Corporation. They do not include other types of expense, chiefly the cost of the peanut programs of 1933–1943 (about $52 million) and the special flax acreage subsidy of 1945 (about $20 million).

and varnish industries. During that period about 56 per cent of the flaxseed used was imported, principally from Argentina. About 15 per cent of the oil used was tung oil, and perilla oil provided a smaller proportion of the amount required. Tung and perilla oils were imported from the Far East until the 1941 season. Thereafter, imports from that area ceased to be available.[79]

In 1932, the price of flaxseed fell to less than half that of the late 1920s. It recovered in 1933, but, though a minor crop, flax was added to the list of basic commodities in 1934.[80] Flax producers were encouraged to plant 2.4 million acres in 1935, as compared with 1.6 million in 1934. The resulting crop, 14.5 million bushels, brought U.S. production back to about 50 per cent of the total amount of flaxseed crushed in the United States.

When the percentage fell off again in later years, the Agricultural Adjustment Act of 1933 had been largely invalidated and any adjustments made would have had to be by other means. Not until 1939 did domestic production again become large enough to supply more than half the amounts crushed in the United States.

The 1936–1941 Program

Under the Soil Conservation and Domestic Allotment Act of 1936, flax was designated as a soil-depleting crop and payments were authorized for diverting flax acreage to soil-conserving crops, and for soil-improving practices. Under that program, government payments of $2,039,000 were made in 1936 but none thereafter.[81] Acreage seeded declined from 2.6 million in 1936 to 1.3 million in 1937, and to 1 million in 1938. It was back up to 2.3 million in 1939 and reached 3.4 million in 1940.

From 1936 on, yields held fairly steady at about 9 bushels per acre but with a slight upward trend. Prices mostly were in the order of $1.50 per bushel, except in 1937 when the increase in business activity raised the price to $1.87. The 1940 crop was double that of the early 1930s and around 50 per cent larger than those of the late 1920s.

79. Until the 1930s, flax producers looked mainly to the tariff as a method of supporting prices for their product. The tariff on flax was raised in the 1920s and had a significant but somewhat uncertain effect on prices because of the large variations in U.S. production and consumption.

80. Under Section 4 of the Jones-Connally Cattle Act (Public Law 142, 73d Cong.). Until then, about half the U.S. supply had been produced domestically. With the short crop of 1933, the proportion produced in the United States dropped to about 33 per cent. Though producers urged that steps be taken to restore the earlier relationship, flaxseed was not included in the Agricultural Adjustment Act of 1933, as its price was then at a more favorable level than that of many other farm products. It was $1.63 in 1933 as compared with about $2.25 to $2.50 in the late 1920s. It had been up to $2.81 in 1929 and down to $ .88 in 1932.

Though not a large or widely produced crop, flax was of some interest as a possible substitute for wheat, which was in heavy oversupply, whereas the domestic production of flaxseed was far below national requirements.

81. *Agricultural Statistics, 1946,* p. 655.

First Support Program Announced in 1941

Flaxseed for oil was one of the commodities for which increased production was requested for defense and war purposes. Under the Steagall Amendment of July 1, 1941 it was thus eligible for price support at 85 per cent of parity. On August 19, 1941 support at $1.85 per bushel for No. 1 grade flaxseed, at Minneapolis, was announced by the Secretary of Agriculture. The price for No. 2 was to be 5 cents lower and no loans were to be made on lower grades.

The program was designed to provide an average price to farmers of $1.70 per bushel. However, increasing war activity strengthened demand and resulted in a season average price to farmers of $1.79. Since this was somewhat above the loan level, there was little demand for loans.

Large surpluses in Argentina and a 50 per cent reduction in the tariff on Argentine flaxseed, as of November 15, 1941, kept the 1941 price relatively low, but by the end of the 1941 season, increases in the Argentine price had more than offset the decrease in import duties. Imports from Argentina amounted to 21 million bushels, about twice the preceding year's volume and the highest since 1936. However, by the end of the season, shipping space had become scarce and shipping charges were being increased substantially.

Price ceilings on linseed oil were put into effect as of December 13, 1941, designed to hold prices at the November 26 level. On January 2, 1942, the price ceiling was raised to the October 1, 1941 price plus 0.75 cent per pound.[82] Ceilings on linseed oil were not effective at that time as average market prices were below the ceiling level, and the prices received by farmers, for flaxseed, were 25 per cent below parity. These were major factors in the decision to exclude linseed oil from price ceilings after February 4, 1942.[83]

Higher Supports and Increased Acreage in 1942

An acreage goal of 4.5 million seeded acres was set for 1942. That was about 30 per cent higher than the acreage sown in 1941. Price support at $2.40 per bushel, for No. 1 flaxseed at Minneapolis, was announced.[84] The methods of support provided were nonrecourse loans and government purchases of flaxseed grading No. 2 or better. The sup-

82. Amendment No. 1 to Price Schedule No. 53. Ceilings generally were placed at the October 1 level or 110 per cent of the November 26 level, whichever was higher. However, the ceilings for soybean and linseed oils were to be at the October 1 level plus 0.75 cent per pound.

83. Amendment No. 2 to Price Schedule No. 53. After the removal of price ceilings, crude oil prices advanced from 10.6 cents to 11.1, at Minneapolis, and were up to 12.6 cents by the end of the season. Flaxseed prices, to farmers, increased from $2.08 per bushel in February to $2.35 at the end of the season but still were 9 per cent below parity.

84. The rate on No. 2 was put at $2.35.

port level worked out to about $2.25 at the farm (approximately 88 per cent of parity as of July 1, 1942).[85]

Since there was active demand for flaxseed for crushing and for use as seed, farmers who were growing oats and barley for cash sale were urged to shift some acreage to flax. Grasses and legumes seeded with flax were added to the list of crops acceptable in meeting the requirement that 20 per cent of the farmer's cropland be in soil-conserving crops (as a condition for establishing eligibility for soil conservation payments). The government also initiated an educational program designed to encourage increased flaxseed production.[86]

To insure the cooperation of flaxseed crushers, the government announced on August 28, 1942 that CCC would make nonrecourse loans on up to 40 per cent of the crusher's total of oil produced from U.S.-grown flaxseed, provided the growers had been paid support prices. Loans were made on raw linseed oil at 12.0 to 12.4 cents per pound and supplemental contracts were entered into to encourage movement of flaxseed to eastern mills and to alleviate bottlenecks at the Midwest crushing mills.[87] Crude oil prices advanced from 12.6 cents in July 1942 to 13.6 cents in February 1943, so that phase of the program had little effect on prices.

With the provisions relating to soil conservation modified to favor flax production, and with no ceiling on flaxseed prices, the acreage sown in 1942 was increased to 4.7 million,[88] about 200,000 in excess of the goal and about 1.2 million more than in 1941. Yields were slightly below those of 1941 but production was up to 41 million bushels, about 28 per cent above the 1941 total.

In the early part of the season, receipts were heavy and the price declined to $2.23 in November, which was only 85 per cent of parity. However, demand increased thereafter as a result of a large decrease in net imports.[89] With no ceilings in effect, the price rose to $3.00 in April 1943, 112 per cent of parity. The season average price to farmers was $2.36.

Further Stimulus Given in 1943 and 1944

Price supports at about 96 per cent of parity were announced for 1943 and 1944. These worked out to $2.85 in 1943 and $2.95 in 1944, for No. 1 grade at Minneapolis.[90] Loans were made available to growers

85. As of that time the required level of support was 85 per cent of parity. The Stabilization Act of October 2, 1942 made 90 per cent support mandatory.
86. See *The Fats and Oils Situation*, April 1942, pp. 11–12, and U.S. Agricultural Adjustment Administration, *Report of the Administrator of the Production and Marketing Administration, 1942*, p. 24.
87. *The Fats and Oils Situation*, September 1942, p. 6.
88. *Agricultural Statistics, 1953*, p. 124.
89. From 21 million bushels in 1941 to less than 5 million in 1942.
90. In this period the official agricultural price parities were rising gradually as a result of increases in the prices of things bought by farmers.

at support level with an allowance of 7 cents per bushel for flaxseed stored on the farm. The loans were contingent on the seeding to flax of 90 per cent or more of the farm's flax acreage goal. However, nonrecourse loans granted in previous years and in 1943 were discontinued in 1944.

Additional support was provided by a pledge to processors that CCC would purchase linseed oil at 0.7 cent per pound below ceiling prices and linseed meal at $2 per ton under ceilings, provided the processor had paid support prices to the producer. Prices for oils and for oil meal were close to ceilings, so the Commodity Credit Corporation suffered little or no loss on the subsidy and price programs of 1943 and 1944.[91]

The acreage sown in 1943 was at a record level of 6.2 million, 32 per cent above that of 1942 and 13 per cent in excess of the national acreage goal. Some shift from wheat to flax had occurred as a result of reduced acreage allotments for the wheat crop. However, it is likely that so large an increase would not have been made if farmers had realized that price ceilings would be imposed about a month before the marketing season was to begin. Yields were down moderately, to 8.8 bushels, but production amounted to 50 million bushels, which was an increase of 22 per cent over that of 1942 on an acreage that was 32 per cent larger.

Acreage Sharply Reduced in 1944

Farm prices were held under ceilings for 1943 crop-year marketings. The season average price to farmers, $2.83, was moderately favorable in terms of parity but not so favorable on a return-per-acre basis as the income that could be derived from competing farm products. With a prospect that ceilings would be continued in 1944, and with likelihood of larger returns from other crops, there was a sizable shift away from flax, particularly to wheat and oats.

Seeded acreage was down to 2.9 million, less than half that of 1943, and the yield was lower. The outturn of 22 million bushels was equal to only 44 per cent of the large 1943 crop. On August 14, 1944, price ceilings were increased to $3.10 (at Minneapolis) and flaxseed for uses other than oil and seeding for the following season were exempted from ceiling regulations.[92] Average farm prices for the 1944 season increased over those of 1943 but only slightly ($2.91 as compared with $2.83). The end-of-season price, $2.92, was about 101 per cent of parity.[93]

91. U.S. Department of Agriculture, *Report of the President of the Commodity Credit Corporation,* 1944, and *The Fats and Oils Situation,* November 1943, p. 15, and January 1944, p. 12.

92. Amendment No. 5 to Maximum Price Regulation 397.

93. There were heavy imports of flaxseed from Canada and Argentina in 1943. These, together with the large 1943 crop, made possible a 23 per cent increase in oil production over 1942. However, the equivalent of about three quarters of the imports was reexported under lend-lease and for other war purposes. Linseed oil stocks, which had been depleted to 192 million pounds at the end of the 1942 season, were built up to an all-time high of 336 million pounds.

The greatly reduced 1944 crop, and a shift to a net export basis as a result of lend-lease shipments, resulted in a 40 per cent decline in oil production, to only 660 million pounds as compared with 1,132 million in 1943. Imports were down from 21 million pounds to 6.5 million. By the end of the season, oil stocks were down to 160 million pounds, the lowest since the war began.

Restrictions on Use of Linseed Oil

During 1943 and 1944, various steps were taken to restrict oil consumption to essential uses and to increase production. As of July 1, 1943, crushers were required to set aside 45 per cent of the oil produced, for purchase by the government if needed.[94] As stocks built up, the order was amended so as to require only a 25 per cent set-aside (after October 26, 1943). It was terminated on January 6, 1944. Purchases by processors in excess of their needs for the remainder of the 1943 marketing season were prohibited on March 1, 1944 (to put restraint on speculation and advance purchases for later use).[95]

Quotas on drying oils for civilian use were established in May 1944, at 70 per cent of the average amounts used in 1940–1941. As the smallness of the 1944 crop became apparent, the civilian quotas were successively lowered, to 60 per cent in July 1944, 50 per cent for January to March 1945 and 40 per cent for April through June.[96]

Efforts to Stimulate Production in 1945

As a result of the severe shortage that had developed, the Congress authorized expenditure of $29.8 million to encourage the planting of flax in the 1945 season.[97] Special payments of $5 per acre were to be made to flax producers for seeding up to the individual farm acreage goal. The national seeded acres goal had been set at 5 million, 72 per cent more than the acreage planted in 1944 but only about four fifths as large as the big crop of 1943.[98]

Price supports were put at $3.00 per bushel (basis No. 1 at Min-

94. Food Distribution Order No. 57, issued June 22, 1943.

95. Food Distribution Order No. 94.

96. There was very heavy demand for linseed oil for export under lend-lease, to Britain for wartime industrial uses and to Russia as a means of supplementing her desperately short supply of food fats. At the same time, Argentine and Canadian production had fallen off by half and shipping had become very scarce for bringing in even the small amounts available from Argentina. (See *Agricultural Statistics, 1945,* p. 120.)

97. Amendment to the Federal Crop Insurance Act of 1938 (58 Stat. 918), approved December 23, 1944 and effective January 16, 1945.

98. Payments would be made only if the land used was suitable for growing flaxseed and if the crop was properly tended throughout the season. Flax is a temperamental crop and is subject to heavy weed infestation on some lands in some years, as, for example, in Iowa and Minnesota in 1943.

neapolis), which was 103 per cent of parity.[99] However, prices remained around ceiling levels ($3.10 at Minneapolis, $2.91 at the farm), so little use was made of government loans. Acreage was increased to about 4 million in 1945, from the 2.9 million of 1944. The increase was apparently due largely to the $5 per acre bonus offered, which was much more effective in the low-yielding spring wheat region than in the heavy-yielding areas of the West. The acreage in California, the principal West Coast producer, declined substantially in 1945 as compared with 1944.

The acreage grown nationally was 21 per cent less than the announced goal but yields were somewhat better than in 1944 and production was up from 22 million bushels to 34.6 million. Without the special acreage payments, it might well have been lower than in the preceding year as other, less risky crops were bringing higher returns per acre. Price ceilings held the average farm price down until May 1946 despite the shortage of supplies. The 1945 season average price to farmers was $2.89, two cents below the 1944 average.

Flaxseed stocks were very low at the beginning of the 1945 season, only 3 million bushels as compared with 12 million a year earlier. Linseed oil production declined to 589 million pounds.[100] However, some 8 million bushels of flaxseed (equivalent to about 150 million pounds of oil) were imported from Canada and Argentina. Exports to Russia were discontinued, but there was a continuing strong demand for oil in Western Europe. Total linseed oil supplies for the year amounted to 694 million pounds as compared with 660 million in 1944. With heavy demand from the domestic drying oil industry, end-of-year linseed oil stocks were the smallest since before the war.[101]

In the 1945 season, CCC encountered losses for the first time in its flaxseed operations. Ceilings on linseed oil remained at the 1943 levels, which allowed only a 10-cent spread between the support level and the ceiling price. Under its contracts with processors, which allowed them to obtain flaxseed at prices that would enable them to sell oil and meal at ceiling prices, CCC had a net loss of $503,000. This was in addition to the government's acreage subsidy of about $20 million.[102]

99. The $5 per acre bonus was in addition to the price received in the market. In areas where yields were low, 8 to 10 bushels per acre, as in most parts of the Middle West, this added as much as 50 cents per bushel. In irrigated areas, such as California, where customary yields might run as high as 30 bushels, the bonus per bushel and the stimulus to production were, of course, much smaller. As a further incentive to expand flax acreage, the Federal Crop Insurance Corporation was authorized to write crop insurance on flax beginning with the 1945 crop.

100. It had been 633 million in 1944, also a year of severe shortages.

101. Processor inventory restrictions were in effect throughout the year but were eased somewhat on September 27. They were tightened again in April 1946.

102. There were in addition to the oilseed programs described above some small ones relating to castor beans and tung oil. These, however, involved costs of only about $300,000 in all. Some other oil-procurement programs were carried on as war measures by other agencies of the government, for example, the babasu nut program undertaken in Brazil.

Price Ceilings Lifted in 1946

Price ceilings on flaxseed were removed on June 30, 1946 and the price advanced sharply thereafter. The 1946 season average price to farmers was $4.04. Acreage was a third lower than in 1945 and production was down to 23 million bushels (from 35 million).

From 1946 on, with strong demand and no price ceilings, both production and prices increased. The season average price to farmers reached an all-time high of $6.15 per bushel in 1947 and was still up to $5.71 in 1948. Acreage went above the 5-million mark in 1948 and remained high in 1949, but by then the shortage of fats and oils was easing off. The price of flaxseed (to farmers) dropped back to $3.63 in 1949 and remained at about that level through 1950, 1951 and 1952. Acreage also declined and by 1952 was only slightly above the 1940 level.[103]

The price-support rate was put at 90 per cent of parity for the 1949 crop but was reduced to 60 per cent in 1950 and 1951. It was raised to 80 per cent in 1952. These percentages worked out to prices of $3.74 per bushel in 1949, $2.57 in 1950, $2.65 in 1951 and $3.77 in 1952.

The support level in 1953 was $3.79, two cents higher than in 1952,[104] but farmers were urged to reduce their 1953 plantings by 10 to 15 per cent. Instead of being reduced, the 1953 acreage was up about 35 per cent and production nearly 22 per cent, though stocks were relatively heavy. About 40 per cent of the crop was put under loan and CCC bought 750,000 bushels in Texas as a price-support operation. Losses on the 1953 operations (reported for fiscal 1954) amounted to $51.3 million, nearly as much as those of the whole period 1946–1951. Stocks of flaxseed and linseed oil as of July 1, 1954 were expected to be more

103. Acreage, production and farm prices in these and the following years were as follows:

Year	*Acreage Planted (Thousands)*	*Production (1,000 Bushels)*	*Season Average Price per Bushel to Farmers*
1945	3,953	34,557	$2.89
1946	2,641	22,588	4.04
1947	4,264	40,618	6.15
1948	5,121	54,803	5.71
1949	5,348	42,976	3.63
1950	4,274	40,236	3.34
1951	4,116	34,696	3.71
1952	3,444	30,174	3.72
1953	4,640	36,668	3.64
1954	5,959	41,534	3.03
1955	5,255 [a]	41,300 [a]	2.88

a. Preliminary estimates.

(*Agricultural Statistics, 1955,* p. 115 and later reports. Prices from *ibid.* and *The Fats and Oils Situation,* July 24, 1956, p. 11.)

From 1947 through 1953, exports exceeded imports. Net exports in 1948 and 1951 were in the order of 4 to 5 million bushels. (*The Fats and Oils Situation,* July 24, 1956, p. 7.)

104. 80 per cent of parity as in 1952.

than adequate to meet requirements for a full year, but heavy sales for export at prices well below domestic prices reduced them in the latter part of the season.[105]

The support level for the 1954 crop was reduced to 70 per cent of parity ($3.14), but acreage and production were again increased over those of the preceding year. CCC losses on the 1954 crop were again heavy ($22.8 million) but not so heavy as in the 1953 season, mainly because the support level was lower. The increase in flax acreage was mostly on land taken out of wheat because of acreage allotments on wheat.[106] About 8.4 million bushels of the 1954 crop were taken over by CCC, but, even so, prices sagged below support levels in the latter part of the 1954 season.

The support level for flaxseed was reduced to $2.91 for the 1955 season (60 per cent of parity), but with continuing pressure to reduce wheat acreage, the acreage sown to flax was still about equal to the high 1948 and 1949 acreages. Because of high yields, production was around that of 1954. Flax production still appeared to be somewhat out of balance, though there was a prospect of smaller government losses because of the lower level of support and an active demand for oil and meal.

Program Costs to 1955

The flaxseed program in the years since 1946 has been one of the most expensive in proportion to the value of the crop. Through June 1953, the costs amounted to $72 million, of which $66.2 million was for price-support programs, almost all incurred in the period 1946–1951. The remainder consisted of $5.8 million from Section 32 funds used in surplus removal programs. There was also an expenditure of some $20 million in 1945 for incentive subsidies to increase acreage, but this can be regarded mainly as a war expense.

Heavy losses were incurred in fiscal 1954 and 1955 ($74.1 million). Thus the total costs, aside from the wartime incentive payments, have been in the order of $146 million, a large amount for a minor crop like flaxseed. The value of the 1952 flaxseed crop was less than 0.6 per cent of the value of all crops produced.

105. *The Fats and Oils Situation,* October 25, 1954, p. 14. Exports were expected to reach the equivalent of 25 million bushels of flaxseed, all from government stocks.
106. *Ibid.,* p. 25.

5

Coarse Grains and Livestock

THE CORN PROGRAM

CORN IS the most important crop grown in the United States.[1] Its farm value in 1952 was approximately $5 billion, as compared with $2.7 billion for wheat and $2.6 billion for cotton. More acreage is used for corn production than for any other crop, and corn tends to be grown on the best lands under cultivation. Though most farmers grow some corn for feed and some of them produce corn for sale, only a small part of the crop is shipped out of the areas where it is grown. The value of the crop depends principally on the value of the livestock products derived from it.

However, even as a cash crop, corn ranks third, after wheat and cotton, though the cash receipts from tobacco are almost as large.[2] About half the corn sold goes to other farmers for use as livestock feed. The other half, usually about 10 per cent of the total crop, is processed as human food and for industrial uses. A small quantity is exported.

The corn crop provides about three quarters of all the grain fed to livestock and two thirds of all concentrate feeds used in livestock production. It is the primary feed for hogs, which consume about half the amount produced. Hog production is so heavily dependent on corn that there is a continuous and usually rather close relationship between hog production and the supply of corn available, and between their prices.

Factors Affecting Corn Prices

The price of corn depends principally on the relation of the supply of corn to the number of animals to be fed, and on the demand for livestock products. There has never been any large volume of corn exports and the demand in markets abroad does not have an important bearing on corn prices.[3] The demand for corn to be used for food and

1. Though it is grown in nearly all parts of the United States, the bulk of it comes from the North Central area known as the Corn Belt.

2. If truck crops are regarded as a single crop, proceeds from the sale of them exceed returns from either corn or tobacco. Several of the livestock industries also show higher cash returns than do any of the crops. (For data and comparisons, see U.S. Department of Agriculture, *Agricultural Statistics, 1953,* p. 610.)

3. Exports were rather large in the period 1896–1900, but even at their highest, in 1897, accounted for only 9.3 per cent of the crop. They were also relatively high in 1919–1922 but not so high as in the late 1890s.

industrial purposes, though stable and rather inelastic, is of minor importance so far as prices are concerned.

The demand in feed uses tends to be relatively inelastic in short periods, but is much more elastic over longer periods. That is, the number of animals to be fed cannot be adjusted quickly and a short corn crop, when there is a big livestock population, can result in relatively high prices for corn, and vice versa. However, the rate of feeding and the weights and finish to which animals are carried can be and are adjusted somewhat, depending on the relative prices of corn and livestock, especially hogs. Even though adjustments of that kind can be and are made, an increase in the size of the corn crop from the average level may reduce corn prices by a larger percentage than the increase in output.

In the short run, the price of corn is not affected directly, to any great extent, by changes in the purchasing power of consumers. Over longer periods it is affected indirectly, and very significantly, through changes in the demand for livestock products, which in turn is affected by the level of consumer purchasing power. The demand for many of the livestock products, especially pork, is more elastic than the demand for corn.

The market price of corn affects the corn producer in a number of ways, most of them indirect, though his principal concern is with the joint return from corn and hogs or corn and beef cattle. The level of corn prices has some bearing on the choices the farmer makes; for example, whether he will sell rather than feed or will carry some of the supply over to another season. More important is the effect of corn prices, as related to livestock prices, on the amount of feeding that will be done, the number of sows retained for breeding, and so on. As a result of changing relationships in prices, particularly those of corn and hogs, there is some tendency for years of large and small production of hogs to recur at fairly regular intervals in what is commonly known as the corn-hog cycle.

Trends in Demand and Supply

The shift from horse power to motor power has reduced the consumption of corn by horses and mules from about 25 per cent of the crop in 1909 to less than 3 per cent in recent years. Demand has also been modified through an increase in the production and use of other feed grains such as grain sorghums, oats and barley. Even more important has been the increased use of by-product protein feeds such as cottonseed and soybean meals. These changes have been more than offset by the increased demand for livestock products.

The acreages of corn grown are fairly stable but have shown a marked downward trend over the past twenty years. However, the trend in yields during that period has been even more significantly upward. The amount of corn produced in the early 1950s, on about 80 million acres, was substantially larger than that produced on about 105 million acres in the early 1930s.[4] Though production as a whole has kept pace with increasing demand, there are variations in corn yields that are very disturbing to livestock producers.

From 1945 to 1955, both production and yields were relatively stable, except for the low-yield crop of 1947. The usual amount produced is in the order of 3 billion bushels, but a drop in yield from 36.7 bushels in 1946 to 28.4 bushels in 1947, together with a fairly sizable cut in acreage, reduced output to 2.35 billion bushels, which was less than the amount needed to carry out usual feeding programs. The years 1934 and 1936 were also marked by extremely low yields as a result of droughts.[5] Even in the 1940s and early 1950s, and with 1947 omitted, production varied from 2.5 billion bushels to 3.6 billion, enough to create serious disturbances in the livestock industry if not offset by some type of supply stabilization.

The stabilization of feed supplies is therefore of great importance to livestock producers, including most commercial growers of corn. If supplies can be stabilized, corn prices tend automatically to be less variable, except for changes that result from major variations in consumer buying power. The regularizing of feed supplies tends also to iron out, to some extent at least, the cyclical changes in livestock production. Hence the importance of dealing with instabilities in feed production through storage operations designed to absorb excesses and offset deficits.

FIRST GOVERNMENT PROGRAM IN 1933

Though corn prices went very low in 1931, the procedures available to and used by the Federal Farm Board did not lend themselves well to efforts to aid the producers of corn and livestock. Furthermore, the most severe decline in corn prices did not come until the fall of 1931 when Farm Board funds were already heavily committed in the wheat, cotton and wool support programs.[6]

Corn acreage had not changed much in the years 1919–1931 except for a slight downward trend in production in the latter part of the decade. However, acreage increased in 1931 and 1932 and the 1932 crop was

4. This was the period in which hybrid seed-corn, a high-yielding type, was introduced suddenly and almost universally in the Corn Belt. In addition, there has been continuous improvement in the productivity and adaptability of varieties, in the use of commercial fertilizer and in the timeliness of operations (as a result of the availability of power machinery).

5. Production was down in 1934 to 1.46 billion bushels and in 1936 to 1.53 billion, as compared with a then customary output of 2 to 2.5 billion bushels.

6. A small corn crop of only 2 billion bushels in 1930 slowed the decline in corn prices. The 1929 crop was somewhat below average and the carry-over into the 1930 season was moderate. The Farm Board did provide some assistance to cooperative livestock marketing associations but did not attempt to support prices directly.

nearly 3 billion bushels, which was close to the record highs of 1906, 1920 and 1921. With demand falling off and hog prices at record lows, the price of corn fell to a season average of 32 cents per bushel in 1931, and was about the same in 1932. The price of hogs, to farmers, had fallen to an all-time low of less than $3.00 per hundredweight by May 1932 and was down to $2.68 in January 1933. It was below $4.00 from December 1931 on.[7] The price in 1929 and early 1930 had been in the order of $9.00 to $10.00.

The large corn crop of 1932 caused the price of corn at the farm to fall below 20 cents per bushel by December of that year. That was less than 25 per cent of the price prevailing in 1928 and 1929. The low corn price in turn contributed to an even heavier oversupply of hogs than in the previous year, since it led to some increase in hog production in 1933 in spite of the low prices prevailing and the poor prospect for any significant increase in exports of pork products.[8]

The very severe depression in the Corn Belt, a major segment of American agriculture, meant, of course, that the Corn Belt farm groups would play an important role in shaping the new agricultural legislation then being drafted and that special attention would be given to the corn-hog economy in the formulation of programs.[9]

In the Agricultural Adjustment Act of 1933, corn and hogs were included in the list of "basic" commodities. Hence, processing taxes could be levied on them and control programs could be undertaken. Since only a small portion of the corn crop is processed, there could be little income from processing taxes on corn. Principal reliance had to be on the tax levied on hogs. Consequently, the two had to be handled in conjunction with each other, for financial reasons if no other.

While most hogs were processed and hence could be subjected to processing taxes, it was recognized that the demand for pork was so elastic that a tax on it would very likely result in a lower price to the producer. That is, in the conditions then existing, a somewhat higher price to consumers might result in their buying smaller quantities of pork and actually spending for pork and its products about the same total amount as they would have spent anyway. If so, there could be little advantage to the producer in taking a lower price in the market and

7. *Agricultural Statistics, 1937,* pp. 40, 262.

8. Pork and lard exports had fallen off considerably in the 1920s and declined still more in the 1930s.

9. Corn Belt groups had been active in the campaign for the McNary-Haugen bill that developed in the 1920s, though they were less directly concerned than were the wheat growers, who were the initial sponsors of the movement. The corn growers recognized that export subsidies could not be expected to solve the problems of the corn grower as such. However, the corn and hog economies were intimately related and it was thought that some improvement in the hog situation might be brought about by reviving the active export trade in pork products and lard that had existed in World War I and in the first years thereafter.

having the reduction offset by a government payment derived from the processing tax. However, processing tax funds could be used in programs designed to reduce production and thus might result in a higher total return to growers, by raising consumer prices enough to more than offset the reduction in market prices caused by the tax.

The 1933–1936 Program

The law permitted the levying of processing taxes at a rate equal to the difference between the price in the market and the "fair-exchange value" (now known as the parity price). However, in order to avoid severe repercussions on the price of hogs in the market, the administrators of the act, in consultation with representatives of the producers, decided to make the initial tax rate low, and to raise it gradually thereafter. The decision to levy processing taxes was announced in August 1933.

The tax was put into effect in October, at a rate of 50 cents per hundredweight for November and December. It was to be increased to $2.00 in January. Subsequently, the schedule was revised so as to defer the $2.00 rate until February 1 and to raise it to $2.25 on the first of March. A processing tax on corn, at 28 cents per bushel, to become effective in November, was also announced in October. The high rate was protested and after a hearing which brought out the adverse effect on the relation of corn to competing products, it was reduced to 5 cents per bushel.

That meant that the processing tax on corn could not supply any large amount of funds for carrying out a production control and price-raising program for corn, the most important and one of the most severely depressed of the farm crops. The language of the Agricultural Adjustment Act seemed to indicate that the processing taxes collected on each commodity were to be used only on programs relating to that commodity. Since corn and hogs were so intimately related, there was a difficult problem both of interpreting the legislation and of planning an appropriate and effective program.

In view of the large supply of hogs in prospect, and the extremely low price prevailing, it was considered essential to initiate a corrective program at the earliest possible time and to find ways of financing it before income from processing taxes could become available. A cutback of production deferred until 1934 and after would mean postponing effective aid to the corn and hog producers for at least a year and possibly longer. As a way of meeting these problems, arrangements were made for the Treasury to make advances against future processing tax collections and for the corn and hog programs to be combined so that processing taxes on hogs could be used in the joint over-all program.

The Pig-Sow Purchase Program

With a view to reducing quickly the hog population and preventing a more extreme glut in the fall and winter of 1933–34, the administrators decided to buy up at premium prices, and to slaughter, a considerable number of brood sows and young pigs.[10] Under that program, the Agricultural Adjustment Administration bought some 6,200,000 pigs and about 220,000 sows. The heavy pigs and sows were converted into dry salt pork and distributed through the Federal Emergency Relief Administration. Light pigs, unsuitable for food use, were converted to grease and tankage for fertilizer.

In spite of this sizable reduction in the hog population, marketings became very heavy in November and December 1933. Hog prices again declined, almost to the level of a year earlier. As a means of easing the situation, the Adjustment Administration arranged with the Federal Emergency Relief Administration to buy live hogs and hog products for relief distribution. Prices recovered moderately by the spring of 1934 but were still below $4.00 in March. They moved up in the 1934 season and were a little above $5.00 in the fall months of that year. The recovery continued in 1935, and by the fall of that year prices were about at the 1928 and 1929 levels. The improvement was due largely to the short corn crop of 1934, to smaller pig crops in the fall of 1934 and the spring of 1935, and to other measures taken to hold down hog production.[11]

The heavy supplemental purchases made in the fall and winter of 1933–34, and turned over to the relief agencies, probably had more influence on prices than did the emergency pig-sow buying program. However, such purchases cannot be regarded as net additions to marketings. Considerable amounts of the pork so handled would probably have found their way into consumption in relief-supported families even if not supplied in that way, but the program did make larger quantities available to them than they would otherwise have been able to buy. In some measure at least, the operation constituted a transfer to people on relief of sizable funds that might otherwise have been paid to farmers as benefit payments or in other ways. However, the incidence of benefits

10. The spring pig crop of 1933 was 4 per cent larger than that of 1932, which had been large enough to reduce prices to less than $3 per hundredweight at the farm, a level that was recognized as disastrous to hog producers. Furthermore, the government pig survey of June 1, 1933 indicated that an unusually large number of sows had been bred for fall farrowing. (See U.S. Agricultural Adjustment Administration, *Agricultural Adjustment in 1934,* p. 88.)

11. Data from *Agricultural Statistics, 1937,* p. 262, and *1951,* p. 340. Further purchases of live animals and of hog products were made, principally in January 1934. Altogether, supplemental purchases of hogs and hog products amounted to about 2 million head. The grand total, including the pig-sow purchases, was equivalent to about 10 per cent of the average number of hogs slaughtered. The total cost was about $13.5 million, of which $11 million came from AAA, that is, from processing taxes, and $2.5 million from the Relief Administration. (*Agricultural Adjustment in 1934,* pp. 88–89.)

is virtually impossible to determine. If the purchases had not been made in that way, the prices paid to farmers for hogs marketed would almost certainly have been lower and thus would have offset some of the possible gain from benefit payments.

The pig-sow slaughter program was widely and severely criticized in the press and by the public generally. However, it was not different in principle from the cotton plow-up campaign, which did not arouse similar public opposition. Both were wasteful, and justifiable, if at all, only as extreme measures designed to bring about quickly a better balance in industries that were heavily overexpanded in terms of the effective markets then available. These strictly emergency programs were quickly replaced in both cotton and hogs by others designed to avoid producing commodities or animals that might have to be destroyed as a means of restoring some measure of health to the badly demoralized markets of that period.[12]

First Price-Support Loan for Corn

A second emergency program with some novel features was initiated in October 1933 by means of the newly created Commodity Credit Corporation.[13] This involved the making of nonrecourse loans on corn stored under seal on the farms where grown. Under that program, farmers might, if they chose, have their corn appraised, measured and put under seal, and could receive a loan on it at a specified rate per bushel, which could later be repaid with interest if they wished to reclaim the corn for feed use or sale. If the price remained below the loan level, and they did not choose to reclaim it, they could turn it over to the Commodity Credit Corporation and be absolved from any obligation to make up the loss that might accrue to the Corporation.

The purposes were twofold: one, to relieve pressure on the corn market and encourage orderly marketing of the crop; the other, to put money into the hands of farmers immediately without forcing them to sell corn and hogs quickly in a glutted market in order to get funds for meeting current obligations. The plan was adopted somewhat reluctantly. It was not, in fact, greatly different in principle from some of the early price-supporting procedures of the Federal Farm Board, which were by then rather thoroughly discredited.

However, the Commodity Credit Corporation procedures were much more flexible and workable than those of the Farm Board, and the setting in which the operation was undertaken was much more favorable.

12. The purchases of marketable hogs, for relief distribution, had rather general public approval though there were awkward problems to be dealt with in getting equitable and effective distribution to the relief recipients.

13. For a fuller explanation of this step and a description of Commodity Credit Corporation procedures, see Murray R. Benedict, *Can We Solve the Farm Problem?*, Twentieth Century Fund, New York, 1955, Chapter 10.

The Farm Board began operation in a period of relatively high prices, and endeavored to hold that level in a period of general and severe price decline. The Commodity Credit Corporation began operations when prices were at rock bottom and had a prospect of more favorable conditions in the years ahead.

Loans were offered at 45 cents per bushel for corn grading No. 4 or better, if properly stored and sealed.[14] The average price of corn at the farm at that time was about 39 cents,[15] so the loan was in excess of 100 per cent of market value. In order that the loan program might contribute to the general plan of production adjustment, eligibility for loans was made conditional on an agreement by the farmer that he would comply with the 1934 corn-hog contracts, which were then being prepared.

Effectiveness and Results of the Program

Corn prices strengthened somewhat in the fall of 1933, partly because of reduced production and the expected effects of the crop adjustment programs then getting under way, but also as a result of the nonrecourse loan program. The oat and barley crops of 1933 were small and corn production was down about 500 million bushels. However, there was no real shortage, as stocks of corn and oats, and of wheat as well, were high.

The aggregate volume of corn stored under the CCC loan program was 271 million bushels,[16] about 13 per cent of the total crop. Perhaps more significant was the fact that this was about half the amount normally sold off the farms where grown in that period. Not only did the action taken serve to strengthen corn prices and get money into the farm areas at a time when it was desperately needed, it also helped to reduce somewhat the incentive for increased hog production and, more important in view of later developments, caused some of the abundant 1933 corn supply to be carried over into 1934, when it was much more useful. The total amount loaned was $121 million.

One of the worst droughts the country had ever experienced occurred in 1934. Corn production was down from 2.4 billion bushels in 1933 to 1.5 billion in 1934. It had been as high as 2.9 billion in 1932. The price of corn, to farmers, was up to nearly 80 cents by the time the 1934 crop began to come on the market and rose to 85 cents later. As a consequence, growers who had borrowed on corn grown in 1933, and had held it, were able to make very substantial gains on the operation. Furthermore, the increase in carry-over helped somewhat in easing the very tight feed situation that developed in the 1934–35 season. The

14. Loans were offered only in the "commercial" corn areas, that is, in the areas where part of the corn produced ordinarily moved into the cash markets.

15. *Agricultural Statistics, 1937,* p. 47.

16. *Agricultural Adjustment in 1934,* p. 91.

Adjustment Administration estimated that the loan program resulted in carrying over as much as 50 million bushels more than would otherwise have been retained.[17]

The success of the 1933–34 corn loan launched the Commodity Credit Corporation on a career that was to make it, later, the primary agency in the effort to improve farm prices and incomes. The Corporation itself made a half-million-dollar profit and the gains to farmers who held their corn over were much larger. The attitude in the Congress in regard to operations of that kind changed markedly from what it had been a year or two earlier. In 1932, when the heavy losses incurred by the Federal Farm Board were being widely and critically discussed, congressional sentiment was, in general, antagonistic to price-pegging activities.

The change in the attitude of the Congress toward price-support loans and purchases became more evident in 1938 and after. Between 1934 and 1938, there were few major surplus problems to deal with because of the severe droughts of 1934 and 1936. Consequently, the CCC operations undertaken in 1933 continued to be looked upon as an outstanding success. In the Agricultural Adjustment Act of 1938, the Congress placed greater reliance on price-support loans of the CCC type and decreased the emphasis on production control. It became willing in later years to provide the Commodity Credit Corporation with much larger funds for carrying out price-support programs by means of nonrecourse loans.

The very satisfactory result of the 1933–34 operation was due in considerable measure to the fact that a year of extremely short supply followed so closely on the heels of one in which supplies were moderately plentiful. The Farm Board had encountered a situation in which supplies continued to increase even though demand was shrinking rapidly. Had 1934 been a year of large corn production it is possible that the CCC experiment would have been regarded as a repetition of the unhappy experience of the Board, rather than as a new and easy way out of the dilemma facing farmers. However, the undertaking, though entered into with some reluctance, did demonstrate that such a procedure, under appropriate conditions and with adequate flexibility and funds, could be beneficial both to farmers and to society. It also restored the price-support loan idea to good standing and revived interest in the idea of year-to-year stabilization of supplies, which had been much discussed in the 1929–1930 period.

Combination Hog and Corn Program in 1934

The 1934 program, as planned, sought to bring corn production into better balance with demand and to avoid further accumulation of stocks.

17. *Ibid.*, p. 92. The year 1934 was one of extreme feed shortage almost all through the country, but especially in the West where millions of cattle and sheep either starved to death or were destroyed to keep them from starving.

It also was designed to hold in check the number of hogs produced. Corn producers were offered contracts under which they would be required to reduce their corn acreages by at least 20 per cent from the average acreages grown in 1929–1933, and to hold hog production down to about 75 per cent of the number grown in the base period. The incentives provided were a payment of 30 cents per bushel on the estimated normal yield of the acres taken out of corn, and a payment of $5.00 per head on 75 per cent of the average number of hogs produced for market from litters farrowed between December 1, 1931 and December 1, 1933.[18]

Contracts were signed by 1,155,000 producers, who represented a little more than half the total acreage in corn. Their contracts provided for cutting down corn production by about 13 million acres, approximately 28.6 per cent of the base acreage to which the contracts were related. The total acreage planted to corn in 1934 was estimated at a little more than 100 million, a reduction of about 9 per cent from that of 1933 but only about 5 per cent below the acreage grown in the base years 1929–1933. Nonparticipating and noncomplying growers apparently increased acreage enough to offset about three quarters of the reduction made by complying participants.[19]

The drought of 1934 eliminated the corn surplus. The crop of that year amounted to less than half the big crop of 1932. The large carryover into the 1934 season, 338 million bushels, was not sufficient to bring the total supply for the season up to normal. However, the number of hogs and cattle to be fed had also been reduced by drought and by special programs. Corn growers redeemed the corn put under loan in 1933 and fed it. Only a small quantity was put under loan in 1934, and even that was redeemed and fed before the end of the season. Stocks were reduced to a very low level by October 1935, about 65 million bushels.[20]

Conclusive evidence on the effectiveness of the corn control program is not obtainable. Estimates of the reduction in plantings range from about 5 to 8 million acres. Since the drought reduced yields to a very low level, the production actually realized was probably only about 75 to 100 million bushels less than it would have been without the program.[21] The base acreage (average for 1929–1933) was a relatively

18. *Agricultural Adjustment in 1934,* p. 93. A contracting producer could, if he chose, receive comparable payment on a reduction of up to 30 per cent of his base acreage of corn.

19. Harvested acreage was only 92.3 million. The difference between that and the figure given above was due mainly to abandonment after planting, because of drought.

20. *Agricultural Statistics, 1945,* p. 45.

21. A study made by the Brookings Institution in that period estimated the acreage reduction at 7.7 million and the cut in production at about 90 million bushels (see Edwin G. Nourse, Joseph S. Davis and John D. Black, *Three Years of the Agricultural Adjustment Administration,* The Brookings Institution, Washington, 1937, p. 129). An analysis made by the Bureau of Agricultural Economics in 1937–1938 (unpublished) put the reduction at 5.8 million acres and 75 to 100 million bushels.

high one. Farmers might not have planted up to that level even if there had been no control program. That is, some of the acres the growers rented to the government possibly would not have been planted to corn if not put under contract, though the tendency for "noncooperating" growers to increase acreage would seem to throw some doubt on that conclusion.[22] Nevertheless, the rental payments did serve to transfer considerable amounts of money into the corn area, though possibly not in all cases or even generally to the individuals most in need of financial aid.

Program Continued in the 1935 Season

A referendum was held in the fall of 1934 and growers voted to continue the program in 1935. However, not quite so many growers signed contracts. Those who did sign represented about 50 per cent of the total acreage of corn, principally in the Corn Belt, which produces most of the corn that is marketed. They put some 12 million acres under contract, about 22 per cent of their base acreages.

Corn plantings for the 1935 season were estimated at about 100 million acres, slightly less than the acreage planted in 1934. The season was more favorable and the crop produced (2.3 billion bushels) was nearly up to the pre-1933 average. The reduction in livestock numbers had been so severe that the amount produced was sufficient to meet feeding requirements and increase carry-over to about the normal level. Apparently, the principal effect of the acreage control program was to check a tendency to increase acreage in order to offset the short crop of 1934.

The price of corn eased off and by December 1935 was down to 53 cents per bushel, at the farm, as compared with 85.3 cents a year earlier.[23] CCC continued to offer nonrecourse loans on the 1934 and 1935 crops. The rate in 1934 was raised to 55 cents but not many loans were made as the price in the market was well above that level. The rate was dropped back to 45 cents for the 1935 season. Producers again put only small amounts under loan and redeemed and fed them later in the season. The price at the farm continued to be moderately above the loan rate throughout the marketing season and moved up sharply in July 1936 as it became evident that another very short crop was in prospect.[24]

22. It should be noted, however, that there are many and varied situations in any industry that includes so many different entrepreneurs. It may be that a good many growers who would have been disposed to reduce acreage regardless of whether there was or was not a program were more receptive to the idea of acreage control contracts than those who planned to expand. On individual farms, contractions and expansions are a normal process. That is one of the reasons why uniform percentage adjustments tend to be unworkable, particularly for a crop such as corn, which is mostly used on the farm.

23. *Agricultural Statistics, 1937,* p. 47.

24. The farm price stood at 61.3 cents on June 15 and was up to 80.2 cents by July 15. The crop actually produced in 1936 was only 1.5 billion bushels as compared with 2.3 billion in 1935. (*Ibid.,* pp. 40, 47.)

In summary, it can be said that the emergency programs applied to corn in the 1933–1935 seasons increased the cash incomes of corn growers to some extent, though not on any large scale. The 1933 loans from CCC raised prices early in the season and made cash available sooner than if the loans had not been made. To the extent that the corn was bought by other farmers, the higher price meant for them a higher cost. The manipulation of corn prices is to some extent a two-edged sword so far as farmers as a whole are concerned, but it does not affect all of them in the same way.[25]

Sales for human consumption and industrial use did bring farmers as a whole a larger return, but that, as already noted, was for a very small portion of the crop. The processing taxes on corn apparently did not affect the prices to growers. They were passed on to consumers. However, they were small in amount, only $12 million for the entire period (November 5, 1933—January 6, 1936). Processing taxes on hogs and funds appropriated by the government provided by far the largest part of the payments made to producers on their corn-hog contracts.

Controls on Hog Production

The hog production phase of the corn-hog program was the more important one, both as a source of processing tax income and as a contributor to increased farm income, though much of the increase in income was a result of direct government subsidies. Hogs are, in fact, the primary product of Corn Belt agriculture. Corn is, to a large extent, an intermediate product. For a very large number of corn producers, the price attributed to corn is largely a matter of bookkeeping rather than one which affects importantly the over-all returns received. If corn is figured at a high price, the corn enterprise shows a larger profit (or smaller loss) and the hogs a smaller one, and vice versa.

However, since there is a significant cash market for corn, higher prices do benefit the grower and seller of corn, mostly at the expense of other farmers many of whom are in other regions. More important is the indirect effect of corn prices on the number of hogs raised. If the corn price is high relative to the price of hogs, hog production tends to be cut down. If it is low, hog production is stimulated. Consequently, the ups and downs of hog production are not, in most periods, direct responses to the prices of hogs themselves but rather to changes in the corn-hog ratio. Thus in the very depressed situation of 1932–1933,

25. Cash receipts to growers who sold corn were probably increased about 10 per cent in 1933. In the 1934 season, the increased carry-over resulting from the program probably about offset such reduction in output as was brought about by the acreage control program. In 1935, the restraints on acreage planted apparently were sufficient to increase receipts from marketings to some extent. It is estimated that, for the three seasons, the gains on account of price-support loans and production controls may have amounted to as much as $27 million, a relatively small addition on a crop with so large a total value.

there was some tendency for hog production to expand even though hog prices were at an extremely low level. The result nevertheless was to make over-all returns to Corn Belt farmers very low.

Pork product outlets had been somewhat disturbed from the middle 1920s on because of a marked decline in exports and some upward trend in hog production in the early 1930s. But much more important was the serious decline in consumer purchasing power that occurred in 1930 and after. Average exports of pork and lard in the 1920–1924 seasons were equivalent to about 10.6 million hogs, some 23 per cent of the inspected slaughter. In the years 1930–1933, exports were equivalent to only about 5.2 million hogs, 11 per cent of the inspected slaughter. The upward trend in hog production was no doubt due in large measure to the low price of corn. The third factor, reduced purchasing power, was, of course, affecting the prices of all farm products disastrously but especially the price of pork as there has long been a recognizable and positive relationship between employment levels and demand for pork.

The pig-sow purchase program more than offset the increased number of pigs saved in the spring of 1933 and resulted in hog numbers that were down to less than 59 million at the end of December 1933 as compared with 62 million at the end of 1932. While the contraction tended to reduce hog marketings, it also cut back on the demand for corn and tended to increase the amount carried over. As things turned out, that proved to be an advantage rather than a disadvantage because of the great need for corn that arose in 1934.

The later purchases of mature, marketable hogs, which were financed jointly by the Adjustment Administration and the Relief Administration, took off about 4 per cent of all hogs slaughtered under federal inspection in the 1933–34 season. While these purchases and distributions can hardly be regarded as a net addition to pork consumption, they did apparently raise hog prices, perhaps by as much as $1.75 per hundredweight over what they would have been without such purchases.[26]

The cost of the operation as a whole, including the pig-sow purchases, was about $44 million to AAA and some $12 to $15 million to the Federal Surplus Relief Corporation. It is probable, of course, that sizable purchases for relief would have been made even if there had been no corn-hog program. Some part even of the AAA contribution should perhaps be regarded as a public contribution to relief as well as an aid to hog producers.

Effect of Corn-Hog Contracts on Hog Production

The corn-hog contracts entered into with growers apparently helped to reduce the number of hogs produced, but it is impossible to estimate

26. See D. A. Fitzgerald, *Livestock under the Agricultural Adjustment Administration,* The Brookings Institution, Washington, 1935, pp. 71–80.

their effect with any assurance. Several factors were affecting the situation. Hog prices were still very low. They did not go above $4 per hundredweight until August 1934. Corn prices were rising and the corn-hog ratio was becoming less favorable to hog producers. The shortage of feed undoubtedly accounted for a good part of the reduction in fall farrowings in the 1934 season. Certain it is, however, that the 1934 pig crop was very much smaller than that of 1933. The number of pigs saved in the spring of 1934 was only 40 million as compared with 53 million in 1933. The fall pig crop was reduced even more drastically (from 31 million to 17 million).

Thus the total pig crop in 1934 was only 57 million as compared with 84 million in 1933.[27] The number of pigs saved in 1935 was about 56 million, a slightly smaller crop than that of 1934. An analysis made by the Bureau of Agricultural Economics in 1938 indicated that the program may have reduced the number of hogs marketed in late 1934 by as much as a million head and in 1935 by 3.4 million.[28]

There were some differences in the contract arrangements as between the 1934 and 1935 seasons. The 1934 contracts provided that growers should not raise more than 75 per cent of the average number of hogs grown in 1932 and 1933. The 1935 contract provided that the number raised should not be more than 90 per cent or less than 25 per cent of the 1932–1933 average. However, the short corn crop of 1934 would have caused growers to hold down pig production even if there had been no control program, so estimates of the effects of the contracts are of dubious value.

A substantial increase in hog prices and a larger corn crop in 1935 led to a marked increase in the number of sows bred for spring farrowing in 1936. The number saved was nearly 66 million as compared with 56 million in 1935. Inspected slaughter in 1936 may have been reduced to some extent by the 1935 control program, but the major influence on pork output was, of course, the very severe drought of 1936, which again reduced corn production to little more than half the usual amount.

The elimination of processing taxes and the termination of the Secretary's authority to enter into control contracts with farmers (January 1936) ended the effort to manage hog production and prices by that means. The removal of processing taxes resulted in some increase in the prices paid to farmers, but that action could not have had much effect on spring farrowings. Prices already were high enough to afford some stimulus to production. As a result of the reductions made in 1934 and 1935, mostly because of reduced feed supplies and higher prices for

27. *Agricultural Statistics, 1951,* p. 340; for hog prices, see *ibid., 1937,* p. 262.

28. Unpublished manuscript prepared for H. B. Rowe as part of a study of the results of the agricultural adjustment programs. The analysis is summarized in U.S. Agricultural Adjustment Administration, *Agricultural Adjustment, 1937–1938,* pp. 139–56.

corn, hog prices were above $9.00 in the 1935–36 season, which was about the 1928–29 level and more than double that of 1932–1934.[29]

Effect of Processing Taxes

Processing taxes reduced the prices paid to hog producers but it is difficult if not impossible to determine their net effect. However, it is apparent that the tax widened the margin between what the producer received and what the consumer paid for the products. The tax affected the prices to all producers, whether they participated in the program or not. Consequently, those who did not take part in the program took the reduction in prices that resulted from the tax and received no benefit payments in return. Their gain, if any, was from such effect as the program may have had on over-all supplies and prices. The cooperating producers shared in the redistribution of taxes collected and in the direct appropriations made, but the funds spent on the pig-sow slaughter program and on purchases made later for relief distribution did, of course, tend to raise prices for all hog producers.

The net amount collected in processing taxes from November 5, 1933 to January 6, 1936 was $261.4 million. The Brookings Institution studies made in that period indicate that the major part of the return from processing taxes on corn and hogs was offset by lower prices received in the market.[30] Later estimates put the amount of the reduction in receipts from marketings at about $240 million.

On the basis of this estimate it would appear that the over-all effect of this phase of the program was to redistribute about $240 million among the various groups of hog and corn producers but not in the same way as the costs were distributed. The total cost of the corn-hog program amounted to $488.7 million.[31] The portion not covered by

29. The unpublished BAE manuscript cited above gives estimates of hog production and prices with and without AAA programs as follows:

Year	*Inspected Slaughter Reported*	*Estimated Inspected Slaughter without AAA Programs*	*Average Price per 100 Pounds Paid by Packers*	
			Reported	*Estimated without AAA Programs*
	(*1,000 Head*)			
1933	47,226	47,946	$3.83	$ 3.55
1934	43,876	48,876	4.52	4.10
1935	26,057	29,457	9.22	10.00
1936	36,055	38,055	9.76	9.20
1937	31,642	32,142	9.94	9.74

30. *Three Years of the Agricultural Adjustment Administration,* p. 303. There was apparently some tendency for the packers to bid more than the free-market price minus the tax in the latter part of the period, after the eventual nullification of the tax came to be regarded as probable (*loc. cit.*).

31. U.S. Department of Agriculture, *Realized Cost of Agricultural and Related Programs, by Function or Purpose, Fiscal Years 1932–1953,* in U.S. Senate Committee on Agriculture and Forestry, *General Farm Program,* Hearings, 83d Cong., 2d sess., Part I, 1954, pp. 74–89 (reproduced in Appendix B in *Can We Solve the Farm Problem?*).

processing taxes was made up by direct appropriations from the U.S. Treasury. The Brookings Institution estimates, as supplemented by later Department of Agriculture computations, indicate that the program as a whole resulted in an increase in producer gross receipts from corn and hogs of about $465 million, of which about $227 million came from the U.S. Treasury. (See Table 31.)

TABLE 31

HOGS: ESTIMATED CASH FARM INCOME, ACTUAL AND WITHOUT AAA PROGRAMS, 1933–1936

(*Millions*)

Year	Actual Income from Sale of Hogs and Hog Products	Benefit Payments on Corn and Hogs	Total, Including Benefit Payments	Estimated without AAA Programs	Net Gain
Total	$2,619	$519	$3,138	$2,673	$465
1933	485	31 [a]	516	450	66
1934	513	159	672	490	182
1935	663	238	901	780	121
1936	958	91	1,049	953	96

Source: Unpublished Bureau of Agricultural Economics manuscript.

a. Value of government purchases of pigs and sows.

An estimate published by the Agricultural Adjustment Administration in 1939 gives over-all figures for the corn and hog program which are not wholly in accord with the figures given above. However, the two do not differ greatly. (See Table 32.)

The decision of the Supreme Court in the Hoosac Mills case ended the corn-hog program as originally set up, except for carrying out commitments already made. The Congress appropriated funds from the Treasury for meeting obligations already incurred but did not thereafter authorize programs relating directly to hogs and pork until World War II. From 1936 on, efforts to aid the producers of corn and hogs were mostly in the form of price supports and other measures for corn rather than under a joint program of the 1933–1936 type. Actions taken in respect to corn did, of course, have collateral effects on hog production and prices, but in ways that varied somewhat from period to period. The maintenance of higher than free-market prices on corn in some seasons no doubt had a tendency to hold down hog production. At other times, as in World War II, the release of government-held corn made it feasible and profitable to increase hog production.

EMERGENCY PURCHASE OF CATTLE AND SHEEP

Other government expenditures to aid livestock producers were made during the middle 1930s but do not appear in the Department of Agri-

TABLE 32

CORN AND HOGS: ESTIMATED CHANGES IN TOTAL CASH INCOME OF PRODUCERS RESULTING FROM AAA PROGRAMS, 1933–1936

(*Millions*)

Total benefit payments on corn and hogs	$519 [a]
Net tax collections on corn and hogs	260
Net governments payments	$259
Estimated amount of hog processing tax absorbed by farmers	$239
Total collections less absorption by farmers	$21
Gain to farmers because of changes in hog supplies caused by AAA [b]	185
Gain to farmers in cash income from sale of corn for industrial uses resulting from AAA loans, production control, etc.	27
Net government payments	259
Total gain	$492

Source: U.S. Agricultural Adjustment Administration, *Agricultural Adjustment, 1937–1938*, p. 145.

a. Includes payments for purchases of pigs and sows in August and September 1933.
b. Primarily on account of surplus purchases.

culture's over-all summary of the cost of farm programs. These related programs were undertaken as emergency operations under special appropriations, not, in the main, as parts of the continuing farm program. The principal activity of that kind was the emergency purchase of cattle and sheep, which came about as a result of the extremely severe droughts of the 1934–1936 period. Though designed partly as a means of preventing starvation of animals that could not be carried on the drought-depleted ranges, the program also served to bring cattle and sheep numbers into better balance with available market outlets.

Slaughter supplies of cattle and calves did not appear to be excessive in 1929–1933 but production was increasing. However, in 1932, cattle prices dropped to less than half and by 1933 were down to about a third the 1929 level.[32] The low level of prices together with relatively abundant feed supplies tended to encourage withholding from the market so long as the feed situation was favorable. The number of cattle on farms at the beginning of 1934 was the largest on record and a third more than at the low point of the cattle cycle in 1928.

Cattle were not included in the list of basic commodities in the Agricultural Adjustment Act of 1933. Many influential members of the cattle industry were opposed to a program for cattle similar to that provided

32. *Agricultural Statistics, 1937*, p. 251.

for hogs. However, with ranges overstocked and with drought conditions beginning to develop in 1933, there came to be more interest in some type of program for cattle. There was an attempt to develop a marketing agreement with the packers but that did not materialize. Proposals for a production control program similar to that for hogs were rejected as impractical.

Consequently, the problem was approached in a somewhat different way. Through an amendment to the Agricultural Adjustment Act approved on April 7, 1934,[33] beef cattle were added to the list of basic commodities and an appropriation of $200 million was authorized for programs designed to reduce the number of cattle on farms and ranches. The act also provided $50 million for purchase of dairy and beef products for distribution to people on relief and for making payments to encourage the elimination of cattle affected by tuberculosis and brucellosis.

The range areas were severely affected by drought throughout 1934 and there was much concern over the fate of millions of head of cattle and sheep that were dependent on them. Since conditions in the country generally were also very depressed, the Congress appropriated an unprecedentedly large fund for use by the President in providing emergency relief of various kinds. Among its provisions was one for drought relief in the agricultural areas. Part of that fund, in addition to funds made available under the Jones-Connally Act, was used in the effort to relieve both human and animal distress in the range areas. The procedure, so far as beef cattle, sheep and goats were concerned, was to buy up animals in the areas where feed supplies were not sufficient to maintain them or finish them for market. Many thousands of head already were dying from starvation.

Purchases Made and Effects of the Program

Cattle buying was begun in June 1934 and was continued until January 1935. Purchase payments ranged from $1 to $14 per head. They were supplemented by benefit payments of $3 to $6 per head. Many of the animals purchased were in the last stages of starvation and were destroyed. Some were moved to other areas where feed was more plentiful.

Cattle purchases amounted to 8.3 million head. The total amount spent for cattle, sheep and goats, but mostly for cattle, amounted to about $120 million (through December 31, 1935). Expenditures for cattle were just under $112 million.[34] The number thus taken over constituted about 30 per cent of the cattle inventories on the farms affected.[35] Though the prices paid were extremely low, the funds thus

33. The Jones-Connally Cattle Act.

34. The number of sheep purchased was 3.6 million head and the number of goats 350,000. The cost for the two combined was about $8 million.

35. U.S. Agricultural Adjustment Administration, *Agricultural Adjustment, 1933–1935*, pp. 66–67.

channeled into the range areas provided important relief to the hard-pressed ranchers and enabled many of them to hang on when they would otherwise have been forced out of business. Many of the cattle sold to the government would not have been marketed at all if not taken over in that way.

The over-all situation in the cattle industry was improved as a result of the operation, though conditions in a large part of the livestock industry still were desperate. The government purchases, together with 1934 commercial marketings, reduced the number of dairy cattle and calves by 2.2 million, about 6 per cent, and the number of beef cattle by 5.5 million, or 17 per cent.[36] The number of cattle on farms was reduced from 74 million head at the beginning of 1934 to 69 million at the beginning of 1935, thus bringing about a better balance between animal numbers and feed supplies than had existed a year earlier. There was also some improvement in the quality of breeding herds and a slight increase in the value of the cattle left on farms.

Additional Purchases Made in 1936

Heavy marketings in the early months of 1936 again threatened to depress prices severely from the higher levels they had attained in 1935. Slaughter in the first six months of 1936 was larger than in any year for which records were available. A program was developed in July to authorize purchase of a maximum of 165,000 head at a cost not to exceed $5 million.[37] Its purpose was to prevent demoralization of the market as a result of heavy receipts of drought-area cattle, by keeping the prices of common cutter and low cutter grades from going below a $2.75–$3.50 range at St. Paul, or comparable prices at other markets.

Apparently, the announcement of the program added some strength to the market, but the operation was too small to be of much significance. Purchases were made in August and September but the number bought was less than 4,000 head and the total cost only $108,000. The program was supplemented by measures designed to redistribute livestock in a way that would make best use of such amounts of roughage as were available. That apparently eased somewhat the pressure to sell drought-area livestock in the very depressed market then existing.

Purchases of Sheep and Lambs

Sheep numbers and lamb slaughter also increased rapidly between 1928 and 1932. The number on farms reached record levels by the end

36. The program included purchase of dairy cattle infected with tuberculosis and Bang's disease as well as the drought relief purchases in the range areas. The disease control phase was an expansion and speeding up of a longer-term, continuing program that had been under way for some years.

37. The funds used were allocated from money made available under Section 32 of the Agricultural Adjustment Act as amended. (See U.S. Agricultural Adjustment Administration, *Agricultural Conservation, 1936,* p. 91.)

of 1934. The drought threatened loss of many of them. Consequently, they, too, were included in the purchase program. From mid-August through December 1934, the Adjustment Administration bought 3.6 million head in the states west of the Mississippi. This figure probably includes a considerable number that would otherwise have been marketed through commercial channels. However, without the purchase program there would no doubt have been some increase in commercial marketings of distress sheep and many would have died from lack of feed and water. The number of stock sheep and lambs on farms was reduced from 48 million at the beginning of 1934 to 46 million at the end of the year. Federal expenditures amounted to about $7 million. Returns to growers were probably increased by at least a similar amount.

The over-all result of economic forces, drought and the government programs was to reduce the number of grain-consuming animal units fed annually from 159 million in 1932 to 131 million in 1934,[38] a reduction of 18 per cent. The supply of concentrate feeds declined from about 115 million tons in 1933 to 82 million in 1934, a drop of 29 per cent. In addition, pasture and forage resources were greatly reduced. Most of the reduction was caused by drought. However, the government programs helped somewhat in conserving livestock that would have been lost. Since there was some increased carry-over of corn from 1933 to 1934 as a result of government programs, total livestock production for the years 1934 and 1935 probably was not much below what it would have been without the programs. Returns to farmers were apparently increased by about the amount put in by the government.

Livestock under the Acts of 1936 and 1938

No special provision was made for aid to livestock growers in the Soil Conservation and Domestic Allotment Act of 1936. The actions described above with respect to the 1933–1935 seasons therefore marked the end of efforts to aid livestock producers directly until the beginning of World War II. However, the conservation and crop adjustment programs did have a bearing on the livestock situation.

That was recognized in the Agricultural Adjustment Act of 1938 and subsequent amendments. In administering the programs, the uses to which land withheld from soil-depleting crops could be put were to be restricted. Acres rented, and the soil-conserving crops grown, were not to be used to increase livestock production to such an extent as to create a "surplus." Producers of crops subject to marketing quotas were enjoined from feeding the excess over quotas in such a way as to increase the marketings of livestock products. Such provisions are, of course, extremely difficult if not impossible to enforce.

38. U.S. Agricultural Marketing Service, *Grain and Feed Statistics through 1954*, Statistical Bulletin 159, March 1955, p. 2.

Hog prices were relatively high in 1936–1939 (about the 1929 level) but declined in 1940 and 1941 to levels that made the corn-hog ratio unfavorable to hog producers.[39] Beginning in 1939, purchases of hog products for relief and for the food stamp program gave some support to the market. Such purchases were continued through fiscal 1942 and amounted in total to about $71 million. Increasing employment after the outbreak of war in Europe also added some strength to the hog market even before the United States became directly involved in the war.

CORN IN THE 1936–1942 PROGRAMS

The Supreme Court's decision in the Hoosac Mills case made continuance of the earlier program in respect to corn and hogs impossible. For some years thereafter, the efforts to deal with the feed grain and livestock problem were confined almost wholly to operations relating to corn. The soil conservation and domestic allotment program, which almost immediately took the place of the agricultural adjustment program, called for reduction in the acreage of crops classified as "soil-depleting."

Corn was classed as a "soil-depleting" crop and the program therefore called for a reduction in the acreage grown. Corn was included in a "general crops" program without a separate system of payments such as those provided for cotton and tobacco. Growers were offered opportunity to participate in a general conservation program under which payments would be made on acres withdrawn from soil-depleting, cash crops and for adopting specified soil-improving practices. The requirement was that at least 20 per cent of the "soil-depleting base" for the farm be given over to soil-building crops and soil-building practices.

Despite this effort to shift production away from corn and into hay and forage crops, the acreage planted to corn in 1936 was 2 per cent larger than that of 1935. However, another severe drought reduced production to about the 1934 level. Not only was there no excess of corn, but livestock feed supplies as a whole were seriously deficient. Stocks on farms as of January 1, 1937 were even lower than those of January 1, 1935 and nearly three quarters of a billion bushels below what might be considered normal. CCC offered loans at 55 cents per bushel, with no condition attached as to the acreage that could be

39. The January 1 farm value per head in the years 1925–1941 was as follows:

1925	$13.15	1931	$11.35	1937	$11.89
1926	15.66	1932	6.13	1938	11.26
1927	17.19	1933	4.21	1939	11.18
1928	13.17	1934	4.09	1940	7.78
1929	12.93	1935	6.31	1941	8.34
1930	13.45	1936	12.71		

(*Agricultural Statistics, 1937,* p. 257, and *1951,* p. 340.)

The January 1 number of head on farms stood at 62 million in 1933, about the same as the high level of 1928. It declined to 39 million in 1935 and increased again to 61 million in 1940.

planted in 1937. Corn prices were much above the loan level, so the offer of loans had no effect on prices.

Corn Plantings Lower in 1937

Though corn prices were high in 1936 (approximately $1 per bushel) and there were no restraints on production in 1937, a smaller acreage was planted in the spring of 1937 than in 1936.[40] The reason lay in the relaxation of controls on wheat and cotton and the relatively high prices for those crops. There was some shift of acreage from corn to cotton in the South, and from corn to wheat along the western edge of the Corn Belt.

The Adjustment Administration had worked out a more definite soil conservation plan for the corn areas than was available in 1936. It proposed planting about 94 million acres, which, with average yields, would produce about 2.3 million bushels. That was thought to be enough to supply feeding requirements and leave a reasonably large carry-over at the end of the 1937 crop year. However, the larger acreage planted and favorable growing conditions brought production up to 2.64 billion bushels, the largest since 1932. The end-of-season carry-over was about 300 million bushels larger than the very small one of 1936 (66 million bushels).[41]

The large crop in prospect caused corn prices at the farm to recede from $1.21 in May to 59 cents in October.[42] A CCC loan of 50 cents (about 59 per cent of parity) was offered. Demand was also strengthened somewhat by a short corn crop in Argentina, which made it possible to export 138 million bushels, a much larger amount than usual. Prices stabilized at about the loan level, averaging 52 cents for the season. Approximately 47 million bushels were put under loan, of which about 45 million were owned by CCC or under loan to it at the end of the season.[43] Most of it was repledged under the 1938 loan program at 57 cents.

Corn under the 1938 Act

The Agricultural Adjustment Act of 1938 contained several provisions relating specifically to corn. It was again included in the list of basic commodities and annual acreage allotments and marketing quotas were authorized under specified conditions. CCC loans were not only authorized but were made mandatory in the "commercial" corn areas if prices were below 75 per cent of parity or if the November estimate of production exceeded a normal year's domestic consumption and exports. A schedule of loan rates was written into the act.

40. 97 million acres as compared with 102 million in 1936.
41. *Agricultural Statistics, 1945,* p. 45.
42. *Grain and Feed Statistics through 1954,* p. 39.
43. *Ibid.,* p. 46.

The 1938 act opened the way for comparatively rigorous controls on production in the areas defined as "commercial" corn areas, that is, primarily in the Corn Belt. Price supports were to be in a prescribed relation to parity,[44] depending on the supply in prospect as related to the legislatively defined "normal" supply. However, the rigorousness of the control over production was more apparent than real. Growers who did not keep within their acreage allotments and the marketing quotas assigned could be deprived of CCC loans and conservation payments but could not practically be prevented from growing larger acreages for home use. Since a very large part of the corn crop is fed on the farms where grown, acreage controls on corn have never been very effective.

The program for 1938, as developed by the Adjustment Administration, contemplated some further reduction in the acreage planted. Allotments were assigned in the "commercial" corn areas and the total acreage planted was reduced from 97 million to about 94.5 million. However, a favorable season again brought a large crop of 2.5 billion bushels. A CCC loan rate of 57 cents was announced. Prices dropped below the loan rate and some 230 million bushels, about 9 per cent of the crop, were put under loan. CCC held at the beginning of the season about 45 million bushels from the 1937 crop and the added stocks taken over from the 1938 crop resulted in CCC holdings of 258 million bushels at the beginning of the 1939 season, nearly half the total U.S. stocks, which amounted to 588 million bushels. This was the beginning of a series of extensive support operations that extended into the war period.

High Production on Reduced Acreage, 1939–1941

Efforts to reduce corn acreage were continued in 1939, 1940 and 1941 and were moderately successful so far as acreage was concerned. The 1939 planted acreage was down to 92 million, that of 1940 to 89 million and that of 1941 to 87 million. However, yields began to increase in 1939 and by 1941 were well above those of the early 1930s. A major technological change in the corn industry was occurring at a very rapid rate. The use of hybrid seed corn, one of the most important biological improvements in the history of corn production, was raising yields to an extent that more than offset the reductions in acreage. The use of hybrid seed had been started around 1930 and by the end of the decade had spread to nearly all farms in the Corn Belt. The 1941 crop (2.7 billion bushels), grown on 87 million acres, was slightly larger than the 1937 crop grown on 97 million acres.

The CCC corn support level was continued at 57 cents (70 per cent

44. That was a significant change from the provisions applicable in earlier years when the Secretary of Agriculture could set the loan rate at such level as he deemed feasible and desirable. It was the beginning of the increasingly rigid requirements as to loan rates that were to come later.

of parity) in 1939 and some 302 million bushels were put under loan. By the end of the season, CCC was holding a record stock of 471 million bushels, about two thirds of the total U.S. stocks, which were large. Commercial holdings declined from 326 million in October 1939 to 217 million in October 1940. The season average price was 56.8 cents, almost exactly the support level. The price would undoubtedly have gone much lower if price supports had not been available.

The number of horses and mules to be fed continued to decline, but the increase in numbers of hogs and cattle more than offset this reduction. However, even with an increase in consumption by meat animals, over-all demand was not sufficient to absorb the large crops produced in the 1938 and 1939 seasons. End-of-season stocks reached all-time highs in those years.

Despite the heavy accumulation of CCC holdings, the loan rate for 1940 was raised to 61 cents (75 per cent of parity).[45] Production was nearly as large as in 1939 but the market was showing more strength. Only 103 million bushels went under loan, as compared with 302 million in the preceding year. CCC holdings as of October 1941 were somewhat smaller than a year earlier (403 million bushels as compared with 471 million). The season average price to farmers was 61.8 cents, just over the support level.

Loan Policies and Their Effects, 1938–1941

Most of the corn put under loan in the 1937 season at 50 cents was continued under loan in 1938 at 57 cents. Some if it was carried through to 1940 when producers were offered opportunity to redeem it at 58 cents or turn it over to the Corporation. Most of it was delivered to the Corporation, with a resulting loss to CCC of 9 cents per bushel in investment costs and carrying charges.

Much of the larger quantity put under loan from the 1938 crop also was carried over until the outbreak of war in Europe. Farmers were given the option of redeeming it on October 1, 1940 at less than the investment in it but were also offered the alternative of resealing it for two more years with the privilege of redeeming it under specified conditions within that period. A considerable amount of corn from the 1939 crop was put under loan but about half of it was redeemed. However, the additions to carry-over raised the October 1940 holdings and commitments of CCC to the record 471 million bushels mentioned above.

When war broke out in Europe, industrial activity increased in the

45. The schedule of loan rates prescribed in the Agricultural Adjustment Act of 1938 was from 52 per cent of parity (if the supply was more than 125 per cent of normal) to 75 per cent if the price of corn was below 75 per cent of parity and if estimated supply was not more than a normal year's consumption and exports. Under the discretionary arrangement, in effect from 1933 to 1937, the range had been from 55 to 66 per cent of parity. Legislation passed in the spring of 1941 required that the loan rate be further increased, to 85 per cent of parity (75 cents per bushel).

United States and there was some pickup in the demand for livestock products. In that period, the heavy stocks of corn held by CCC acted as a brake on what would no doubt otherwise have been a more rapid increase in corn prices. Prices moved up moderately in the spring and summer of 1941 and reached 70.8 cents by September (as compared with 61.9 cents a year earlier and 56.2 cents in September 1939).[46] The 61-cent loan rate (at 75 per cent of parity) was not high enough to affect the situation importantly. A smaller quantity of 1940 corn was put under loan and most of it was redeemed within the season.

With prices rising generally and the demand for livestock increasing, corn prices for the 1941 crop continued to move up and reached 86 cents in July 1942, but with a big 1942 crop in prospect they eased off in the fall months. The loan rate for the 1941 crop had been put at 85 per cent of parity (75 cents per bushel) as required by law. However, demand was strong enough to absorb all of the moderate-sized 1941 crop and liquidate some of the stocks acquired under the 1938 and 1939 programs.

Total stocks, and CCC holdings as well, were at their peak (688 million bushels for the two combined) in October 1939. They were reduced slightly (to 645 million) in 1940 and were down to 491 million in October 1942. Somewhat more than half of the CCC holdings and commitments had been liquidated by the fall of 1942 and almost all of them by the fall of 1943.[47]

Demand Strong in 1942

For the 1942 season, demand was strong enough to absorb all of the new crop of more than 3 billion bushels and to make further liquidation of stocks possible. CCC holdings were down to only 8 million bushels by October 1943, but that was due partly to larger private holdings. Privately held stocks increased from 242 million bushels in October 1941 to 376 million in October 1943. Total stocks in October 1943 were only about 300 million bushels below the peak level of October 1940, but there had been a pronounced shift from government to private ownership of the stocks held. The rise in the general price level put the 85 per cent of parity loan rate for the 1942 season at 83 cents per bushel, but only 56 million bushels were put under loan as the price

46. *Grain and Feed Statistics through 1954,* p. 39.

47. *Ibid.,* p. 46. CCC holdings and commitments and total stocks at the end of the season, that is, as of October 1 of the following year, were as follows (in millions of bushels):

Crop Year	*CCC Holdings and Commitments*	*Total Stocks*
1938	257.8	583.7
1939	471.1	687.6
1940	403.0	644.7
1941	196.6	490.7
1942	8.3	384.1

in the market was above the loan rate. Producers were required to redeem or deliver the corn held under loan by a specified date in 1943, and by the end of the 1942 marketing season CCC had liquidated substantially all of its holdings and commitments without loss.

This, of course, was not a normal outcome for that type of operation. It was due to the war-induced advance in prices. However, the CCC operations did help to stabilize prices in the 1938, 1939 and 1940 seasons and, as it turned out, provided a very useful backlog of feed supplies. Without the increase in demand that grew out of the war, the stocks held would undoubtedly have resulted in sizable losses.

If demand had continued weak, the level of price support would probably have been kept at 70 per cent of parity or below and production might have been kept lower than it was, though the rapidly increasing yield might have kept it above desired amounts. There is not much evidence that acreage allotments and marketing quotas would have been successful in holding production down, since it is difficult to make them effective for a feed crop that is used mainly on the farms where it is grown. CCC's actual losses for the period as a whole were, for the reasons given, very moderate, about $20 million, mostly on corn carried over from the 1937 crop.[48]

THE FEED GRAINS IN THE WAR PERIOD

During the 1937 and 1938 seasons, hog production was increasing as a result of the favorable hog-corn price ratio of that period, but hog prices were declining as is usual in such situations. They continued to decline in 1939 and 1940. The price of corn advanced and the corn-hog ratio became unfavorable to hog producers. However, increased employment and the inauguration of the lend-lease program in 1941 strengthened the demand for pork products and re-established a corn-hog ratio that was favorable to hog production. There was more active demand for corn and accumulated supplies began to be reduced.

In view of the need for increased production of livestock products, the Department of Agriculture undertook to encourage expansion, particularly of pork and lard. Corn was to be made available from government stocks at prices that would make hog production attractive, even though that might involve some loss on government-held stocks.[49] An-

48. Though it is evident that much of the success of the corn operation of 1937–1941 was a result of an unforeseeable development, namely, the outbreak of war, the experience does emphasize the fact that large and unpredictable needs do arise from time to time as a result of droughts, wars and other disasters. That suggests a need for larger reserve stocks than will normally be carried by the trade and a warrant for an outlay of funds to implement some type of "prudent reserve" operation, especially in times of disturbed and unsettled world conditions. However, if such accumulations come into being merely as a result of price-support operations, they may become unwieldy and socially undesirable or may even be too small in critical periods.

49. Corn was sold at somewhat less than book value and, though market prices were advancing, the government took a loss of $10 to $15 million. That was, in essence, a first step in the subsidization of food production.

nouncement was also made that loans would be called on wheat, and that up to 100 million bushels of wheat would be sold at feed prices (about the price of corn) as a means of encouraging livestock production. That program was later expanded by direction of the Congress, and the feeding of wheat to livestock, much of it at subsidized prices, reached a total of nearly a billion and a half bushels for the war period as a whole. Normal feed use would have been in the order of 500 million bushels for the four-year period.

The continuance of an 85 per cent of parity support price on corn in the 1942 season, rather than at 90 per cent, was due to specific action by the President, in accordance with legislation that authorized him to set a rate of less than 90 per cent of parity if that was deemed necessary in order to prevent an increase in the cost of feed for livestock. The rate was continued at 85 per cent in 1943 but was raised to 90 per cent in 1944. The actual support rates were 83 cents in 1942 and 90 cents in 1943. Prices received by farmers were almost continuously above support levels from 1941 on and only negligible amounts were put under loan. Almost none of the crop passed into CCC hands from 1941 to 1948.

Ceilings were imposed on corn prices in January 1943, at 100 per cent of parity ($1.05 per bushel). That tended to discourage speculative holding of corn for further price advances. Before the end of the season a serious shortage of corn for feed developed. Such loans on corn as were still outstanding were called in order to increase the supplies available to livestock producers. Hog production had been increased greatly between 1941 and 1943. Slaughter in the 1943 season was 40 per cent above that of 1941 (73 million head as compared with 52 million).[50] Pork became so plentiful that it was taken off rationing for a time in the 1943–44 season.

Corn Program Modified in 1943

Some further changes were made in the corn program in the 1943 season. There was a shift from emphasis on production control to encouragement of increased output. The conditions for obtaining loans were changed from a requirement that plantings be kept within allotments to one that the farmer plant up to at least 90 per cent of the production goal set for his farm. The advance in prices had eliminated the conditions under which parity and conservation payments could be made.

The supply of corn became so short by the end of the season that special measures were taken to meet the needs of corn processors, and the corn-hog ratio had become so favorable to hog producers that extensive black marketing developed. The measures taken to meet the

50. *Agricultural Statistics, 1951*, p. 349.

needs of processors included set-aside orders directing elevators to sell to designated purchasers, requirements that elevators in some areas sell to the government and the refund of import duties on corn brought in from Argentina. In the meantime production remained at about the 3-billion-bushel level, but that was not sufficient to meet the greatly expanded demand.

As a consequence, the loan rate was increased to 90 per cent of parity in 1944 and remained at that level through the war and postwar years. The support rate in 1944 was 98 cents per bushel. However, only a small amount of corn was put under loan and all of it was redeemed. Purchases at ceiling prices were authorized when necessary to cover lend-lease and other government requirements. The higher prices for corn had resulted in about a 10 per cent increase in acreage between 1941 and 1944 but the 3-billion-bushel crop of 1944 was about the same as that of 1942. Acreage fell off again in 1945 and continued to decline throughout the remainder of the decade except for a small increase in 1949.[51]

The efforts to increase production of other crops, especially soybeans, and the scarcity and increased cost of labor contributed to reduced plantings in the 1945 season. Also, price ceilings kept corn prices at a level that tended to discourage plantings. The need for corn became so urgent that farmers were offered a bonus of 30 cents per bushel above ceiling prices for deliveries made to the Commodity Credit Corporation. In this way the Corporation obtained about 34 million bushels. Only small amounts of corn were put under loan and all of it was redeemed.

In the last years of the war, the great demand for livestock and the large amount of it produced not only absorbed all of the accumulated stocks of corn but also huge quantities of wheat, a large volume of grain imported from Canada and increased quantities of by-product feeds.

LIVESTOCK IN THE WAR YEARS

During the war years, there was an enormous expansion in the demand for livestock products, especially meats. Part of it stemmed from the large purchases of pork and lard made through lend-lease, but the greater part grew out of increased employment in the United States, higher buying power, more strenuous physical exertion and the large

51. Acreages and production in these years were as follows:

Year	*Acres Planted (Millions)*	*Production (Billion Bushels)*	*Year*	*Acres Planted (Millions)*	*Production (Billion Bushels)*
1939	91.6	2.6	1945	89.3	2.9
1940	88.7	2.5	1946	88.9	3.2
1941	86.8	2.7	1947	85.0	2.4
1942	88.8	3.0	1948	85.5	3.6
1943	94.3	3.0	1949	86.7	3.2
1944	95.5	3.0	1950	82.7	3.0

(*Agricultural Statistics, 1953*, p. 31.)

needs of the U.S. armed services. The demand was held in check to some extent by rationing, but prices were also held down by price controls and consumer subsidies. However, meat was a key item throughout the war and the tendency for producers and handlers to make black-market sales was difficult to control.

The heavy stockpile of feed grains carried into the war proved an important war asset and would have been even more vital had production conditions turned out to be unfavorable, as they were in World War I. The maintenance of support prices on corn in the late 1930s, without corresponding supports or controls on hogs, shifted the balance strongly toward corn production and against hog production.

The normal average relationship between hog and corn prices is in the order of a value per hundredweight for live hogs that is some 11 to 13 times the value of a bushel of corn. In 1938, the ratio was 16 to 1, which was very favorable to hog producers, but it dropped off to 13.3 in 1939 and was down to 9.2 in 1940.[52] That unfavorable relationship, largely a result of the support price on corn, caused hog producers to cut back on pig production. The number of pigs saved in 1939 was 87 million, which was a larger pig crop than the big ones of 1931–1933, but the number was cut back to about 80 million in 1940.

The spring crop of 1941 was about the same as that of 1940, but a strong appeal was made for a larger fall crop. The Secretary of Agriculture announced, in the spring of 1941, that the prices of hogs, dairy products, chickens and eggs would be supported at prices substantially higher than those then prevailing. The fall pig crop was increased by more than 5 million, thus bringing the year's total up to 85 million head. A reduction in the number farrowed had been indicated by the low 1940 corn-hog ratio and was confidently expected until the government stepped in with its promise of higher prices.[53]

Supports under Wartime Legislation

Since the Secretary of Agriculture had asked for an increase in hog production, price support at 85 per cent of parity was authorized automatically, from July 1, 1941 on, in accordance with the provisions of the Steagall Amendment. Subsequently, in 1942, the support level for Steagall commodities was raised to 90 per cent of parity and continuing support for two years following the close of hostilities was promised.

52. *Agricultural Statistics, 1945*, p. 46.

53. The price at Chicago was $7.60 in March 1941, when lend-lease purchases were begun, and had been below $5 at the farm earlier in the spring. The support price of $9.00, at Chicago, was announced in April, too late to affect the spring pig crop but early enough to have a very significant effect on the fall crop. The procedure to be used, if needed, was government purchase of pork and lard. As of that time, and through the war years, an outlet was available by way of lend-lease for almost any quantity the government might have occasion to buy in its price-support operations.

In the meantime, steps had been taken to make feed grains available at attractive prices as described above.

With feed abundant and low in price, hog production was stepped up very rapidly. The number of pigs saved increased from 85 million in 1941 to 105 million in 1942, and to 122 million in 1943. Heavy feeding made the increase in pork production even larger.[54] By 1943, pork production had expanded so much that no further increase seemed desirable. The feed stockpile was being pulled down rapidly and both the government and the processors were faced with the problem of how to use effectively the huge volumes of pork that were entering the market.

Prices began to weaken and fell below the ceilings in the latter part of 1943 and through most of 1944. As a result, farmers cut back farrowings about 25 per cent in 1944. The number of pigs saved dropped from 122 million to 87 million. Prices advanced beyond the ceiling level and costs to consumers were held down by means of government subsidies until decontrol after the close of the war.[55] Pig production remained about the same in 1945 as in 1944 but fell off to about 83 million head in 1946, largely as a result of rising prices and greater scarcity of feed supplies.

Subsidies designed to keep down the price of meats to consumers had been initiated in 1943. Beginning in June, prices were rolled back about 3 cents per pound at retail and about 2 cents at wholesale. The subsidies were paid to slaughterers so as to enable them to buy hogs, cattle, sheep and lambs at the prices prevailing in the market and sell them at the ceiling prices for meat. Later, in 1945, subsidies were also paid to feeders of cattle, sheep and lambs to encourage maintenance of production under the price controls then being maintained. They were administered through the packers, in conjunction with the subsidies being paid to them.

The consumer subsidies were paid by the Reconstruction Finance Corporation. Payments to slaughterers from June 1943 to the end of the control period amounted to $1,548 million. The direct subsidy to cattle feeders in 1945 and 1946 was about $40 million and to sheep and lamb feeders and producers about $43 million.

54. The 1942 pig crop was still considered inadequate to meet the rapidly rising requirements. The Secretary of Agriculture asked for a 15 per cent increase in the 1943 pig crop and, in the spring of 1943, promised to support the price, at Chicago, at $13.75 per hundredweight. He also undertook to assure farmers that ceiling prices on live hogs would not be imposed at a level that would discourage hog production. The actual increase was a little over 16 per cent.

55. Price ceilings were imposed on live hogs in October 1943 and were reduced moderately, for heavy hogs, in May 1944. The reduced ceiling on heavy hogs was intended to discourage heavy feeding since the corn situation was tight. Later in 1944, the support level was also reduced, with a view to encouraging a better adjustment of hog numbers to feed supplies. That action apparently had no significant effect on either production or prices as the price in the market was again pressing against ceilings. Some purchases were made in early 1944 in order to make good on price-support promises, but with the sharp reduction in pig numbers prices did not again decline to the support level.

DEVELOPMENTS IN THE POSTWAR YEARS

Hog production in the first postwar years was only moderately larger than at the beginning of the war but demand was much stronger. Prices moved up sharply after decontrol and were well above support levels until 1948. The average cost to packers at Chicago, per hundredweight, in the 1945–46 season was $15.73. In 1946–47, it was $23.58 and in 1947–48, it reached $24.08.[56] However, the corn-hog ratio was not markedly favorable to hog production since corn, wheat and other feed grains were scarce and high in price.

Price supports were continued at 90 per cent of parity in the years 1946 through 1949 but no support operations were required as prices were mostly well above the support levels.[57] The price declined in 1949, to $17.44 as a season average. Other goods were by then becoming more readily available and consumers were tending to shift more of their spending to nonfood items. Exports of pork declined sharply after the close of the war but stabilized at a lower level after 1946. Lard exports fell off in the 1946–1948 period but rose again to about the wartime level in 1949. They were also high in 1951 and 1952.

The price of hogs advanced moderately in 1951 but dropped again in 1952, to about the 1950 level. Another upswing carried hog prices to a new high of $25.70 per hundredweight in May 1954, but there was a sharp decline thereafter as the large 1954 hog crop began to come on the market. The price was down to $17 at the farm in December and January 1954–55.[58] By August and September 1955, the farm price had fallen to $15.70 (about 75 per cent of parity). Price-supporting purchases were being considered by the Department of Agriculture to check the decline and ease the situation until readjustments could be made.

A notable feature of the hog situation throughout the period here described is the speed with which adjustments were made to changes in the corn-hog price ratio and the very large variations in numbers of pigs raised. This does not mean necessarily that an increase in pig production occurs in response to a high price for pork or vice versa. If corn and other feeds are high in price, hog production may not expand, even though hog prices are high. The high hog prices of 1947 and 1948 brought only moderate increases in the numbers of pigs produced. In like manner, low prices for corn may result in large production of hogs even though the joint return from the two is much below what farmers regard as satisfactory.

56. *Agricultural Statistics, 1951,* p. 351.

57. The support level, Chicago basis, was $13.60 to $15.60 in 1946–47 (depending on season); $16.10 to $16.90 in 1947–48; $16.80 to $17.00 in 1948–49 and $16.40 in 1950. (U.S. Production and Marketing Administration, *CCC Price Support Statistical Handbook,* 1952, p. 47.)

58. *Agricultural Prices,* January 28, 1955, pp. 4, 5.

Cattle Numbers Greatly Increased

The number of cattle other than milk cows increased steadily during the war years. January 1 numbers moved up from 43 million in 1940 to about 58 million in 1945. A rather heavy liquidation in the years 1945–1948 tended to hold prices in check for a time after the removal of controls. Beef prices did not advance as rapidly as hog prices. However, by 1948 the price of beef steers at Chicago was nearly twice the 1945 price and almost three times the 1941 price.[59]

A sharp drop in prices in 1949 caused a good deal of concern to cattle growers. However, it was actually a readjustment from the very high 1948 level to a more normal relationship to the prices of other farm products. Even after the severe decline of 1949, beef cattle prices were at 115 per cent of parity as of January 15, 1950, a parity ratio that was above that of any of the other farm products except tobacco, lemons, veal calves and lambs.[60]

Prices moved up again in 1950 and 1951 to all-time highs. The average cost to slaughterers for cattle and calves in 1951 was $31.88 per hundredweight as compared with $24.32 in 1948.[61] Even with parity computed by the revised formula, beef cattle stood at 146 per cent of parity in July 1951, a level exceeded only by wool, which stood at 157 per cent of parity.[62]

From 1952 on, there was heavy liquidation of the overlarge beef cattle inventory, partly as a result of droughts in the southern range areas. Prices fell drastically and by December 1953 were down to $14.80 per hundredweight at the farm, only 70 per cent of the revised parity level.[63] There was some recovery in 1954 and 1955 and by June 1955 the price to farmers was $16.50, 77 per cent of parity as then computed.[64]

With beef cattle prices at all-time highs and much higher relatively than most other farm products during most of the first decade following the war, there was not much demand for government programs relating to them, except in drought areas and in the period of severe price decline

59. Average prices per hundred pounds for all grades of beef steers at Chicago in these years were as follows:

Year	Price	Year	Price
1941	$11.33	1946	$19.16
1942	13.79	1947	25.83
1943	15.30	1948	30.88
1944	15.44	1949	25.80
1945	16.18	1950	29.35

(*Agricultural Statistics, 1951,* p. 338.)

60. *Agricultural Prices,* January 31, 1950, pp. 4, 5. That was in terms of the revised or "modernized" parity, which gave beef cattle a parity price about 25 per cent higher than it would have been under the "old" formula.

61. *Agricultural Statistics, 1953,* p. 347. Figure given is for all cattle and calves slaughtered under federal inspection.

62. *Agricultural Prices,* July 29, 1952, p. 5.

63. *Ibid.,* December 30, 1953, p. 5.

64. *Ibid.,* June 30, 1955, pp. 4, 5.

of 1952–1953. Some minor beef purchase and drought relief programs were carried out but no national beef cattle program was undertaken, or in fact urged by the more influential groups in the cattle-producing areas. The beef cattle groups have in general tended to prefer self-directed readjustment rather than large-scale government programs, except in times of acute emergency.

Sheep numbers declined drastically during and after the war and lamb supplies were reduced accordingly. Since the wool program, in which lambs were a by-product, is described in Chapter 8, it is not discussed here. In general, lamb prices tended to follow about the same pattern as beef cattle prices.

The high level of employment and consumer income led to a markedly higher per capita consumption of meats, particularly of beef, in the postwar years. The per capita consumption of beef in the 1948–1952 period reached 69 pounds, as compared with 63 pounds in 1935–1939. By 1953, it was expected to reach or exceed the record high of 73 pounds set in 1909.[65] That was due in part, however, to a reduction of some 10 pounds per capita in the amount of pork available, as compared with the 1952 situation. The higher per capita level of meat consumption seemed to be rather well established and likely to continue if employment and earnings remained high.

THE CORN PROBLEM IN THE POSTWAR YEARS

During the postwar years, the heavy demand for meat animals, which carried their prices to all-time highs and put the index of meat-animal prices higher than that of any other group except tobacco, had, of course, a significant effect on the demand for and prices of the feed grains. However, feed grain prices did not reach the levels attained by the meat-animal group [66] since grain production had already been greatly expanded, as a result of war demands and favorable crop conditions. For some of the grains, particularly wheat, the volume of production was much above the amounts needed in a peacetime economy, unless the excess could be used in the feeding of livestock. Until 1949, the heavy demand for wheat in meeting food needs abroad took wheat out of the feed class and returned livestock producers to their normal reliance on the coarse grains. Thereafter, most of the excess production found its way into government-held stocks, instead of being used for feed as in the early years of World War II.

65. *The Livestock and Meat Situation,* May–July 1953, p. 3.

66. In 1951 meat-animal prices reached a level of 411 per cent of the 1910–1914 average. The only groups that went higher were tobacco (436 per cent) and wool (501 per cent). The average for all farm products was 302 per cent. Feed grains were at 220 per cent of the 1910–1914 level but moved up to 227 per cent in 1952. Food grains stood at 243 per cent in 1951 and 244 per cent in 1952. (*Agricultural Statistics, 1953,* p. 602.)

When the war ended, corn prices were pressing against ceilings. The large war-year crops and the stocks accumulated before the war had been used up. Stocks were low. The number of grain-consuming animals had been reduced from the high point reached in 1943 but still was larger than at the outbreak of war in Europe. In accordance with the guarantees provided in the war-period legislation, prices were to be supported at 90 per cent of parity, but that provision was of little significance as prices continued to be above support levels. No immediate action in respect to either corn or livestock appeared to be needed.

With the abandonment of price controls in 1946, the price of corn advanced rapidly, reaching $1.80 in August, as against an early-season level of $1.10 to $1.13. The increase was too late to have any significant effect on corn production and the 1946 acreage continued well below that of 1943 and 1944. However, weather conditions were favorable and the yield (36.7 bushels) was the highest of record. Production amounted to three and a quarter billion bushels, also a record high. Prices receded and by December 1946 and January 1947 were down nearly to the early 1946 level. They recovered later as weather damage made it evident that the 1947 crop would be very short. By September 1947, the price was at an all-time high of $2.40 per bushel.[67]

The support price on the 1946 crop was $1.15, but only a small amount of corn was put under loan and nearly all of it was redeemed. However, the commercial carry-over was increased (to 283 million bushels) and was larger than had been customary in the prewar years.

The high prices of the 1946 season came too late to stimulate plantings in 1947. The 1947 acreage was smaller than that of 1946. Severe droughts cut the yield to 28.4 bushels on harvested acreage,[68] nearly 25 per cent below that of 1946. Production was down to 2.4 billion bushels, the lowest since 1936. The short crop forced some reduction in livestock feeding and both corn and livestock prices reached new high yearly averages in 1948. The carry-over into the 1948 season was the lowest since 1936–37. The 1947 experience again emphasized the importance of stabilizing feed supplies from season to season as the impact of the short crop on livestock producers was very severe.

Program Modified in 1948 and 1949

The wartime commitments to provide support at 90 per cent of parity were intended as a safeguard against a sharp postwar decline of the 1920 type and as a way of providing opportunity for a review of the prewar programs to see what changes might be needed. New legislation

67. *Grain and Feed Statistics through 1954,* p. 39. Not only was U.S. demand strong but the extreme shortage of grain in Europe resulted in exports of nearly 130 million bushels of U.S. corn, the largest volume since 1937.

68. There was also a heavier abandonment than normal.

was passed in 1948 (the Agricultural Act of 1948). It amended the Agricultural Adjustment Act of 1938 in important ways but looked in general to a gradual return to a program in which there would be a good deal of flexibility and some safeguards against top-heavy accumulations of the kind that had caused difficulty in 1932 and were again shaping up at the beginning of World War II.

These revisions were contained in Title II of the 1948 act (the Senate version) and were presumably to go into effect in 1949 when the wartime commitments would have expired. However, Title I of the act (the House version), which was added to the other rather than substituted for it, postponed the effective date of Title II until 1950. Essentially, it continued the wartime support arrangements without change, so far as the basic crops were concerned.[69] Subsequent legislation continued the mandatory 90 per cent of parity support arrangement for the basic crops until 1955.

By that action, one of the most favorable opportunities for reversion to more normal marketing arrangements was passed up. As of 1948, stocks were not burdensome and the economy as a whole was so active and prosperous that a start could have been made in readjusting from the forced-draft production program of the war and early postwar years without any heavy accumulation of burdensome stocks to hamper it. The readjustment had to be undertaken later under less favorable conditions. With a promise of price supports at 90 per cent of parity, which was a very high level for the major field crops, there was almost no incentive for farmers to make a start on the complicated and difficult adjustments that are inevitable after the distortions that develop in wartime.

The most significant change made in the Agricultural Act of 1948, as compared with that of 1938, was the prescribing of a new method of computing parity prices so that changes in the relative supply and demand conditions for the different farm products could be reflected in the parity prices assigned to them.[70] The revised formula would have increased the parity prices of those products for which demand had been greatly increased and would have lowered those for products which were in less urgent demand, or where lowered costs would make it attractive to produce excess quantities if the earlier price relationships were maintained. However, the average level of parity prices for all of the farm products would not have been changed as a result of the new method of computing parities.

Thus the change specified, if price supports were readjusted accordingly, would have provided powerful incentives for farmers to make the

69. The support arrangements on the nonbasics, that is, on the Steagall commodities, were relaxed and made more flexible.

70. For a fuller explanation of this change, see *Can We Solve the Farm Problem?*, Appendix A.

kinds of adjustment in production that were most needed. The revised formula would have reduced the computed parity for corn and would have raised it for livestock products. As of June 15, 1948, the parity price of corn would have been $1.42 per bushel instead of $1.61, as it was when computed by the "old" formula. That, even with a 90 per cent of parity level of support, would have put the loan commitment on corn at $1.28 instead of $1.45. For hogs, the new formula would have increased the computed parity slightly, from $18.20 to $18.65 per hundredweight. These modifications would have changed rather significantly the results of feeding operations and would have put more of a premium on livestock products, which were the end products society was really concerned with.

Full Adoption Postponed

The new method of computing parities was not allowed to go into effect at that time and, for the basic crops, was deferred until 1956. The Agricultural Act of 1949, which superseded most parts of the act of 1948 before it could come into effect, raised the average level of parities, by providing that for the basic crops the new formula would be used for any particular crop or product if it resulted in a higher parity standard, but the old formula would be applied if use of the revised formula would yield a lower parity price.[71]

The 1948 and 1949 acts made other changes that affected the levels of price-support loans. In the Agricultural Adjustment Act of 1938, the loan rates on corn specified were to be within a range of 52–75 per cent of parity, depending on the relation of the supply available to the legislatively defined "normal" supply. In the act of 1948, this range was changed to 60–90 per cent.[72] In either case, the Secretary of Agriculture had some discretion in fixing the rate within the range.

Since the 1949 act was passed before the act of 1948 became effective, it superseded and to a large extent nullified the 1948 act, though some of the same principles were included. The method of computing parity under the old and new formulae was not changed,[73] but provision was

71. The act of 1948 provided for a transitional parity arrangement whereby, if a shift from the old to the revised formula would reduce the computed parity for a given commodity, such reduction was to be made only at a rate of 5 per cent a year. That was intended as a means of avoiding a sudden severe reduction in the support level for particular commodities, mainly wheat and corn. The restriction on use of the revised formula where it would result in lower computed parities for certain crops expired at the end of 1955 but the provision for a gradual transition from the old to the new basis of computation was retained, thus slowing up the full adoption of the new formula and keeping certain crops, especially wheat and corn, overpriced relatively for some years beyond 1955. The revised formula was adopted for the nonbasics and for such of the basics as would have their parities raised thereby, thus raising somewhat the over-all level of computed parity prices.

72. If marketing quotas were in effect, the range was to be 72–90 per cent.

73. Except for the requirement that the one that would yield the highest parity price must be used.

made for including in the list of prices paid by farmers the wages paid to hired labor. That raised the level of parity prices but did not affect the relationships of the parities for the different products significantly. Putting into effect the revised formula, in computing parities for the basic commodities, was again postponed and the 90 per cent level of support was continued.

Two other changes of some significance were made. The carry-over allowance for consumption and exports of corn was raised from 7 to 10 per cent, in computing normal supply, and the conditions specified for liquidation of CCC stocks were modified.[74] The increase in the carry-over provision permitted stocks to reach higher levels before acreage allotments and marketing quotas would have to be imposed.

The conditions placed on sale of government stocks are very important in handling the kinds of problems that arise when market prices are declining. Before World War II, stocks could be disposed of at such prices and times as the administrators might consider desirable. With a rising price level, stocks can usually be disposed of at a profit, or at no great loss; but if the market is falling, government stocks must, if sold at all, be sold at a loss. During the early part of the war, the Administration used its discretionary powers in disposing of accumulated stocks of corn at some loss, as a way of helping to meet the need for increased production of livestock products.

Subsequently, by agreement with members of Congress and by legislative conditions attached to other acts, the sale of corn and other grain feeds was restricted in order to protect the corn market. The Agricultural Act of 1948 prescribed conditions of sale but they were revised in the act of 1949. The most significant provisions relating to corn were: one, that sales policies should be worked out in such a way as not to discourage the private trade from acquiring and carrying normal inventories and, two, that CCC could not sell at less than 5 per cent above the current support price plus reasonable carrying charges. However, these restrictions were not to apply to sales for new or by-product uses, to sales made because of deterioration in quality or to sales for export.

Record Crop and Lower Prices in 1948–1949

Only 85.5 million acres of corn were planted in 1948, but the yield of 42.5 bushels was far above any previously recorded. Production was at a record level of 3.6 billion bushels. The huge crop, together with a somewhat reduced hog population, provided a supply that was more than adequate to meet current needs and restore carry-overs to normal levels.[75] Farm prices generally were easing off from the very high levels

74. The allowance for normal carry-over was further increased, to 15 per cent, in the Agricultural Act of 1954.

75. The number of hogs on farms, including pigs, as of January 1, 1948 was 55 million. A year earlier there had been about 57 million, and the number had been as high as 83.7 million in 1944. (*Agricultural Statistics, 1951*, p. 340.)

of 1946–1948, which were due to heavy requirements for postwar feeding abroad, to the very severe drought in Europe in 1947, to the high level of domestic activity and, of course, to the very short U.S. corn crop of 1947.[76]

The price of corn had been far above parity in the 1947 season, reaching the wholly unprecedented level of $2.46 at the farm (155 per cent of parity) in January 1948. It continued above $2 until July (except for a drop to $1.92 in February) and then eased off as the large 1948 crop became a more assured prospect. It was down to $1.21 (about 80 per cent of parity) by November 1948 and remained around there for the remainder of the season. The season average price was $1.28 as compared with $2.16 in the preceding year.[77]

CCC loans were available at 90 per cent of parity ($1.44 per bushel) in the 1948 season. Nearly a sixth of the crop (551 million bushels) was put under loan. Almost 500 million of it was under loan to or owned by CCC at the end of the season and total stocks held privately and by government were at an all-time high of 813 million bushels.

Another large crop of 3.4 billion bushels in 1949, together with declining farm prices generally and a severe downward adjustment in cattle and hog prices, caused corn prices to decline further in the 1949 season. The price reached a low of $1.02 in November but moved up again, reaching $1.44 in the summer of 1950, after the outbreak of war in Korea. The season average price was $1.24.

The support loan offered in 1949 was $1.40. The amount put under loan (387 million bushels) was sizable but not so large as that from the 1948 crop. Furthermore, the bulk of it was redeemed before the end of the season. The net addition to CCC holdings was about 157 million bushels. CCC holdings and commitments at the end of the 1949 season, that is, in October 1950, reached a new high of 650 million bushels, but nongovernment holdings were decreased, so total stocks at the end of the marketing year were only moderately higher than a year earlier.[78]

76. Farm prices as a whole were well above parity from 1942 through 1948. They declined to 100 in 1949 and 1950. There was much uneasiness about the severe drop in farm prices in 1949. It is evident, however, that it was, in the main, a readjustment toward a more normal relationship between farm and nonfarm prices. A ratio of 100 was in fact a more favorable one than had prevailed at any time between 1921 and 1941. However, there was concern as to whether the drop recorded in 1949 might be the beginning of a long-expected farm recession similar to that of the early 1920s.

The ratios of prices received by farmers to those paid by farmers in these years were as follows, with the period 1910–1914 as 100:

1941	93	1946	113
1942	105	1947	115
1943	113	1948	110
1944	108	1949	100
1945	109	1950	100

(*Ibid.*, p. 581.)

77. *Grain and Feed Statistics through 1954*, pp. 39, 40.

78. They were up to 845 million bushels as compared with 813 million. (*Ibid.*, p. 46.)

Government supports undoubtedly strengthened corn prices in the 1948 and 1949 crop years though the farm price remained below the loan rate until July 1950. Nevertheless, it is probable that it would have gone below a dollar if CCC had not taken off the market the amounts it did. Just what the over-all significance of the operation was cannot be estimated with any assurance. Hog production probably was discouraged somewhat, but in many cases the producers of hogs, the feeders of cattle and the growers of corn were the same people.

Cheaper corn and heavier feeding might have put more money into one pocket, higher corn prices into the other. Something in the order of $1.5 billion of government money was put into the corn areas, but the government held about 650 million bushels of corn that might serve to offset a shortage in later years or might reduce prices if released when supplies were plentiful. That is the dilemma which is inevitably created by heavy accumulations of that kind. The long-run effects are especially difficult to appraise in dealing with a crop like corn, which is, for many farmers, one part of a joint product.[79]

Stronger Demand and Smaller Crops, 1950 and 1951

Demand for nearly all kinds of farm products increased in 1950 and 1951 as a result of the inflationary upsurge in prices that accompanied the outbreak of war in Korea. Also, the 1950 and 1951 corn crops were somewhat smaller (3.0 billion and 2.9 billion bushels). Demand was sufficient to permit some reduction in CCC stocks, though the Corporation's holdings and commitments still stood at 306 million bushels at the end of the 1951 season, about two thirds as large as the heavy stocks held in 1939 and 1940.

Acreage allotments were reinstated for the 1950 crop. The allotment for the "commercial" corn areas was 46 million acres, which was 3 million more than the acreage allotted in 1943 though the total area in corn in 1949 had been some 6 million acres below that of 1943 and still had been large enough to result in substantial additions to CCC holdings. The allotments probably had little effect on plantings. The planted acreage was reduced from 87 to 83 million, but that was in line with the trend and probably would have come about anyway as a result of the low prices of the previous two years. Yields continued high and production was only 163 million bushels smaller than the large crop of 1949.

The 1950 loan rate was $1.47, but only 54 million bushels were put under support. The season average price of $1.52 was slightly above the loan rate and the net result for the year was a reduction of about 160 million bushels in CCC holdings. Acreage allotments were not continued

79. Exports were in excess of 100 million bushels in both the 1948 and 1949 seasons, which adds a further complication in judging the results of the program.

in 1951, but the increase in acreage planted was only about 400,000, roughly half of 1 per cent. The support price in the 1951 season was $1.57. The amount pledged to CCC was even smaller than in 1950 (26 million bushels). Again the season average price ($1.66) was above the loan rate and there was a further net reduction of about 180 million bushels in CCC holdings. Net exports in 1950 were 109 million bushels and in 1951, 75 million. That volume of exports was larger than normal and no doubt contributed to the easing down of CCC stocks.

1952 Corn Crop Again Large

Price supports for the 1952 crop, at $1.60 per bushel, were announced on February 11. The acreage planted was about the same as in 1950 and slightly below that of 1951. However, a 40.6-bushel yield, second only to that of 1948, resulted in production of 3.3 billion bushels, which was more than enough to feed out the livestock on hand. Corn prices eased off from the $1.60–$1.70 level of the 1951 season to about $1.50.

Some 417 million bushels were put under loan and CCC holdings and commitments were increased to 579 million bushels as of the end of the season, the second highest on record. Total end-of-season stocks were also high, though not up to the levels of 1948 and 1949. The support program undoubtedly prevented prices from going lower than they did, though it did not hold them fully up to the support level. The season average price was $1.51 as compared with $1.66 a year earlier. The price maintenance was achieved, however, by adding to government holdings on a scale that foreshadowed difficulties to come.

The 1953 support level was again put at $1.60 and an even larger quantity was put under loan (471 million bushels). The acreage harvested was down slightly from that of 1952, but yields were high (39.6 bushels) and production amounted to 3.18 billion bushels. Prices were slightly below those of the 1952 season though the season average of $1.48 was only 3 cents below that of the preceding year. Again the support program undoubtedly helped to keep prices up, but at the cost of another large increase in CCC holdings and commitments, which brought them up to an all-time high of 760 million bushels as of the end of the season. Total stocks, which amounted to 920 million bushels, were also much above any previously recorded. There was obviously trouble ahead unless production and use could be brought into better balance.

Acreage Allotments Resumed in 1954

By 1954, the increasing size of CCC holdings led the government to attempt again to restrain production by means of acreage allotments. The allotment announced for the "commercial" corn area (about 47 million acres) was some 16.5 per cent below the 1951–1953 average, but the acreage harvested, for the nation as a whole, was 80.2 million, only slightly less than the 80.5 million harvested in 1953. So far as feeds were concerned, the difference was more than made up by an increase in the acreage put into oats, barley and grain sorghums. The yield per acre was down slightly and total production amounted to 3.1 billion bushels, only about 200 million bushels less than in 1953.

A support price of $1.62 (90 per cent of parity) was announced for the 1954 crop, for producers in the "commercial" corn areas if they were in compliance with acreage allotments. The support level in "noncommercial" areas was at 75 per cent of the rate in the "commercial" areas, that is, at $1.215.[80] The amount put under loan was 258 million bushels, about 36 per cent of the 750 million bushels eligible for loans. Production in the "commercial" areas approximated 2,440 million bushels, but only about 40 per cent of the farmers who produced corn in that area were in compliance and thus eligible for price-support loans. Probably no more than 30 per cent of the corn itself was eligible for support loans since production on the noncomplying farms averaged considerably higher than on the complying farms.

As of September 1955, the October 1 carry-over was expected to be about 1,050 million bushels, the largest on record and more than 300 million bushels above the 1949–1953 average. Of this, CCC holdings and commitments of some 850 to 900 million bushels were anticipated.[81] Stocks of other feed grains also were at record levels. However, the number of grain-consuming units of livestock, particularly hogs, was expected to increase. With larger production of corn outside the "commercial" areas, there was prospect that more would be fed, but the 3.1-billion-bushel crop was expected to result in some further increase in carry-over at the end of the 1955 season.[82]

The Agricultural Act of 1954 provided that the support rate on corn and other basic commodities would be within the range 82.5–90 per cent of parity for the 1955 crop. Thereafter, the 75–90 per cent rate specified in the Agricultural Act of 1949 presumably would apply.[83] The rate announced for 1955 was $1.58 (87 per cent of the February 15 parity price).[84] Price supports for oats, barley and sorghum grains were to be about a fifth lower than in 1954.

The Department of Agriculture announced, in November 1954, that acreage allotments would be in effect for the 1955 crop. However, the Secretary stated in December that the "cross-compliance" provision, which had been announced in June, would not be in effect. Under that

80. *The Feed Situation,* April 1, 1954, p. 3.
81. *The Feed Situation,* September 22, 1955, p. 7.
82. *Ibid.,* pp. 7, 9.
83. Subject, of course, to the possibility that it might be changed by later legislation.
84. *The Feed Situation,* March 31, 1955, p. 3. From 1944 to 1954, a 90 per cent rate was required by law.

arrangement, a farmer would have had to be in compliance on all crop allotments established for his farm for 1955 in order to be eligible for price supports on any crop. Removal of the restriction meant that the only production controls applying would be acreage allotments on the individual crop concerned, and compliance with marketing quotas if they were voted. For example, a farmer could overplant his corn allotment and still be eligible for price support on wheat or other crops. This meant that there would be little restraint on the uses to which diverted acres might be put.[85]

Continuing Unbalance Seemed in Prospect

As of 1955, there appeared to be prospect of a continuing supply of feed grains that would be in excess of the amount that could be sold at prices comparable to those prevailing in the 1950–1954 period, unless severe droughts or other disasters should reduce yields markedly. However, the moderate reduction in required support levels seemed to give promise of establishing a better balance between feed-grain prices and those of livestock, or at least one that would encourage some expansion of livestock production. The situation did not appear to be so far out of balance as to be unmanageable with some rather moderate readjustment in prices and possibly a few years in which production conditions would not be so favorable as in the 1948–1955 period.

Some steps were, of course, being taken to reduce the overabundant stocks held by CCC. Space does not permit a detailed description or analysis of them here and they had not, as of 1955, become an important factor in the situation. In April 1954, the Department of Agriculture offered approximately 170 million bushels of 1948 and 1949 corn at local market prices or at not less than 20 cents under the 1953 loan rate for No. 3 yellow, if local market prices were above that level. In addition, other off-grade corn owned by CCC was offered at the same price.[86]

In May 1954, the Department announced a program in which feed grains would be made available for export at prices below those in the domestic market and approximately in line with world prices.[87] Through these and other measures, the build-up of stocks had been slowed down but not eliminated. However, the principal problem still appeared to be that of reducing stocks already held to a more desirable level without disturbing the domestic markets unduly or incurring excessive costs to the government.

85. *Ibid.*, January 4, 1955, p. 16. Since corn, wheat, barley, oats and various other crops can be used somewhat interchangeably as feed for livestock, this meant, of course, a relaxation of controls on over-all feed production, which had been strongly advocated by some groups.

86. *Ibid.*, p. 12.

87. The export allowance on corn was 15 cents per bushel, on oats 10 cents and on barley 15 cents. (See *ibid.*, July 26, 1954, p. 16.)

Cost of the Corn Program

The cost of the various programs relating to corn can be stated only in terms of realized costs as of any given time. There are, in all situations where CCC stocks have been built up to levels above those needed as prudent reserves, prospective and as yet unrealized costs which cannot be determined until they do become "realized." For the earlier programs, data are available on a realized cost basis but there is no way of knowing what return the government will obtain from stocks still held by CCC.[88]

Under the Agricultural Adjustment Act of 1933, program costs for corn and hogs combined amounted to $488.7 million, of which $261.4 million was met by receipts from processing taxes. Agricultural conservation payments in the 1936–1943 period amounted to $441 million and parity payments in the same period to $347.5 million.[89] In addition, there were expenditures of Section 32 funds on corn and corn meal in the amount of some $18.4 million, the bulk of it for corn meal, of which about half was used in the food stamp program. The food stamp expenditures are presumably a relief item. Most of the remainder, a relatively small amount, was used in providing export subsidies. Relief purchases and surplus removal for pork products, under Section 32 funds, was a much larger item ($64.3 million), of which more than half went into the food stamp program.

Realized costs for CCC operations in corn had amounted to $227.1 million as of June 30, 1955. These were allocated to various periods as follows: for the period 1933–1941, $20 million; for 1941 to 1946, $14 million; for 1946 to 1951, $17.8 million; and the remainder, $175.3 million, to the fiscal years 1952 to 1955. The largest losses ($80.5 million and $75.7 million) were in the fiscal years 1954 and 1955.[90] The total outlay under all of the corn and hog programs, as of June 30, 1955, was thus in the order of $1,587 million.

SUPPORT ON OTHER FEED GRAINS

Price-support loans were offered on barley and grain sorghums from 1940 on, and on oats in 1945 and after. These programs, especially in the postwar years, were designed partly to protect corn prices and partly

88. As of June 30, 1955, CCC had a corn inventory valued at about $986 million and loans outstanding of about $470 million. During fiscal 1955, corn valued at $224 million was sold for approximately $185 million. There was a total net loss in fiscal 1955, on these and other inventory operations in corn, of a little over $75 million. (See Commodity Credit Corporation, *Report of Financial Condition and Operations as of June 30, 1955*, pp. 33, 41.)

89. *Realized Cost of Agricultural and Related Programs.*

90. Commodity Credit Corporation, *Report of Financial Condition and Operations as of June 30, 1955*, p. 31. There were, of course, additional losses in prospect on the heavy stocks then held.

to aid growers of these other crops. During the war years, the barley and grain supports were partly for the purpose of encouraging the production of feed grains. (See Table 33.)

TABLE 33

OATS, BARLEY AND GRAIN SORGHUMS: PRICE SUPPORTS AND QUANTITY PLACED UNDER PRICE SUPPORT, 1940–1955 [a]

	Oats		Barley		Grain Sorghums	
Crop Year	National Average Price Support per Bushel	Placed under Price Support [b]	National Average Price Support per Bushel	Placed under Price Support [b]	National Average Price Support per Cwt.	Placed under Price Support [b]
		(1,000 Bushels)		*(1,000 Bushels)*		*(1,000 Cwt.)*
1940			$ .35	7,499	$ .54	44
1941			.45	16,297	.71	191
1942			.55	15,199	.98	68
1943			.75	761	1.52	26
1944			.85	3,302	1.70	4,601
1945	$ .48	2,933	.80	1,027	1.65	6
1946	.53	788	.83	491	1.72	309
1947	.63	244	1.03	337	2.12	42
1948	.70	23,396	1.15	49,260	2.31	22,262
1949	.69	41,006	1.09	32,951	2.09	47,274
1950	.71	14,974	1.10	30,620	1.87	33,780
1951	.72	13,125	1.11	16,912	2.17	8,359
1952	.78	21,583	1.22	9,890	2.38	2,061
1953	.80	55,955	1.24	45,176	2.43	25,497
1954	.75	74,956	1.15	115,108	2.28	64,136
1955	.61	68,317 [c]	.94	96,007 [c]	1.78	59,556 [c]

Source: U.S. Agricultural Marketing Service, *Grain and Feed Statistics through 1954,* Statistical Bulletin 159, March 1955, p. 46, and *The Feed Situation,* May 21, 1956, p. 21.

a. Loan program for oats started in 1945. Loans on all three grains varied by counties from 1945 to date.

b. Total quantity placed under loan, 1940–1947, and under loan and purchase agreement, 1948 to date.

c. Preliminary.

Though corn is the dominant feed grain, the losses incurred on the other coarse grains have been large; for the postwar years nearly as large as those on corn. For the years 1946–1955, they amounted in total, for the three crops, to about $130 million, of which well over half ($84.8 million) was on the grain sorghums.[91] Temporary price advances in

91. *Ibid.* There was a small loss of $40,000 on operations in barley during the war years, and a larger one of $437,000 on grain sorghums. However, there were no large operations in these secondary coarse-grain support programs until after the close of the war. Considerable quantities of wheat and oats were imported from Canada during the war but as a supply operation, not as a price-support program.

1950 and 1951 made possible some sales at a small profit, but these profits were much more than offset by the heavy losses in fiscal 1954 and fiscal 1955.

Operations were on a modest scale until 1948. In that year, 23 million bushels of oats, 49 million bushels of barley and 22 million hundredweight of grain sorghums were put under price support.[92] The barley and grain sorghum commitments amounted to 16 and 30 per cent of the respective crops. Support levels were at 75 per cent of parity for barley, 70 per cent for oats and 77 per cent for grain sorghums.

CCC operations in oats and grain sorghums were even larger in 1949. All three still were being supported extensively in the 1950 season but operations dropped off to negligible amounts in 1951 and 1952. By 1953 and 1954, very extensive loan programs were in operation for all three crops. In 1954 the volumes put under loan amounted to 74 million bushels of oats, 114 million bushels of barley and 64 million hundredweight of grain sorghums. These amounted to 56 per cent of the grain sorghum crop, 31 per cent of the barley crop and 5 per cent of the oat crop. Stocks in CCC hands at the end of the 1954 season, as of July 1, 1955, included 40.5 million bushels of oats, 73.5 million bushels of barley, and 52 million hundredweight of grain sorghums. In addition, CCC had outstanding loans in the amount of $15.6 million on oats, $14.3 million on barley and $795,000 on grain sorghums.[93]

OVER-ALL PROGRAM RESULTS

The acreage control programs for corn do not seem to have had any important effect on the amounts produced. Acreage allotments were assigned in only a few of the years: 1934, 1935, 1938–1940, 1950, 1954 and 1955. In most of these years, many of the growers did not find the inducements to comply sufficiently attractive to cause them to participate in the program. There is, in fact, much reason to question whether acreage allotments and marketing quotas can be made effective on a crop which is so largely used on the farms where it is grown. Also, the limitation of the program to the areas defined as "commercial" has left a large part of the corn crop uncontrolled. Acreage controls have not been applied to the other feed grains and, for the reasons mentioned above, probably would not have been effective if they had been applied.

One reason for the failure of corn acreage controls to be effective in reducing production has been the rapid increase in yields. The acreage of corn harvested was reduced by some 27 per cent between 1932 and 1955. Yet production was about 20 per cent larger in 1955 than in 1932 despite the fact that the 1932 yield was a relatively high one for that

92. *Grain and Feed Statistics through 1954*, p. 46.

93. Commodity Credit Corporation, *Report of Financial Condition and Operations as of June 30, 1955*, pp. 33, 41.

period. Customary yields have increased some 50 per cent between the early 1930s and the early 1950s. Under these circumstances, cutbacks related to a historical base could be little more than an official approval of an adjustment that would be made anyway. The release from allotments in the war years, and during most of the postwar period, left farmers free in most years to adjust their corn acreages to economic conditions as they saw them.

The conservation programs of the late 1930s probably contributed some to higher yields. They did not have much restraining influence on acreages grown. Perhaps half or more of the increase in yield was due to increased use of hybrid seed, but other factors were important as well. Fertilizer use in the six leading corn states increased from less than a million tons just prior to World War II to more than 3.5 million tons in 1950.[94] Some low-yielding acres were eliminated and legume rotations came into more general use, partly as a result of the conservation programs.

The adjustment and conservation payments made between 1933 and 1943 were very helpful to corn producers in a period when farm incomes were extremely low. They did not affect prices significantly but did, of course, involve subsidization of corn producers by nonfarm people.

Price Supports and Stability

For the twenty-year period here under discussion, the price-support program for corn apparently contributed to stability of feed supplies and to some extent to stability in the amount of money currently available for farmers to use. That result was to some extent fortuitous, since the apparent success of the program was due in part to the severe drought of 1934 and to World War II and the Korean War, which came at times when corn stocks might well have been considered burdensome and unduly expensive. Reserve stocks would have been helpful in 1947 but were not then available. However, the heavy stocks acquired in 1954 and 1955 point to weaknesses in such a program as well as advantages. The program has been operated largely in a period of rising prices. It would not work so well in a period of declining prices.

The price-support programs do not seem to have had much effect on the utilization of feed grains. Neither increased exports nor special-use programs have been important factors in the situation. There has apparently been some tendency for corn production to be concentrated more heavily in the "commercial" corn areas, and the heavy accumulations by CCC have probably caused more corn to be sold off the farms where grown than would otherwise have been disposed of in that way, but

94. Richard J. Foote, John W. Klein and Malcolm Clough, *The Demand and Price Structure for Corn and Total Feed Concentrates,* U.S. Department of Agriculture, Technical Bulletin No. 1061, October 1952, p. 11.

usually it has not moved out of the general area in which it was grown. Only about half the corn is grown in the areas designated as "commercial." Continuous restrictions in that area could be offset by expansions outside of it.

The desirable size of carry-overs calls for further study and continuous review. Some students of the problem contend that a carry-over of up to a billion bushels need not be a cause for alarm. It is pointed out that the drop in production between 1946 and 1947 amounted to more than 850 million bushels, which would have absorbed most of a billion-bushel reserve. However, the validity of that line of argument rests to a considerable extent on the assumption that usual production and usual need are fairly well in balance. If production is rather continuously in excess of needs, the tendency is, of course, for stocks to be built up to levels that are unneeded, unduly expensive to maintain and possibly ultimately unstabilizing in their effects.

Continuing to use the unrevised parity formula in computing parities for corn, for price-support purposes, has led to some distortion of price relationships. Use of the revised formula from 1950 on would have reduced the parity price of corn about 15 per cent, which, even with 90 per cent support, might have been enough to result in a fairly good balance between supply and demand without resort to acreage allotments. Discretionary application of loan rates within a moderate range could very possibly have encouraged the feeding of more corn to hogs and might have reduced the losses taken by cattle feeders in 1952 and 1953.

Relation to the Livestock Economy

The demand for livestock products constitutes the principal, though indirect, demand for feed grains. It is heavily dependent on the level of consumer purchasing power. Since livestock production must to a considerable extent be adjusted to the supply of feed grains, stabilizing the grain supply has a tendency to stabilize the livestock industry as well, except when there are major changes in the general level of consumer demand.

Experience in the war years demonstrated that livestock production, especially of hogs, can be increased very much and very fast, provided feed grains can be supplied at prices that are attractive in relation to those paid for livestock products. In the postwar years, the large increase in the supply of livestock products has been due largely to the abundance of feed grains. From 1950 on, meat supplies increased at a more rapid rate than population.

For the most part, the livestock growers, operating in a rapidly expanding market, were able to make needed adjustments throughout the period 1945 to 1955 without government aid. Prices during most of the period were favorable as compared with those of most other farm products. The readjustments of 1949–1950 and 1952–1953 were severe but the one in 1949–1950, at least, was in large part a return to a more normal relationship between the prices of meat animals and the prices of farm products generally.

A 1952 study made in the U.S. Department of Agriculture for congressional use concluded that, on the whole, "the price support and storage programs in force during the twelve to fifteen years preceding that date may have reduced the earlier variability of corn consumption by livestock as much as 50 per cent." [95] That conclusion must, of course, be related to the extremely dynamic and changing situations in the period covered by the study. So large an amount of stabilization effect could not be anticipated in a period of similar length when conditions are more stable.

On the whole, programs designed for direct control of livestock production, or support of livestock prices, were not an important part of the grain and livestock program except in the period 1933–1936 and in the war years. Significant assistance was given in the readjustment of the hog and cattle populations in 1933 and 1934. There was a substantial amount of production and price management during the war, both through incentive prices, for hogs, and through government assistance in assuring adequate supplies of feeds. Both hog and cattle prices were affected somewhat in the opposite direction by price ceilings and rationing but were strengthened, at least for pork products, by heavy shipments under the lend-lease program.

From 1945 to 1955, there was comparatively little direct government action relating to meat animals. Some relatively minor programs for purchase of beef and pork were undertaken, and drought relief was provided in some areas. In the main, however, the livestock growers tended to make their adjustments individually, in response to market influences and production costs rather than through government programs.

95. *Reserve Levels for Storage Farm Products,* U.S. Senate Doc. No. 30, 83d Cong., 2d sess., May 13, 1952, p. 41.

6

Butter, Cheese, Poultry and Eggs

THE DAIRY AND POULTRY industries are among the largest producers of cash farm income in the United States, ranking second only to meat animals.[1] The groups of products dealt with in the following pages are not homogeneous nor are the problems faced by their producers identical. However, poultry products and manufactured dairy products do tend to be handled in somewhat the same channels of trade and there are similarities in the problems and programs relating to them.

The various manufactured dairy products are interrelated in a production sense but serve different purposes in the diet and are not directly interchangeable at the consumer level.[2] Poultry products also have different types of outlet, but production can be modified so as to increase egg production and de-emphasize poultry for meat or vice versa. There are, of course, interconnections in the demands for both eggs and poultry for meat with those for livestock and for cheese.

Very marked differences exist in respect to consumption trends. The per capita consumption of poultry and eggs has been on the increase. So also has the consumption of cheese. Butter, on the other hand, has experienced the largest and most rapid decline in per capita consumption of any important food product.[3] While these differences exist, the industries here discussed also have some features in common. For one thing, the products are perishable or semiperishable. Though storable for moderate periods in special types of storage facilities, they are not "storable" in the sense that cotton, tobacco, wool, wheat and the other grains are. Both dairy and poultry products are produced in almost every part of the United States and by vast numbers of very small producing units.

1. In 1952, cash receipts from cattle and calves amounted to $6.2 billion; from hogs, $3.5 billion; and from sheep and lambs, $394 million, making a grand total of $10.1 billion. The income from poultry and eggs was $3.4 billion and from dairy products $4.5 billion. Receipts from each of the three groups exceeded those from food grains, feed grains, cotton and tobacco. (U.S. Department of Agriculture, *Agricultural Statistics, 1953,* p. 610.)

2. A very large and growing part of the dairy industry finds its outlet in direct consumption as fluid milk. That portion of the dairy problem is discussed separately in Chapter 11 and hence is touched on only incidentally here.

3. Civilian consumption per capita stood at 17.2 pounds in 1939 and had been slightly higher in the early 1930s. By 1952, it was down to 8.7 pounds. (*Agricultural Statistics, 1953,* p. 428.)

That type of industry organization does not lend itself well to coordinated action either economically or politically.

Though the producers of dairy products are strongly organized nationally, and in some cases regionally or locally, their internal conflicts or differences of interest, for example those of the fluid milk producers as compared with those of butter and cheese producers, make strong, unified action difficult. The poultry producers also have strong organizations but mainly on a local or regional basis and for marketing and service activities rather than for political action. The situation is further complicated by the fact that entry or withdrawal by the individual producer is comparatively easy in both industries. That makes for relatively quick expansion and contraction, especially of poultry output, in times when prices are favorable or when prices and feeding ratios become unfavorable.

For these and other reasons, proposals for special programs relating to manufactured dairy products and to chickens and eggs did not assume large importance prior to World War II. However, both had been given considerable emphasis in the various longer-term programs of the U.S. Department of Agriculture and by the state experiment stations and educational institutions. Much of the activity of these agencies, dating back to periods much earlier than the 1930s, had to do with improved and more economical dairy and poultry production, such as breeding for higher output per cow or per hen, improved methods of feeding, culling procedures, disease control and so on.

Congressional support for programs of these types has been continuous and generous, but because of the almost nationwide character of the industries concerned there has not been intense pressure for special, regionally oriented types of legislation such as those sought by the wheat, cotton and tobacco growers. In the 1920s, there was, in fact, a good deal of positive encouragement for farmers to shift into dairy and poultry production as a less speculative and more constructive alternative to heavy reliance on one-crop agriculture.

PROBLEMS AND PROGRAMS IN BUTTER AND CHEESE

Butter prices, unlike those of most other farm products, held up moderately well in the period following World War I. From a customary range of about 25 to 28 cents per pound in the prewar years the annual average price of butterfat to farmers rose to 55.5 cents in 1920. It dropped off to 37.0 and 35.9 cents in 1921 and 1922 but was back up to 42.2 cents in 1923. The price remained above 40 cents through 1929 and was at parity or above in 1923, 1926, 1927 and 1928. It was almost at the parity level in all of the other years of the 1920 decade except 1922, when its index was 95.[4]

4. U.S. Bureau of Agricultural Economics, *Dairy Statistics and Related Series*, Statistical Bulletin 100, June 1951, pp. 31, 33.

Butterfat prices eased off in 1930 and dropped sharply thereafter, reaching 17.9 cents in 1932, which was less than 75 per cent of the 1909 price and less than 50 per cent of the level prevailing in the 1920s.[5] Cheese prices also held about steady during the 1920s but with a slight upward trend from 1921 on. The wholesale price for fresh, single daisies, at Chicago, was 20.5 cents per pound in 1921 and moved up to the 24–25-cent range in 1927 and 1928. The price fell off sooner than that of butterfat and was down to 18.3 cents by 1930. It reached a low of 11.9 cents in 1932 and remained below 15 cents until 1940.

Farm Board Butter Stabilization

Land O' Lakes Creameries, Inc., a producer cooperative established in the 1920s, undertook, with some assistance from the Federal Farm Board, to check the downswing in butter prices that began in December 1929. The Board's main emphasis was on strengthening the regional dairy marketing cooperatives, especially Land O' Lakes of the North Central dairy states, Challenge Cream and Butter Association of California, United Dairymen's Association of Washington and Idaho, Interstate Associated Creameries of Oregon and some others. It encouraged interregional cooperative arrangements, particularly between Land O' Lakes and Challenge, whereby each would handle products of the other in the markets principally served by it. That is, Challenge would sell Land O' Lakes butter in California under the Challenge brand and Land O' Lakes would sell Challenge's dried skim milk and surplus butter if they were shipped east of the Rockies.[6]

In January 1930, the Board granted a loan to Land O' Lakes to enable it to withhold some of its own butter from the market and to peg the price of butter on the exchange by offers to buy at specified prices. The operation was designed mainly to overcome a seasonal weakness in butter prices and to steady the situation in a period when farm prices generally were falling rapidly.

5. Butterfat prices in these years were as follows:

Year	*Price of Butterfat (Cents per Pound)*	*Parity Ratio*	*Year*	*Price of Butterfat (Cents per Pound)*	*Parity Ratio*
1909	25.5				
1920	55.5	105	1926	41.6	100
1921	37.0	99	1927	44.5	106
1922	35.9	95	1928	46.1	104
1923	42.2	107	1929	45.2	99
1924	40.4	98	1930	34.5	80
1925	42.4	99	1931	24.8	66
			1932	17.9	56
			1933	18.8	59

(*Loc. cit.*)

6. See fuller explanation of the arrangement in William H. Nicholls, *Postwar Developments in the Marketing of Butter,* Iowa Agricultural Experiment Station, Research Bulletin 250, February 1939, pp. 341–42.

These rather limited objectives seem to have been achieved though the operation was not a large one and was not of long duration. It involved only about 5.2 million pounds of butter. By March 15, prices stiffened and Land O' Lakes disposed of its holdings at a profit.[7] That operation, though modest in scale, probably had some influence in holding butter prices to a slower decline than those of cheese and many other farm products. However, the later sale of these stocks may have depressed prices about as much as they were increased during the period of acquisition.[8] Whatever effect these later sales may have had was partly or wholly offset by short pastures and a somewhat lower volume of butter production in the summer of 1930 than in 1929. Butterfat prices held about at the January 1930 level until December of that year. The price of cheese declined from 20.4 cents per pound in January to 16.5 cents in July and remained mostly below 18 cents for the rest of the year. The price index for farm products as a whole declined from 147 in January to 107 in December.[9]

Dairy Programs, 1933 and After

The assistance given to butter producers by the Federal Farm Board was of short duration and small in scale. It had very little lasting effect on either prices or industry organization. However, some contribution was probably made to strengthening and developing several of the large cooperatives already existing or then being formed.

Following passage of the Agricultural Adjustment Act of 1933, an effort was made to devise a marketing agreement for butter. However, the plan was abandoned because of difficulty in getting agreement among the various interests concerned. Also, many felt that a marketing agreement could add very little to prices of butter and cheese. Generally speaking, action in respect to the dairy industry (except in fluid milk) was slower than that relating to some of the other commodities. The pressure for government aid was not so strong as in respect to wheat, cotton, corn and hogs, except on one or two occasions when the price of butter dropped precipitately. Many doubted that production control could be made practical for dairy products. There was also some predisposition to oppose restriction on output because of the widely held view that people should eat more dairy products rather than less.

Following the breakdown of negotiations for a marketing agreement,

7. *Ibid.*

8. See John D. Black, *The Dairy Industry and the AAA,* The Brookings Institution, Washington, 1935, p. 358.

9. *Dairy Statistics and Related Series,* pp. 31, 44, and U.S. Bureau of Agricultural Economics, *Index Numbers of Prices Received by Farmers, 1910–1943,* February 1944, p. 22. There were, of course, other factors in the situation. As Black points out, autumn stocks of butter were low, as a result of poor pastures, and the price could be pegged through curtailment of current sales and offers to purchase by any agency with sufficient financial backing. If the price weakness is only temporary, such an operation can be helpful. In a prolonged depression its usefulness is very much subject to question.

the Adjustment Administration authorized the purchase of substantial quantities of butter, partly through Land O' Lakes Creameries and partly through the Dairy Marketing Corporation.[10] Land O' Lakes bought 11 million pounds of butter and Dairy Marketing Corporation 17 million in the second half of 1933. Later, in 1934, the Federal Surplus Relief Corporation bought 25 million pounds.

These purchases, which were of essentially the same type as those made with Federal Farm Board funds in 1930, seemed to strengthen the market for a time though the principal influence assigned by Black was the "pseudo-inflation" of that period.[11] The price of butter held about steady from June 1933 through November at 22–23 cents but dropped to 19.4 cents in January 1934. Heavy relief distributions made in January and February relieved the top-heavy government stock situation and the price recovered to about the 24–25-cent level, where it remained for the first half of 1934.[12] The strength in the spring and summer of 1934 was almost certainly due to the severe drought and the short supply of pasture grass that accompanied it.

It soon became evident that no lasting gain could be achieved merely by buying up butter and holding it. Stocks owned or financed by government were up to 40 million pounds by January 1934. Secretary Wallace announced on December 16, 1933 that the butter acquired would be turned over to the Federal Emergency Relief Administration and that enough more would be bought to bring commercial holdings down to within 7 million pounds of the five-year average.

Scale of Butter Purchase Operations to 1953

Total government purchases from August 1933 to April 1934 amounted to 51.6 million pounds.[13] All of it was distributed to families on relief. Black estimated that government purchases may have raised the average annual price to producers by one or two cents per pound but probably not more than a cent.[14] The program was terminated in 1934, except for purchases by FERA, because of fund complications.[15]

10. The Dairy Marketing Corporation was a private agency of which the stockholders were the National Co-Operative Milk Producers' Federation, the American Association of Creamery Butter Manufacturers, the International Milk Dealers Association and the National Cheese Institute. It operated as a broker or buying agent for the government. It bought on confidential orders from the government and was financed by it. (See *The Dairy Industry and the AAA*, pp. 354–63.)

11. *Ibid.*, p. 357.

12. For 92-score creamery butter at Chicago as given in *Dairy Statistics and Related Series*, p. 51.

13. Nicholls, *op. cit.*, p. 346. Black gives a figure of 68 million pounds for the first two years of operation.

14. *The Dairy Industry and the AAA*, p. 359.

15. There was, however, a related program, financed by the government, which affected the balance between cow numbers and the demand for dairy products. Beginning in 1934, the government undertook an expanded program of tuberculosis and brucellosis eradication in dairy cattle. That, together with droughts and low prices, resulted

The expectation in August 1933 was that processing taxes would be levied and that these would provide reimbursement to the Secretary's emergency fund. Hearings were held but no processing taxes were levied. Secretary Wallace insisted that processing taxes, if levied, should be used to finance some plan of production control. Since no such plan was agreed on or adopted, the plan to collect processing taxes fell through.[16]

There were relatively small purchases by the newly created Federal Surplus Commodities Corporation in the years 1934–35 to 1936–37 but as business improved they dropped off to 1.7 million pounds in 1936–37. The business recession of 1937–1938 depressed butter prices, and purchases were increased to 9.8 million pounds.[17]

Government purchases of butter to remove price-depressing surpluses became very large in 1938, reaching a total of 142 million pounds for the year. The volume of purchases fell off sharply thereafter, to 25 million pounds in 1939 and to about 11 million in 1940 and 1941.[18] From 1941 on, butter was in short supply and had to be rationed. There was no occasion for price-support purchases from 1942 through 1948. Large-scale government buying was resumed in 1949.

By far the largest part of the funds used from 1936 until the early 1950s was derived from customs receipts assigned to the Secretary of Agriculture under Section 32 of the Agricultural Adjustment Act amendments of 1935. Total Section 32 expenditures on butter from 1936 to 1952 amounted to $93.2 million. Of that amount, $26.2 million was used in the food stamp plan. Realized losses on Commodity Credit Corporation purchases up to that time amounted to $48.3 million.

For the period August 1933 to June 30, 1953, surplus removal purchases of butter amounted in all to $110.1 million, of which $16.9 million came from sources other than Section 32 funds, chiefly those supplied by AAA and the Federal Relief Administration in the years 1933–1935. There were in addition, from 1954 on, much larger Commodity Credit Corporation outlays, which are described in a later section (see pp. 245–50).

---

in a decrease in the number of milk cows and heifers from about 38 million head in 1934 to 34.8 million in 1938. Thereafter the number expanded, reaching 41.3 million in 1944. (*Agricultural Statistics, 1951,* p. 325.)

16. *The Dairy Industry and the AAA,* pp. 362–63.

17. From May 1938 on, part of the purchasing was done by the Dairy Products Marketing Association, a nonprofit organization of eight regional butter marketing cooperatives set up by the government to help operate the government loan program for butter. Receipts from sales in excess of loans were to be turned over to the Surplus Marketing Administration. (See U.S Bureau of Agricultural Economics, *The Dairy Situation,* December 1941, p. 8.)

18. U.S. Bureau of Agricultural Economics, *Changes in the Dairy Industry, United States, 1920–50,* statement submitted July 21, 1950 in a Public Hearing before a Subcommittee of the Senate Committee on Agriculture and Forestry, 81st Cong., 2d sess., pursuant to Senate Resolutions 36 and 198, pp. 2013–15.

Purchase Operations in Cheese

Some support was given to the cheese industry in much the same way as that provided for butter. About 18 million pounds of cheese were purchased in 1934, but thereafter purchases were small or negligible until 1949 when relatively heavy buying was resumed. Some 3.5 to 4.5 million pounds were bought in each of the years 1938 and 1940 and small amounts in 1935–1937 but none at all in 1939 or 1941–1948.

Total expenditures on cheese, for surplus removal, in the period August 1933 to June 30, 1953 amounted to $3.7 million. Almost all of it ($3 million) came from Section 32 funds. The cheese purchased in surplus removal operations was virtually all used in relief activities. Here, as in butter, there were later heavy expenditures for price support by way of the Commodity Credit Corporation.

Some government purchases of evaporated milk and dry skim milk also were made in 1933–1941 but they were not very important to the industry as a whole. Evaporated milk purchases were largest in 1935 (47 million pounds) and in 1940 (66 million pounds). Dry skim milk purchases were nominal in 1936, 1939 and 1940 but reached 16 million, 23 million and 31 million pounds in 1935, 1937 and 1938.

The purchases of manufactured dairy products as a whole cannot have had any large effect on the price situation in the years 1933–1941. Only in 1938 and 1939 did such purchases, on a whole-milk-equivalent basis, for all products combined (that is, for butter, cheese and evaporated and dried milk) account for as much as 1 per cent of total milk production. Usually they were much less than 1 per cent. In 1938 and 1939 total purchases did reach 1 to 2 per cent of total production and no doubt provided some strength to the very weak markets of those years. The buying program helped somewhat in easing down burdensome accumulations in certain years and, in any event, could probably be well justified as a method of supplying needy families with foods that might otherwise have deteriorated or have served to depress prices further.

On the whole, butterfat prices were somewhat less favorable during the 1930s than the average of all farm prices. The pattern was similar but the butterfat parity ratio was usually from one to several points below that of farm prices generally. Such steps as were taken by the government, except in the fluid milk markets, were of minor consequence and probably affected prices very little and production not at all.

Dairy Products in World War II

The war brought extensive changes in the dairy market situation, some of which have had lasting effects on the industry. Whereas in the

1930–1941 period dairymen were continually plagued by excess supplies and low prices, the problem soon became that of inducing dairymen to produce enough milk and milk products to supply the rapidly increasing demand.

Milk production had been increasing gradually during the 1930s, except in the drought years. By 1939, it stood at about 107 billion pounds as compared with 100 billion in 1930. There was a sharp increase, to 109.5 billion pounds, in 1940. The price of butterfat, to farmers, was up from 1939 but was lower than in 1936 and 1937. Milk sold at wholesale showed about the same relationship.[19]

The heavy demand for cheese and evaporated milk to supply British requirements under lend-lease upset customary price relationships from the spring of 1941 on. In most of the fluid milk markets the price of butter was an important factor in the formula used in determining the price to be paid for fluid milk. With higher prices being paid for milk going into evaporated form and into cheese, but not for butter, there were, of course, repercussions in the fluid milk industry.

Other important changes were occurring. Labor was becoming scarce and high-priced, and dairying is an industry in which labor costs bulk large. The prices of grain concentrates also were rising as a result of the rapidly increasing demand for meat. The more speculative types of agriculture were becoming more attractive as compared with dairying, which had long been regarded as a stable but not a high-income type of farming.

Some changes in milk utilization began to be made, partly at the behest of government. From a nutritional standpoint, butterfat is one of the less essential parts of milk. Emphasis was shifting to greater use of milk-solids-not-fat and the demand for fluid milk was increasing. Plants were equipping themselves for dried milk production and some new plants were being built. All of these changes implied a need for

19. Prices received by farmers and price parities in that period were as follows:

	Milk Sold at Wholesale		*Butterfat*	
Year	*Price to Farmers*	*Parity Price*	*Price to Farmers*	*Parity Price*
	(*Cents per Cwt.*)		(*Cents per Pound*)	
1930	222	254	34.5	41.8
1931	170	224	24.8	36.8
1932	128	198	17.9	32.6
1933	131	190	18.8	31.3
1934	155	205	22.7	33.7
1935	172	205	28.1	33.7
1936	189	203	32.2	33.4
1937	198	211	33.3	34.7
1938	175	202	26.3	33.1
1939	170	197	23.9	32.3
1940	184	198	28.1	32.6
1941	221	210	34.2	34.5

(U.S. Production and Marketing Administration, *Federal Milk Marketing Orders and Dairy Programs in World War II,* Agriculture Monograph No. 12, August 1951, p. 8.)

more total milk production. But the opportunities in other types of farm production, and rising costs and labor scarcities in the dairy industry, were tending to impede the needed expansion.

Milk production increased to nearly 119 billion pounds in 1942 but dropped off slightly in 1943 and 1944. A support price of 31 cents for butter (92-score at Chicago) was announced in April 1941 but it was too low to be attractive to farmers in view of the rising costs they were faced with. It was followed in 1942 by price ceilings and rationing of butter in an effort to keep the cost of living down. The result was a price squeeze on dairymen that led to the leveling off of milk production in 1943 and 1944.

Supply and Production Programs

After passage of the Lend-Lease Act in March 1941, the government programs relating to dairy products had several objectives. One phase was the supply program, the principal purpose of which was to procure the products needed for Britain, and later Russia, under lend-lease commitments and, as the war developed, for the U.S. armed forces. A second emphasis was stimulation of production, particularly of fluid milk, for domestic use along with the desired increase in the amounts of dried milk and cheese available for export. In making that shift, butter tended to be de-emphasized because of the larger nutritional significance of milk solids in the supply programs. A third factor in the situation was the desire to hold down the prices of important food products like milk, butter and cheese as a means of controlling inflation.

From 1941 until 1949, there was no need for price-support purchases to carry out government commitments under the Steagall Amendment. Dairy products were continually above parity. The problem was to keep prices from going higher than would be in keeping with over-all price stabilization objectives and to induce farmers to expand production enough to supply the quantities desired by the government and the general public.

No one of these objectives was entirely achieved, though no severe shortages or price increases resulted. Supplies of fluid milk were tight at times, and both rationing and price control were used in the effort to keep consumption in balance with production without sharp price increases. Producer and consumer subsidies were used for the dual purpose of increasing output and holding down prices to consumers. The most severe impact was on butter since it was given a lower priority in the domestic and foreign food programs than were the products that made fuller use of all of the food elements in milk. Butter supplies to domestic consumers were severely rationed and much of the deficit was made up by increased use of margarine.

Though government purchases for price-support purposes were discontinued, there were very extensive purchases under the supply program. These had, of course, a price-raising effect, but in terms of a tendency to raise prices above required support levels rather than to keep them up to the levels guaranteed under government commitments.

There were important changes in the relative demands for different types of manufactured dairy products. Shipping was critically short and all products sent to allied nations had to be in the form of highly concentrated foods. As a consequence, the U.S. government took vigorous steps to increase the production of dried milk and cheese. Production capacity in the dried milk industry was expanded far beyond normal peacetime requirements, a change that gave rise to some of the more acute postwar problems in the dairy industry. The shift from butter to margarine was also an important factor in creating the postwar problems to be described later.

These measures were supplemented by others designed to change patterns of distribution and to control movement. The rationing arrangements have already been mentioned. They applied particularly to butter, cheese and canned milk. For cheese, relatively low ration-point values were put on the non-Cheddar types, partly as a means of conserving Cheddar and partly because of the perishability of many of the other types.[20] Much more important were the various set-aside orders under which directives were issued to processing establishments requiring them to set aside specified portions of their output for government purchase. From June 1943 through April 1944, producers were required to set aside 75 per cent of both spray and roller type nonfat dry milk solids. The percentage was later reduced as production began to catch up with demand. Set-asides were continued on roller production until September 1944 and on spray production until September 1945. Set-asides were reinstated on both types for the period May–July 1946.[21]

Efforts to Increase Milk Production

A major phase of the over-all program was the effort to increase or maintain milk production in the face of rising costs and attractive opportunities in other types of agricultural production. That phase was the one that resulted in the heaviest expenditure of government funds, the largest outlay in fact that was made in connection with any of the farm products during the war years. Producer subsidies on milk ranged generally from 30 to 90 cents per hundredweight, those on butter from 4 to 17 cents per pound. These were in addition to the rollback consumer subsidies provided as a means of keeping consumer prices at or below

20. This, together with the relatively favorable price ceilings on non-Cheddar types, resulted in a shift toward increased production of the non-Cheddar types, which led later to the issuance of a restraining order. See Hugh L. Cook and George H. Day, *The Dry Milk Industry*, American Dry Milk Institute, Inc., Chicago, September 1947, p. 12.

21. *Ibid.*, p. 13.

the April 1943 level, as directed in the President's "hold-the-line" order of April 8.

The subsidies provided took a number of forms. The principal ones were as follows: [22]

1. Cheddar cheese, December 1, 1942 to January 31, 1946. Rate, 3.75 to 4.00 cents per pound. Purpose, to prevent diversion of milk to other uses in view of the relatively low ceiling prices on cheese. Cost, $67.6 million.

2. Fluid milk, April 8, 1943 to June 30, 1946. Rate, 20 to 30 cents per hundredweight. Purpose, to offset increases in prices to producers in specified markets and enable distributors to sell at ceiling prices. Cost, $38.1 million.

3. Butter production payments (to creameries), June 1, 1943 to October 31, 1945. Rate, 5 cents per pound. Purpose, to offset rollback in retail price of butter. Cost, $181.6 million.

4. Dairy production payments, October 1, 1943 to June 30, 1946. Rate (on whole milk), 36.3 to 60.4 cents per hundredweight of milk; on butterfat, 4.2 to 16.3 cents per pound. Purpose, production incentive to offset rising feed and other costs. Cost, $1,204.7 million.

The total of these subsidies amounted to $1,492 million, the largest item in the wartime food subsidy program. The programs were carried out in various ways, some by the Commodity Credit Corporation through Dairy Products Marketing Association, with payments made to manufacturers (for cheese); some by CCC payments through milk market administrators (for fluid milk); some by the Reconstruction Finance Corporation through Defense Supplies Corporation (to creameries); and some by CCC through county AAA committees (to farmers). Direct payments to farmers constituted by far the largest item in the total ($1.2 billion out of approximately $1.5 billion).

Incidence of the Subsidy Program

Although by far the largest part of the subsidy on dairy products went directly or indirectly to farmers, it cannot properly be regarded as a special aid to agriculture or a part of the price-support program. The payments were made as an inducement for farmers to maintain or increase production and to hold down prices to consumers. The expanded production desired was a matter of national objectives, not of farmer aspirations. Prices in the market might have been allowed to rise as did those of most other farm products. The results from the standpoint of the dairy producer would have been about the same.

22. Data as given in U.S. Production and Marketing Administration, *Federal Milk Marketing Orders and the Dairy Program in World War II* (hereafter referred to as *Dairy Program in World War II*), Agriculture Monograph No. 12, August 1951, pp. 44–45.

Most dairy spokesmen were opposed to the subsidy program and urged that prices be allowed to rise enough to cause farmers to produce the amounts needed. That would have meant higher prices to consumers, which the farmer spokesmen contended they were well able to pay. Actually, dairy prices and consumption were held down more rigorously through price ceilings and rationing than those of many other farm products. For broader reasons related to the effort to hold living costs and wages stable, the government chose the subsidy route rather than the higher-market-price route. There were, of course, logical reasons for that decision but they were in terms of national objectives, not of farm program objectives.

That the very large payments made were not a windfall to dairy farmers is evidenced by the fact that dairy product prices did not rise by a notably larger percentage in the war years than did the prices of farm products as a whole and by the fact that the production of milk was not stimulated significantly. Dairy products rose from an index of 120 in 1940 (1910–1914=100) to 230 in 1945, an increase of about 108 per cent. Farm products as a whole rose 106 per cent. Milk production held about steady through 1942, 1943 and 1944.[23]

During 1945 production increased markedly and it may be that this implies a higher than necessary price in 1943 and 1944, as it takes some time to expand dairy facilities and cow numbers. However, the larger 1945 production was not in excess of estimated needs and was not fully maintained in succeeding years. Many dairy farmers could have, and probably would have, turned to other types of production had dairy prices been kept down to ceiling levels without providing increased returns for keeping dairying on an approximately even keel with other types of agricultural production.

Milk-Drying Capacity Overexpanded

As a result of the emphasis put on increased production of dried milk, that branch of the industry was overexpanded in relation to peacetime needs. Nearly all types of dairy products continued at prices well above support levels until 1949 but it became necessary to make price-support purchases of dried milk in 1947. Some 211 million pounds of nonfat dry milk solids were purchased for price-support purposes.[24] The milk thus acquired was later sold to other government agencies for use in occupied countries and foreign relief.

Postwar Supports

The heavy purchases in connection with the foreign-aid programs, and the high level of domestic demand, kept prices of nearly all the farm

23. *Agricultural Statistics, 1951,* p. 581, and *Dairy Programs in World War II,* p. 8.
24. *Dairy Programs in World War II,* p. 11.

products, including those of the dairy industry, well above support levels through 1948. By 1949, with a recession in business and a slacking off of abnormal demand, prices sagged and sizable quantities not only of dried milk but also of butter and cheese were bought by the government in an effort to maintain prices. In that year, the Commodity Credit Corporation bought 128 million pounds of butter, 109 million pounds of cheese and 325 million pounds of nonfat dry milk solids. The need for readjustment either in quantities produced or in the levels of support prices began to be more apparent.

Thereafter, almost all of the price-support operations were carried out by the Commodity Credit Corporation. The losses incurred therefore appear in its reports, except those that are potential and not yet measurable. However, various devices were used to ease down the stocks built up then and after. Most of the commodities concerned were of the semiperishable type. That is, they had to be kept in cold storage, which was expensive, and even so could not be kept indefinitely. Some were fed into the foreign-aid supply programs, some into school lunches and some were disposed of in other ways. However, the excess stock situation continued to be a perplexing one. Though not so large in scale as the wheat and cotton surpluses, the butter and cheese surpluses attracted almost equal attention in the press.

CCC Operations to 1951–52

Except for purchases under the supply program, there were no CCC operations in butter until after the close of World War II. Price-support purchases were begun in April 1949, in accordance with an announcement made on February 8 that butterfat would be supported nationally at 90 per cent of parity. By June 30, the Corporation had acquired 6.4 million pounds at a cost of $3.8 million. This was intended as a price-stabilizing operation and it was expected that the butter acquired could be sold later without loss.

Purchase operations became much more extensive in fiscal 1950 (July 1949–June 1950). Through December 1949, the operations were carried out under the provisions of the Agricultural Act of 1948. From January 1950, they were in accordance with the Agricultural Act of 1949. The support price for grade A butter was put at 59 cents for deliveries made before July 27 and 62 cents for deliveries made thereafter. The purpose of the differential was to encourage normal storage of butter. Supports were also announced for nonfat dry milk solids and for Cheddar cheese, dried milk at 11 to 12.75 cents per pound depending on type and time of delivery, and cheese at 31.75 cents per pound.[25]

25. U.S. Production and Marketing Administration, *Review of Operations—Commodity Credit Corporation—Fiscal Year 1950,* pp. 7–9.

It should be noted that program years do not coincide with fiscal years in the data presented here and elsewhere. The program year for butter and cheese was April 1 to

As of the end of fiscal 1949, CCC still held inventories from the previous year's operation in the amount of 6.4 million pounds of butter and 83.4 million pounds of dry milk solids. During fiscal 1950 (July 1949–June 1950), CCC purchased 190.6 million pounds of butter at a cost of $115.2 million and 234 million pounds of dry milk solids, which cost $28.3 million. It also bought 25.5 million pounds of Cheddar cheese at a cost of $8.4 million.[26] Thus the serious stock problem of the early 1950s was beginning to take shape.

Small portions of the butter and cheese stocks were disposed of during fiscal 1950, through donation, sales and some small amount of spoilage. Net realized losses and donations amounted to about $4 million for butter and $13,000 for cheese. A very large part of the dry milk solids (183 million pounds) was sold for export at a net loss of $11.5 million, and 25 million pounds were donated for foreign and domestic assistance at a cost to CCC of $3.3 million.

Supports were continued at about the same rate in 1950 but were increased in 1951 to 66 cents per pound for butter, 36 cents for cheese and 13–15 cents for dry milk solids. Those of the 1950–51 marketing year were designed to reflect an average price of not less than $3.07 per hundredweight for manufacturing milk and 60 cents per pound for butterfat. These rates were approximately 79 per cent of parity for manufacturing milk and 86 per cent for butterfat. The corresponding rates for the 1951–52 season were $3.60 per hundredweight for manufacturing milk (87 per cent of parity) and 67.6 cents per pound for butterfat (90 per cent of parity).[27]

Butter stocks held by the Commodity Credit Corporation were low at the beginning of the 1950 fiscal year, that is, on June 30, 1949, amounting to 6.4 million pounds valued at $3.8 million. There were heavy purchases for price-support purposes during that year, a total of 190.6 million pounds valued at $115.2 million. The end-of-year inventory (June 30, 1950) amounted to nearly 162 million pounds valued at just under $100 million.[28]

The upsurge in demand which resulted from the Korean War carried prices above the support level and there was almost no purchase of butter by CCC in the 1951 fiscal year. The principal CCC activity was in disposing of the heavy inventories acquired under the 1949 and 1950 programs. Donations valued at $42 million and sales amounting to $84 million brought the June 30, 1951 inventory down almost to zero. Losses taken by CCC on the year's operations amounted to $44.2 million.[29]

---

the following March 31. The fiscal year, in accordance with long-established government practice, runs from July 1 to the following June 30. The operations in a given fiscal year may therefore include parts of two program years.

26. *Ibid.*
27. *Ibid.*, fiscal 1951, p. 7.
28. *Ibid.*, fiscal 1950, p. 32.
29. *Ibid.*, fiscal 1951, table on Dairy Branch Program Activity during Fiscal Year 1951.

No program activities in butter were reported for fiscal 1952, except disposal of the inconsequential amount of butter held at the beginning of the year (221,000 pounds). That was sold at a profit of $41,571.[30]

Heavy Accumulations in 1953 and 1954

The price of butterfat (in cream) reached 105 per cent of parity in February 1952 and held at or around the 100 per cent level through the remainder of the 1952 fiscal year. Early in fiscal 1953 it began to weaken and by December was down to 85 per cent of parity. Heavy purchases of butter were made by CCC in carrying out the government's commitment to support prices at 90 per cent of parity.[31] At the end of the year CCC owned 231 million pounds valued at $154 million, a larger quantity than in any previous season. The butter problem was emerging as one of the most perplexing aspects of the farm problem as a whole. Though the values involved were not so large as in some of the crop programs, the perishability of butter, and the costliness of storage for it, made it especially important that steps be taken to reduce inventories.

During fiscal 1954, CCC bought 377 million pounds of butter at a cost of $237 million. Of that, about 75 per cent was bought in connection with the 1953 program and about 25 per cent under the 1954 program. As of June 30, 1954, CCC had an inventory of 467 million pounds carried on its books at $304 million.[32] Sales during the year amounted to $59.3 million on butter which had cost CCC $71.7 million. Other dispositions accounted for butter which had cost the Corporation $22.5 million. Net loss for the year, on butter, was $34.8 million.

Per capita butter consumption was continuing its long decline and was down to 8.7 pounds in 1953, which was not much over half what it had been in the 1930s. Margarine consumption, on a per capita basis, had increased from about 2.5 to 3 pounds in the late 1930s to 7.9 pounds in 1953. There was also some increase in per capita consumption of other edible oils, from about 5 to 7 pounds in the 1930s to 9.2 pounds in 1953. Total per capita consumption of all food fats, including lard, was about the same in 1953 as in the 1930s, butter having been replaced to a considerable extent by margarine and "edible oils" such as those used in salad dressings and for similar purposes.[33]

The repeal of the special federal tax on colored margarine, effective July 1, 1950, gave further impetus to the increase in per capita consump-

30. Except for a very small amount donated (less than $400 worth). (*Ibid.*, fiscal 1952.)

31. It bought 143 million pounds at a cost of $97 million under the 1952 program and 111 million pounds under the 1953 program. (*Ibid.*, fiscal 1953, table showing Dairy Branch Program Activity.)

32. Commodity Credit Corporation, *Report of the President and Report of Financial Operations, June 30, 1954,* pp. 37, 38.

33. U.S. Agricultural Marketing Service, *The Fats and Oils Situation,* May 28, 1954, p. 17.

tion of margarine, which had nearly doubled in the 1940s, partly as a result of shortages of butter. Several states followed the lead of the federal government in removing restrictions on the sale of margarine colored to look like butter. That increased the convenience and attractiveness of margarine and contributed to a shift that was already occurring as consumers became more accustomed to using margarine. Also, there was a widening spread between the prices of margarine and butter as a result of lower prices for cottonseed and soybean oils, the principal ingredients of margarine.[34]

Support Rate on Butter Reduced

Until January 1, 1950, the price of butterfat was supported at 90 per cent of parity. The rate was lowered to 79 per cent in January 1950 but was raised to 87 per cent on April 1 and remained at that level until March 31, 1951 when it was raised to 90 per cent. It remained at 90 per cent until March 31, 1954.[35] By the winter of 1953–54, it had become evident that continued support at the 90 per cent rate would not only be very costly from the standpoint of the government but that the maintenance of high-level supports for butter was contributing to the shift from butter to margarine as a food fat.

The situation was different from that in wheat. Butter production was not overexpanded in terms of prewar per capita requirements. The problem was how to help the industry adjust to a major shift in food habits which had reduced severely the per capita consumption of butter. Investments in dairy farms, dairy equipment and production know-how were heavy and widely dispersed over the nation. Dairy farming had long been encouraged by state and federal agencies, banks and others as a desirable and stable type of agriculture. Yet the continuous buying up and storing of butter and other dairy products was obviously not a satisfactory solution for the dilemma facing butter producers and the government.

Not only was the cost of the program reaching proportions that were a matter of grave concern; there was also a prospect that large losses might occur through spoilage and deterioration, which could result in adverse public reaction similar to that caused by the diversion and destruction of large quantities of potatoes in 1949 and 1950. Further-

34. See *The Dairy Situation,* January–February 1952, p. 11. Per capita consumption of margarine increased from 6.0 pounds in 1950 to 7.9 pounds in 1953, partly because of the relatively high price of butter and partly for the reasons given above.

35. The Secretary of Agriculture had authority from 1950 on to support the prices of dairy products at 75 to 90 per cent of parity. In the opinion of many observers, the readjustment in support levels that was made in 1954 was delayed longer than it should have been. Earlier action would probably have eased the situation with respect to excess stocks and reduced government losses, and would have resulted in an earlier start on the inescapable readjustments confronting the dairy industry. (Price-support levels are as given in U.S. Production and Marketing Administration, *CCC Price Support Statistical Handbook,* April 1952, p. 20.)

more, there was very real danger that the market for butter was being irreparably damaged by throwing the competitive advantage so heavily in the direction of increased reliance on margarine as a customary spread and cooking fat.

In view of these considerations, the Secretary of Agriculture lowered the support price on butter to 75 per cent of parity as of April 1, 1954, the beginning of the new marketing year. The first effects of reducing the support rate were to increase consumption of butter and reduce government purchases. The long decline in per capita domestic consumption was checked temporarily at least. The domestic consumption of butter in both the 1954 and 1955 seasons exceeded that of the 1953 season. Lower prices together with increasing consumption encouraged the trade to carry larger holdings. Increasing consumption and smaller purchases, together with a stepped-up disposal program, had almost eliminated the surplus stocks of butter held by CCC by the end of the 1955 season.

The problem had also been made somewhat less acute by the continuing shift of areas formerly engaged in butter and cheese production into the production of fluid milk to supply the increasing demand for that product. However, many butter-producing dairymen were not so situated as to be able to sell in the fluid milk markets, and even the rapidly expanding fluid milk markets could, of course, be swamped by any general shift from butter and cheese to fluid milk as an outlet. Also, a considerable portion of the income to fluid milk suppliers is derived from products manufactured from surplus milk used in the manufacture of butter and other dairy products. Adjustment to a new set of price relationships between closely competitive products like butter and margarine remained a difficult one for which there was no easy and simple solution.

Program Costs as of June 1955

During fiscal 1955, additional butter purchases in the amount of $104 million were made, and very sizable donations and other abnormal types of inventory reduction were carried out. Butter sales brought a return of $31.4 million for butter that had cost CCC $46 million. Disposition by other means, that is, donations, relief shipments and so on, including butter oil, accounted for a quantity in which CCC had an investment of $196 million. The net loss for the year on butter operations was $219 million.[36] However, end-of-year inventories, though still large, were substantially smaller than a year earlier (274 million pounds of butter and 7.7 million pounds of butter oil as against 467 million pounds of butter at the end of fiscal 1954).

Much of the loss that became a realized cost in fiscal 1954 and 1955 resulted from the 1952 and 1953 purchase programs. As of July 1, 1953,

36. Commodity Credit Corporation, *Report of Financial Condition and Operations as of June 30, 1955,* p. 41.

CCC held 120 million pounds of butter purchased under the 1952 program and 111 million acquired in carrying out the 1953 program, which was then just getting started. As of July 1, 1954, the Corporation still had on hand 42 million pounds from the 1952 program and 322 million acquired under the 1953 program. In addition, 103 million pounds had been purchased in carrying out the 1954 program.

The fiscal 1955 disposal operations and costs relate to these combined holdings of some 467 million pounds. Part of the loss was due to the decision to reduce the support level on butter (and other dairy products) from 90 per cent of parity to 75 per cent, on April 1, 1954. Butter stocks held when the support level was lowered had, of course, to be sold in a market that was lower than that in which they were acquired. The reduction in support level lowered CCC purchase prices by 8.25 cents per pound for butter, 4.75 cents for cheese and 1 cent for dry milk.[37]

For the period October 1933 to June 30, 1955, as a whole, government costs in supporting the price of butter amounted to $413.8 million, not counting additional costs that were to be expected on the stocks held by CCC as of June 30, 1955 (274 million pounds of butter and 7.7 million pounds of butter oil). As noted, these stocks were mostly liquidated in the 1955 season but the record of costs was not yet available.

The figure given above does not include $182 million spent on butter subsidies during World War II, which are regarded as primarily a subsidy to consumers. Disregarding consumer subsidies, the costs assignable to the butter program (including the losses on butter oil) consist of $303.7 million in CCC losses and $110.1 million in surplus removal programs, mostly financed with Section 32 funds, thus making an overall total of $413.8 million. Of the Section 32 fund expenditures, $26.2 million were used in the food stamp plan of 1939–1943. The remainder under the "surplus removal" category went to domestic and foreign relief and school lunches.[38]

Taken as a whole, the butter program was one of the relatively expensive ones of the postwar period. However, the figures as of the dates here used reflect more fully the losses incurred than do those for some of the less perishable products, since butter by its nature required some sort of action to reduce stocks within a year or two after their acquisition. Hence losses incurred became realized costs more quickly than for such crops as wheat and cotton.

37. *The Dairy Situation,* March 1, 1954, p. 3.

38. Commodity Credit Corporation, *Report of Financial Condition and Operations as of June 30, 1955,* pp. 31, 41; U.S. Department of Agriculture, *Realized Cost of Agricultural and Related Programs, by Function or Purpose, Fiscal Years 1932–1953,* in U.S. Senate Committee on Agriculture and Forestry, *General Farm Program,* 83d Cong., 2d sess., 1954, pp. 74–89 (reproduced in Appendix B in Murray R. Benedict, *Can We Solve the Farm Problem?,* Twentieth Century Fund, New York, 1955); and U.S. Production and Marketing Administration, *Section 32 Handbook,* 1953, p 31.

THE CHEESE AND DRY MILK PROGRAMS

The postwar price-support programs relating to cheese and dry milk followed a somewhat similar pattern to that of butter and for much the same reasons. The cheese industry was not affected so severely by the increased use of a cheaper substitute. However, since cheese is an alternative product of milk that might otherwise go into butter production, there are interconnections between the two. Dry milk, on the other hand, suffered not so much from the rise of a competitive product as from overexpansion of capacity during the war years.

Cheese was not subsidized heavily with Section 32 funds. The total amount used, through June 1952, was $3 million. Section 32 expenditures on milk were much larger, $46.7 million, but much of the amount spent was for fluid milk rather than for processed milk. Purchases amounted to $33.4 million, diversion to $13.2 million, and a very small amount, $112,000, was spent on export subsidies.[39] In addition, the Agricultural Act of 1954 authorized, for the period September 1, 1954 to June 30, 1956, expenditure of up to $50 million to increase the consumption of fluid milk by children in nonprofit schools and presumably comparable annual amounts thereafter.

For cheese as for butter, the principal price-support costs came in the postwar years, especially in the 1950s after the inflation that resulted from the Korean War had eased off. A heavy subsidy on cheese was provided during World War II, from December 1, 1942 to January 31, 1946. Its purpose was to prevent diversion of milk from cheese manufacture because of the relatively low ceiling prices on cheese. The costs incurred were thus, in the main, consumer subsidies and indirect contributions to the government's supply program. Payments of 3.75 to 4.00 cents per pound were made to cheese manufacturers through Dairy Products Marketing Association. The total cost was $67.6 million.[40]

The Steagall Amendment made it mandatory that cheese be supported at 90 per cent of parity through 1948. The Agricultural Act of 1948 (Title I) continued the 90 per cent support rate on milk and its products to January 1, 1950. Thereafter, under the Agricultural Act of 1949, support could be at such rate between 75 and 90 per cent of parity as the Secretary of Agriculture "determines necessary in order to assure an adequate supply." The 75–90 per cent support rate, at the discretion of the Secretary of Agriculture, was retained in the Agricultural Act of 1954.

Under these authorizations and directives, the price support on the principal products made from milk (American cheese, evaporated milk and butter)[41] remained at 90 per cent of parity through 1949. The rates

39. *Section 32 Handbook,* p. 31.
40. *Dairy Programs in World War II,* p. 44.
41. In terms of parity price for the milk used rather than on the products themselves.

on cheese and dry milk, like those for butter, were reduced to 79 per cent for the period January 1, 1950 to March 31, 1950 and were then raised to 87 per cent. They were further increased, to 90 per cent, on April 1, 1951 and remained at that level until April 1, 1954. The support provided from 1949 on was through offers to purchase. Consequently, such amounts as did not move at approximately support prices or above passed into the hands of CCC.

Cheese Purchases from 1949 On

The only price-support purchases made in the period August 29, 1941 to December 31, 1948 were those of nonfat dry milk solids.[42] During fiscal 1950, prices declined and 69.5 million pounds of cheese were bought by CCC (25.5 million pounds under the 1949 program and 44 million under the 1950 program). Most of it (59 million pounds) was still held at the end of the year. A loss of about $1 million was taken on the cheese sold.[43] There were further heavy purchases of about 65 million pounds in fiscal 1951, but the upsurge in demand, together with donations of about 26 million pounds, made it possible by the end of the fiscal year to dispose of practically all of the cheese acquired by CCC up to that time. However, the year's operations involved a loss to CCC of about $24 million.[44] The operations in fiscal 1952 were very minor and resulted in a small net gain of $35,000.

In fiscal 1953, cheese purchases in sizable amounts were resumed in carrying out price-support commitments. CCC bought 161 million pounds and still held 160 million pounds at the end of the year.[45] There was a small realized gain on the year's operations ($13,700) but heavy stocks had been acquired on which later losses could be anticipated. By fiscal 1954, the cheese operations assumed major proportions and began to be a matter of grave concern to the administrators of the program. Cheese purchases by CCC amounted to 423 million pounds and the end-of-year inventory (June 30, 1954) was 419 million pounds.[46]

Heavy losses were in prospect and it was obvious that a special effort would have to be made to reduce holdings not only of cheese but of other manufactured dairy products as well. The loss actually realized in that year was $12.7 million, but it was evident that further heavy losses would have to be taken.

It was hoped that putting support prices at a lower level (75 per cent of parity), in a period when consumer incomes were at all-time highs,

42. *Dairy Programs in World War II,* p. 11. CCC bought 211 million pounds of nonfat dry milk solids in 1946–47. This stockpile was later sold to other government agencies at a profit.

43. Commodity Credit Corporation, *Review of Operations,* fiscal 1950, p. 8.

44. *Ibid.,* fiscal 1951, table showing program activities of the Dairy Branch (unnumbered).

45. *Ibid.,* fiscal 1953, table showing Dairy Branch activity (unnumbered).

46. *Ibid.,* fiscal 1954, table showing Livestock and Dairy Activities.

would result in absorption by the market of nearly all current supplies, thus avoiding the necessity of further additions to CCC holdings. But demand and supply were not sufficiently elastic to bring about such an adjustment, at least not in any short period of time. Even with a lower level of support prices, purchases in fiscal 1955 amounted to 135 million pounds. Forty-two million pounds of cheese were sold during the year and "other dispositions" (donations and so on) accounted for 163 million pounds. As of the end of the fiscal year CCC still had on hand 350 million pounds. The realized loss for the year amounted to $76.1 million, the largest for any year up to that time, but holdings still were large. Losses on the 350 million pounds still held would undoubtedly be heavy.

Realized CCC losses on cheese for the whole period August 1933 to June 30, 1955 amounted to $113.8 million, more than half of it in fiscal 1955. The other period of heavy loss ($25 million) was in 1946–1951, mainly in fiscal 1951 on the 1949 and 1950 programs. Small gains were recorded in fiscal 1952 and fiscal 1953. Heavy losses began to reappear in fiscal 1954 and reached record levels in fiscal 1955. Total cost of the cheese programs, including the $3 million in Section 32 funds used and ignoring relief and war purchases, amounted to $116.8 million by June 30, 1955.

The Dry Milk Program

As previously stated, the dry milk problem arose largely out of the heavy emphasis on increased capacity and larger production which developed in the war period.[47] Nutritionists have long deplored the waste of the nonfat solids in milk used for butter production since they include many valuable nutritional elements, especially minerals, vitamins and proteins. However, no large demand for such products was apparent in the domestic or foreign markets prior to 1941. U.S. consumers were relatively well supplied with these nutrients through heavy consumption of milk in fluid form, though nutritionists, dairymen and others had long contended that, even in the United States, the consumption of dairy products, especially of fluid milk, was less than it should be from a health standpoint.

Civilian consumption of nonfat milk solids increased during the interwar years but only slowly and from a start that was so small as to be negligible. Per capita consumption in the United States stood at 0.2 pound per capita in 1920 and had increased to 2.2 pounds by 1940. Total consumption, as of 1940, was 295 million pounds and total disappearance only 305 million pounds.[48] Per capita consumption declined moderately during the war but rose in the postwar years as a result of

47. The production of nonfat dry milk solids increased from an average of 438 million pounds in the 1937–1941 period to 935 million pounds in 1949. (*Agricultural Statistics, 1945,* p. 363, and *1953,* p. 423.)

48. *Agricultural Statistics, 1953,* p. 429.

abundant supplies and continuous pressure by nutritionists for wider and more diverse use of the product. By 1952, per capita consumption had increased to 4.4 pounds per capita and total civilian use to 690 million pounds. Total disappearance amounted to 771 million pounds.

During the war years, with shipping at a premium, strenuous efforts were made to supply the allied nations, particularly Britain, with very compact but highly nutritious foodstuffs. Dry milk was one of the commodities that met this requirement. As a consequence, special efforts were made by the government to encourage and facilitate the installation of additional milk-drying equipment and increased output. U.S. civilian consumption was held in check by set-aside orders applied at the manufacturing level. Exports of nonfat dry milk solids, mostly under lend-lease, increased from 17 million pounds in 1940 to 223 million in 1942.[49] They fell off moderately thereafter but were increased again in the postwar period as part of the foreign-relief program. The amount exported in 1947 was 259 million pounds, some fifteen times as much as was exported in 1940.

The production of nonfat dry milk solids for human consumption showed a moderate upward trend during the late 1930s, from 188 million pounds in 1935 to 322 million in 1940. Thereafter, the increase was rapid, reaching 565 million pounds in 1942 and 643 million in 1945. The upward trend continued in the postwar years and was at an all-time high of 935 million pounds in 1949, nearly twice the wartime level. There was a moderate decline in 1950 and after, but production still amounted to 842 million pounds in 1952, nearly three times the prewar level.[50]

Price Supports Tended to Encourage Overproduction

Since, under the laws applying, dry milk was supported at the same levels as were provided for butter and cheese, which had not been so greatly expanded in the war years, the effect of the price-support program was to encourage continuance of a volume of dry milk production that was excessive in view of the declining demand for it. Hence, large quantities could find outlet only in the form of additions to government inventories. During the early postwar years, considerable amounts of the excess could be and were used in the foreign-aid programs, but as

49. *Agricultural Statistics, 1951,* p. 469.

50. *Dairy Statistics and Related Series,* p. 21. Dry whole milk was increased even more in percentage terms. However, in absolute amount it was much less important. Production rose from 29 million pounds in 1940 to 217 million in 1945. From that time on, it declined rather rapidly and only 98 million pounds were produced in 1952. Dry whole milk is more perishable than nonfat dry milk solids and hence less storable or exportable. Also, the amounts of fat required for minimum adequate diets can usually be supplied more cheaply in other ways than by including butterfat, which is relatively expensive. Nonfat dry milk solids were therefore considered more suitable for lend-lease, military and relief uses and for many types of domestic civilian use.

the need for emergency food programs eased off, the dry milk program became increasingly difficult to handle since there was no way under the laws then in effect of cutting back more heavily on dry milk production than on production of butter and cheese.

Purchases made under the various supply programs, with specially appropriated funds, helped to ease the situation during the early postwar years, but surpluses began to appear as early as 1946 and 1947 and CCC found it necessary to make purchases in order to maintain the prices guaranteed in the wartime price-support legislation. In fiscal 1947 the Corporation bought 118 million pounds at a cost of $11.5 million. Further purchases were made in July and August 1947 in the amount of 88.6 million pounds, but by June 30, 1948, all of the stocks had been sold to other government agencies at a modest profit ($416,000).[51]

Purchases were resumed in fiscal 1949 with the take-over of 91 million pounds at a cost of $10.6 million. As of June 30, 1949, CCC held 83 million pounds. During that period, much of the surplus was being absorbed by the government's supply programs and hence does not appear as price-support purchases. Supply purchases, made by CCC but not financed by it, amounted to 215 million pounds at a cost of $30.6 million.[52]

The 1949–50 fiscal year brought the first really burdensome stock situation in the dry-milk phase of the program. CCC bought 464 million pounds and year-end stocks were up to 363 million pounds, which represented an investment of $46 million. Losses in the amount of $14.7 million were realized within the year and there was, of course, a prospect of heavy loss on the large inventory held at year end.

Support Level Reduced in 1950

The 1950 program, in which the Secretary of Agriculture for the first time after the war had authority to adjust supports to less than 90 per cent of parity, was put on a different basis. For the period January 1, 1950 to March 31, 1951, milk used in manufacturing was to be supported at 79 per cent of parity ($3.07 per hundredweight as a yearly average). The level was raised to 87 per cent of parity for the year April 1, 1951 to March 31, 1952 and thereafter was at 90 per cent of parity until it was reduced to 75 per cent in 1954. Butterfat was to be supported at 86 per cent of parity (about 60 cents per pound) to March 31, 1951 and thereafter at 90 per cent until it, too, was reduced to 75 per cent of parity in 1954.[53]

Further purchases of dried milk were made in the 1950–51 season (132 million pounds) but there was very heavy liquidation of stocks,

51. Commodity Credit Corporation, *Review of Operations,* fiscal 1948, p. 6.
52. *Ibid.,* fiscal 1949, p. 8.
53. *Ibid.,* fiscal 1951, p. 7, and *Price Support Statistical Handbook,* pp. 19, 20.

339 million pounds through sales and 123 million by donations. The year-end inventory was down to 32 million pounds, partly as a result of the favorable opportunity for stock liquidation generally which resulted from the Korean War. Realized losses on dried milk for the year amounted to $42.6 million.

The 1951–52 program was on a relatively small scale as prices of most farm products were above support levels. Only 56 million pounds of dried milk were purchased by CCC and the year-end inventory (30 million pounds) was about the same as a year earlier. A net loss of $1.2 million was taken on the dry-milk operation as a whole.

Heavier Purchases in 1953 and After

The year 1952–53 brought a revival of large-scale buying by CCC (362 million pounds). CCC holdings as of June 30, 1953 amounted to 328 million pounds valued at $55 million. Losses of $4.8 million had been realized during the year. The build-up continued in 1953–54 with purchases of 676 million pounds, about three quarters of a year's production. Sales amounted to 463 million pounds and "other dispositions" to 102 million pounds but the realized loss was high ($82 million). CCC still held 440 million pounds as of June 30, 1954. Purchases were smaller in 1954–55 and holdings were down to 198 million pounds on June 30.

Heavy losses were also experienced in the operations of 1954–55. Sales were made at sacrifice prices in order to liquidate the unwieldy surplus that had been built up. Part of the loss was due also to the reduction in prices that resulted from the lowering of support levels in the spring of 1954. Dry milk in which CCC had an investment of $69.7 million was sold for $16.4 million, partly for use as livestock feed. In addition, milk valued at $64.5 million was donated for use by various public agencies. Net loss on the year's operations was $117.8 million. The year-end inventory, as of June 30, 1955, was 198 million pounds.[54]

Considering the whole period here under review, losses on dry milk solids amounted to $262.9 million by June 30, 1955. Most of the loss related to the support programs of 1949, 1950, 1953, 1954 and 1955. Losses in the 1946–1951 period, mostly in 1949–1951, amounted to $56.8 million. Those for fiscal 1952 and 1953 were minor, less than $6 million in all. The big losses of $82 million and $118 million were taken in fiscal 1954 and fiscal 1955, though the situations and programs that brought them about were a hang-over from an earlier period, principally that which grew out of World War II.

Capacity Excessive in Most Years from 1949 On

It is apparent from the chronology of operations listed above that dry milk production had outrun peacetime requirements by 1949. There

54. Commodity Credit Corporation, *Report of Financial Condition and Operations as of June 30, 1955,* pp. 28, 39.

was need either for a readjustment in capacity and output or for greatly expanded use of the product. A temporary respite came in 1951 and 1952, but excess output again became a serious problem in 1953 and 1954. The loss resulting from the attempt to continue price supports at the levels prevailing in those years and on so large a volume of output was heavy and undoubtedly socially wasteful. Some of the product was channeled into livestock feed in order to get rid of it.

Nutritionists rather generally agreed that more dry milk solids might well be used, both in domestic diets and in other countries. However, the devising of workable programs for bringing that about proved difficult and frustrating. More dry milk solids could apparently be used domestically to improve the nutritional value and palatability of breads and other bakery products, but inducing bakers to use more and persuading the public to buy more nutritious breads proved to be a slow process, though there seemed to be a gradually growing appreciation of the dietary merits of dry milk solids.

The development of effective outlets by way of foreign-aid programs required both improved methods of operation and an increased willingness on the part of the Congress to provide financial support for programs of that kind. The development of export outlets through normal commercial channels presented, of course, the same types of difficulty as did achieving higher levels of domestic consumption but probably they were even harder to overcome.

Uniform Levels of Support Not Appropriate

Part of the problem arose from the tendency of the Congress to apply uniform standards and methods of price support to diverse arrays of products where the surrounding circumstances were different. The increased capacity for and output of dry milk solids were much more clearly a phase of the war program than were the developments in butter and cheese. Yet because the three products are essentially different outlets for the same raw material, and because dairy products were by 1949 in long supply, the same levels of price support were applied to all three during most of the period to 1955.

Though the larger output of dry milk was needed and useful through 1948, that phase of the industry clearly called for differential treatment thereafter. It is also clear that a purchase and storage program, even if feasible for some other products, is not well suited to semiperishables of the type here discussed. Storage as a method of evening out year-to-year ups and downs of demand or supply cannot be used effectively for products that must be consumed within a year's time to avoid spoilage, deterioration or excessive storage costs. Such products must flow into use fairly promptly if waste is to be avoided.

If prices are to be supported at a level above what the market will pay, some procedure other than accumulation in government-owned stocks is needed, together with aggressive measures for increasing consumption of products which, in the interest of society, might well be produced and consumed on a larger scale.

EGGS AND POULTRY

The poultry industry is the nation's third largest producer of cash farm income. In 1952, the $3.4 billion return from poultry products was exceeded only by the $10.1 billion income from meat animals and the $4.6 billion derived from dairy products. About 80 per cent of the farms of the United States produce some chickens but, as with many of the other farm products, the tendency in recent decades has been for commercial egg and poultry production to be concentrated in certain areas which specialize in that type of farming. However, these commercial poultry areas are numerous and widely scattered.

The principal concern about government programs centers in the areas where poultry and eggs provide a substantial part of the farm income. On the great majority of the farms, poultry production is a minor sideline and much of the product is used locally.[55] These small flocks do, however, create problems for the larger, more specialized growers in that production from them tends to be less responsive to egg and poultry feed-price ratios than that of the growers who buy most or all of the feeds used.

Many of the small flocks subsist largely on waste materials and are cared for by family labor that does not add to the over-all expense of operating the farm. Though the production from each flock is small, the number of flocks is so large that the over-all production can have an important effect on prices, especially in some seasons. Egg production from flocks of that kind tends to be more seasonal than on specialized poultry farms, and egg quality in particular is likely to be poorer and less uniform. These considerations apply especially to the large Midwest areas where poultry production is a minor sideline for many farm families.

Farm flocks are kept principally for eggs. In the period 1947–1951, sales of farm-produced chickens and eggs accounted for about three fourths of the total national cash income from poultry and eggs. Of that amount, two thirds consisted of receipts derived from the sale of eggs. The cash receipts from broiler and turkey production, which are now highly specialized industries, amounted to about a fourth of the total income from poultry products.

55. The data given in the following pages do not include the production of poultry and eggs in small nonfarm establishments. It is estimated that such flocks produce about 10 per cent of the total but most of their product is for home use. The figures do include large amounts of egg and poultry production from small farm flocks where the income from poultry and eggs constitutes only a small part of the total income of the farm.

Another characteristic of the industry is the relative speed with which production adjustments can be made in the specialized producing areas. If prices or price ratios become markedly favorable or unfavorable, rather large changes in flock sizes can be made in a single season. For beef cattle, sheep, dairy production and hogs, such adjustments take longer and, even for many of the crops, they are more difficult.

Price-Support Operations Mainly in Eggs

Egg price supports in the period 1936–1951 were among the most expensive of the government operations relating to farm products. Through 1951, government costs amounted to more than $230 million and were second only to those on potatoes.[56] Government expenditures on egg price supports in that period (including expenditures of Section 32 funds) amounted to about 16 per cent of the cost of all price-support operations relating to perishables. Much of the pre-1941 expenditure ($34.9 million) could be looked upon as primarily a relief program which was at least as much for the benefit of consumers as for egg producers.

The costs here shown for the 1941–1951 period were primarily for price support. They do not include the very large purchases made with lend-lease funds for shipment abroad during the war years. Those purchases were for other purposes but did provide a strong market for a greatly expanded volume of dried egg production. The steps taken to make such shipments possible also, of course, contributed materially to the overexpansion of the industry which gave rise to the need for a post-war price-support program.

Characteristics of the Market

The domestic annual demand for eggs is relatively inelastic,[57] probably more so than the demand for any of the other livestock products. Because of this inelasticity of demand, price-support operations through purchases for diversion and export may, under some conditions, increase returns to farmers by more than the cost to the government. That would depend on whether government purchases actually operate to reduce supplies available to consumers or consist in part of purchases of eggs that would not be produced if the government did not supply an outlet for them.

In a fully employed economy where consumer incomes are high, it is very difficult to find outlets for significant additional quantities of eggs

56. See U.S. Senate, *Price Supports for Perishable Products: A Review of Experience*, Committee on Agriculture and Forestry, 82d Cong., 1st sess., Committee print, October 17, 1951, pp. 2, 3. Supports were available on farm chickens but were not used. No supports were authorized for broilers. Support provisions for turkeys were available but were used in only two of the seasons prior to 1952.

57. Shepherd puts it at −.4, Fox at −.3 and Mehren at −.42 (as of 1950).

without depressing prices severely, as most consumers buy about as many eggs as they want. Except in wartime, export markets are very limited and there is not a large domestic market for processed eggs. Shell eggs are very perishable and must be moved into consumption within the season in which they are produced.

The production of eggs is highly responsive to the prices received in the preceding season. Since pullets begin laying about six months after hatching, an advance in price can bring a quick response. Moreover, the relatively small amount of additional labor and capital required to make substantial additions to flocks contributes to easy and quick expansion of output. Because of that, and because of the wide distribution of egg and poultry producers and the relatively small amount of specialization in the industry, direct controls on production are virtually impossible. Consequently, they have not been tried. The government programs have consisted entirely of purchases for direct distribution and export.

The numbers of chickens raised and pullets kept for laying show a close relationship to the egg-feed price ratio early in the season, but egg production from pullets raised in any given year does not affect the supply of eggs significantly until the next season. The price support provided in one season may therefore affect production in the succeeding season and can, to some extent, direct production. The egg-feed price ratio also may guide production. However, the prices of feeds used by chickens cannot be adjusted except as over-all feed prices are controlled. Consequently, planned modification of egg-feed price ratios can come about only by actions that affect the price of eggs.

THE POULTRY AND EGG PROGRAMS

There was little effort to aid poultry and egg producers until the Agricultural Adjustment Administration came into being. The Federal Farm Board made some loans to poultry and egg cooperatives, beginning in the first year of its operations, but did not undertake to stabilize egg prices. However, the loan made to one cooperative did include a small sum that was intended for use in a commodity support operation. The bulk of the loan funds provided was for facilities and for aid in merchandising.

During the lifetime of the Board, loans to 33 associations in the amount of $1,138,000 were approved. By May 26, 1933, when the assets of the Farm Board were transferred to the Farm Credit Administration, the outstanding loans had been reduced to $409,000. All of them had been liquidated by the end of 1940. In the meantime, the Farm Credit Administration had continued to make loans to poultry cooperatives through the banks for cooperatives. None of these activities had any important effect on egg and poultry prices. They were designed to strengthen and aid the cooperative associations in providing better and more effective marketing services.

First Phases of the AAA Program

The Agricultural Adjustment Act of 1933 contained no specific reference to poultry and eggs. However, since egg prices had fallen by more than 50 per cent as a result of the depression,[58] support purchases were considered in the fall of 1933 with a view to diverting as much as a million cases of storage eggs from usual commercial outlets. The Adjustment Act authorized use of any available funds for expansion of markets and removal of surplus agricultural commodities.

The Adjustment Administration did not favor the levying of a processing tax on eggs and the funds otherwise available were not sufficient to meet the demands made on them. However, late in 1933, the relief agencies authorized the Department of Agriculture to purchase storage eggs and some 314,000 cases were bought in December and January. In addition, the state emergency relief administrations bought 313,000 cases for which they were reimbursed by the Federal Surplus Relief Corporation.

The purchase and distribution for relief of some 600,000 cases eased the situation somewhat and possibly contributed to a slightly better marketing season in 1934. The very low price of around 10 cents per dozen in the spring of 1933 had led to a heavy accumulation of storage eggs (around 9.5 million cases as of August 1). Movement out of storage was slow and prices fell to very low levels in December. By the early part of February, relief purchases had reduced storage holdings to low levels and prices improved somewhat. The usual seasonal decline was under way but 1934 spring prices, at the farm, were a third higher than in the previous season.

Had the purchases been made at the highest level of storage, in July and August, prices probably would have been higher in the late fall and early winter months. Under conditions of that kind, a relatively minor support operation may have a significant effect in stabilizing the market and improving prices, but the level of support in relation to the prices of feedstuffs and to the demand for eggs has an important bearing on the success of the operation.

Though the tone of the market was healthier in 1934, the season average price of 17 cents at the farm was only slightly above the 13.8-cent level of 1933. The number of eggs sold was about 2 per cent smaller than in 1933, which, with other factors, may have accounted for the difference. By 1935, with a small further reduction in marketings and some general economic recovery, the farm price rose to 23.4 cents, which was about the 1930 level but about 6 cents below that of 1929.[59]

58. The farm price of eggs was approximately 30 cents per dozen in 1929. It had fallen to 13.8 cents by 1933. Cash receipts from eggs had declined from $740 million to $309 million. (U.S. Bureau of Agricultural Economics, *Farm Production, Disposition and Income from Chickens and Eggs, 1909–44*, revised, July 1953, p. 60.)
59. *Ibid.*

The Situation in 1936 and After

Beginning in 1936, funds became available for diverting surpluses and encouraging exports by means of customs receipts assigned to the Secretary of Agriculture under Section 32 of the Adjustment Act amendments of August 1935. Egg producers could be given assistance under the terms of that act if the Secretary of Agriculture so decided. Egg production increased about 10 per cent between 1935 and 1937 and prices declined slightly, standing at 21.8 cents per dozen as a season average in 1936 and 21.3 cents in 1937. Purchases were made in the early and late months of 1937 in an effort to strengthen weak markets but they apparently had no large effect. Production leveled off but did not decline significantly.

Production moved up to new highs in 1939 and 1940 and prices again declined, almost to the level of the mid-1930s. The season average farm price in 1938 was only 17.4 cents and in 1940, 18 cents. The inauguration of the food stamp plan in 1939 and the taking of larger quantities in 1940, together with some increase in direct distribution, contributed some strength to the market, but mainly as an offset to the increase in production. The 1940 price to farmers was almost the same as in 1939.

Sales under the food stamp plan and purchases for direct distribution, in the 1940 season, amounted to about 2.5 per cent of total production. Purchases were so distributed as to support the market in the periods of heaviest sales by farmers. They are thought to have resulted in a price to farmers that was about 1 cent per dozen higher than it would otherwise have been.[60]

One of the most serious defects of the prewar program was a confusion in objectives. That confusion is revealed in the press releases and dockets presented as justification for the programs. For example, the releases announcing the 1937 program [61] stated that one of the purposes of the purchases and of the desired increase in the price of eggs to farmers was "to encourage the hatching of a normal number of chickens," that is, to discourage a prospective reduction in hatchings. However, a 1938 press release calling attention to the seeming success of the 1937 operation stated that its purpose was to buy up surplus eggs.[62] Price-support purchases designed specifically to encourage increased production were begun in the spring of 1941, even before passage of the Lend-Lease Act, in March, and the Steagall Amendment, in July.

60. An increase in price of 1 cent per dozen, if achieved, would mean about a $25 million increase in cash receipts to egg producers.

61. 1034–37, January 16, 1937; 1082–37, January 27; and 1206–37, February 24.

62. 1482–38, March 24, 1938.

Eggs and the Food Stamp Plan

Eggs proved to be the most popular of the surplus foods made available to relief families under the food stamp plan. In 1939, about one fourth of the blue stamps provided were used for the purchase of eggs. Later, the addition of pork to the list of foods available for purchase with blue stamps resulted in some shift from eggs to pork. During the period in which the food stamp plan was in operation, relief families obtained by that means 140 million dozen eggs that would have cost at retail $43.6 million, which was about one sixth of the total value of foodstuffs distributed under the food stamp arrangement.[63]

Distribution through the food stamp plan was developed as an alternative to direct distribution. In 1939 and 1940, more eggs were distributed directly to consumers by means of school lunches and in other ways than through the food stamp plan. During 1941, 1942 and 1943, food stamp distributions accounted for a larger part of the total. The volume provided in that way declined from 1942 on because of the large increase in employment, the reduced need for relief distribution and the beginning of large-scale lend-lease purchases. The food stamp program was discontinued in 1943. (All government purchases during the period 1933–1941, together with egg production and prices, are given in Table 34.)

The stamp plan for eggs, and for other foodstuffs as well, was both a farmer relief and a consumer relief measure. Eggs are recognized as having high nutritive value but low-income families commonly consider them too expensive to use freely. They tend to concentrate on cereals and potatoes instead and buy only small amounts of eggs and pork. An analysis of the data available in 1940 indicated that relief families receiving blue stamps consumed more eggs than those that did not receive stamps, which, of course, is to be expected since they could obtain eggs at very low cost. However, food stamp purchases did apparently increase to some extent the total consumer demand for eggs.[64] (Section 32 funds used for eggs, under the food stamp plan, are shown in Table 35.)

EGG PROGRAMS OF THE WAR PERIOD

War developments in Europe soon were reflected in an increased demand for foodstuffs from the United States. Eggs were among the

63. That does not mean, of course, that egg sales were increased by that much. Undoubtedly the families on relief would have bought some eggs anyway but not nearly so many.

64. See Norman Leon Gold, A. C. Hoffman and Frederick V. Waugh, *Economic Analysis of the Food Stamp Plan,* A Special Report by the Bureau of Agricultural Economics and the Surplus Marketing Administration of the Department of Agriculture, 1940. Since the demand for eggs by the higher-income consumers is relatively inelastic, an increase in takings by the lower-income groups presumably increased total demand and the prices paid in the market, though the market price effect probably was not large for programs operated on the scale of those of the late 1930s and early 1940s.

TABLE 34

EGGS: U.S. DEPARTMENT OF AGRICULTURE PURCHASES FOR PRICE SUPPORT AND SURPLUS REMOVAL, 1933–1941 [a]

Year [b]	Total Production	Average Farm Price	Purchases	Purchases as Per Cent of Total Production
	(1,000 Cases)	*(Cents per Dozen)*	*(1,000 Cases)*	
1933 [c]	98,650	13.8	627	0.6
1935	93,358	23.4	—	—
1936	95,928	21.8	31	0.03
1937	104,344	21.3	501 [d]	0.4
1938	103,767	20.3	61	0.05
1939	107,897	17.4	268	0.2
1940	110,264	18.0	2,317	2.1
1941	116,328	23.5	206	0.1

Sources: U.S. Bureau of Agricultural Economics, *1952 Agricultural Outlook Charts,* October 1951, p. 57, and *The Poultry and Egg Situation,* September–October 1952, p. 20; also records of the Commodity Programs Division, Poultry Research, U.S. Production and Marketing Administration.

a. All price-support and surplus removal purchases in this period were of shell eggs. Stamp plan sales 1939–1941 not included.

b. Purchases in most years were spread throughout the year, with the largest part being made in January through August. In 1940, purchases were made in every month January through August with the greatest concentration in May and June.

c. Purchases of 1933 storage eggs in December 1933 and January 1934 and, in addition, State Emergency Relief Administrations' purchases of 313,000 cases, for which they were reimbursed by the Federal Surplus Relief Corporation.

d. Some of these stored eggs were purchased in 1938.

TABLE 35

EGGS: SECTION 32 FUNDS USED FOR EGGS IN THE FOOD STAMP PLAN, 1939–1943

Fiscal Year	Shell Eggs	Cost
	(1,000 Cases)	*(Thousands)*
Total	4,663	$43,568
1939	5	38
1940	407	2,655
1941	1,548	11,534
1942	1,975	20,327
1943	728	9,014

Source: U.S. Production and Marketing Administration, Office of Budget, Table, "Removal of Surplus Agricultural Commodities (Section 32), Egg Programs—Fiscal Years 1936–1952," August 15, 1951, revised October 30, 1952.

items for which the United Kingdom began to negotiate for larger supplies. The Lend-Lease Act of March 11, 1941 provided the means whereby increased purchases for export could be financed. On April 3, 1941, the Secretary of Agriculture issued a statement urging farmers to expand the production of specified commodities, including chickens and eggs, and promised price support on such commodities through June 1943. Subsequently, in July 1941, the Steagall Amendment directed that support prices for such commodities were to be at 85 per cent of parity. The rate was raised to 90 per cent in 1942. Thus the basis for the war programs relating to chickens and eggs was established early in the war period.

The low level of egg prices in 1940 and the relatively low egg-feed price ratio would normally have discouraged egg production in 1941. However, the stabilization purchases undertaken in 1940, and the Secretary's promise of April 1941 that egg prices would be supported at 22 cents per dozen, more than offset these retarding influences. Egg production was increased by about 5 per cent in 1941. Feed supplies were abundant, so all that was needed was the promise of a price sufficient to make production attractive.

The announcement by the Secretary of Agriculture was notable in two respects: (1) it was the first experiment with forward pricing, and (2) it extended support to chickens as well as to eggs. Egg-support purchases had previously been made only as a way of meeting emergencies. They were not pledged in advance. Furthermore, no specific price objectives had been announced. The addition of chickens was in effect an extension of the price support on eggs since, for the most part, they were joint products of the same industry, chickens being the lesser of the two.[65] Turkeys were added to the list as another item for which demand was likely to increase greatly.

The support level of 22 cents per dozen, Chicago base, was about in line with the then current market. That is, the assurance provided was that if poultrymen increased production as requested they would not be penalized by having to take lower prices as a result of the increase in output. The support level of 22 cents at Chicago, which is in the heart of a large egg producing and shipping area, was comparable to a national season average farm price of 24.2 cents per dozen. The level was such that when the Steagall Amendment requiring 85 per cent of parity came into effect it was not necessary to change the support price on eggs. The season average price to farmers was 23.5 cents.

The offer to support chickens at 15 cents per pound live weight was higher than the required 85 per cent of parity. However, the average price received by farmers, 15.8 cents, was above the support level and no price-support purchases were needed.

65. The support was later limited to chickens weighing 3.5 pounds or more, which was intended as a way of avoiding support for broiler production, a specialized enterprise.

Lend-Lease Shipments Heavy

Lend-lease shipments to Britain were begun in 1941 and were continued throughout the war. Purchases, mostly in dried-egg form, were very heavy in the years 1942–1944. These operations were carried out as a supply operation, not as a means of supporting prices, though they did, of course, greatly enlarge and strengthen the market. The funds were provided through the Lend-Lease Administration and hence do not appear as costs of the farm program.

Purchases in 1941 amounted to nearly 6 per cent of total production. Over the following three years they ranged from 14 to 17 per cent of production but tapered off thereafter. Buying for war purposes declined in 1945 but was continued on a more moderate scale into 1947, as a supply operation for relief and other purposes. (See Table 36.)

TABLE 36

EGGS: U.S. DEPARTMENT OF AGRICULTURE PURCHASES FOR SUPPLY PROGRAMS, 1941–1947

		Purchases						
			Frozen		Dried			
Year	Production	Shell Eggs	Actual	Shell Egg Equivalent	Actual	Shell Egg Equivalent	Total in Terms of Shell Eggs	Purchases as Per Cent of Production
	(1,000 Cases)	*(1,000 Cases)*	*(1,000 Pounds)*	*(1,000 Cases)*	*(1,000 Pounds)*	*(1,000 Cases)*	*(1,000 Cases)*	
1941	116,328	1,549	65,558	1,748	35,249	3,456	6,753	5.8
1942	134,992				208,266	20,418	20,418	15.1
1943	151,497	219			208,777	20,468	20,687	13.6
1944	162,583				275,444	27,004	27,004	16.6
1945	155,161				35,931	3,523	3,523	2.2
1946	154,417		12,015	320	97,407	9,550	9,870	6.3
1947	153,478				29,470	2,889	2,889	1.8

Sources: U.S. Bureau of Agricultural Economics, *The Poultry and Egg Situation,* April 1950, and *1952 Agricultural Outlook Charts,* October 1951, p. 57.

Egg production was greatly expanded during the war years, moving up from about 40 billion in 1940 to 58.5 billion in 1944. The rate of production was sufficient in 1941 and after to meet foreign-aid commitments, permit continuance of food stamp distributions in 1942 and 1943, and take care of domestic and military requirements. There was also a very substantial increase in per capita consumption by U.S. civilians. In fact, production increased at such a rapid rate that there was a surplus of eggs in 1944.

The rapid and large increase in output during those years illustrates the great elasticity of supply in poultry production and its quick response to favorable price relationships. The egg-feed price ratio increased from 10.4 in 1940 to 14.7 in 1943. As noted, the ratio in 1940 was low and resulted in some reduction in the number of hens and pullets on hand at the beginning of 1941. However, the smaller number of laying hens on hand was more than offset by the rate of lay in 1941. Heavier feeding and the encouragement provided by purchase operations in 1940, and by promises of price support in 1941, initiated the rapid increase in production that characterized the succeeding years. By 1943, the number of chickens raised was up some 50 per cent, and the 58 billion egg output of 1944 was 60 per cent above prewar production.

During the war years, the Department of Agriculture made annual announcements of production goals for poultry and eggs, but they were usually too late to have much effect on production in the next season. Actual production outran the goals.[66]

Price Ceilings and Price Supports

Price ceilings for eggs were established in 1942, but through most of the war period the supply available was sufficient to keep prices below ceiling levels. Ceilings may have checked price advances in a few brief periods. Prices reached seasonally adjusted ceilings in July 1943 and in the fall months of that year. Eggs were scarce in some areas and it became necessary to resort to set-asides in order to obtain the quantities desired by the military services in 1943. The continuance of price ceilings despite an egg surplus in 1944 was criticized as creating a tendency for retailers to maintain higher prices than were justified by the supply situation.

Price-support levels were increased in October 1942, as a result both of general price increases that were raising the parity price itself and of the required increase of the rate from 85 to 90 per cent of parity. The level was raised to 98 per cent of parity in 1943, an incentive level rather than one required by law. It was 95 per cent in 1944 though by then a surplus of eggs was beginning to appear.[67] However, price ad-

66. See Gerson Levin, "Government Egg Programs during Wartime, A Review and Appraisal," *Journal of Farm Economics*, November 1946, pp. 888–93.

67. The average support levels in cents per dozen eggs in the years 1941–1950 were as follows:

	Support Price	*Per Cent of Parity*	*Season Average Price to Farmers*
1941	24.2	85	23.5
1942			30.0
Jan.–Sept	27.2	85	
Oct.–Dec.	28.8	90	
1943	34.0	98	37.1
1944	34.0	95	32.5
1945	33.3	90	37.7
1946	37.4	90	37.5
1947	44.8	90	45.3
1948	48.2	90	47.2
1949	47.1	90	45.2
1950	37.0	75	36.2

(*CCC Price Support Statistical Handbook*, April 1952, p. 53.)

vances in the market kept prices above support levels until 1944 and no important price-support operations were needed. Some small purchases were made in the South in 1942 and 1943 for the purpose of bringing farm prices in some of the southern states more nearly into line with those in the states where eggs were being bought for drying to supply lend-lease requirements. By 1944, production had expanded so much that prices fell to the support level.

The Egg Surplus of 1944

The war demand for eggs reached its peak in 1943 and the favorable egg-feed price ratio pointed to increased production and an egg surplus in 1944. Apparently neither the supply prospect nor the demand outlook was accurately appraised. Late in 1943 the Department of Agriculture announced a goal that called for an increase in the production of eggs. In any case, the announcement was too late to have much effect.

Early in 1944, it became evident that price-support purchases would be necessary. Buying for military and lend-lease requirements would not in themselves maintain prices. Though civilian per capita consumption had been increasing, a surplus of pork was reducing the demand for eggs. To meet the situation, the War Food Administration ordered an extension of operations so as to provide for buying eggs on current delivery at designated markets throughout the country. Prices broke to the support level in April.

Specific schedules of prices as applying to 64 markets had been issued in February and March, and government agents were authorized to purchase on government account. By that time, the foreign-supply program had been shifted entirely to dried eggs because of difficulties encountered in handling shell and frozen eggs. But the egg-drying plants were unable to keep abreast of a surplus which came from a March–July production that was at an all-time high.

As a further complication, there was a shortage of unoccupied cold storage space suitable for storing shell eggs. An official of the War Food Administration took to the radio to plead with housewives to buy and hold an extra dozen or two in family refrigerators. At the same time, the Department of Agriculture supplemented its purchases of dried eggs by buying 4.8 million cases of shell eggs over a three-month period. The records on that operation are incomplete but one aspect of it was that for about 200,000 cases the highest order-of-use that could be found was to convert them into tankage for animal food.

During this hectic period, the Department also found that dried egg purchases, originally conceived as a procurement operation, required adaptations if they were to be used as a price-support operation. The egg driers naturally were buying their eggs at the lowest prevailing prices, which were not necessarily in line with prices the War Food Administration had pledged itself to maintain or with operating margins needed to return reasonable profits to the processors. The Food Administration therefore amended the outstanding contracts with egg driers to provide that the price paid them for dried eggs would be the cost of shell eggs plus 16 cents per pound as a processing charge. This resulted in a decrease in the paying price for dried eggs that may for a time have been as much as 10 cents per pound. Shortly thereafter, the contracts were changed again so as to specify the payment of minimum prices to farmers for the eggs bought by the driers.

Purchases for the supply program amounted to 27 million cases, which was somewhat in excess of current requirements. In addition, the Department bought 5.6 million cases as a surplus removal operation. The total under the two programs constituted about 20 per cent of total production. The price was held close to the support level in the months of heaviest production and rose above it in the later months of the year. The price received by farmers averaged 32.5 cents for the season. This was 1.5 cents less than the announced objective. However, it did meet the Steagall Amendment requirement of 90 per cent of parity.

CCC reported a net loss of $11,956,000 on the price-support operations of 1944.[68] Taking account of excess stocks of dried eggs held at the end of the year, the actual surplus for the year amounted to approximately 12 million cases or about 7 per cent of the then current requirements. Had the price-support purchases not been made in addition to current requirements, the average price received by farmers probably would have been below 30 cents. (For a summary of price-support purchases through 1946, see Table 37.)

Chicken and Turkey Programs Not Needed

The requirement that the prices of chickens and turkeys be supported did not result in any cost to the government during the war years. An increase of more than 50 per cent in production was absorbed by increased demand and at prices that were well above support levels.

The real problem in the war years was to maintain price ceilings on chickens and turkeys. In fact, price controls virtually broke down because of direct consumer purchases or trucker deliveries that short-circuited normal channels of distribution. Freezer-locker plants and home deep freezers were widely used by consumers to store larger supplies than they usually carried.

It became difficult to obtain the quantities of chickens and turkeys desired for the armed services. Set-aside orders on stocks held in public

68. This does not, of course, include expenditures under the supply program. Lend-lease purchases probably were more liberal than they would have been had eggs not been in long supply. Dried eggs at over a dollar per pound were a very expensive item in the lend-lease food program and the possibility of some cutback in the quantities supplied to Britain was being considered from 1943 on.

TABLE 37

EGGS: U.S. DEPARTMENT OF AGRICULTURE PURCHASES FOR SURPLUS REMOVAL AND PRICE SUPPORT, 1942–1946 [a]

		Purchases						
			Frozen		Dried			
Year	Production	Shell Eggs	Actual	Shell Egg Equivalent	Actual	Shell Egg Equivalent	Total in Terms of Shell Eggs	Purchases as Per Cent of Production
	(1,000 Cases)	*(1,000 Cases)*	*(1,000 Pounds)*	*(1,000 Cases)*	*(1,000 Pounds)*	*(1,000 Cases)*	*(1,000 Cases)*	
1942	134,992	502					502	0.3
1943	151,497	19					19	0.01
1944	162,583	5,593					5,593	3.4
1945	155,161	5					5	0.003
1946	154,417		4,223	113	100	10	123	0.07

Sources: U.S. Bureau of Agricultural Economics, *The Poultry and Egg Situation,* April 1950, and *1952 Agricultural Outlook Charts,* October 1951, p. 57.

a. Includes quantities purchased with Section 32 funds and certain purchases with CCC funds for price support, but not stamp plan expenditures of Section 32 funds, 1942–1943.

storage were resorted to in 1943. Set-aside orders for turkeys were used each year as a means of obtaining supplies for holiday dinners and other special occasions. Before the end of the war, black-market operations resulted in an almost complete breakdown of usual marketing practices. In 1945, reduced purchases by the armed services and the cessation of hostilities in Europe, together with the seasonal increase in the marketing of chickens, broke the black markets. The prices of chickens and heavy turkeys fell below ceilings within a short time.

Developments in 1945 and 1946

It was apparent in 1944 that a readjustment in egg production would be necessary as the abnormal war demand slacked off. The huge carry-over of frozen and dried eggs would provide a good portion of the lend-lease needs for the following year and it was expected that lend-lease takings would be reduced.

Domestic consumption of eggs had increased greatly in 1944 because of abundant supplies and low prices. It was therefore not to be expected that civilian purchases would be increased enough to offset the reduction in other requirements. In early 1944, the egg-feed price ratio was some 20 per cent lower than in 1943 and was at a level that would be expected to discourage chicken production. Reports indicated that the number of chickens raised in 1944 would be 15 to 20 per cent below that of a year earlier. However, as a result of heavy government purchases and the large stocks held off the market, the ratio became more favorable in the latter part of the year.

Production goals for 1945 were announced on November 15, 1944, again too late to have much effect on output. This first announcement called for a 16 per cent reduction in egg output and a 25 per cent reduction in the number of hens and pullets on farms as of January 1, 1945. In January the goals were readjusted to bring them more in line with realities. Only a 9 per cent decrease in egg production was suggested but some consideration was given to devising ways of inducing chicken raisers to cull potential layers more heavily.

When the January estimates were in, it was found that the number of potential layers was down only 10 per cent from the number on hand in January 1944. The number of pullets had been reduced 14 per cent but the higher prices of the preceding fall and winter had caused farmers to retain more laying hens, thus offsetting in part the reduction in the number of pullets raised. There was also some increase in the rate of lay per hen, so egg production actually was down only 4.5 per cent from the high level of 1944.

Again the prospective demand for eggs was not correctly appraised. There was some reduction in the amount of pork available and civilian egg consumption increased. That increase, together with military and foreign-aid requirements, was sufficient to absorb the 1945 production, and some of the excessive carry-over, at prices that averaged above the 90 per cent support level. In fact, egg prices pressed against ceilings during most of 1945.[69]

The number of potential layers at the beginning of 1946 was about the same as in 1945. The egg-feed price ratio had improved in 1945, but only moderately, and the result had been a 7 per cent increase in the number of chickens raised. The market outlook appeared less favorable than in 1945 since lend-lease and military requirements would be eliminated or reduced.

Egg prices declined to the seasonally adjusted support level. However, supply purchases were increased to 10 million cases and a small volume of frozen eggs was purchased for price-support purposes. These early purchases relieved the market of the danger of excessive storage stocks. The demand for eggs increased as the season advanced, largely as a result of higher prices for pork and other meats. Prices advanced somewhat more than in the previous season though the averages for the two

69. Some purchases of dried eggs were made early in the 1945 season when prices were seasonally high, 105 per cent of parity, and far above the 90 per cent support level. This added to the tight supply situation of that year. The amount purchased was about 35 million pounds (Levin, "Government Egg Programs during Wartime," p. 898).

years were practically identical. The season average price was almost exactly at the support level.[70]

Support Purchases of 1947 and After

Despite high-level production and reduced foreign demand, the government was committed under the Steagall Amendment to support prices at the high wartime levels, at least through 1947 and 1948. Title I of the Agricultural Act of 1949 made it mandatory for the 90 per cent of parity rate to be continued through 1949. Not until 1950 could the support price be put at a lower percentage of parity. At that time the rate was reduced to 75 per cent. Production continued at about the 1945 level through 1948 but was beginning to increase again by 1949, reaching about the 1944 level in 1950 and going even higher in 1951 and 1952.

Supply purchases for foreign governments continued through 1946 and into the early months of 1947. Thereafter, the Commodity Credit Corporation undertook to maintain the required price level, primarily by purchases for diversion and export.[71] Fortunately, domestic demand for eggs continued high, but even so CCC had to make sizable purchases through the postwar years until 1951 and the losses incurred were substantial.

Dried and frozen eggs were purchased from vendors who had paid producers not less than the support prices specified. Such purchases amounted to about 87 million pounds by June 30, 1947 (at a cost of $59 million). These stocks had been reduced to 77 million by June 30 but still were so large as to be a matter of serious concern in view of the declining outlet for dried eggs. At the same time, heavy purchases (amounting to $82 million) were made by CCC for other government agencies.[72] Section 32 fund purchases were resumed in 1947 and CCC

70. The prices in cents per dozen at the farm in 1944–1949 were as follows:

	Season Average Price	*Support Level*
1944	32.5	34.0
1945	37.7	33.3
1946	37.6	37.4
1947	45.3	44.8
1948	47.2	48.2
1949	45.2	47.1

(U.S. Department of Agriculture, *Farm Production, Disposition and Income from Chickens and Eggs, 1909–44,* p. 60; *1945–1949,* p. 13; and *CCC Price Support Statistical Handbook,* p. 53.)

71. Partly with Section 32 funds.

72. Commodity Credit Corporation, *Review of Operations,* fiscal 1947, p. 8. The interconnections between the supply program and the price-support program in this period are not stated clearly in the reports and it is virtually impossible to say with assurance what the total cost of price-support activities was since considerable quantities of CCC stocks were transferred to other government agencies, some at sacrifice prices based on caloric values equivalent to those of wheat, others presumably at the cost to CCC.

losses were put at $11.5 million. Total purchases in the calendar year 1947 were about 4 per cent of total production and are estimated to have kept prices about 4 cents per dozen over what they would have been without such purchases.[73]

Egg production was reduced slightly in 1948 and the quantities offered to the government were much smaller than in 1947. Total purchases were equivalent to about 2.7 million cases of shell eggs, roughly 1.7 per cent of total production as compared with 4 per cent in 1947. The Army took some of the dried eggs for distribution in Germany and substantial sales were made through the Economic Coöperation Administration. A larger quantity was transferred to Section 32 account for direct distribution and CCC itself took a sizable loss in the form of donations.[74] Purchases were concentrated in the spring months. The need for price-support operations arose primarily out of heavy production of eggs in the Midwest.[75]

Egg production increased in 1949, to about the 1945 level, which was the highest of record up to that time except for the very large output of 1944.[76] Civilian consumption remained at about the 1948 level and as a consequence heavy purchases had to be made by the government in order to maintain the required level of support.

At the beginning of the fiscal year (July 1, 1948), the inventory consisted of 6.8 million pounds of dried eggs and 44 million pounds of 1947 frozen eggs valued at a total of $24.4 million. Purchases, all in dried form, amounted to 67 million pounds. No large realized loss was shown for fiscal 1949 as most of the dried eggs purchased were still on hand at the end of June, which was the close of the fiscal year. Virtually all of the frozen egg stocks, from the 1947 program, had been disposed of at some profit as prices had increased after they were acquired. Sales to the Army and ECA, under Section 112 (e) of the Foreign Assistance Act, amounted to about $2 million, of which half was paid by the recipient agency and half came from Section 32 funds. The total realized loss to CCC for fiscal 1949 was small, only $773,000.[77]

73. There was a small price-support operation in turkeys from February to June 1947. The price of turkeys was mostly above support levels. The scale of operations was small ($548,000) and resulted in a net loss to CCC of $3,708; see *ibid.*, fiscal 1948, p. 26.

74. CCC began the fiscal year (1947–48) with an inventory of 24 million pounds of dried eggs and 52 million pounds of frozen eggs valued in total at $48 million. Net losses for the year were put at $25.9 million, mostly through transfer of eggs under the Foreign Aid Act of 1947 (Public Law 389, December 17, 1947) at prices equivalent to their caloric value in terms of wheat. (See *ibid.*, fiscal 1948, pp. 26–27.)

75. See U.S. Department of Agriculture, *Report of the Administrator of the Production and Marketing Administration, 1948*, pp. 68–69.

76. The 1949 production was 56.2 billion, almost identical with that of 1945. The 1944 output was 58.5 billion, which was about 47 per cent above that of 1939. The lowest production of the postwar years, in 1948, was 54.9 billion. (*Agricultural Statistics, 1953*, p. 470.)

77. Commodity Credit Corporation, *Review of Operations*, fiscal 1949, pp. 32–33 and summary table for the Poultry Branch.

Heavier Surpluses in 1950

Though the 1950 support level was reduced from 90 per cent of parity to 75 per cent (47 cents per dozen to 37 cents), the 1950 production was slightly higher than that of the record year 1944. Even with this lower level of support prices, the government found it necessary to buy about 5 per cent of the total production. The season average price to farmers was substantially lower than in 1949 (36.3 cents as compared with 45.2 cents), reflecting both the lower support price and the heavy volume of production.

Per capita consumption was up slightly (about 1 per cent) but not enough to absorb the additional production.[78] There was a small volume of exports, through sales to foreign governments, and much larger quantities were disposed of by way of ECA. Heavy losses were taken by CCC on exports and donations, by far the largest volume going to the United Kingdom on contracts which involved substantial losses.

Even so, the June 30, 1950 inventory was 94 million pounds of dried eggs, about 50 per cent more than that of a year earlier. Net loss for the year amounted to $41.6 million, the largest up to that time. The closing inventory had a cost value of $103.3 million but very large reserves for expected losses on it had been set up.[79] There was a small operation in frozen turkeys during August to December 1949. Purchases amounted to $3.5 million (at 40 cents per pound). There was a small gain of $44,000 on the operation.

Further Increase in Egg Production in 1951

As a result of lower prices in 1950, there was a substantial decrease in the number of potential layers on farms as of January 1, 1951. However, a lower culling rate and increased production per hen more than offset the reduction in numbers at the beginning of the year. The January 1 inventory of layers was down 13.5 million but the average number on farms during the year was reduced by only about 3 million. The rate of lay per hen was up to 175 eggs as compared with 172 in 1950 and only

78. Per capita consumption had been increasing consistently from 1940 on. It had moved up from about 300 eggs per person per year in the late 1930s to 383 in 1950, the highest of record except for an approximately equal number in 1948. It was to go still higher, to 407, in 1952. (*Agricultural Statistics, 1953,* p. 472.)

79. Net loss per pound on the 1948 and 1949 stocks disposed of in the 1950 fiscal year amounted to 83 cents per pound against an average cost of $1.31 per pound. Sales amounted to 44 million pounds at a loss of $33.6 million. Donations under Section 416 of the Agricultural Act of 1949 (for domestic relief, school lunches and so on and for foreign assistance) accounted for 3.9 million pounds. Of the quantity sold, the major portion was delivered to ECA under Section 112 (e) of the Foreign Assistance Act of 1948 under which proceeds were derived largely from ECA and Section 32 funds. See Commodity Credit Corporation, *Review of Operations,* fiscal 1950, pp. 27–28 and summary table for the Poultry Branch.

134 in 1940. Domestic civilian consumption was up about 3 per cent, largely because of increases in the price of meat.

As in previous years, the heavy surpluses were in the Midwest. For that area, the 1950 season support was designed to assure producers a return of 25 cents per dozen at the farm though the national average farm price was to be 37 cents. During fiscal 1951, CCC bought 25 million pounds of 1950 crop dried eggs at a cost of $24 million. As of July 1, 1950, the Corporation already held 57 million pounds of 1950 crop eggs and had an investment in them of $55.5 million. During the fiscal year, that is, to June 30, 1951, the Corporation sold 24.7 million pounds for only $11.5 million and donated 17 million pounds which had cost $17 million. The result was a net realized loss of $30.1 million.

In other inventory operations, all but nominal amounts of the 1948 and 1949 program eggs were disposed of, 18.6 million pounds being sold and 18 million pounds donated, with a resulting net loss of $45.9 million. Total realized losses for the fiscal year, on eggs, amounted to $76 million, of which 53 per cent consisted of donations. CCC ended the year with an inventory of 40.4 million pounds of dried eggs, almost all from the 1950 program.[80] There was also a small continuation of the 1949 turkey program, which carried over into July 1950. Purchases amounted to only $2.4 million and the birds were later sold at a small loss of $29,000.

The price of eggs, as of most other farm products, rose sharply in 1951. The national average farm price was 47.8 cents per dozen as compared with 36.3 cents in 1950.[81] The result was a fairly sharp increase (9.5 million) in the number of hens and pullets on hand at the beginning of 1952 though apparently later disposals brought the average number for the year down to some 3 million more than in 1951. However, total egg production for the year was at an all-time high of 61 billion.

Egg prices were running mostly at over 90 per cent of parity [82] and there was no government purchase program for 1951. CCC activity in

80. *Ibid.*, fiscal 1951, pp. 32–33 and summary table on Dairy Branch operations.

81. *Agricultural Statistics, 1953,* p. 470.

82. In compliance with the Agricultural Acts of 1948 and 1949, parity prices for eggs were being computed at the levels provided in the "transitional" formula, which would later result in their being computed in accordance with the "modernized" formula; this, for eggs, was lower than parity according to the "old" formula. As computed under this procedure, the "transitional" parity for 1950 was 5 per cent lower than if computed by the formula used in 1949; 10 per cent lower in 1951 and 15 per cent lower in 1952. The transition was completed in 1953, and thereafter parity prices were computed in accordance with the "modernized" parity formula.

These changes in the method of computing parity affect, of course, not only any price supports authorized in terms of percentages of parity but also any price ceilings that may be established on a parity price basis. There also were changes which reduced somewhat the parities for chickens (4 per cent) and for turkeys (1 per cent). (For fuller explanation, see *The Poultry and Egg Situation,* November–December 1949, pp. 10–12, and January–February 1952, p. 16.)

respect to eggs consisted of steps taken to dispose of the stocks held at the beginning of the year. Of the 40 million pounds held, 26 million were sold and 8.6 million were donated. The loss recorded for the year was $29.3 million, incurred chiefly through sale for $6.2 million of eggs that cost $26.8 million. Donations represented costs of $8.7 million. The end-of-year inventory was reduced to a relatively nominal amount, 5.3 million pounds, almost all from the 1950 program, valued at $5.4 million on a cost basis.

Egg Program Liquidated in 1953

From 1950 to December 1955, no new egg or poultry price-support programs were undertaken. The last of the inventory acquired under the 1949 and 1950 programs was disposed of in fiscal 1953. The 5.3 million pounds still held were sold or donated. Liquidation was chiefly through sales at very low prices. Eggs that had cost $4.7 million were sold for $1.17 million. Donations amounted to $743,000 in terms of cost to CCC. The net realized cost for the year, on eggs, was $4.2 million.[83]

Egg production continued to increase in 1953 and 1954, reaching 65.3 billion in 1954, which was more than 10 per cent above the 1950 level that had given rise to large-scale purchases and heavy losses on price-support operations. Egg prices, without support, held up strongly through 1953 despite the large number produced (62.3 billion). The season average price to farmers was 47.7 cents per dozen, only 0.1 cent below the record high of 47.8 cents in 1951. The price declined sharply in 1954 and averaged only 36.8 cents for the season.

As of June 1, 1955, a substantial readjustment appeared to be in the making. The number of young chickens on farms was about 18 per cent below that of a year earlier.[84] Early season prices in 1955 were about the same as in 1954, reflecting the heavy 1954 population of hens and pullets. Egg supplies were so large in the fall and winter of 1954 that the usual seasonal advance in prices did not occur. Prices were about at the 1950 level, which was the low point following the high-price years 1947–1949 and preceding the high-price period 1951–1953 associated with the general upsurge of prices in the Korean War.[85] Egg prices to farmers were up to 80 per cent of parity in August 1955 as compared with 75

83. Commodity Credit Corporation, *Review of Program Operations,* fiscal 1953, pp. 15–16 and summary table for the Poultry Branch. Later reports show a small net return in fiscal 1954 ($92,000) and a loss ($4,793) in fiscal 1955, which presumably are readjustments on earlier transactions. See Commodity Credit Corporation, *Report of Financial Condition and Operations as of June 30, 1955,* p. 31.

84. *The Poultry and Egg Situation,* July 18, 1955, p. 3.

85. It should be noted, however, that there were heavy government purchases of eggs in the 1947–1949 period as well as in 1950 and that prices in those years would undoubtedly have been substantially lower if such purchases had not been made. Government purchases were not a factor from 1950 on. The most striking development of the 1951–1953 period was the absorption at relatively high prices of the greatly increased volume of output.

per cent in August 1954 and 76 per cent in July 1955. The 1944–1953 average for August was 93 per cent of parity.[86]

The large 1954 increase in the number of laying hens was due in considerable measure to a favorable egg-feed price ratio in 1953, 12.3 as compared with a 1944–1953 average of 11.1, which included some years in which the ratio was above 13 and which, in general, was sufficiently favorable to cause a rapid and continuous expansion of egg production.[87] The ratio dropped to 9.4 in 1954, the lowest recorded from 1940 on and .6 below the previous low of 10.0 in 1952. Low egg-feed price ratios of that kind usually lead to sizable readjustments in egg output in the following year. The mid-August 1955 ratio was 11.1, about the same as the 1944–1953 average.

Over-All Results of the Egg Program

Except as new programs might be initiated, the postwar egg program could be looked upon as carried to completion by early 1953, though there were some very minor cleanups and adjustments in fiscal 1954 and 1955. The carrying out of wartime commitments of 90 per cent of parity support through 1949 under the Steagall Amendment and the 1950 support program at 75 per cent of parity resulted in heavy losses to the government. Part of the difficulty arose from the fact that the "old" parity formula based on 1910–1914 price relationships, which was used through 1949 and with only slight modification in 1950, yielded a parity price for eggs that was high relative to that for many of the other farm products. Maintaining a uniform support at 90 per cent of parity on that basis made chicken and egg production attractive and tended to over-stimulate the industry.

The rapid increase in egg production per hen, and other technological improvements, also affected the situation and caused grower adjustments in numbers of layers to have less effect on egg production than would

86. *The Poultry and Egg Situation,* October 3, 1955, p. 2 (latest available as of this writing).

87. *The Poultry and Egg Situation,* October 4, 1954 (Outlook Issue 1955), p. 12, and October 3, 1955, pp. 2, 27. Customary egg-feed ratios had been higher in the 1920s and 1930s but in the meantime breed improvements and better methods of feeding and caring for laying hens had increased the efficiency of egg production in such a way that somewhat lower egg-feed price ratios were sufficiently favorable to stimulate production. For ratios going back to 1925, see *ibid.,* January–February 1953, p. 5.

There had been a very large increase in the gross income from eggs and chickens in the 1940s and early 1950s. Cash receipts from eggs moved up from $468 million in 1940 to $1.9 billion in 1948. They amounted to $1.6 billion even in 1950 in spite of the sharp decline in prices that occurred in that year. Cash receipts were above $2 billion in 1951 and nearly as high in 1952 (*Agricultural Statistics, 1953,* p. 470). Cash receipts from chickens moved up from $196 million in 1940 to $688 million in 1943 but declined gradually thereafter to $393 million in 1952. They were well above $600 million in the years 1944–1946 (*ibid.,* p. 441). These large wartime returns and the expanded capacity that went with them no doubt facilitated and encouraged the overproduction of the late 1940s and 1950.

otherwise have resulted. Egg production per hen was nearly 50 per cent higher in the early 1950s than in 1940.

The stimulus given by means of price-support promises resulted in an abundance of eggs during the war, not only for supplying a greatly increased domestic demand but for the large-scale shipments of dried eggs to Britain. The need for a downward adjustment in production began to be apparent as early as 1945 and probably could have been brought about in the two years following the close of hostilities without severe hardship on poultry producers if the program requirements as specified by law had been less rigid. A moderately lower and possibly declining rate of support in 1946–1948 would almost certainly have brought production more nearly into line with requirements. The continuance of high supports through 1949 gave rise to the largest, most costly and most wasteful of the postwar egg programs.

During the years 1946–1948, production was undoubtedly larger than would have been called for by plans realistically related to foreign-relief needs, government costs and alternative types of production. However, the surplus acquired in those years was, for the most part, put to constructive, humanitarian use. The later heavy accumulations, some of them downgraded to livestock feed use and some supplied to other agencies at prices comparable to those for similar caloric values in the form of wheat, were wasteful and socially undesirable. There is reason to believe that poultry producers could and would have made production adjustments to bring output into line with demand about as easily in 1947 and 1948 as in the 1950s when such action did become necessary.

There is also reason to believe that they could and would have expanded operations enough in the early 1950s to take care of the sudden and unexpected increase in demand. In other words, egg production appears to be one of the types of farming in which adjustments can be and are made rather quickly and effectively, except in periods of extreme general depression such as that of the 1930s. There is reason to question the desirability from the standpoint of either society or the poultry producers of massive buying programs that overstimulate the industry and lead to waste and heavy government expense.

However, minor or temporary buying programs such as those used in the 1930s apparently can, if wisely administered, help in strengthening the season average price and providing some measure of support until needed adjustments can be made. Such action, to be constructive and effective, requires much skill and judgment and cannot be carried out in a satisfactory way under rigidly prescribed legislative requirements.

Taken as a whole, the egg programs cost the government $331.6 million for the period 1932–1953 (June 30).[88] Of that total, $189.7 million was in the form of costs by way of the Commodity Credit Cor-

88. *Realized Cost of Agricultural and Related Programs.*

poration and $141.9 million in the form of surplus removal operations.[89] There was a further and sizable expenditure which was partly a result of price-support operations but which cannot be segregated. Undoubtedly, lend-lease shipments were kept somewhat higher in the latter part of the war than they would have been if eggs had not been so abundant. Also, eggs probably bulked larger in the postwar foreign-relief and armed service foreign-feeding programs than they would have if the Department of Agriculture had not been seeking actively to unburden itself of excess supplies.

The Chicken and Turkey Programs

The price of chickens, other than broilers, which were not under support, did not fall to levels that required government purchases. Hence no losses on chickens are recorded. For turkeys, the small CCC operations do not show any loss. There was, in fact, a small gain of $11,070 in the 1946–1951 period. The Steagall commitment on turkeys was completed with the end of the 1949 season. Thereafter, support was permissive, not mandatory. However, production was increasing and the government undertook extensive purchase operations in 1952.[90] As of June 30, 1953, surplus removal programs (with Section 32 funds) showed a total cost of $33.4 million, of which all but $6.2 million was a result of the 1952 program.[91]

89. The small plus and minus adjustments made in 1954 and 1955 did not alter the Commodity Credit Corporation total significantly.

Some part of the surplus removal expenditure, especially in the 1930s, should, of course, be regarded as an aid to consumers. The contributions to foreign relief in 1946–1949 also were for consumer benefit in a broader sense but possibly were not the most efficient way of providing such assistance.

90. Turkey production in 1952 was up 50 per cent over that of 1949.

91. *Realized Cost of Agricultural and Related Programs,* and *Section 32 Handbook,* March 1953, p. 31.

7

Sugar

THE UNITED STATES does not produce enough sugar or wool to supply its own needs. The national policy problems relating to these commodities are therefore quite different from those discussed in earlier chapters. Though both sugar and wool are deficit crops, there are important differences between them which have influenced the policies and programs adopted. Both the methods of production and the interarea relationships differ significantly. The principal offshore supplies of sugar come from areas and countries which have close political and economic ties with the United States. Wool imports come from countries that have both a wider world market and a less close political relationship with ours.[1]

The U.S. sugar supply comes from three principal sources: (1) the sugar beet and cane areas of the U.S. mainland, (2) U.S.-controlled offshore areas such as Hawaii and Puerto Rico, and (3) other offshore areas such as Cuba and the Philippines, which, though not controlled by the United States, have long been closely associated with it. Internally, there are problems of equity between the sugar beet and sugar cane areas and also between growers on the mainland and those in U.S. offshore areas.

In addition, there are important problems of safeguarding food supplies that are likely to be necessary in case of war. Cuba, which has long supplied a large part of our sugar, and a still larger part in war periods, is closer to the U.S. mainland than our own island areas and therefore less easily cut off. Furthermore, we have very important reasons for wanting to keep the Cuban economy, based largely on sugar, in a healthy condition and its government on friendly terms with ours.

U.S. sugar production, particularly in the sugar beet areas, has, in the past at least, been heavily dependent on an abundant supply of cheap labor. In wartime, domestic sugar production tends to be cut back rather than expanded. In World War II, we relied very heavily on expanded production in Cuba to make up deficits in this country. The increasing mechanization of sugar-crop production on the mainland may reduce the tendency for cutbacks in time of war, but it is not likely to reduce materially our need for large amounts of sugar from Cuba both in peacetime and in time of war.

1. The wool problem and the programs relating to it are discussed in Chapter 8.

Other considerations are important in arriving at a logical and practical sugar policy. Generally speaking, sugar is produced at much lower cost in the tropical and semitropical cane areas than in the sugar beet areas. A large part of the world's sugar beet production has been developed artificially, through tariffs, subsidies, embargoes and similar devices. Originally at least, a desire for self-sufficiency in time of war was an important consideration in the policies adopted in regard to this crop. Once the industry was established, the desire to maintain it and keep it prosperous has, of course, been a factor. Probably no other major crop has been so much manipulated by the governments of the world as sugar.

From the standpoint of the general public, it seems apparent that a good part of the sugar used in the United States could be obtained more cheaply in peacetime by importation than by home production. There is, therefore, some conflict of interest between domestic sugar producers and the consuming public. There is also a question as to how far consumers should be expected to go in paying a higher price for all sugar used in order that the growers who supply roughly a third of it may receive higher returns.

Sugar has long been a matter of general international concern as well since it is a commodity that is peculiarly subject to periods of oversupply and undersupply in the world markets. Shortages, partly caused by shipping difficulties, have occurred mainly in war periods. The more usual situation is a tendency to overproduce on a world basis and thus to bring about severe depression in the principal cane-producing areas of the world.

Main Reliance on Tariffs until 1934

Until 1934, the sugar tariff was almost the only type of assistance given to the domestic sugar industry. Through most of our history, the principal purpose of the sugar tariffs was not to protect the domestic industry but rather to provide revenue for the federal government. From 1789 to 1860, some two thirds to nine tenths of all ordinary revenues of the government came from customs duties. As late as 1900, the proportion was almost half. Sugar alone produced up to a fifth of all tariff revenue until about 1890. By that time, however, the duty on sugar, which ranged from 1 to more than 3 cents per pound, had come to be looked on as a protective device as well as a source of revenue.[2]

In the McKinley Tariff of 1890, the duty on sugar was removed and, in order not to destroy the small and struggling beet sugar industry, a bounty of 2 cents per pound was provided for sugar grown in the United

2. Until after the Civil War, there was little in the way of a domestic sugar industry to protect. As late as 1860, Louisiana produced no more than 10 per cent of the sugar used in the United States and the amount of beet sugar produced was negligible.

States. This caused serious difficulty for the Treasury. An important source of income had been cut off and at the same time a large annual expenditure had been authorized. The sugar bounty was repealed in 1894 and the policy of providing protection and revenue by means of tariffs was resumed.

The tariff was reduced in the Underwood-Simmons Act of 1913 but was raised again in 1921 and twice thereafter, in 1922 and 1930. Under the Emergency Tariff of 1921, the duty on Cuban sugar was raised from 1 cent per pound to 1.6 cents. This was further increased to 1.76 cents in 1922 and to 2 cents in 1930.[3]

Unexpected Results of the Sugar Tariffs

It was expected that the tariff increases provided in the 1920s and in 1930 would raise returns to sugar growers in the mainland producing areas. Instead, the tariff increases stimulated sugar production in the U.S. offshore areas and these consequently supplied a much larger part of the sugar used in the United States, thus taking over part of the market formerly supplied by Cuba. Cuba was not within the duty-free area, as were our own island areas, which at that time included the Philippine Islands. The higher tariffs therefore put the U.S. offshore areas in a much stronger competitive position than they were before.

Prices to beet and cane growers on the U.S. mainland were apparently strengthened, but not enough for the industry to maintain acreage at the 1920 and 1921 levels.[4] Beet sugar production had expanded to a little over a million tons in 1920 and 1921 but fell off sharply in 1922. It then recovered to about the 1920–1921 level. In the 1930s, with labor plentiful and cheap, there was a substantial increase. Production rose to 1.6 million tons in 1933 in spite of lower prices.

The big change was in the U.S. offshore areas. Their production was about 1.7 million tons at the close of World War I. By 1933–34, it had increased to 3.9 million tons. U.S. imports from foreign countries, chiefly Cuba, fell off correspondingly. They dropped from 4 million tons in 1922–23 to 1.4 million in 1933–34 and to even lower levels in succeeding years.

From 1902 to 1929, Cuba supplied almost half the sugar used in the

3. These rates, in accordance with the Convention of Commercial Reciprocity of 1902 and the implementing act of 1903, are 20 per cent below those applying on sugar imported from other foreign countries.

4. However, the acreages grown in the 1920s were somewhat above those of the pre-World War I years. Sugar beets, at the farm, stood at $5.69 per ton in 1913. The price fell off slightly in 1914 and then rose steadily during the war years, reaching $11.74 in 1919. It remained high ($11.63) in 1920 but fell off to $6.35 in 1921. The price held mostly at $7.00 to $8.00 through the 1920s but had fallen to $5.13 by 1933.

The price of sugar cane (in Louisiana at the farm) moved down during the 1920s. It was only $3.77 per ton in 1929 as compared with $3.63 in 1921, $5.83 in 1922 and $7.09 in 1923. (*Agricultural Statistics, 1937,* pp. 107, 111.) There is little evidence that the tariff increases raised prices significantly in these years.

United States. During the years 1930–1933, the portion drawn from there was less than 30 per cent. In contrast, Hawaii, the Philippines and Puerto Rico increased their share of the U.S. market to about 45 per cent. It had been around 25 per cent in the period between 1902 and 1929 and about 30 per cent in 1927–1929. Since Cuba, with a one-crop economy, was unable to reduce acreage enough to offset these increases in the U.S. offshore areas, the effect was to force Cuban prices down and demoralize the Cuban market.[5]

It would be unwarranted to assume that there would have been no increase in U.S. offshore production if tariffs had not been raised. However, the differential that was set up did give domestic suppliers in the offshore areas a marked advantage over Cuba. The Cuban sugar industry was so dependent on the U.S. market that it had no choice but to meet the competition from the duty-free island areas by reducing its price, thus absorbing most of the tariff increase. That is the principal reason why the higher tariffs did not cause significant increases in U.S. sugar prices.

The U.S. Department of Agriculture, in a recent report, summarizes the effect of the tariff increases as follows:

> The net effect of a higher tariff was to bring greater overproduction in the domestic areas and ever increasing depression in the world market. Imports from Cuba were cut in half and the Cuban price fell below one cent per pound. Economic ruin and political revolution were the consequences. By 1933 it had become evident that the tariff was no longer adequate to insure either a healthy domestic industry or a dependable source of foreign supplies. By that time it had also become evident that the destruction of our import trade was tearing down our export trade. This was injuring cotton growers, grain growers, and the producers of our other export commodities.[6]

Cuba an Important Factor in U.S. Sugar Policy

The situation in Cuba touches very closely the interests of the United States in many ways. Not only is it important that friendly and cooperative relationships be maintained with a nation so near to our own shores but there are also moral obligations to foster Cuba's prosperity and well-being, in view of our historic role in helping it to become an independent nation. In addition, there are economic and military considerations.

5. An internal quota system was put into effect in Cuba in 1930, but it apparently served more as a way of distributing the greatly reduced volume of exports to different producers than as a method of exerting a positive influence on prices. Later, the same device was used in allocating shares in the very profitable export market that developed during the war. For a brief account of the steps taken in Cuba, see Boris C. Swerling, "Domestic Control of an Export Industry: Cuban Sugar," *Journal of Farm Economics,* August 1951, pp. 346–56. From the Cuban standpoint, the problem was similar to and possibly even more difficult than that faced by U.S. growers of export crops such as wheat and cotton.

6. U.S. Production and Marketing Administration, *Sugar Reports,* No. 11, June 27, 1951, p. 2.

During World War II, Cuba was a vital asset to the Western Hemisphere, as a source of sugar supplies that could not be obtained in any other way. Philippine supplies were cut off almost immediately. Shipments from Hawaii were of dubious dependability, and production on the U.S. mainland declined instead of expanding. Had it not been for the very large supplies obtained from Cuba, made possible in part by a substantial increase in Cuban production, U.S. supplies would have been even shorter than they were. At best, a quick and very costly shift to sugar production on the mainland would have been necessary and much manpower that was badly needed elsewhere would have had to be transferred to the production of sugar beets and the construction of facilities for processing them.

Failure to take account of Cuba's place in the sugar economy could also cause trouble in peacetime. The Cuban output, if handled without reference to the U.S. sugar industry, could demoralize the world market and might possibly create grave difficulties in administering any program set up by the United States alone.

Serious disturbances to the Cuban economy could also involve the United States in other ways. Under the Platt Amendment of 1901, the United States stipulated, as a condition of its withdrawal of troops, that it would have the right to intervene in the event of a threat to Cuban independence or to the stability of its government. Consequently, any major economic crisis in Cuba would create embarrassing political problems for the United States. The Platt Amendment was repealed in 1934 but it still would be a matter of grave concern if serious disturbances were to occur in a nation so close to our borders.

Sugar accounts for about 90 per cent of Cuba's exports and she normally ships a very large part of it to the United States. Also, Cuba is a natural and very accessible purchaser of both agricultural and industrial exports from the United States, and large amounts of U.S. capital are invested in Cuban sugar processing plants and sugar plantations.[7]

In recognition of the close ties implied by the Platt Amendment, the Convention of Commercial Reciprocity of 1902 provided for a mutual 20 per cent tariff preference in dealings between the two countries. An act of Congress, December 17, 1903, implemented this tariff preference. The 20 per cent preferential tariff has been in effect since that time.

Tariff Increases a Serious Blow to Cuba

The three successive increases in the tariff on Cuban sugar, coming at a time when the Cuban economy was already in the throes of a major depression, naturally caused serious difficulties for Cuban government

7. Though Cuba has a population of only about 5.5 million, it provides an important outlet for U.S. products. Between 1948 and 1951, the annual value of U.S. exports to Cuba ranged from $380 million to $540 million. On a per capita basis, Cuba ranks very high as an importer of U.S. goods.

officials. The collapse of the sugar economy led to the revolution of 1933 and the expulsion of President Machado. It was followed by extremely unsettled conditions and became a matter of great concern to the United States.

The Tariff Act of 1922 had included a provision for "flexible" tariffs based on differences in costs of production. However, even this rather dubious method of adjusting tariffs was not made effective. A Tariff Commission study of the relative costs of sugar production, made in 1926, indicated that on the basis of the comparative-cost principle the sugar tariff should be reduced. No reduction was made and the tariff was raised to 2.0 cents in 1930. In 1932, the sugar problem became so acute that another cost-of-production study was undertaken by the Tariff Commission. This study, completed in the spring of 1933, led to the conclusion that some solution other than the maintenance of a high tariff on Cuban sugar must be found. On April 11, the Chairman of the Commission wrote to the President as follows:

> It is evident from our study that the duty on sugar cannot justly be based on a difference between domestic and foreign costs of production. The situation in Cuba, which is the chief competing foreign country, is such that the higher the American tariff may be, the lower are the costs of producing sugar in Cuba.
>
> Cuba must fix the price at which she sells sugar at a point which will enable her product to enter the American market. The result is that the price has gone down to a point which is disastrous both for American and for Cuban sugar producers. It is evident that no increase of the American tariff can relieve the resulting situation in this country or in Cuba.[8]

U.S. Sugar Consumption and Supplies

The people of the United States consume, on the average, about 100 pounds of sugar yearly and require currently around 8 million tons to supply their needs.[9] The U.S. mainland provides less than 30 per cent of this amount (about 2.3 million tons made up of approximately 1.8 million tons of beet sugar and about 500,000 tons of cane sugar). U.S. offshore areas, Hawaii, Puerto Rico and the Virgin Islands, supply about 2.1 million tons. Most of the remainder, somewhat over 3.5 million tons, is imported from Cuba and the Philippine Islands, except for some small quantities obtained from other foreign countries.

Principal Sugar Beet Areas

Sugar beets are grown principally in three regions: the Pacific Coast states (chiefly in California and Washington), the Mountain and Inter-

8. *Sugar Reports,* No. 11, June 27, 1951, appendix entitled "The Background and Operations of the Sugar Acts," p. 10.

9. Unless otherwise stated, all data are on the basis of short tons "raw value." The conversion factor for translating this into refined sugar is .9346, which means that 107 pounds of raw sugar are required to produce 100 pounds of refined sugar.

mountain area (Colorado, Wyoming, Montana, Utah and Idaho) and the Central region, which includes a group of North Central states extending roughly from the Dakotas and Nebraska on the west to Ohio on the east. Until recently, Michigan was the most important producer of sugar beets in the North Central states area, but Minnesota and Nebraska now have as large or larger acreages.[10]

The regional distribution of the industry has changed significantly during the past quarter century. California had more than 20 per cent of the beet acreage of the United States in 1953 and more than twice as much land in beets as in the years 1928–1932. Both the North Central region and the Mountain states area have declined in relative importance and in acreage grown. Colorado, the largest producer aside from California, had an average acreage of 202,000 in 1928–1932 but was down to 121,000 in 1953. Michigan, the third largest producer, was down to 56,000 acres as compared with an average of 112,000 in the period 1933–1942.[11]

Total acreage for the United States fell off sharply in the war years. It recovered in 1950 but was again down nearly to the wartime level in 1952. Acreage and production increased again in 1953 and 1954.[12]

Cane Sugar Production

The U.S. mainland acreage in sugar cane has been much more constant than that in sugar beets and has shown a rather steady increase over the past quarter century. The acreage harvested in 1929 was 192,000. It dropped off a little in 1930 and 1931 but thereafter moved up to 316,000 in 1949. After declining slightly in 1950 and 1951 it increased again to 318,000 in 1952. The bulk of the U.S. cane sugar crop is grown in Louisiana. Florida, the other cane-producing state, has about one eighth

10. In the Pacific Coast states, beets are grown under irrigation and yields are high (16.4 tons per acre in California for the years 1939–1948). In the mountain states, though the beet lands are irrigated, yields are usually lower (for example, an average of 13.2 tons per acre for Colorado for the years 1939–1948). In Michigan, where the lands are not irrigated, yields for the same period were 8.7 tons. There are some small beet-producing areas in other states but they are of minor importance.

11. Harvested acreages as given in *Agricultural Statistics, 1937,* p. 107, *1945,* p. 87, and *1954,* p. 70. Nebraska, Minnesota and Idaho harvested larger acreages in 1952 than did Michigan. They, together with California, have increased in relative importance during recent years.

12. Acreages planted for the years 1929 through 1954 were as follows (in thousands):

Year	Acreage	Year	Acreage	Year	Acreage
1929	772	1938	985	1947	968
1930	821	1939	993	1948	800
1931	760	1940	971	1949	768
1932	812	1941	796	1950	1,014
1933	1,036	1942	1,048	1951	758
1934	945	1943	619	1952	719
1935	809	1944	633	1953	795
1936	855	1945	775	1954	956
1937	813	1946	905		

(*Agricultural Statistics, 1953,* p. 82, and later reports.)

as many acres as Louisiana but, because of higher yields, produces more than a sixth of the crop.

Cuba's production was in the order of 3 to 4 million tons from 1935 through 1944 but was greatly expanded in the postwar years. It was above 6 million tons in most years after 1944 and reached the record-breaking total of 7,964,000 tons in 1951. Hawaiian production declined from more than a million tons in 1935 to about 875,000 in the war years. It began to expand again in 1948 and reached 1,075,000 tons in 1952.

The Philippine industry, with a prewar production of more than a million tons, was virtually destroyed during the war, but began to come back in 1947. By 1951, it reached 1,077,000 tons, which was approximately its prewar output.[13] Puerto Rico, the other principal cane sugar producer, maintained a rather steady output of around a million tons from 1935 through 1946. It expanded production in 1947 and was producing at the rate of 1,325,000 tons in 1951. Its production dropped back to 1,190,000 tons in 1952. The percentage expansion in the Virgin Islands has been large but the total quantity produced is not important in the over-all sugar situation (15,000 tons in 1952).

Relation of Production Changes to U.S. Policy

From the standpoint of U.S. sugar policy, from 1933 on, the most significant features of the cane sugar situation are the relatively stable production on the U.S. mainland and in Hawaii, Puerto Rico and the Philippines,[14] and the very large expansion in Cuba. The Cuban supply has an important bearing on U.S. policy in two ways: (1) it supplies a very large part of the sugar used in the United States, but its production cannot be directly controlled by the U.S. government; (2) it has shown itself to be better able to expand production to offset U.S. deficits than the areas directly under U.S. control. It therefore constitutes a strategic reserve of great importance to the United States.

The world pattern of sugar production and consumption that existed before 1914 has been greatly changed and no settled relationships have come into being since. Many countries that formerly relied heavily on low-cost, cane sugar areas for much of their supply have provided subsidies of various kinds for building up beet sugar production within their own boundaries. This has narrowed the markets for the cane-producing areas and has increased the danger of overproduction and unsettled economic conditions in the areas that rely heavily on sugar as a source of

13. Philippine production had been up to nearly 1,600,000 tons in its record-breaking year 1933. It was cut back very heavily under the sugar program of 1934, to only 700,000 tons. The large production of 1933 was due in part to efforts to get the crop onto the market before the sugar program restrictions were applied. Philippine production in 1952 was 1,165,000 tons.

14. Except in the war years.

foreign exchange. The United States has, of course, an important political as well as economic interest in helping to stabilize both the domestic and foreign industries.

INTERNATIONAL CONTROL OF SUGAR

Because of the international character of the sugar market, and the serious instability that has marked it, there have been many attempts to achieve stability through international agreement. These efforts have generally been aimed at overcoming the nationalistic policies to which sugar has been subjected, particularly on the European continent. High tariffs and other import restrictions so expanded beet production in several countries that they became exporters rather than importers.

This led to export subsidies as a way of disposing of such surpluses. By the end of the nineteenth century, much of the sugar that moved in international trade carried export subsidies and was generally referred to as bonus-fed sugar. For some countries, export subsidies on sugar constituted a severe drain on the national treasuries.

As early as 1864, the United Kingdom, France, the Netherlands and Belgium attempted to control export subsidies by means of an international convention. The plan was not successful and the sugar market continued to be marked by instability and cutthroat practices. A second attempt was made in the Brussels Convention of 1901. Seven European countries agreed to suppress direct and indirect bounties to producers and to refrain from providing export subsidies. They further agreed to impose special import duties on bonus-fed sugar. This agreement was in effect from 1903 until the outbreak of World War I and was moderately successful.

The Chadbourne Agreement

World War I so disrupted the European sugar industry that the problem did not again become troublesome until 1927.[15] Attempts were then

15. Though the United States seemed to be somewhat insulated from the problems facing the sugar-exporting countries in this period, its insulation was more apparent than real. The sugar tariff could not hold domestic prices at satisfactory levels if its principal effect was to lower the prices received by countries exporting to the United States.

The most significant cause of trouble in the world market was the rapid expansion in production without an equivalent expansion in consumption. The principal factors in the expansion of output were technological progress and the growth of economic nationalism. World sugar production recovered to about its pre-World War I level (20.8 million tons) by 1922–23. It rose rapidly thereafter to 31.5 million tons by 1930–31 (*Agricultural Statistics, 1937,* p. 116). There was no corresponding increase in market outlets. Visible stocks more than doubled and the world price of raw sugar fell from an average of about 4 cents per pound to less than 2 cents. In 1932, the Cuban price averaged only 0.7 cent per pound. As a consequence, government controls on sugar were tightened, tariffs and bounties were increased, and the free, world sugar market became seriously demoralized. The world sugar depression was transmitted to the United States by way of Cuba.

made to bring about an international arrangement for handling sugar surpluses but no general agreement was reached until 1931. At that time, the Chadbourne Agreement was approved. The signatory countries represented about half the world's sugar production and 90 per cent of the sugar entering into world trade. The Agreement bore the name of a prominent New York attorney, who took a major part in drafting it. He was acting in behalf of a group of New York banks interested in Cuban sugar because of the failure of many Cuban-American sugar companies.

Under this plan, the signatory powers agreed to limit exports to specified annual quotas and to take steps to eliminate the surpluses that had been accumulating since the middle 1920s. To live within the terms of the Agreement the signatory nations reduced their production by about 40 per cent. However, the nonagreement countries expanded their production by about 15 per cent. The Agreement was terminated in 1935, not only because of this expansion in the areas not covered but because by that time the United States and Britain, both nonsignatory powers, had undertaken production controls and the limitation of imports. A new situation had developed and new methods were being shaped to handle it.[16]

The International Sugar Agreement of 1937

By 1937, both the United States and the United Kingdom had so changed their views on sugar that they were ready to welcome an intergovernmental attack on the problem. In that year, twenty-one countries signed an International Sugar Agreement. They represented 85 to 90 per cent of the world's sugar production and about 85 per cent of the consumption. Importing countries agreed to limit expansion of their domestic sugar industries, while exporting nations agreed to observe market quotas. The Agreement had no specific price provisions though it was recognized that some price influence was implied in the quota arrangements.

The Agreement was to remain in effect for five years, but its major provisions were suspended shortly after the outbreak of war. They were not put into operation after the close of World War II. Instead, the signatory powers, from time to time, extended the life of the Agreement. There was continuing discussion looking to the development of a new international sugar agreement under United Nations auspices. These negotiations led to the adoption of a new sugar agreement.

16. The international agreements are discussed more fully in Boris C. Swerling's *International Control of Sugar, 1918–1948*, Stanford University Press, Commodity Policy Studies No. 7, 1949. See also Joseph S. Davis, "Experience under International Commodity Agreements," *Journal of Political Economy*, June 1946, pp. 202–05, and *idem, International Commodity Agreements: Hope, Illusion or Menace*, Committee on International Economic Policy in Cooperation with the Carnegie Endowment for International Peace, New York, 1947.

The Sugar Agreement of 1953

The text of the new agreement was worked out in London and was approved on October 1, 1953 subject to ratification by the signatory nations. It went into effect on January 1, 1954.[17] Its stated objectives are ". . . to assure supplies of sugar to importing countries and markets for sugar to exporting countries at equitable and stable prices; to increase the consumption of sugar throughout the world; and to maintain the purchasing power in world markets of countries or areas whose economies are largely dependent upon the production or export of sugar by providing adequate returns to producers and making it possible to maintain fair standards of labor conditions and wages." [18]

"Operationally the agreement is of the standard export-quota form modified only by consumer representation and a target 'zone of stabilized prices.' " [19] The "target zone of stabilized prices" was for a range of 3.25 cents to 4.35 cents per pound in the "free market" f.a.s. Cuba, that is, in that part of the international trade in sugar for which there was no special protection or privilege in the country of destination. The primary aim was the achievement of stability plus some reasonable measure of equity and the creation of incentives for making needed longer-term adjustments.

Though some fears were expressed that the agreement might prove to be a gigantic cartel for the exploitation of consumers, qualified observers predicted that it would be more difficult to hold prices up to the target level than to keep them down enough so that consumers would not be exploited.[20] It is obviously too early to predict the success or failure of the new agreement. While the objectives agreed on appear to have met with rather general approval, critics point to the looseness of some of the provisions and to the difficulty of holding production in check when war demand is not present to give strength to the market. International sugar agreements have in the past proved very difficult to carry out and have not been notably successful.

Swerling, a long-time student of the international sugar economy, comments, "What is at fault with the present agreement is that it accepts as its main objective the reconciliation of essentially irreconcilable national sugar policies, while failing to come to grips with identifiable underlying problems. There may be possibilities of experimentation in political, commercial, monetary, and fiscal directions, that a strictly commodity conference is in no position to explore. From the inter-

17. For details and text of the Agreement, see *International Sugar Agreement,* Message from the President of the United States Transmitting International Sugar Agreement, dated London, October 1, 1953, Senate Executive Document B, 1954, 36 pp.

18. Chapter I, Article 1, general objectives.

19. Boris C. Swerling, "The International Sugar Agreement of 1953," *American Economic Review,* December 1954, p. 837.

20. See, for example, *ibid.*, p. 838.

national instrument now in effect little can be expected." [21] Others, recognizing that many of the nations concerned are now making a more conscious effort to develop economic and political cooperation than in the past, and that there is now a larger background of experience to draw on than in earlier periods, are more optimistic.

Even those who are skeptical about the results likely to flow from the current agreement concede that great instability is characteristic of the international market for sugar and that it poses a continuing threat to the economies of nations heavily dependent on sugar exports as a source of international exchange. It is to be expected that, barring a new outbreak of war, the opportunity which the agreement affords for continuing consultation and gradual evolution of the mechanics of operation will lead to improvements and possibly eventually to a more stable world sugar economy. The great instability of a completely unregulated world sugar economy and the notable inconsistencies inherent in the policies followed in the past by many of the sugar-producing nations seem likely to encourage continuing effort to develop more orderly ways of dealing with the problems that have so long plagued the sugar industry.

THE DOMESTIC SUGAR PROGRAM

The sugar problem was given some consideration during the period of Farm Board operations. A conference of sugar beet and sugar cane growers from the various producing areas in continental United States, arranged by the Board in 1930, led to the establishment of a Sugar Beet and Sugar Cane Advisory Committee. That group met with the Board at various times in 1930 and 1931. However, since no surplus in the usual sense of the word could be said to exist, and since these crops were not well suited to the Farm Board purchase and storage type of operation, no specific sugar program was undertaken. Sugar did not again come into prominence in farm program discussions until 1933 when the far-reaching New Deal programs were launched.

First Steps in the AAA Program

Since sugar was not defined as a basic crop in the Agricultural Adjustment Act of 1933, any action taken in respect to it at that time would have had to be under the marketing agreement provisions of the act. With this approach in mind, an industry conference was convened in Washington in June 1933 and a draft marketing agreement known as the Sugar Stabilization Plan was drawn up. This plan, designed to run for three years, allocated quotas to the areas supplying the U.S. market. It also established a minimum price for raw sugar—the level to be determined by formula.

21. *Ibid.*, p. 853.

The proposed quotas, 1,525,000 tons for beet sugar and 310,000 tons for cane sugar, were very favorable to growers in continental United States. Instead of a reduction, the beet sugar quota allowed a larger tonnage than had ever been produced up to that time.[22] The quota proposed for cane sugar in continental United States was larger than the actual production of any year between 1921 and 1933.[23] Cuba, which had supplied about 3.5 million tons annually from 1926 through 1929, was given a quota of 1.7 million tons. Its exports to the United States had fallen off sharply after 1930, averaging only 1.95 million tons from 1931 through 1933.

In the hearings on this plan, held in August 1933, there was opposition to the plan as proposed. The domestic beet growers objected to any limitation whatever on their output and the refiners were not in agreement with the proposals made. The Administration advised abandonment of the plan unless the grower and refiner interests could reach agreement.

A revised plan, agreed to by all of the interested parties except Cuba and the Philippines, was presented a few days later. This raised the quota for continental beet growers to 1,750,000 tons. The increase was made possible, however, only by raising the domestic consumption estimate from 6,350,000 tons to 6,725,000 tons.

It is probable that offering that amount of sugar on the domestic market at that time would have had a price-depressing effect. The Secretary of Agriculture announced, on October 9, that he would not act on the industry's Sugar Stabilization Plan. He stated that the proposed agreement appeared to emphasize unduly the interests of processors rather than the interests of farmers. The proposed agreement was also unsatisfactory in that it contained no effective provision for the control of production.

The Jones-Costigan Act of 1934

The next move came from the Administration itself. On February 8, 1934, the President sent a message to the Congress in which he asked for special legislation to achieve the following objectives: "(1) to maintain the existing acreage of sugar beets and sugarcane in the Continental United States, but to limit further expansion, (2) to increase returns to domestic growers, (3) to stabilize production in the insular areas, and (4) to check the decline of imports of Cuban sugar as a means of

22. The 1933 tonnage, not yet harvested at the time this agreement was drafted, was 1,642,000. From 1920 through 1931, production ranged between 675,000 and 1,208,000 tons. In most years it amounted to a little over a million tons. The 1932 production was 1,357,000 tons. (*Agricultural Statistics, 1937,* p. 107.)

23. The 1921 production, 334,000 tons of raw sugar, was abnormally high. Production was much lower in the years immediately preceding 1921 and in all of the years from then until 1934.

restoring Cuba's power to purchase American agricultural products."[24] In his letter, the President went so far as to propose a set of "preliminary and tentative quotas." These are shown in Table 38.

TABLE 38

SOURCES OF UNITED STATES SUGAR, 1926–1929, 1931–1933 AND FIRST QUOTAS AUTHORIZED UNDER SUGAR ACTS AND OTHER PROPOSALS

(*Thousands of Tons, Raw Value*)

(1) Geographic Source	(2) Average Amount Supplied, 1926–1929	(3) Average Amount Supplied, 1931–1933	(4) Proposed Sugar Stabilization Plan, 8/21/33	(5) Pres. Roosevelt's Proposal of 2/18/34	(6) 1934 Quotas: First Year of Jones-Costigan Act	(7) 1937 Quotas: First Year of 1937 Sugar Act	(8) 1948 Quotas: First Year of 1948 Sugar Act [a]
Total	6,686	6,452	6,725	6,452	6,475	7,044	7,800
Continental United States							
Beet	1,063	1,342	1,750	1,450	1,556	1,633	1,800
Cane	114	227	310	260	261	443	500
U.S. territories							
Hawaiian Islands	812	1,012	975	935	916	989	1,052
Puerto Rico	572	843	875	821	803	841	910
Virgin Islands	7	4	15	5	5	9	6
Philippine Islands	548	1,049	1,100	1,037	1,015	1,085	982
Cuba	3,543	1,948	1,700	1,944	1,902	2,015	2,515
Other countries	27	27	—	—	17	28	35

Source: Sugar Branch, U.S. Production and Marketing Administration.

a. In clarification of the quota operations of the 1948 act it should be noted that, through changes in the consumption estimate and through reallocation of deficits, the quotas of the various producing areas were finally adjusted as follows: continental beet 1,687,738 tons, continental cane 413,260 tons, Hawaiian Islands 825,000 tons, Virgin Islands 6,159 tons, Philippine Islands 240,000 tons, Cuba 2,940,467 tons, and other areas 63,620 tons.

As a result of the President's message, the Congress passed the Jones-Costigan Amendment to the Agricultural Adjustment Act. That amendment, approved on May 9, 1934, defined both sugar beets and sugar cane as basic agricultural commodities, thus giving the Secretary of Agriculture authority to make rental or benefit payments in connection with acreage and/or marketing restrictions. It required the Secretary of Agriculture to determine American sugar requirements and to establish quotas applicable to noncontinental areas.

Quotas for continental United States were spelled out in the legislation (1,550,000 tons for beet sugar and 260,000 tons for cane sugar). The beet sugar quota was 1,000 tons in excess of that recommended by

24. Edwin G. Nourse, Joseph S. Davis and John D. Black, *Three Years of the Agricultural Adjustment Administration,* The Brookings Institution, Washington, 1937, p. 107.

the President. It exceeded the production of any previous year except the record output of 1933. Quotas for noncontinental U.S. areas were to be determined by the Secretary of Agriculture on the basis of receipts from each contributing area in the three most representative years of the period 1925–1933.

An important provision of the new act was the imposition of a processing tax of ½ cent per pound on all sugar consumed in the United States and its territories. This was accompanied by an equal downward adjustment of the tariff. The proceeds of the tax were to be segregated for use in making payments to domestic producers.

The Secretary of Agriculture was authorized to impose controls on the growers of sugar crops and also to assign quotas to processors. He was given wide discretionary powers in determining the amounts required to meet domestic consumption needs and could increase or decrease allotments if the data for any given year indicated that consumption would exceed or fall short of the amounts allotted.[25] If any production area proved unable to produce and deliver its allotted amount, the deficit could be prorated to other areas on the basis of their respective quotas. Quotas could also be reduced to offset surplus sugar stocks accumulated in the area during the preceding year.

These provisions placed control of the flow of sugar, both domestic and imported, in the hands of the Secretary of Agriculture. They also gave him a certain amount of control over the regional structure of the industry and over the profits of processors, though obviously these could not practically be used in such a way as to distort customary margins very markedly. The arrangement did, however, make possible very sharp changes in the amounts produced in the insular areas as compared with production on the mainland.

Since the processing industry consisted of a small number of units—less than 250 in all—such controls appeared to be administratively feasible, especially since the industry itself approved the general character of the plan. Its own proposed Sugar Stabilization Plan included equally stringent government controls.

Control over Wages and Child Labor

The act contained a labor provision that marked a new departure in agricultural relief legislation. This section, 8a (3), provided that ". . . all agreements authorized by this Act relating to sugar beets, sugarcane, or the products thereof may contain provisions which will limit or regulate child labor, and will fix minimum wages for workers or growers employed by the producers and/or processors of sugar beets and/or sugarcane who are parties to such agreements . . ." In addition, the

25. If consumption requirements were increased, not less than 30 per cent of the amount in excess of 6,452,000 tons was to be allotted to continental U.S. producers.

Secretary was authorized to adjudicate any disputes about this or other provisions of the agreement and his decision was to be final.[26]

The sugar industry had long been recognized as one in which worker incomes were low and living conditions bad. It was also one in which child and woman labor were used extensively. The field workers were ordinarily hired on a contract basis at so much per acre. Many of the families were migrant and of foreign nationality. All members of the family, including children as young as eight or nine, worked in the fields along with the adult male workers.

Earnings in the industry as a whole, both domestic and foreign, were barely sufficient for subsistence at a very meager level. Production costs in the offshore tropical cane sugar areas were so much lower that even the relatively high protection afforded the growers in continental United States could do little more than offset some of the natural disadvantages of the mainland growers. It did little to improve the incomes of field workers.[27] Their living conditions continued to be little better than those of sugar workers in the tropical areas, which were among the lowest in the world.

The rapid introduction of labor-saving machinery, and increases in farm wages generally, were soon to change this situation but, as of the time the act was passed, there was obvious need to protect the living standards of this labor group and especially for restraints on the use of child labor. The later increases in wage rates, which resulted from war and postwar demands for labor, were to improve the incomes of field workers but would not necessarily do away with child labor.[28] Under

26. This was the only agricultural act that contained specific provision for minimum wages or the abolition of child labor. Agriculture was, in fact, specifically exempted from the more general labor laws that were beginning to take shape during this period. There was growing demand for more equitable division of benefit payments between landlords and their tenants or croppers, and provisions governing this were gradually written into the laws and regulations, especially those relating to cotton, but these did not apply to wage workers.

27. Part of the cost differential between U.S. mainland and offshore sugar production derives from the extremely low wages and poor living conditions in the tropical areas, except in Hawaii. However, the natural advantages of these areas probably will continue to make them lower-cost producers of sugar than the sugar beet areas of the U.S. mainland, even if insular wage rates are raised and made comparable to those on the mainland. The mainland beet industry is being very rapidly and generally mechanized and this may eventually offset the advantages of the tropical areas and put the two types of production on a more equal competitive basis.

28. It is often said that the sugar beet industry is depression-oriented; that is, it requires large amounts of labor but cannot compete for it except in times of low employment. Changes now occurring will undoubtedly modify that situation a good deal. In the 1940s, when labor supplies were tight and the competition from other crops keen, the production of sugar beets on mechanized farms increased. In U.S. areas not considered to be mechanized, the annual labor requirement is 75 to 100 hours per acre. In California, where mechanization is rather far advanced, it is less than 40 hours. However, even this large decrease is not so striking as that which has occurred in some competing lines of crop production. Even the "unmechanized" areas now customarily use tractor power in preparing the land. That amount of mechanization reduced labor requirements by about 9 hours per acre. (See Warren R. Bailey, *Economics of Sugar-Beet Mechaniza-*

the contract system of payment that is common in the industry, higher wages might even intensify that problem. Mechanization has tended to ameliorate both conditions but has not eliminated them.

The Problem of Requirements and Allocation

One of the crucial problems was to determine the consumption requirement. A liberal estimate would mean that surpluses would appear in the market and the price would settle to or near the "free-market" level, that is, the external price plus the duty. If the Secretary should establish a very low estimate, prices would be above the "free-market" level and would automatically ration the short supplies. The 1934 consumption estimate was put at 6,476,000 tons, which was about the amount proposed in the President's message. That estimate had, of course, originated in the Department of Agriculture and was its guess as to how much would be consumed at approximately the prevailing level of prices.

While the continental quotas were settled by the act, the insular and foreign quotas were not. The method of sharing some 70 per cent of the U.S. sugar market among those areas was of great concern, not only to them but also to the East Coast and Gulf refining industries. The quotas authorized were based on deliveries in the years 1931, 1932 and 1933, except that for Hawaii the years 1930, 1931 and 1932 were used.[29] The quotas were later revised. The legislation had provided for reallocation of quotas if requirement estimates were changed or if it became apparent that a supplying area could not meet its quota.

In the 1933–34 production year, the output of Puerto Rico and the Philippines was very high. The Philippines had in fact shipped very large quantities of sugar to the United States before the quotas were announced and even before the Jones-Costigan Act was approved. This was done largely in the hope of getting the sugar in early enough so it would not be regarded as part of the Philippine quota.

However, on June 21, 1934, only a few days after the quotas were assigned, the Secretary of Agriculture announced that the Philippine quota for 1934 had been filled. All later shipments were stored under Customs Service control and were not released until January 1, 1935, at which time they were charged against the Philippine quota for that year. The excess over quota in 1934 was about 450,000 tons.

The amounts produced in excess of 1934 quotas for other areas were as follows: continental United States, 191,000 tons; Puerto Rico, 251,000 tons and Hawaii, 73,000 tons.[30] These excess supplies were not

---

tion in California, U.S. Department of Agriculture, Circular No. 907, August 1952, pp. 2, 17.)

29. The quotas assigned in 1934 are shown in Column 6, Table 38.

30. John E. Dalton, *Sugar, A Case Study of Government Control,* Macmillan, New York, 1937, p. 127.

allowed to enter channels of consumption and were stored for distribution in 1935 (against 1935 quotas). To liquidate them and bring the industry into balance under the quota pattern adopted, the 1935 production in Puerto Rico, the Philippines and Hawaii had to be cut substantially below the quotas.[31] This problem resulted largely from the fact that marketing controls were applied in 1934 while production controls were not put into effect until 1935.

In the continental and insular areas, a tonnage allotment was assigned to each factory district.[32] These quotas were then converted to acreage allotments, using normal yields. Within each factory district, individual growers were given a choice of basing their acreage allotments on the five-year, four-year, three-year or two-year average for the years immediately preceding 1934.

Payments to Beet Growers—1934

For the 1934 crop, beet growers were guaranteed benefit payments, termed "fair exchange value" payments,[33] of at least $1.25 per ton of beets, on actual production or on estimated production using normal yields. The payments made amounted to $2.60 per ton of beets produced in that year.[34] No production adjustment was required in order to qualify for these payments.

The farm price of beets was $5.16 per ton, as compared with $5.13 in 1933. This, together with the $2.60 in benefit payments, made an over-all return of $7.76 per ton in 1934. However, the gross return to farmers was only a little larger than that for the big crop of 1933. The 11-million-ton crop of 1933, at $5.13 per ton, brought approximately $56.6 million. The 7.5 million tons grown in 1934 brought $38.8 million at the factories. This plus $19.6 million in government payments gave the growers a gross return of $58.4 million, or about 3 per cent more than the 1933 return.[35]

31. Strong production restraints were applied only in Puerto Rico and the Philippines. In Hawaii, the adjustment was carried out mainly on a voluntary basis.

32. The acreage allotment to each company district for 1935 was not less than 90 per cent of the acreage planted in 1933 and not more than 100 per cent. Since the 1933 beet acreage was the largest on record, this was a liberal allowance for the continental beet areas.

33. These were essentially the same thing as the "parity" payments made on certain crops in later years. In the earlier legislation, the term "fair exchange value" was used instead of "parity," which came into use later.

34. Both acreages harvested and yields were down substantially in 1934, as compared with 1933, largely as a result of the severe droughts of that year. The district allotments for 1935 were not announced until December 22, 1934. The 1934 crop had already been planted when the program for that year was announced.

35. For data on prices and government payments, see Table 39, which is based on information supplied by the Sugar Branch, U.S. Production and Marketing Administration. These data differ slightly from some of those published in other sources.

Sugar Beet Production in 1935 and 1936

Beet acreage allotments for 1935 totaled 975,000 acres, but drought conditions at planting time over much of the sugar beet area prevented full use of the quotas assigned. Only 847,000 acres were planted and only 763,000 acres were harvested. The amount of sugar produced was 1,185,000 tons.[36] The remainder of the 1,556,000-ton quota was drawn from stocks carried over from the 1933 crop.

Rainfall still was very inadequate in 1936 and production in that year was only 1,313,000 tons, which meant that the supply of continental beet sugar was about 200,000 tons short of the quota. The downward adjustment made in these years resulted from weather conditions, not from restrictions on output.[37] However, the acreage reductions in Puerto Rico and the Philippines were very severe. It was here that the principal restrictive effect of the program was felt. Even without individual grower allotments, a severe restriction on the amounts the processors can sell in their customary markets causes them to cut back on the amounts they will grow, or purchase from the growers dependent on them for an outlet.

The payments made were, in effect, direct transfers from consumers to growers in amounts that restored the purchasing power of sugar (with bonuses included) to about the 1910–1914 relationship with the prices of commodities purchased. However, they were conditional in that growers were required to maintain a modest minimum wage and to eliminate child labor in order to be eligible for them.

The Supreme Court's Hoosac Mills decision of January 6, 1936[38] ruled out the use of acreage control contracts between the Secretary of Agriculture and the growers. Hence, the acreage control feature of the program was not in effect for 1936, except for payment of obligations carried over from the 1935 operation. However, the Congress passed a resolution providing that the quota provisions with respect to offshore sugar would continue to be in effect. As a result, both the excess stocks and the overexpanded production in the island areas were brought down to a more normal relationship with demand.

For the 1936 crop, payments were made under the Soil Conservation and Domestic Allotment Act passed in February of that year, for compliance with acreage control plans provided specified conservation practices were carried out. Participating growers received payments averaging 39 cents per ton for beets and 20 cents per ton for cane.

36. *Agricultural Statistics, 1937,* p. 107.

37. In 1935, the acreage allotments constituted technically a restraint on production, but this did not cause growers to give up any acreage they would otherwise have grown since they did not plant as much as was permitted under the allotments.

38. *U.S.* v. *Butler et al., Receivers of Hoosac Mills Corporation,* 297 U.S. 1 (1936).

The Cane Sugar Program

The 261,000-ton continental cane sugar quota was generous. It was higher than the amount produced in any year between 1922 and 1934. However, the trend was slightly upward in the early 1930s and there was a large expansion of output in 1935 and 1936 (approximately 50 per cent).[39]

Though acreage allotment determinations were made in respect to the 1935 crop, no restrictive program was carried out. Producers were given "fair exchange value" payments to supplement incomes and as a *quid pro quo* for paying the prescribed rates of wage and eliminating child labor. Such payments, in 1934, amounted to $2.50 per ton of cane and, in 1935, to 74 cents per ton. The price received by farmers per ton of cane was $2.33 in 1934 and $3.18 in 1935. The 1934 payment thus more than doubled the return to the grower. In 1935, it added more than 20 per cent to the amount received from the processors. The price paid for cane in these years was mostly below even the low levels of 1932 and 1933, which were about 25 per cent below prices in the middle 1920s.

Over-All Effects of the Jones-Costigan Act

The program which resulted from the Jones-Costigan Act accomplished several of the purposes for which it was designed. It protected the continental sugar producers from being flooded out by supplies from offshore areas and did it more effectively than the tariff had done previously. It gave continental U.S. growers an assured outlet for more sugar than they had produced in previous years. The quota restrictions on offshore areas forced a readjustment in their output and made possible the absorption of surpluses that had accumulated in the Philippines and Puerto Rico. The rapid expansion in these areas was halted and the sugar market as a whole was brought into a healthier condition. This was accomplished almost wholly, however, by extremely vigorous pressure on growers in the offshore areas.[40]

The price of sugar beets was stabilized but was not raised significantly

39. This was due largely to increased yields. Acreage was about 210,000 to 220,000 in 1932 and 1933. It moved up to more than 250,000 in 1935 and 1936. Production increased from 246,000 tons in 1933 to 397,000 in 1936. (*Agricultural Statistics, 1937,* p. 111.) However, the 1920s were not a representative period for Louisiana, for disease curtailed production very severely in that area. The Florida industry hardly existed in the years prior to 1929.

40. Unquestionably the procedure used discriminated in favor of U.S. mainland sugar producers. Their representatives had votes in the Congress while those from the island areas did not. However, the maladjustments had become much more serious in the island areas than on the mainland. Even if mainland quotas had been set at the actual production levels of the preceding years, the allocation to the insular areas could not have been much more liberal.

until 1936. By that time, sugar supplies had been brought into better balance with demand. The increase from $5.13 per ton in 1933 to $6.05 in 1936 brought the price back to about the 1931 level, but it still was 15 to 20 per cent below the prices prevailing in the late 1920s when large surpluses were already piling up. The principal financial effect on beet growers, aside from the prevention of further demoralization of the market, was a sizable direct transfer of income to them in 1934 and a much smaller one in 1935. This came out of funds derived from the processing tax. Part of the income supplement was, however, a replacement of returns that would have come to them in higher prices for their product if the processing tax had not been levied. (See later analysis, pp. 318–21.)[41]

The 1934 payment, $19.6 million, approximately equaled the reduction in return from sale of beets which resulted from the short crop of 1934. The payments made on the 1935 crop, $9.5 million, again supplemented the returns from sale of beets in such a way as to keep the total return at about the 1933 level. Gross returns, including government payments, were $56.6 million in 1933, $58.2 million in 1934 and $55.1 million in 1935.[42] The 1936 return, with quotas in effect but no supplementary payments except those provided under the soil conservation program, was $55.2 million.[43] Except for the big crop of 1933, beet sugar production was at about the level which prevailed between 1927 and 1932.

Thus, in these years, the beet sugar program acted as an income stabilizer but had no significant influence on mainland output either as a restraint or as a stimulus. However, if the severe droughts of 1934 and 1935 had not occurred, it is probable that acreages would have been above those of 1927–1932 and the 1935 program very possibly would have had the effect of slowing down the rate of increase.

Effects in the Cane Sugar Areas

As of November 30, 1936, continental cane producers had received about $10.7 million in supplemental payments on the 1934 and 1935 crops and the U.S. offshore cane areas about $40.8 million.[44] The total return per ton to sugar cane growers was stepped up sharply in 1934, to about 25 to 50 per cent over the prices that had prevailed from 1927

41. It is probable that the beet growers gained substantially from the 1934 transfer payments. The processing tax was collected on the total domestic supply. Since the 1934 crop was small, the payment, based on representative yields, was more than enough to offset the price-reducing effect of the processing tax. The sugar cane growers also apparently received much larger returns in 1934 than they would have if the program had not been in effect.

42. See Dalton, *op. cit.*, p. 155.

43. *Agricultural Statistics, 1937,* p. 107.

44. AAA press release of November 30, 1936, as quoted by Dalton, *op. cit.*, p. 140. Further payments amounting to about $5 million were made later, but the figures here shown indicate the general magnitude of the transfers.

on. For the 1935 crop, the combined return dropped back to about the level prevailing in 1928 and 1929, which was around 20 per cent higher than the 1930–1933 level. (See Table 39.)

TABLE 39

SUGAR BEETS AND CONTINENTAL SUGAR CANE: PRICES AND GOVERNMENT PAYMENTS RECEIVED BY FARMERS, PER TON, 1930–1951

	Sugar Beets			Sugar Cane		
Crop Year	Prices Received from Processors	Government Payments [a]	Total	Prices Received from Processors	Government Payments [a]	Total
1930	$7.14		$7.14	$3.31		$3.31
1931	5.94		5.94	3.21		3.21
1932	5.26		5.26	2.98		2.98
1933	5.13	$ .23	5.36	3.13		3.13
1934	5.16	2.60	7.76	2.33	$2.50	4.83
1935	5.76	1.20	6.96	3.15	.74	3.89
1936	6.05		6.05	3.67		3.67
1937	5.27	1.97	7.24	2.90	.91	3.81
1938	4.65	1.93	6.58	2.71	.94	3.65
1939	4.77	2.02	6.79	2.84	.96	3.80
1940	5.11	1.92	7.03	2.88	1.04	3.92
1941	6.46	1.89	8.35	3.95	.97	4.92
1942	6.78	2.59	9.37	4.40	1.29	5.69
1943	7.48	4.09	11.57	4.27	1.51	5.78
1944	7.74	5.67	13.41	4.20	1.92	6.12
1945	8.03	4.75	12.78	4.22	2.56	6.78
1946	11.10	2.55	13.65	6.62	1.19	7.81
1947	10.60	3.84	14.44	7.17	1.30	8.47
1948	10.34	2.56	12.90	5.76	1.15	6.91
1949	10.80	2.54	13.34	6.25	1.16	7.41
1950	11.20	2.49	13.69	7.80	1.21	9.01
1951	11.60	2.50	14.10	6.37	1.15	7.52

Source: Sugar Branch, U.S. Production and Marketing Administration.

a. Includes Sugar Act and CCC payments but not agricultural conservation payments.

The principal gain to the sugar cane areas aside from about $51.5 million in direct government payments (for the two years 1934 and 1935),[45] which was partly offset by lower prices for cane, was in the readjustment of production and stocks in the insular areas. This relieved

45. The benefit payments to cane growers were distributed as follows (in millions): to Louisiana and Florida, $10.7; to Hawaii, $13.3; to Puerto Rico, $12.1; to the Philippines, $15.4. (Dalton, *op. cit.*, p. 140.)

the industry of the threat of demoralization from continuing expansion in the island areas and thus brought about greater stability and better balance between supply and demand. The continuance of quotas on sugar made it possible to avoid recurrence of the flooding of the domestic market through re-expansion of the shipments from offshore areas. It strengthened the U.S. price as compared with the price in the world market generally. Dalton estimates this price advantage at four tenths of a cent in 1935 and seven tenths of a cent in 1936.[46]

Acreages grown in the offshore areas remained relatively stable during the late 1930s but stocks increased again around the end of the decade. These accumulations were due mainly to increased acreage and production in the continental cane and beet areas.

Price to Consumers Not Affected

There is little indication that the imposition of a one-half cent tax on domestically consumed sugar, and the related reciprocal reductions in tariff, affected prices paid by U.S. consumers.[47] The retail price remained almost constant from 1931 through 1941, mostly at about 5.5 cents, except that the 1932 price was down about one half cent.[48]

The program seems therefore to have affected the interrelationships within the industry and the general receipts of the U.S. Treasury rather than U.S. consumers. About $102 million in processing taxes on sugar were collected from June 1934 through December 31, 1936.[49] The duty on Cuban sugar was reduced from 2 cents to 1.5 cents in June 1934, by presidential proclamation under an authorization contained in the Jones-Costigan Act. It was further reduced, to nine tenths of a cent, in August 1934 under the reciprocal trade agreement entered into with Cuba at that time. Additional tariff concessions were granted in the 1940s. The duty (on sugar from Cuba) was reduced to .75 cent in the trade agreement of January 1942 and to .5 cent in the Geneva agreement of 1948.[50]

The loss to U.S. Treasury general receipts was the difference between 2 cents per pound on the amounts imported from Cuba and the duties actually levied on them in this period, that is, 1.1 cents per pound from

46. *Op. cit.*, p. 235. When the program was begun, there were surplus stocks of about one million tons: 300,000 in beet sugar, 300,000 in the Philippines, 250,000 in Puerto Rico and 150,000 in Hawaii. (Joshua Bernhardt, *The Sugar Industry and the Federal Government,* Sugar Statistics Service, Washington, 1948, p. 194.)

47. The reduction in tariff would probably have had some tendency to reduce the prices paid by U.S. consumers and received by U.S. producers had it not been for the quota system, which was introduced at the same time. However, for reasons already mentioned, there is little likelihood that U.S. prices would have been reduced by the amount of the tariff reduction. A good part of the adjustment would still have been in the form of a higher price to Cuban producers.

48. *Agricultural Statistics, 1937,* p. 117, and *1945,* p. 97.

49. U.S. Agricultural Adjustment Administration, *Agricultural Conservation, 1936,* p. 138.

50. U.S. Tariff Commission, *Summaries of Tariff Information,* Vol. 5, *Sugar, Molasses and Manufactures,* 1948, p. 1.

August 1934 on.[51] Total imports, June 1934 to December 31, 1936, virtually all from Cuba, were roughly 6.4 million tons. For this period, the Treasury receipts foregone thus were in the order of $125 million to $130 million.[52]

During this first period, Cuba gained by having an assured outlet for a sizable portion of her crop at a price that was higher than it would have been without quotas, and, after August 1934, from a reduction in the tariff which more than offset the processing and excise taxes. If Dalton's estimate of the price-raising effect of the quota limitations is accepted, and can be assumed to have averaged roughly one half cent, it would appear that the gain to Cuban producers, in this form, may have been in the order of $25 million per year.[53]

Until August 1934, the one-half cent reduction in tariff was offset by the one-half cent processing tax and probably had little if any effect on the returns to Cuban exporters. From August 1934 to January 6, 1936, the effective reduction (tariff reduction minus processing tax) was six tenths of a cent. Through most of 1936, the tariff reduction of 1.1 cents was presumably reflected largely in increased returns to Cuban sugar producers. To assume that all of it was passed on in that way would almost certainly be unwarranted. Some of it no doubt was absorbed by handlers, and there probably was some effect on U.S. prices, though apparently not a large one. There is indication, however, that most of the gain (on imported sugar) accrued to the Cuban industry.[54]

51. The amount collected as processing tax, though an offset to part of the tariff reduction, did not go into the Treasury general fund. It was made available to the Secretary of Agriculture for payments to sugar-crop producers (in 1934 and 1935 only). Thereafter, the excise tax collected went into the general fund but with a tacit understanding that a good part of it would be appropriated for payments to sugar-crop producers. Since the tax apparently did not raise prices to consumers, its principal effect was to lower the price of raw sugar. Thus it affected Cuban sugar producers in much the same way as though the tariff had been that much higher. It also reduced the market returns to U.S. growers by about the amount of the tax. Such effects are seldom as precise as this analysis implies but the general results appear to have been about as here stated.

52. The time during which the tariff reduction was in effect is not the same as the period during which the processing tax was collected. The tax was discontinued in January 1936.

53. Since the Cuban sugar came in under quota, it presumably had approximately the same effect on the supply-demand situation, and hence on the price, regardless of the amount of tariff on it. Actually the U.S. price on foreign sugar, duty-paid, moved up moderately, from 2.969 cents per pound in June 1934 to 3.503 cents in September 1935 and 3.806 cents in December 1936. (*Sugar Economics, Statistics and Documents,* United States Cane Sugar Refiners Association, New York, 1938, p. 29.) This apparently was, in the main, the price rise occasioned by the imposition of quotas and tends to bear out the estimate made by Dalton.

54. The Cuban situation improved materially between 1932 and 1936, mainly but not wholly as a result of U.S. actions. Its 1929 crop was valued at $191 million. This return shrank to $37 million in 1932 but recovered to $54 million in 1933. By 1936, it had reached $108 million, or about 56 per cent of its 1929 level. (Dalton, *op. cit.,* p. 254.)

Gains to U.S. Growers

When final settlements were made, U.S. growers had received about $85 million in direct payments on the 1934 and 1935 programs, out of the fund derived from the processing tax on sugar.[55] It can be assumed that a considerable portion of this would have gone to them in higher prices for beets and cane had there been only the quota plan but no processing tax. The quota system would apparently have kept the wholesale price, duty and tax paid, about as it was. Hence processors, unless they were to absorb the tax, had to make their payments to growers enough lower to offset the tax.[56]

The effect on grower incomes from processing taxes and conditional payments was thus to substitute in considerable measure a payment from the government for payment of a higher price by the processors, except in 1934 when payments per ton were large because of the short crop. The difference was mainly that the fund thus built up could be used to help in bringing about planned adjustments in the industry, whereas payments made directly to the growers by the processors could not be so used.

However, there was an increment to the fund which came about through reduced income to the U.S. Treasury, rather than through reduced returns to the growers. This was the one-half cent tax collected on imported sugar, which, so far as the importers were concerned, was in effect a substitute for part of the tariff duty. It was merely a payment to the special fund rather than to the general fund of the Treasury. It added about $40 million to the sugar adustment fund, essentially from the U.S. Treasury, without a corresponding reduction in processor payments to the growers.

Conservation Payments Made Available in 1936

The Jones-Costigan program, like most of the other AAA programs, was in liquidation in 1936. However, under the Soil Conservation and Domestic Allotment Act of 1936, sugar-crop growers were allowed to earn payments for soil-conserving practices, though no provision was made for diverting acreage formerly in sugar beets and sugar cane.[57]

55. *Agricultural Conservation, 1936,* p. 139.

56. Manufacturers' spread, for beet factories, remained about constant during 1934 and 1935 but showed some increase in 1936, possibly because the repeal of the processing tax came after production plans and contracts had been made. (See *Sugar Economics, Statistics and Documents,* p. 37.) However, processors' return on investment rose sharply in 1935 and 1936 to 11.36 and 12.64 per cent, but dropped off to about the 1933 and 1934 levels (around 8 per cent) in 1937, 1938 and 1939. (U.S. Agricultural Adjustment Administration, *Agricultural Adjustment, 1939–1940,* p. 90.)

57. These payments were computed on the basis of 12½ cents per 100 pounds of raw sugar (*Agricultural Conservation, 1936,* p. 103). Though the gross amount is not specifically stated, the AAA reported payments on 1,056,735 tons of sugar in 1936 (*ibid.,* p. 194), which would indicate payments of about $2.6 million. The figure given for 1937 is $3,734,000 (*Agricultural Adjustment, 1937–1938,* p. 298).

Both sugar beets and sugar cane were classed as soil-depleting crops, but, since the program did not call for reductions in acreage, growers could obtain conservation payments by planting soil-conserving crops on acreages amounting to 25 per cent of the land in sugar beets and sugar cane.[58] Soil conservation payments have been continued in the years since 1936 but are not included in the analysis here presented. Though they added to growers' incomes, they had no direct effect on prices and were not for the same purpose as the conditional payments on sugar crops discussed in the preceding pages.

The Sugar Act of 1937

Government payments at the 1936 levels were not acceptable to the growers, since they had been receiving much larger payments in 1934 and 1935. Considerable pressure developed for the passage of new sugar legislation. This took shape in the Sugar Act of 1937. That act included the essential features of the Jones-Costigan Act, namely, (1) provision for annual estimates of consumption requirements, (2) the portioning out of estimated requirements among continental, offshore and foreign areas, and (3) allotment of "proportionate shares" to domestic growers of beets and cane, these to be the bases for "conditional" payments and, at the same time, the bases to which acreage restrictions would be applied if necessary. The processing tax, invalidated by the 1936 Supreme Court decision, was replaced by an excise tax at the same rate, one-half cent per pound.

One important feature of the 1934 act, the parity or "fair-exchange-value" concept, was dropped. However, the retention of the excise tax and authorization for conditional payments implied that the government would continue to supplement the prices received from the processors.[59]

The 1937 act called for a different and more explicit method of determining quotas. The Secretary of Agriculture was required to allot 55.59 per cent of the annual consumption estimate to U.S. areas but was not to make the total allotment to these areas less than 3,715,000 tons. The quota determined for U.S. areas was to be subdivided as follows: to continental beet growers, 41.72 per cent (of the 55.59 per cent allotted to U.S. areas); to continental cane producers, 11.31 per

58. See *Agricultural Conservation, 1936,* p. 102. The Sugar Act of 1937 did not come into effect until September 1937. From January 1936 to September 1937, the quota arrangement and the soil conservation program were the only forms of aid provided for sugar producers.

59. Under the 1937 act, the method of handling wage-rate requirements also was changed. Instead of acting as adjudicator in wage disputes, the Secretary of Agriculture established definite minimum rates. Hourly earnings in the beet areas rose from 31 cents in 1934 to an average of 40 cents in 1939, 1940 and 1941. The 1934 rate was above the rates paid generally for farm workers at that time. However, the increase between then and the end of the decade was somewhat smaller than for farm wage rates as a whole.

cent; to the Hawaiian Islands, 25.25 per cent; to Puerto Rico, 21.48 per cent; and to the Virgin Islands, 0.24 per cent.

The remaining 44.41 per cent was to be allotted as follows: to the Commonwealth of the Philippine Islands, 34.70 per cent; to Cuba, 64.41 per cent; and to other countries, 0.89 per cent.[60] However, the quota for the Philippines was in no case to be less than that already established in the Philippine Independence Act of 1934.[61] If the Philippines were unable to fill their quota in any year, the deficits were to be reallocated to foreign countries other than Cuba. Deficits in other areas were to be reallocated on the basis of prorations then in effect.

Payments to Growers

Growers were to be paid 60 cents per 100 pounds of recoverable raw sugar for keeping within the quotas provided and for complying with other requirements of the law.[62] These payments worked out to about $1.04 per ton of sugar cane and $1.87 per ton of beets. Payments to growers for the ten-month period September 1937 through June 1938 amounted to about $36,847,000.[63] It was estimated that these payments, in addition to the prices received for beets and cane, would result in a total return to growers for the 1937 crop that would approximate the parity price.

The higher returns received by growers in these years apparently were

60. Cuba had benefited materially from the quota system and the reduction in tariffs. While the tariff on Cuban sugar had been reduced from 2 cents to .9 cent, the full duty applying to other foreign areas had been reduced only to 1.875 cents (from 2.50 cents). Thus, Cuba's differential advantage had increased from .5 cent to .975 cent. By the end of 1936, the price at Havana warehouses was nearly double what it had been at the beginning of 1934 (1.86 as compared to 1.02). (See *Sugar Economics, Statistics and Documents,* p. 77.)

61. A gradual change from colonial to independent status for the Philippine commonwealth was authorized in the Philippine Independence Act of March 24, 1934. A ten-year period of readjustment was to lead to complete independence on July 4, 1946. In the meantime, the Philippine government was to levy a gradually increasing export tax on sugar, which would eventually be replaced by the standard duties imposed by the United States. These provisions were modified by the act of 1946, which permitted entry without payment of duty, for Philippine sugar exports permitted under the quotas, until 1954. See U.S. Tariff Commission, *United States–Philippine Trade,* Report No. 118, Second Series, 1937, pp. 52–56, 195–205, and U.S. House Committee on Insular Affairs, *Appendix to Hearings,* 79th Cong., 2d sess., *To Provide for Rehabilitation of the Philippine Islands,* 1946.

62. This rate was to be decreased as the amount of sugar produced on the farm or plantation increased, reaching a minimum of 30 cents per hundredweight for a farm producing 30,000 tons or more. The 60-cent rate applied on farms producing less than 500 tons. (This upper limit on acreage eligible for full payment was reduced to 350 tons in the 1948 act.) The other requirements for eligibility to receive payments were: (1) the elimination of child labor, except that of members of the grower's immediate family; (2) payment of the minimum wage specified by the Secretary of Agriculture; and (3) carrying out soil-conserving practices. The soil conservation requirements were much the same as those of the 1936 and 1937 soil conservation programs. The rate of payment was raised in 1942 to 80 cents per 100 pounds of recoverable sugar.

63. *Agricultural Adjustment, 1937–1938,* p. 60.

due almost wholly to quota limitations on imports rather than to the collection and distribution of the excise tax. The wholesale price of refined sugar, net excluding tax, was 4.112 cents per pound for the period September 1937–June 1938 as compared with 4.684 cents in the same period of the preceding year (*Agricultural Adjustment, 1937–1938,* p. 60). This seems to bear out the conclusion that the price was reduced by about the amount of the tax.[64]

World Market Still Weak

The world market for sugar continued weak through the late 1930s. The U.S. industry was insulated to some extent, but not entirely, from the depressing influence of the external market. In 1938 and 1939, prices for the raw product were even lower than in the early years of the depression. (See *Agricultural Statistics, 1952,* pp. 97 and 102.) Though the quotas provided a more effective and more easily administered control over supplies than that which was being attempted for the export crops (through acreage adjustments and marketing quotas), they did not in themselves overcome the maladjustments in the world markets.

The world sugar market still was demoralized and unstable. Concern over its possible adverse effect on the U.S. program, and other interests of the United States, lay back of the efforts then being made to stabilize the sugar market on a broader scale by means of an international agreement.[65] However, the international situation as a whole was greatly changed by the outbreak of war in 1939. Shortly thereafter the world sugar problem became one of concern about the adequacy of supplies rather than of unmanageable surpluses.

Acreage Restrictions Imposed in 1939

Sugar beet acreage increased sharply in 1938 and mainland sugar production as a whole was up by some 546,000 tons over that of 1937.[66] As a consequence, genuine acreage restrictions were then imposed for the first time. These called for a 25 per cent reduction as compared with the acreage grown in 1938, except for small growers who were exempted from acreage restrictions.

64. Payments on the 1938 crop are not reported separately but presumably were at least as large as those for the 1937 crop, possibly in the order of $40 million. For the 1939 crop, payments are reported as $46,259,417.17. (*Agricultural Adjustment, 1939–1940,* p. 146.)

65. Prices in the market to U.S. growers in 1938 and 1939 were lower than at any time since the early 1900s. Government payments for these years were at a rate of about $2 per ton for beets and $1 per ton for cane. In addition, the price was held up to some extent by the quota system, possibly by as much as ½ to 1 cent over what it would have been otherwise.

66. *Agricultural Statistics, 1945,* p. 97. U.S. sugar stocks were large in September 1939 (1,592,000 tons). This was the largest amount recorded for that time of year since comparable records became available in 1935. (U.S. Bureau of Agricultural Economics, *Sugar during World War II,* War Records Monograph 3, June 1946, p. 2.)

These restrictions were partly lifted in 1940 through a provision in the new legislation that permitted growers to market up to 110 per cent of their proportionate shares, or that share plus 25 acres, whichever was larger. They were reimposed in 1941 because of a sharp increase in stocks of sugar on hand. These amounted to 1,750,000 tons on January 1, 1941, as compared with 1,415,000 tons in the previous year and about 1 million tons in earlier years.[67]

The growing demand for sugar and the loss of Philippine supplies led to the lifting of this restriction in October 1942. Growers were permitted to market in excess of their allotments without losing their conditional payments but were not to be given payments on the excess acreage. Quotas on offshore and domestic sugar were also suspended in April 1942. Payments under the 1940 sugar program amounted to $45,064,167.75, those for 1941 to $43,959,428.[68]

Sugar Quotas Suspended—September 1939

Sugar quotas were suspended by Presidential proclamation in September 1939 but were reimposed on December 26 (effective January 1, 1940). The outbreak of war had resulted in a wave of buying which carried the New York price for raw sugar, duty-paid, from $2.93 on August 31 to $3.86 on September 6. The wholesale price of refined sugar rose from $4.31 to $5.63 in the same period.[69] This contributed little to increased grower returns since the processors were, in the main, under long-term contracts and the contract prices to them were, of course, reflected in their agreements with growers. Sugar stocks were ample and the price increase was due almost wholly to feverish buying and speculative activity.

The suspension of quotas steadied the situation and the wholesale price of refined sugar for the year as a whole differed little from the prices that prevailed in 1938 and 1940.[70] However, there were some important incidental effects. The beet industry (and to a lesser extent Hawaii) was able to market without restriction a considerable volume of sugar that would otherwise have been carried over into 1940 and charged against the 1940 quota. As a result, the outlet for Cuba was reduced in 1940 and restrictions on beet production were delayed until 1941.

The quota provisions of the Sugar Act of 1937 were due to expire

67. *Report of the Administrator of the Agricultural Adjustment Administration, 1941,* p. 64.

68. *Ibid.,* p. 89, and *Report of the Administrator of the Agricultural Conservation and Adjustment Administration, 1942,* p. 131.

69. *Agricultural Adjustment, 1939–1940,* p. 85. Suspension of the quota system automatically restored the 1.5-cent rate of duty on Cuban sugar. It dropped back to .9 cent on the reinstitution of quotas in December.

70. 1938, 4.481 cents; 1939, 4.572 cents; 1940, 4.337 cents. (*Agricultural Statistics, 1945,* p. 97.)

on December 31, 1940. Hearings were held in April 1940 but did not bring agreement on new legislation. As a consequence, a resolution continuing the existing legislation was passed on October 15, 1940.[71]

SUGAR IN WORLD WAR II

Sugar was plentiful when war broke out in September 1939. The world price of raw sugar, basis New York, was about 1.95 cents. The sharp rise of more than a cent per pound in the month of September, which led to the suspension of quotas, did not continue and prices became more stable. The average for 1941 was about 2.5 cents c.i.f. New York and 3.4 cents duty-paid.[72]

On August 14, 1941, a ceiling of 3.5 cents, basis New York duty-paid, was established.[73] However, as the war progressed, pressure against the ceiling increased and it was adjusted upward to 3.74 cents in January 1942, 3.75 cents in September 1944 and 4.205 cents in February 1946.[74] Mainly because of changes in the cost of Cuban sugar, the ceiling was raised sharply in August 1947 to 6.32 cents. Quotas were suspended in April 1942 and were not reinstated until November 1947 (effective January 1, 1948). Rationing was imposed in May 1942 and remained in effect until July 28, 1947. Sugar was the first product rationed and the last to be freed from rationing.[75]

The most important factors in the wartime shortage of sugar were the loss of the Philippines and the shortage of shipping. Next in importance was the drop in production of beet sugar on the U.S. mainland. The acreage planted fell from a prewar level of just under a million to an average of 626,000 for the years 1943 and 1944. Beet sugar production fell farther below the goals than any other farm commodity.

A further reason for the shortage was the urgent need for sugar in the production of industrial alcohol and synthetic rubber.[76] Cuban ship-

71. This resolution also reinstated limitations on Hawaiian and Puerto Rican refined sugar. These restrictions had expired in February 1940 and were strongly opposed by the President. In 1941, the expiration date of the Sugar Act was again extended for a three-year period, and the basic rate of payment to growers was increased by 33⅓ per cent, to 80 cents per hundredweight of sugar.

72. *Agricultural Statistics, 1945,* p. 97. The tariff on Cuban sugar was reduced from 1.5 cents to .9 cent under the first Supplementary Trade Agreement with Cuba, effective December 23, 1939. However, the reduction was not put into effect until quotas were re-established on December 27, 1939.

73. This action was taken by the Office of Price Administration and Civilian Supply (OPACS) on August 13, 1941, just before the Office of Price Administration was created by Executive Order 8875 (August 14, 1941).

74. The tariff on Cuban sugar was adjusted in January 1942, being reduced from .9 cent to .75 cent.

75. For a general summary of U.S. sugar policy in this period, see *Sugar during World War II.* Data on government regulations relating to the sugar industry in this period are from *Sugar, Facts and Figures,* published by the U.S.-Cuban Sugar Council, New York, 1948, pp. 153–54.

76. Manufactured sugar was not used in the production of alcohol for the synthetic rubber program. Instead, Cuba was asked to supply large quantities of high-test molasses

ments to the United States were greatly expanded during the war years. Had it not been for these larger imports from Cuba, sugar rations in the United States would have had to be much smaller than they were. Cuban shipments for U.S. consumption during 1937–1939 were at a level of 2,009,000 tons per year. They were increased to 3,618,000 tons in 1944 and averaged 3,100,000 tons for the years 1943 through 1947.

U.S. sugar consumption, which averaged just over 100 pounds per capita in the late 1930s, reached a low of 80.5 pounds in 1946. U.S. consumers were enabled to maintain a much higher level of consumption than prevailed in most other belligerent countries, but only because of the enormous production of Cuba, most of which was available for shipment to the United States if shipping could be supplied to bring it over.

U.S. Sole Purchaser of Cuban Supplies

The U.S. government became the sole wartime purchaser of Cuban sugar exports beginning with the 1941–42 crop and carrying through the 1947 crop, except for minor amounts sold mostly to Latin American countries.[77] It also purchased the entire output of Puerto Rico, beginning with the 1942–43 crop and continuing through the 1946 crop year.[78]

The cost of the operation is difficult to measure accurately and it is perhaps not important to do so. It took various forms in addition to the direct costs of purchase and resale.[79] Transportation subsidies were provided and the collection of import duties was suspended for some government agencies from 1942 and for nearly all of them, including the Commodity Credit Corporation and the Defense Supplies Corporation, from May 1944 to the end of 1946. Other subsidies of various kinds were provided for the purpose of encouraging production.[80]

---

in lieu of sugar, to supplement the supplies of blackstrap and other materials in producing alcohol. The effect on supplies was the same, however, as if sugar had been used.

77. However, some of the sugar purchased from Cuba was shared with allied countries.

78. The 1941–42, 1942–43 and 1943–44 crops were bought at 2.65 cents per pound at Cuban ports. The 1944–45 crop was bought by the Commodity Credit Corporation at 3.10 cents but with provision for upward adjustment if prices and living costs in the United States advanced. Beginning with 1941–42, the Defense Supplies Corporation bought blackstrap molasses and also, in 1943–44, invert molasses (suitable for making sugar) equivalent to 900,000 tons of sugar. In 1943–44 it also bought some alcohol made from sugar.

79. Up to June 1947, these costs were more than offset so far as CCC was concerned by the privilege of bringing in its imports free of duty. It sold to the trade at the OPA ceiling price, reflecting normal acquisition costs including the duty. As a result, CCC showed a net gain of $24 million on its wartime sugar operations to June 30, 1947. This was not a true gain, as the Treasury suffered an offsetting loss through the suspension of duties. (See *Report on Audit of the Commodity Credit Corporation and Its Affiliate War Hemp Industries, Inc.*, House Doc. 615, 81st Cong., 2d sess., p. 44.)

80. Incentive payments of 20 cents per hundredweight of sugar were made to growers in Puerto Rico and Hawaii in 1944. These were raised to 55 cents in 1945. Growers in Louisiana were given incentive payments of 33 cents in 1943, 85 cents in 1944 and $1.60 in 1945. Florida growers received the $1.60 in 1945. Incentive payments to beet growers

The transportation subsidies were purely a war measure designed to offset the higher shipping costs that resulted from war risks. The foregoing of tariff was largely a bookkeeping matter since a U.S. government agency bought the import sugar in Cuba. To have paid duty on it would have meant higher costs to CCC and Defense Supplies Corporation and a correspondingly larger payment to the Treasury. The amount of customs revenue foregone is, however, a cost of the program, as compared with earlier ones, which does not appear in the CCC and DSC costs on the operation. The sugar purchases of this period constitute a phase of the war program and are not in any important way a part of the longer-term farm program.

The arrangements made did, however, allow the prices paid to sugar beet and sugar cane growers to move up significantly without a corresponding increase in the prices paid by consumers. The price paid by processors for sugar beets increased from $5.11 in 1940 to $11.10 in 1946, which was somewhat less than the increase in prices of farm products as a whole.[81] However, the difference was more than made up by the supplementary payments to sugar-crop growers. For sugar beets, government payments moved up from $1.92 per ton in 1940 to $5.67 in 1944, but were down again to $2.55 by 1946.[82] Total returns per ton (including government payments) advanced from $7.03 in 1940 to $13.41 in 1944 and stood at $13.65 in 1946 despite the lower level of direct government payments then being made.

For sugar cane, the increase in market price was from $2.88 per ton in 1940 to $6.62 in 1946.[83] Government payments increased from $1.04 per ton in 1940 to $1.92 in 1944, and had been reduced to $1.19 by 1946. The advance in total receipts per ton was from $3.92 in 1940 to $6.12 in 1944 and to $7.81 in 1946, a gain of about 100 per cent. During this period, the general level of prices received by farmers increased by 134 per cent.[84]

Amounts Paid to Growers, 1942–1946

During the war years, conditional payments to growers were of the same type as in the prewar years but at a basic rate of 80 cents per 100 pounds of sugar instead of 60 cents. During the years 1942 through 1946, such payments were made in the following amounts: [85] in 1942,

---

were $1.50 per ton of beets in 1943 and $3.00 per ton in 1944 and 1945. CCC absorbed 45 cents per hundredweight on the sugar bought in 1945. (See *Sugar during World War II*, p. 11.)

81. Farm prices in general advanced 139 per cent between 1940 and 1946; those of sugar beets, 117 per cent.

82. See Table 39.

83. *Agricultural Statistics, 1951*, p. 88.

84. *Agricultural Statistics, 1952*, p. 618.

85. From annual reports of administrative agencies.

$57,916,034; 1943, $43,382,410; 1944, $47,759,000; 1945, $50,–565,000; and 1946, $56,742,000.

THE SUGAR ACT OF 1948

The Sugar Act of 1948, which in amended form is presumably to remain in effect through 1956, continued the main features of the quota legislation of 1934 and 1937.[86] It did, however, make some changes in the quota provisions. It established statutory quotas in absolute terms for the continental and insular areas of the United States and for the Philippines.[87] The basic beet sugar quota was raised from 1,556,000 tons in 1934, and 1,633,000 tons in the 1937 act, to 1,800,000 tons. The continental cane quota was increased from the 260,000 tons allotted in 1934 to 500,000 tons.

This was a departure from one of the implied purposes of the act of 1934, that is, the prevention of an expansion of continental sugar production beyond the levels prevailing in the early 1930s. However, one provision in the act of 1948 tends to limit expansion of continental sugar production. Further increases in consumption are to be reflected in additions to the quotas of foreign areas. Thus Cuba, with a basic quota which is essentially the same as that established in the two earlier acts, is almost the sole beneficiary of further consumption increases so long as the current legislation is left as it now stands.[88]

The Secretary of Agriculture is instructed to base requirement estimates on: (1) the amount of sugar entering distribution channels in the previous year, (2) the level of sugar inventories, and (3) changes in population and other demand factors.[89] In addition, he is to consider the relationship between refined sugar prices and the cost of living as reflected in the relationship that existed in the first ten months of 1947, with a view to maintaining "prices which will not be excessive to con-

86. The 1948 act was to expire at the end of 1952, but an amendment passed in 1951 extended it through 1956. The amendment also raised the Puerto Rican quota from 910,000 tons to 1,080,000 tons and increased slightly the quotas assigned to full-duty countries.

87. The amounts are shown in Table 38, column 8.

88. Unfilled quotas are to be reallocated to areas able to fill them, in proportion to the shares of the total quota assigned to each area, except that Cuba is to receive 95 per cent of the deficits in Philippine shipments. This was included because of the destruction of the Philippine industry in the war years. Between 1935 and 1939, that area shipped an average of 970,000 tons to the U.S. mainland. The first postwar shipment, in 1948, was only 252,000 tons. In 1949 and 1950, Philippine exports recovered to nearly 500,000 tons. The 1948 act put the quota for the Philippines at 952,000 tons, commercial weight, as specified in Section 211 of the Philippine Trade Act of 1946. This has worked out to a raw value quota of about 982,000 tons.

89. The provision that the estimate could not be below a certain rate per capita multiplied by the number of people was deleted. This removed an element of protection to consumers but made it possible to adjust to changing per capita rates of consumption if these should move downward.

sumers and which will fairly and equitably maintain and protect the welfare of the domestic sugar industry." [90]

Conditional payments to growers at a basic rate of 80 cents per 100 pounds of recoverable raw sugar were continued, together with the downward graduation of such payments to 30 cents per hundredweight on production in excess of 30,000 tons on any one plantation. The conditions for obtaining these payments remained about the same as in the 1937 act, except that the soil conservation requirement was dropped.[91]

The labor provisions denying payments where children under fourteen are employed, or where children between the ages of fourteen and sixteen are allowed to work more than eight hours per day, were retained.[92] Also, the requirement that minimum wages be paid to workers was continued, though still at an unspecified rate to be determined by the Secretary of Agriculture. This was in part a recognition of the widely varying conditions prevailing in the various sugar-producing areas, even those under U.S. jurisdiction. The Secretary was allowed to establish different standards for different areas.

Per Capita Demand Not Expanding

The buoyant economic conditions which have prevailed since the 1948 act was passed have not resulted in higher per capita consumption of sugar. In fact, consumption per person, which averaged 95.4 pounds in the period 1948–1952, was slightly below the 1935–1939 rate of 98.1

90. This is the so-called parity-price clause and has been the focus of producer and industrial consumer disagreement about the size of the consumption estimate. In the first months of 1947, sugar had not yet been decontrolled. However, sugar prices had risen sharply as a result of the escalator clause in the Cuban purchase contract. They were then at the highest level since 1920.

91. Conditional payments based on one third of normal yield were to be made on lands abandoned because of drought, flood or other disaster. This constituted a mild form of crop insurance. The downward graduation of the rates of payment was a gesture in the direction of small-unit agriculture but one that did not take much account of the realities of the industry or of relative efficiencies as between large and small operations in sugar. Sugar beets can be grown on comparatively small acreages without much loss in efficiency. Sugar cane is produced mainly on large plantations. That provision tends, therefore, to favor the beet areas as against the cane areas rather than to encourage smaller-scale operations generally.

92. The labor provisions of the program, while indicating a desire to improve conditions in an industry in which low wages, bad living conditions and much use of child labor are common, have not provided a solution for this problem. The regulations in regard to child labor have not been well enforced, and the minimum-wage scales established are not impressive as a step in the direction of better labor conditions in the industry. In the early years of the program, a grower became ineligible for payments if he employed any child labor other than his own children. This was changed in 1939 so as to provide that a deduction of $10 per day would be made if children were employed. Penalties assessed under this regulation have been negligible. (See *Migratory Labor in American Agriculture,* Report of the President's Commission on Migratory Labor, Washington, 1951, p. 163.) The steps taken can be regarded more as a recognition of the problem than as a solution to it.

pounds.[93] Since sugar prices have lagged behind in the upward movement of food prices, this indicates that there is little likelihood of significant expansion of demand through higher per capita consumption. It is a matter of concern to those responsible for administering the Sugar Act since increasing pressure for access to the U.S. market is anticipated.

However, the rapid growth of population resulted in a sizable increase in the amount of sugar used, raising it from 6.7 million tons in 1935–1939 to 7.7 million tons in 1951. The pressure on the Department of Agriculture for larger quotas, though continuous, was moderated somewhat during most of the postwar period by the heavy demand from areas under military occupation and those being supplied by means of ECA funds.

Cuba, for example, though it had only relatively small prewar markets outside the United States, was able in 1948 and 1949 to ship more than two million tons to other countries. However, Cuban production was greatly expanded in the war and postwar years and troublesome surpluses appear to be in prospect. Cuba's 1950 crop was nearly as large as the record crop of 1947 and the 1951 crop was a million and a half tons larger, thus setting an all-time high for Cuban production.[94] A substantial reduction in 1952 and 1953 indicates that an important readjustment is being made, but the prospect of continuing large-scale shipments to countries other than the United States is not promising. European and other countries are expanding production and are not likely to be good markets in the future. The Director of the Sugar Branch of the U.S. Department of Agriculture commented in 1952, "World sugar surplus problems cannot be avoided much longer." [95]

Changed Relation of U.S. to World Price

Though the quota system, under the 1948 act, was handled in much the same way as under the earlier acts, its effect from mid-1950 to the end of 1951 was markedly different. Until then, the quota arrangement resulted in U.S. prices that were at times as much as 1.6 cents above the world price, though usually the differential was less than a cent.

When the world price of sugar rose rapidly, from about 4.5 cents in early 1950 to nearly 8 cents in mid-1951, this situation was reversed. From June 1950 until December 1951, the U.S. price was for the most part about one half cent lower than the world price. It was nearly 2 cents

93. This does not constitute a reduction in total amount of sweeteners used, but reflects the increasing use of corn sweeteners as substitutes for sugar in manufactured products. (See U.S. Production and Marketing Administration, *Competitive Relations between Sugar and Corn Sweeteners,* June 1951, Table 2.)

94. See *Agricultural Statistics, 1954,* p. 79. The peak production of 1951, owing partly to carry-overs from 1950, was 7,964,000 tons. Production was down to 5,680,000 tons in 1952 but still was some 75 per cent higher than in the years 1939–1941.

95. *Sugar Reports,* No. 15, April 9, 1952, p. 48.

lower in mid-1951. The reason for this apparent anomaly lay in the fact that Cuba was well aware of the benefits accruing to her from the quota system. It was to her advantage not only to have the system maintained but to fulfill her quota so it would not be reduced. Furthermore, it was not in her interest to create a situation which might encourage further expansion of U.S. mainland sugar production.

Since Cuba would fill its assigned quota, U.S. importers were in a position to bargain on price without fear of a reduction in the quantity offered. As a result of this unanticipated development, U.S. consumers had a temporary advantage over those dependent on world market supplies. During this period, they apparently got sugar for about one half cent less than if there had been no quota system. This conclusion must be taken with reservation, however, since there is no way of knowing how much sugar would have been produced in U.S.-controlled areas, particularly in Puerto Rico and Hawaii, if quotas had not been in effect.[96]

The situation of Cuba was similar to that of a manufacturer who concludes that it is to his advantage to continue to supply an old and important customer at an established price in spite of a probably short-lived opportunity to sell elsewhere at higher prices. The quota arrangement thus apparently contributed to stability of U.S. prices and supplies in that period, and probably also helped to avoid a temporary and possibly expensive speculative expansion of the industry in the United States. The longer-term outlook is still for excessive supplies and low prices in the world market.

The strength of the U.S. position as the dominant purchaser of Cuban sugar had been demonstrated during the war years. Acting as a single purchaser, with great power to aid or injure the Cuban industry in succeeding years, it was able to keep the price of sugar surprisingly stable even with demand greatly increased. While the U.S. government is no longer buying the Cuban crop outright, the quota allotment is, in effect, a block purchase which has somewhat similar significance in the bargaining arrangements.

Price-Support Programs

In addition to the conditional payments described above, the Commodity Credit Corporation guaranteed prices for the years 1946 and 1947.[97] The first of these programs, covering the 1946 crop, was an-

96. It should also be recognized that conditions of this kind are not likely to occur again in the near future.

97. Because of the increase in ceiling prices, sugar beet producers were receiving from the processors around $11 per ton of beets in 1946 and 1947, and sugar cane growers were getting about $7 per ton of cane. Prices to farmers remained at about these levels through 1951 (see Table 39). Conditional payments amounted to $2.55 per ton in 1946

nounced in August 1945. In Louisiana and Florida, the market outlook was such that no program was put into operation. The Puerto Rican program was an adjunct of the sugar purchases made from Cuba and does not appear as a separate item. Substantial payments were anticipated for the Hawaiian crop (about $2.10 per ton) but were greatly reduced as a result of the higher prices paid for sugar. The subsidy finally paid was at the rate of about 35 cents per 100 pounds of sugar, including 15 cents to assist in meeting increased processing costs.[98]

For 1947, CCC guaranteed processors of beet sugar reimbursement to the extent that refined cane sugar fell below $8.20 per 100 pounds, on condition that they had paid growers not less than $14.50 per ton of beets of average sugar content ($1.00 per ton more than the guaranteed return on the 1946 crop).[99] The 1947 support program cost the Corporation $16,505,000. The price-support program for Hawaii was completed at no cost to CCC.[100]

No price-support program on sugar was instituted for the 1948 crop because of the protection afforded by the Sugar Act of 1948. During that period the Philippines and Hawaii still were not producing up to their quotas and the deficits were reassigned, mainly to Cuba, giving that country a quota for 1949 of a little over 3 million tons and one for 1950 which amounted to 2.6 million tons.[101]

Sugar purchases, other than for the armed services (220,000 tons), were discontinued in 1950 but were resumed on a modest scale in 1951 in order to check the rapid rise in the price of Cuban sugar in the U.S. market. CCC purchased 555,000 tons at 5.38 cents per pound and transferred some 428,000 tons of this to U.S. refiners. In a similar way, it assigned 104,000 tons to the United Kingdom. A small amount was shipped to Germany under the ECA program. This was a price-stabilizing rather than a price-raising operation.

During 1950, negotiations were undertaken for revival of the 1937

---

and $3.84 in 1947. For cane, the rates were $1.19 and $1.30. For the years 1947 through 1950, the amounts paid out in the form of conditional payments were as follows:

1947	$61,777,000 [a]
1948	53,681,000 [b]
1949	59,841,000 [c]
1950	59,229,000 [c]

a. *Report of the Administrator of the Production and Marketing Administration, 1949,* p. 60.
b. *Ibid., 1950,* p. 59.
c. *Ibid., 1951,* p. 71.

98. *Ibid., 1947,* p. 68. The gross amount of these payments, made in the fiscal year ending June 30, 1948, was $6,369,000. Similar payments on the Puerto Rican and Virgin Islands crops amounted to $8,600,000. (*Ibid., 1948,* pp. 73–74.)

99. The purpose of this guarantee was to obtain an increase in the acreage of sugar beets in order to meet the goal of 1,069,000 acres.

100. *Ibid., 1949,* p. 61. The returns received by growers as shown in Table 39 include the CCC payments as well as the conditional payments under the Sugar Act of 1937.

101. *Ibid., 1950,* p. 55.

International Sugar Agreement, and a draft was prepared but final agreement was not reached. The outbreak of war in Korea removed temporarily the concern over possible excessive accumulations. However, negotiations for a new agreement were continued and culminated in the International Sugar Agreement of 1953. (See pp. 290–91.)

PROTECTION TO U.S. MAINLAND REFINERS

All three of the sugar acts contained rigorous quantitative restrictions on the importation to the U.S. mainland of refined sugar, even that coming from Puerto Rico and the Hawaiian Islands. These constituted a form of protection to the mainland refining industry that went beyond the special protection afforded by the tariff prior to 1933, since it restricted the refining industry in the U.S. offshore areas as well as in Cuba and the Philippines.

In the 1934 act, the imports of refined sugar from Cuba were limited to 418,000 tons raw value, about 22 per cent of her quota. This constituted a sharp cutback as compared to the amounts imported in the years immediately preceding 1934. However, the expansion of the Cuban refining industry had come about rather recently.[102] Puerto Rico was limited to 133,000 tons, Hawaii to 26,000 tons and the Philippines to about 80,000 tons.[103] These quotas were the maximum amounts shipped by the island areas in any one of the preceding three years. Thus the limit, except that for Cuba, was a barrier to further expansion, not an actual cutback.

When the 1934 limitations were imposed, the continental refineries, like most other businesses, were in difficulties. A case could be made for a temporary standstill on further expansion of offshore processing facilities, but the case for continuing such a policy is much less apparent. Even in 1934, these provisions were sharply criticized by President Roosevelt. Nevertheless, they were continued in the act of 1937 at an even lower level (375,000 tons for Cuba), but the Administration succeeded in getting a provision that the quotas on refined sugar would expire one year earlier than the act itself.

The quotas were discontinued in February 1940, and for some months there was a free flow of refined sugar from U.S. offshore areas to the mainland, limited only by the over-all quotas. When the Sugar Act was extended in 1940, the limitation on imports of refined sugar was reimposed. In the act of 1948, the Cuban quota for refined sugar was again set at 375,000 tons. The Puerto Rican and the Hawaiian quotas were

102. This increase of sugar refining in Cuba resulted partly from a quirk in the Smoot-Hawley Tariff Act of 1930. The tariff on sugar was raised but the relationship between the tariff rates on raw and refined sugar became such that it was advantageous for Cuba to increase sugar refining and to supply a larger part of her exports to the United States in refined form.

103. Also in terms of raw value.

left about the same as in the acts of 1934 and 1937. The importation of refined sugar from the Philippines was limited to 59,920 tons.

It is hard to see the justification for this extreme form of protection to refiners on the U.S. mainland. Prior to 1934, protection had been given them in the form of a higher duty on refined sugar than on raw sugar. The quota arrangement gives them a rigorous kind of protection, not only against foreign competition but also against the competition of U.S. insular refiners, who would not have been under any handicap at all under a tariff type of protection.

The government of Puerto Rico sought relief in the courts and carried the case to the U.S. Supreme Court. The basis of its attack was the contention that this legislation limited the freedom of U.S. citizens to engage in sugar refining in the United States. The Supreme Court rendered a unanimous decision in favor of the restrictions [104] though the warrant for such action is by no means clear. Many observers who are prepared to accept the sugar legislation as a defensible piece of farm legislation do not extend their approval to the quotas on refined sugar. They look upon that as the result of a deal considered necessary to gain approval of the other parts of the quota system.[105]

COST OF THE PROGRAM

The cost of the program can be only very roughly approximated, and even these rough estimates rest heavily on the assumptions made. Comparisons may be with costs under the high tariff in effect at the time the program was initiated or with the price situation that might prevail if there were no tariff at all. Part of the cost consists of direct government payments, collected initially from sugar consumers. Another part consists of losses in revenue sustained by the general fund of the U.S. Treasury, and still another of higher prices paid by consumers, in most years. Also, part of the gain has accrued to non-U.S. producers as well as to those in the United States. These, however, are producer groups in whose welfare we have both economic and strategic interests.

Effects of Changes in Tariffs and Excise Taxes

The data available indicate that so long as Cuban production was overabundant and demand weak, much of the cost of the tariff was

104. *Secretary of Agriculture* v. *Central Roig Refining Company,* 338 U.S. 604 (1950).

105. Some contend that if the restriction on sugar refining, particularly in the U.S. insular areas, had been examined on its own merits, rather than as part of a more general piece of farm legislation, it would not have gained the approval of Congress. It is in obvious conflict with efforts of the U.S. government to improve conditions in Puerto Rico and Hawaii. See, for example, Nathan Koenig, *A Comprehensive Agricultural Program for Puerto Rico,* U.S. Department of Agriculture in cooperation with the Commonwealth of Puerto Rico, 1953, pp. 235–40. Koenig states (pp. 238 ff.): ". . . the amount of sugar now permitted to be refined is only about one half the refining capacity on the

borne by Cuban producers in the form of lower prices for their product. Cuban sugar had to move to the United States and had to be sold at what the U.S. market would pay, minus the tariff. Hence, in the period preceding 1934, the U.S. Treasury was apparently profiting to the extent of around $70 million to $100 million a year, mostly at the expense of Cuba.[106]

The fund derived from the processing and excise taxes came out of what would otherwise have been U.S. Treasury receipts but only that part of it paid on imported sugar. Since there is little evidence that the excise tax raised the price to consumers, the part of it collected on domestically grown sugar came mostly out of grower incomes and was returned to them as a *quid pro quo* for compliance with the program. For the amount of tax collected on imported sugar, they gained, at the expense of the Treasury, insofar as these receipts were transferred to them.

The amount of excise tax collected by the Treasury has usually been some $15 million to $20 million a year more than was paid out to growers. The amount collected on imported sugar was, in effect, an addition to the duty on foreign sugar. Except for the fact that, by implication at least, it went into an earmarked fund for use in the conditional payment program, it could as well have been a part of the regular duty on sugar.

From 1942 on, the market for Cuban sugar became stronger and the effect of continuing duties at the 1930 rates would apparently have been to raise the price to U.S. consumers. This was largely avoided by reducing the rate of duty and suspending import duties, from May 1944 to the end of 1946, the years in which the U.S. government purchased the Cuban crop in Cuba. This was a gain to U.S. consumers at the expense of the Treasury if the former price and the 2-cent duty are taken as the norms to which the later situation is related.[107] (The U.S.

---

island. The remaining plant capacity represents a luxury which the economy of Puerto Rico can ill afford to maintain in imposed idleness. An increase of 225,000 to 230,000 tons in the shipment quota would pave the way for putting those facilities to work."

106. Price adjustments resulting from tariff changes are seldom or never complete and clear-cut and they do not remain the same from period to period. Some part, probably a small one in this case, is reflected in losses or gains to handlers and processors, U.S. consumers or other groups.

107. Until 1945, the purchase and sale prices were so arranged that the government took the customary peacetime margin. In 1945, the price paid for Cuban sugar was raised from $2.65 per hundredweight to $3.10, but the prices to dealers were left unchanged. The government absorbed the difference. (*Sugar during World War II*, p. 17.) This was part of the wartime food subsidy program. Production subsidies were also paid to growers of beets and cane in the United States. The tariff suspensions provided under Executive Orders from 1942 through 1946 did not apply on all sugar imported but only on that purchased by specified government agencies. Until August 1, 1944, when Executive Order 9495 extended this provision to the two principal sugar-importing agencies, the effect on Treasury income was not large.

retail price, the Cuban price, and the returns to U.S. mainland sugar crop growers are shown in Table 40.)

TABLE 40

SUGAR: U.S. RETAIL PRICE, CUBAN (WHOLESALE) PRICE AND PRICES PAID TO GROWERS, 1941–1953

Year	U.S. Retail Price, Granulated	Wholesale Price, Raw Sugar, Havana	Prices Paid to Growers: Sugar Beets	Prices Paid to Growers: Sugar Cane
	(Cents per Pound)		*(Dollars per Ton)*	
1941	5.7	1.67	6.43	3.95
1942	6.8	2.492	6.84	4.40
1943	6.8	2.407	8.81	4.57
1944	6.8	2.436	10.60	4.95
1945	6.7	2.907	10.20	5.67
1946	7.7	3.502	11.10	6.62
1947	9.7	4.736	11.80	7.17
1948	9.4	4.174	10.60	5.76
1949	9.5	4.345	10.80	6.25
1950	9.7	4.98	11.20	7.80
1951	10.1	5.67	11.70	6.37
1952	10.3	4.17	12.00	6.96
1953	10.6	3.41	12.00	7.27

Sources: U.S. Department of Agriculture, *Agricultural Statistics, 1951,* p. 97, and *1954,* pp. 73, 85.

At present, Cuban sugar is subject to a one-half cent duty, and it, together with that grown in the United States, is subject to a one-half cent excise tax. The effect on prices to consumers is essentially the same as though the duty were 1 cent per pound. This, in a period of active world demand such as that of the late 1940s, probably resulted in an additional cost to American consumers of around 1 cent per pound.

As Cuban supplies again become redundant and Cuba so heavily dependent on the U.S. market that she must sell in the United States at less than the general world price plus the tariff, the advantage of the lower tariff will presumably redound principally to Cuban producers.[108] Under those conditions, neither the present tariff nor the higher one in effect from 1930 to 1934 would have much effect on the prices paid by U.S. consumers or received by U.S. producers.

If we assume the price effect of the quotas to be in the order of .5 to .75 of a cent, the quotas are adding some $80 million to $100 million per year to the cost of sugar used in the United States. About 30 per cent

108. As the law now stands, the tariff provisions of the Hawley-Smoot Tariff Act would come into effect if no quotas were established.

of this goes to sugar-crop growers on the U.S. mainland in the form of higher prices, about 30 per cent to Cuban producers and the remainder to growers in the U.S. insular areas and the Philippines. As already noted, the effect of quotas in periods of high world demand and short supply has apparently been to keep U.S. prices down. Thus, it may be looked upon as a stabilizing device which in most years will be an expense but, under some conditions, will result in gains to U.S. consumers. If the industry can be stabilized and kept in reasonably healthy condition both here and in the offshore areas, there are intangible gains which do not appear in these figures. (Treasury receipts from the tariff and from processing and excise taxes on sugar in the years since 1930 are shown in Table 41.)

AGGREGATE PAYMENTS TO GROWERS

The amounts paid to growers on the U.S. mainland and in the various territorial areas, from 1933 through 1952, are shown in Table 42.

In broad terms, the cost of these payments was not borne by the consumers or the U.S. government. The processing and excise taxes had much the same effect on the prices paid to growers as an increase in processing and marketing costs or an increase in freight charges. The price at which sugar could be sold was established by the amount that could be put on the market under the quotas, and the effective demand for it. Hence, any payment assessed against the processor or handler would have to be reflected mainly in lower prices to producers whether in this country or in other producing areas. U.S. growers no doubt profit to some extent from this interchange if most of the excise tax collected is distributed to them. The excise tax is collected on all sugar used, not just on that produced by U.S. growers.[109]

OVER-ALL RESULTS OF THE PROGRAM

The purpose of the sugar program was to improve returns to U.S. sugar producers and to strengthen the Cuban economy by assuring a

109. The Bureau of Agricultural Economics stated, in 1937, "The definite conclusion is that the [processing] tax did not affect either the supply of or demand for sugar in the retail market, and hence did not affect retail prices paid by consumers." *An Analysis of the Effects of the Processing Taxes Levied under the Agricultural Adjustment Act,* prepared by the Bureau of Agricultural Economics for the Bureau of Internal Revenue, 1937, p. 67, mimeo. The study further reported (p. 73): "It appears, therefore, that, as in the case of sugarcane, the growers of sugar beets bore the immediate burden of the tax, but were reimbursed by the receipt of benefit payments which in the end resulted merely in a temporary diversion of funds realized from the sale of the finished sugar."
A later study by the Tariff Commission led to a similar conclusion. It stated: "The excise tax on sugar refined in this country probably results in a corresponding reduction in the price paid by refiners for raw sugar, domestic or imported. Assuming that the tax is thus shifted to the growers, conditional payments received by domestic growers of sugarcane and beets serve in general to offset the effect of the tax for domestic producers." (*Summaries of Tariff Information,* Vol. 5, *Sugar, Molasses and Manufactures,* U.S. Tariff Commission, 1948, p. 16.)

TABLE 41

SUGAR: RECEIPTS FROM DUTY [a] AND FROM PROCESSING AND EXCISE TAXES, 1930–1954

Year	Treasury Income from Duty	Receipts from Processing and Excise Taxes
1930	$116,809,000	
1931	99,631,000	
1932	76,061,000	
1933	67,408,000	
1934	43,706,000	$102,000,000.00 (1934–1936)
1935	39,985,000	
1936	40,578,000	
1937	45,371,000	—
1938	45,506,000	30,569,130.14
1939	46,218,000	65,414,058.42
1940	42,826,000	68,145,357.56
1941	63,586,000	74,834,839.60
1942	36,056,000	68,229,803.06
1943	55,730,000	53,551,776.72
1944	29,096,000	68,788,910.31
1945	10,430,000	73,293,966.35
1946	10,167,000	56,731,986.36
1947	67,280,000	59,151,922.36
1948	34,665,000	71,246,833.76
1949	37,206,000	76,174,356.09
1950	37,635,000	71,188,028.96
1951	34,957,000	80,191,884.29
1952	36,045,000	78,473,191.00
1953	35,845,000	78,129,860.00
1954	34,748,000	74,477,000.00

Sources: Receipts from duty: *Statistical Abstract, 1950,* p. 867, and *1955,* p. 925; and receipts from processing and excise taxes: for June 1934 through December 1936, as reported in U.S. Agricultural Adjustment Administration, *Agricultural Conservation, 1936,* p. 138 (the collection of processing taxes was discontinued after the adverse court decision of January 6, 1936); for 1938 through 1954, Annual Reports of the Commissioner of Internal Revenue, Fiscal Years Ending June 30, 1939, p. 98; 1941, p. 105; 1943, p. 112; 1945, p. 110; 1947, p. 120; 1949, p. 119; 1951, p. 129; 1952, p. 107; 1954, p. 74.

a. There have been numerous changes in the tariffs applicable on sugar during the period shown. Also, the tariff provisions relating to different foreign areas were not the same. Emergency war purchases of dutiable goods were permitted free entry under varying conditions and in varying amounts from 1942 to 1947. However, even in 1945 and 1946 when most of the foreign sugar purchased came in duty-free, there were some imports on which duty was paid, for example, those imported by private importers from areas not included in block purchases. In general, the effect of these changes on Treasury receipts was to reduce them by half to two thirds as compared with those of 1930. For a summary of tariff changes, see C. F. Wells, *United States Tariff Rates on Agricultural Products,* U.S. Bureau of Agricultural Economics, May 1951, pp. 10–17, mimeo.

TABLE 42

SUGAR BEETS AND SUGAR CANE: AGGREGATE GOVERNMENT PAYMENTS TO PRODUCERS, 1933–1953 [a]

(*Millions*)

Crop Year	Continental			Insular				Grand Total
	Beets	Cane	Total	Hawaii	Puerto Rico	Virgin Islands	Total	
1933	$ 2.6	—	$ 2.6	—	—	—	—	$ 2.6
1934	19.6	$8.9	28.5	$4.7	—	—	$ 4.7 [b]	33.2
1935	9.5	3.4	12.9	8.6	$14.5	—	23.1 [b]	36.0
1936	—	—	—	—	—	—	—	—
1937	17.1	5.4	22.5	4.2	9.5	—	13.7	36.2
1938	22.1	6.2	28.3	8.6	8.9	—	17.5	45.8
1939	21.2	5.5	26.7	9.0	10.6	—	19.6	46.3
1940	22.9	3.9	26.8	8.9	9.6	—	18.5	45.3
1941	19.1	4.6	23.7	8.6	11.2	—	19.8	43.5
1942	30.2	7.0	37.2	8.1	13.1	[c]	21.2	58.4
1943	26.8	7.4	34.2	8.3	12.2	$ .1	20.6	54.8
1944	38.4	6.7	45.1	8.2	13.1	[c]	21.3	66.4
1945	41.2	6.9	48.1	7.8	13.3	.1	21.2	69.3
1946	27.8	6.5	34.3	6.6	15.1	.1	21.8	56.1
1947	32.3	6.3	38.6	8.1	15.5	[c]	23.6	62.2
1948	23.2	7.2	30.4	7.6	17.7	.1	25.4	55.8
1949	27.0	7.0	34.1	8.4	17.5	.2	26.0	60.1
1950	33.7	7.8	41.5	8.5	17.1	.2	25.8	67.3
1951	25.9	6.5	33.3	9.1	19.0	.1	28.2	54.2
1952	24.7	8.0	32.7	9.4	16.9	.15	26.5	59.2
1953	30.4 [d]	8.6 [d]	39.0	10.2 [d]	16.5 [d]	.17 [d]	26.9	65.9

Sources: Sugar Branch, U.S. Production and Marketing Administration; and U.S. Department of Agriculture, *Agricultural Statistics, 1953,* pp. 675, 676, and *1954,* pp. 533, 534. Note that some of the amounts shown in this table differ from those previously given which were taken from earlier reports. The difference is presumably a result of later and more complete audits. For 1942, 1943, 1944 and 1945, the totals given here include other government subsidies as well as the conditional payments mentioned earlier.

a. Includes Sugar Act and CCC payments.
b. Aggregate payments to the Philippine Islands on the 1934 and 1935 crops were $15.4 million.
c. Less than $50,000.
d. Estimated.

more profitable though smaller market in the United States. Presumably, U.S. consumers were also to be protected by avoiding actions that would increase domestic sugar prices unduly. The steps taken involved three types of action: (1) lowering the duty on foreign sugar, (2) imposing a processing or excise tax on domestic consumption, and (3) establishing quotas which would restrict production in and shipments from the offshore areas. There was also a potential restriction on sugar produced on the U.S. mainland.

The quotas apparently raised the U.S. sugar price during the 1930s by something in the order of .5 cent a pound. This was, in effect, a monopoly gain to U.S. growers which stemmed from the ability of the government to regulate and limit the supplies put on the U.S. market.

During the 1940s, the fact that the United States had adopted a quota system, even though it was not in effect from 1942 to 1947, undoubtedly increased the bargaining power of the United States and thus enabled it to buy sugar at a lower price than would have been likely in a free market. That was particularly true during the war years and for a time thereafter. The advantage thus derived was due to the fact that the U.S. government was able to operate essentially as a single buyer for the quantities purchased from Cuba. However, the bargaining power enjoyed by the United States as a result of its control over shipping would perhaps have enabled it to buy on about the same terms even if there had been no quota system. Also, the American scale of prices was attractive to Cuban growers.

Nevertheless, Cuba was anxious to retain her right to sell a specified amount in the U.S. market under a preferential and lowered tariff and was willing to sell to the United States at a lower price than she could have exacted had these longer-term considerations not been involved. This gain was passed on to U.S. consumers, but there is no dependable way of estimating how much it amounted to since there is no way of knowing what the Cuban price would have been if there had been no quota to protect. The saving was undoubtedly sizable during the years 1942 to 1952.

Sugar Program as a Stabilizing Influence

It is possible that, over the period as a whole, U.S. consumers would have paid less for their sugar if there had been no government controls, assuming the changes in tariffs that actually were made. But offsetting these gains would have been the probability of a demoralized domestic industry and increasing chaos in the Cuban economy. On the positive side, it seems clear that the U.S. sugar industry was stabilized, and Cuba was helped in getting her sugar industry into healthier condition. Also, an important strategic reserve food resource was kept intact and in condition to aid importantly in providing supplies that were much needed in the 1940s.[110]

Taking the program as a whole, including the tariff and tax adjustments, together with the specific conditions of deep depression and high war demand that marked the 1930s and 1940s, it seems reasonable to

110. For a very critical view of the program, see William C. Pendleton, "American Sugar Policy—1948 Version," *Journal of Farm Economics,* May 1948, pp. 226–42.

conclude that the principal effect of the program was in furthering stability rather than in increasing or decreasing prices. This is not to say that the effect would be the same over a long period of more normal demand conditions. In an industry prone to overproduction, the quota arrangement may be expected to result in a U.S. price that is higher than it would otherwise be.

This does not, of course, supply a conclusive answer as to how high the U.S. price should be. U.S. consumers could obtain their sugar at lower cost by permitting freer entry of low-cost, offshore supplies, but this would probably mean liquidation of part of the mainland industry. There is some indication that the prices now being paid are about at the levels required to maintain the mainland industry when other farm products are at about current levels. If the prices of other farm products should decline, or if labor should become plentiful and cheap, or if mechanization were to lead to sharp reductions in cost, the maintenance of a full parity return on the sugar crops would probably result in rapid expansion of production on the U.S. mainland unless restrictions were imposed.

MORE GENERAL PROBLEMS OF SUGAR POLICY

Past policy, both under the Sugar Acts and under the earlier tariff system, does not seem to anticipate that continental or total U.S. sugar production will be expanded enough to make either the United States or the mainland self-sufficient. How high the price should be is therefore indeterminate. More beets and sugar cane can be grown on the U.S. mainland, or the mainland industry can be allowed to shrink and more of the supply can be drawn from offshore areas. The prices at which sugar crops are supported will largely determine which direction the industry will take, if no restraints on production are applied.

The quotas established in 1934 implied a policy of stabilizing production on the U.S. mainland at about the level arrived at under the earlier policy of tariff protection. That policy has been modified since but not greatly. It implies an intention to retain for American producers some modest gains arising from the cartel arrangements set up. It is a technique that could be abused to the disadvantage both of offshore areas and of U.S. consumers. As of now, it seems not to have been so used. In fact, the primary concern during the 1940s was to induce growers to produce enough to fill the quotas, except those of Cuba and Puerto Rico.

However, it is characteristic of cartels that a first step is to restrict output by imposing quotas. Thereafter, the tendency is for each participating group to seek enlargement of its quota at the expense of the others. Since it is the U.S. mainland areas that have the voting members in Congress, the possibility of eventual severe distortions in the over-all pattern of production cannot be ignored. Restrictive devices that may be needed and well justified in overcoming severe maladjustments at a given time are not necessarily well suited to longer-run situations.

The sugar beet industry continues to be an artificially maintained segment of the farm economy of the U.S. mainland.[111] Justification for it, if it is justified, rests on strategic considerations rather than comparative advantage. There seems to be little ground logically either for maintaining prices that will expand the mainland industry materially or for creating a situation that will destroy the values and property already built up under the protective policies of the past.[112]

A modest level of home production, possibly an amount comparable to that now being maintained, appears to be desirable as a strategic reserve which would at least provide a nucleus for expansion in the event that contact with the offshore areas should be seriously disturbed. If, in later years, there should come to be more pressure on U.S. food resources as a result of population growth, and if the prospect of continuing world peace were to improve, it might become desirable to rely more fully on the low-cost production of the offshore areas and use more of the continental resources for other kinds of food production for which returns would presumably be more attractive.

The increased stability achieved in the offshore areas seems to be in the national interest as well as that of the offshore areas themselves. This argues for retention of the quota system if it can be maintained without prejudice to the important U.S. interest in maintaining stability in the world sugar market as a whole. The structure of the industry is such that both the quotas established and the production on farms can be more easily and effectively controlled than for most farm products.

The quota system is not necessarily inconsistent with an international or intergovernmental approach to world sugar problems but it requires a precarious balancing of the interests of the various areas concerned. It has been possible thus far to keep these conflicts of interest at a minimum because of an expansion in U.S. mainland consumption, from about 6.5 million tons to nearly 8 million tons, and the abnormal demand and supply conditions of the 1940s. The tensions resulting from the program may well become severe in the years ahead.

The current program does not satisfy wholly the desires of producers

111. It is not a large part of U.S. agriculture. Barger and Landsberg estimated that in 1935–1939 sugar beets accounted for about .7 per cent of total agricultural production. (Harold Barger and Hans H. Landsberg, *American Agriculture, 1899–1939,* National Bureau of Economic Research, New York, 1942, p. 27.) In the period 1947–1951, sugar beets accounted for .4 per cent of cash receipts from farm marketings.

112. In view of the importance of Cuba both as a dependable supplier of sugar in time of war and as a market for U.S. exports, it would seem unwise from the standpoint of national interest to expand mainland quotas significantly at the expense of Cuba and the other offshore areas. Serious depression or economic disturbances in those areas could, in the present state of world affairs, be very detrimental to the interests of the United States.

in the various producing areas. Each area would like to have a bigger share in the large and vital U.S. market. But to grant free access to the U.S. market without restraints on production would apparently result, as it did in the late 1920s and the early 1930s, in a demoralized and oversupplied market and low prices. It appears, therefore, that the mild restraints applied up to now, by means of the quota system, have not been an unduly high price to pay for the greater stability achieved. However, the tendency toward overproduction for the general world market which appears now to be developing may create other problems that cannot be solved in that way. Also, such increase in stability as has been achieved has been less effective for Cuba than for the U.S.-controlled offshore areas.

It should be recognized also that the current type of legislation could be used to the disadvantage of U.S. consumers and could result in arbitrary and undesirable dictation of the relative amounts of sugar produced in the various areas, both offshore and on the U.S. mainland. Production might be frozen in areas that should be partly replaced by others that have become more efficient because of technological changes.

The collection of an excise tax on sugar, and its redistribution as conditional payments to growers, appears to be a cumbersome and somewhat pointless procedure since it apparently does not increase significantly the returns to growers. It is essentially a collection from the growers of an amount that is returned to them but only after incurring the expense and bother of determining eligibility, issuing checks and supervising compliance.[113] If the policy adopted is designed to increase returns to growers, this can best be done by adjusting consumption estimates and quotas so as to maintain the U.S. price at a level the Congress deems appropriate. However, so long as the excise tax and benefit payment procedures are used, any severe restriction on imports would show up as a Treasury loss. Thus the program now in operation may act to some extent as a restraint on unduly severe quota restrictions designed to protect or favor vested interests in the United States. The sugar industry is regulated to an extent that approaches that of a public utility. This gives the Congress and the Secretary of Agriculture very broad powers in determining the price of sugar to consumers and the way in which the income from sugar will be distributed.

The labor provisions of the sugar legislation were intended as a way of eliminating child labor in the sugar beet fields and preventing extreme exploitation of sugar beet labor through low wages in times of depres-

113. Conditional payments, as now provided, do result in some redistribution of returns because of the progressively lower rates paid to the larger farms and plantations. However, in spite of this feature, some of the government checks are for very large amounts. If this redistribution of incomes is considered sufficiently important to warrant the procedure now used, that would, of course, argue for retention of the present arrangement. There is reason to doubt that the plan now used has any large effect on the relative sizes of farms producing sugar crops.

sion. However, there is little in the way of procedure for enforcing the labor provisions of the act and there are complaints that, except in Hawaii, the workers are not sufficiently represented in the wage determinations made by the Secretary of Agriculture. The use of child labor could be outlawed by direct legislation. The problem of enforcement would still remain but this apparently exists even under the present system. The minimum-wage provisions do not seem to be highly significant except in periods of acute depression.

There does not appear to be any legitimate reason for limiting the amount of refined sugar that can be shipped to the mainland from U.S.-controlled areas. Puerto Rico and Hawaii are parts of the United States and should have the same access to U.S. markets as other U.S. areas, except for restraints applied equitably for the purpose of stabilizing the industry as a whole.

8

Wool

THE PROBLEMS of the wool producer are different from those in wheat, cotton and tobacco, and in most other commodities except sugar. Normally, U.S. wool production is not adequate to supply our own needs. In time of war it falls far below U.S. requirements. Consequently, the wool programs adopted or advocated have had special characteristics of their own.

Since wool has been almost continually on an import basis, wool growers have placed heavy emphasis on tariffs as a way of supporting prices and encouraging production. Though they are not heavily dependent on export outlets as are the growers of wheat, cotton and tobacco, their industry is nevertheless greatly dependent on the health and vigor of the international wool markets. Even more important is the tendency for wool prices to be affected profoundly by changes in domestic demand. Supply changes are not the dominant factor affecting prices. Hence, efforts to restrict or expand production have had little place in the wool program, except for the current effort to increase the amounts produced domestically.

Since wool is a strategic commodity, national interests are heavily involved in time of war, or threat of war. All belligerents take steps to assure adequate supplies in such periods. Wool prices and stocks tend therefore to be more largely affected by state trading than do those of most other farm products. The fluctuations that grow out of government demand are usually more important than those that result from changes in peacetime business activity. However, the presence or absence of war demand is by no means the only reason for price instability in the wool industry. Sudden changes in national prosperity, and also the nature of the industry itself, give rise to very important fluctuations in the demand for raw wool. In a population as well clothed as that of the United States, the demand for new clothing and for other products made from wool can drop off very sharply in a period of acute depression. Thus the demand for raw wool is less continuous and stable than the demand for foodstuffs.

Furthermore, the manufacturing and distributing system is such that considerable amounts of wool and wool products are normally in the pipelines, as stocks in the hands of mills, importers, speculators and others, and stocks of finished goods held by garment makers and wholesale and retail handlers. Consequently, if consumer demand falls off suddenly, the mills and the wool trade generally tend to discontinue the buying of raw wool almost completely for a time while they dispose of inventories already in their hands. In such periods, speculative buying is also likely to be very inactive.

Disturbances of the kind mentioned above are clearly evident in the severe depressions of the early 1920s and 1930s. During 1919 and the first part of 1920, wool prices to farmers were fairly steady at about 50 to 53 cents per pound. Beginning in June 1920, they began to fall off rapidly and by June 1921 were down to 15.4 cents, a decline in one year to about 30 per cent of the 1920 level.[1] In the same period the general level of prices received by farmers fell from an index of 212 to 124, which was about 58 per cent of the 1920 level.[2] Wool prices remained at this low level through the last half of 1921 but recovered substantially in 1922.

In the early 1930s, the decline in wool prices extended over a longer period but the level reached was even lower, both in cents per pound and as a percentage of the level that prevailed in the preceding period. In 1928 and 1929, prices to growers ranged in the main from about 30 to 36 cents per pound. By July 1932, they were down to 7 cents, only about 20 per cent of the price prevailing in the late 1920s.[3] The drop in all farm prices between 1929 and 1932 was from 148 to 65, that is, to about 44 per cent of the level prevailing in 1929.

Price Stability Not Achieved

While these very severe declines in demand are characteristic of the industry, it is also true that wool prices have tended to recover more quickly than those of other farm products. This points to a need for more emphasis on stability than on production control. It also raises a question as to the effectiveness of tariffs in aiding the industry in times when it is most in need of assistance.

Though price support by means of tariffs has long been the procedure most favored by wool growers, it has not been as uniformly effective as many assume. Wool prices have fluctuated widely under both high and low tariffs. The drastic decline of 1921 may have been affected to some extent by the preceding period in which wool was on the free list, but only in a very limited way. The even lower prices reached in 1932 were experienced when wool tariffs were at an all-time high. Even in other periods, when war and depression have not been dominant factors, the relation between wool prices and the level of tariffs has not been close or consistent.

1. U.S. Agricultural Marketing Service, *Wool Statistics and Related Data,* Statistical Bulletin 142, September 1954, p. 78.
2. U.S. Department of Agriculture, *Agricultural Statistics, 1953,* p. 546.
3. *Wool Statistics and Related Data,* p. 78.

In 1910, with a tariff of 11 cents per pound in the grease (25 cents scoured), the average price to farmers was 21.7 cents.[4] In 1911, with no change in the rate of duty, the price was 15.8 cents. Prices rose slightly in 1912 and 1913, to about 17 cents, but averaged 16.6 cents in 1914 when wool was on the free list.[5] War demand kept prices high during the war years, but they declined sharply in 1920 and were below 16 cents in the last half of 1921. This was less than one cent above the tariff rate itself.

Tariffs were reimposed in 1921 and 1922 and have remained at relatively high levels in the years since. The Emergency Tariff of May 1921 put the duty at 15 cents in the grease and the act of 1922 provided a rate of 31 cents on the clean content.[6] The rate was raised to 34 cents per clean pound in the Hawley-Smoot Act of 1930 and remained there until January 1, 1948 when it was reduced to 25½ cents.[7]

The price of wool stabilized at about 30 to 40 cents between 1923 and 1929 but dropped to 19.5 cents in 1930 and to 13.6 cents in 1931.[8]

4. *Ibid.*, p. 79. The tariff rates used here and elsewhere are for clothing-type wools, which constitute the bulk of U.S. imports aside from carpet wools. Other rates are prescribed for special types of wool and for woolen materials in various stages of manufacture.

5. The war influence apparently was not significant in the price received in 1914. When the war began, in August, a good part of the clip had already been sent to market. From 1914 on, war demand was obviously a controlling factor. The price moved up to 22.1 cents in 1915, to 26.1 cents in 1916 and to 41.6 cents in 1917. It averaged 57.7 cents in 1918. (*Ibid.*, p. 79.) For a more detailed discussion of the wool situation in these years, see Thomas J. Maycock, *The Government and Wool*, U.S. Bureau of Agricultural Economics, Agricultural History Series No. 6, 1943.

6. The sharp decline of 1920–21 was apparently due in part to the decline in business activity which occurred at that time, but the market was also weakened by the prospective release of war stocks that had ceased to be needed as strategic reserves. Also, substantial amounts of wool were still being imported in spite of low prices and weak demand. Imports reached 378 million pounds in 1918 but were down to 219 million in 1920. In the years 1909 to 1913, the amounts imported averaged about 100 million pounds but were as low as 54 million in 1911 and as high as 176 million in 1909. (*Wool Statistics and Related Data*, p. 38.)

7. The import duty on fine territory wools was 24 per cent of the average Boston price in 1923, 73 per cent in 1932, 33 per cent in 1937 and 41 per cent in 1939. (*Department of State Bulletin*, November 3, 1946, p. 784.) With a fixed duty in terms of cents per pound, the tariff as a percentage of value varies markedly with changes in the price of wool.

8. The prices (to farmers) in these years were as follows (in cents per pound):

Year	Price	Year	Price
1922	27.1	1928	36.2
1923	39.4	1929	30.2
1924	36.6	1930	19.5
1925	39.5	1931	13.6
1926	34.0	1932	8.6
1927	30.3		

Imports for the same period (in millions of pounds) were:

Year	Imports	Year	Imports
1922	194	1928	91
1923	266	1929	102
1924	122	1930	71
1925	179	1931	43
1926	184	1932	17
1927	120		

(*Wool Statistics and Related Data*, pp. 38, 79 and 80.)

Though the tariff was increased by about 10 per cent in 1930, wool prices continued to decline. They averaged only 8.6 cents in 1932, even though the Federal Farm Board had in the meantime undertaken to support the market at higher levels.

Production Increases of the 1920s and 1930s

Wool prices were above parity from 1923 through 1929. After dropping to 43 per cent of parity in 1932, they recovered to 115 per cent in 1936 and were at parity or above also in 1937 and the latter part of 1939.[9] Thus, during most of the period 1920–1940, wool growers received more favorable prices than the growers of most other farm products.

These relatively favorable prices gave rise to a mild upward trend in wool production, which continued until 1942. Production of shorn wool had reached a low of 228 million pounds in 1922. This was about 80 million pounds below the previous all-time high in 1909.[10] By 1930, production was up to 352 million pounds. It continued high through the 1930s and early 1940s, reaching 388 million pounds in 1942. Thereafter it fell off rapidly and amounted to only 213 million pounds in 1949.

Wool production does not vary sharply from year to year. Sizable changes in output have occurred during the past forty years but usually only slowly. There was a slight downward trend from 1909 to 1922 and an upward trend from 1923 to 1942, but year-to-year variations have been small, even from 1943 to 1950 when the industry was experiencing the most severe decline in its history.

Price changes are due more to fluctuations in demand than to changes in the amounts produced domestically. The severe break in wool prices in 1921, and in the early 1930s, resulted from glutted markets and weak demand, not from changes in the amounts of wool produced. This sensitivity to demand changes can be seen also in the sharp price increase that occurred during the brief recovery of 1937 and the 40 per cent drop that followed in 1938, a year of business recession.[11]

9. The specific percentages of parity (annual averages) for the years 1923 to 1939 were:

Year	%	Year	%	Year	%
1923	123	1929	102	1935	82
1924	122	1930	72	1936	115
1925	128	1931	55	1937	125
1926	108	1932	43	1938	85
1927	102	1933	81	1939	101
1928	118	1934	94		

(U.S. Bureau of Agricultural Economics, *Wool Statistics*, 1949, p. 50.)

10. However, production had been declining in the years immediately preceding World War I. The data given here do not include pulled wool, which is the wool taken from the pelts at packing houses. Production of pulled wool ranged from 40 million pounds in 1910 to 73.5 million in 1944.

11. The price to farmers reached a high of 33.2 cents in April 1937 but was down to 18.0 cents by June 1938. The annual averages for the two years were 32.0 cents and 19.1 cents. (*Wool Statistics and Related Data*, pp. 78 and 80.)

Similar abrupt changes in price occurred in the mild recession of 1910–1911 when the price dropped from 24.9 cents in March 1910 to 14.7 cents in May 1911. Again in 1925–1927 wool prices fell sharply, from 43.2 cents in February 1925 to 31.1 cents in February 1927, even though business activity was high.[12]

In the early years of a depression, the tariff cannot have much effect since the mills are virtually out of the market for new supplies of wool. Their own stocks, and those in the pipelines, are sufficient to enable them to carry on without importing much foreign wool or even competing effectively for the current domestic clips. Consequently, prices can go very low without causing much increase in the amounts purchased by the mills. Once these owned or readily available stocks are used up, imported wools, if used, must come in over the tariff and the price of domestic wool tends to improve rather quickly. Quick recovery of that kind is not usual in the markets for products of which there is an export surplus. The relatively favorable wool prices of the 1920s (from 1922 on) and of the 1930s (from 1933 on) were strikingly at variance with the prices of most of the other farm products. It is in such situations that the tariff probably has its most significant effect.

Imports Chief Form of Supply Adjustment

Since the amounts of wool produced domestically do not vary much from year to year, the principal method of adjusting to increased or decreased demand is through variations in amounts imported. The large requirements for military use and stockpiling in World War I were met mainly by sharply increased imports, from about 100 million pounds annually in the prewar years to more than 300 million in the years 1915 through 1919. Imports fell off during the early 1920s but not as much as might have been expected in view of the depressed condition of the U.S. wool industry.

During the 1930s, the adjustment to the greatly reduced domestic demand was much more significant. U.S. wool production continued high all through the 1930s but imports fell off sharply.[13] In the late

12. *Ibid.*, p. 78.

13. Imports during the 1930s were as follows (in millions of pounds):

1930	71	1935	42
1931	43	1936	111
1932	17	1937	150
1933	60	1938	31
1934	29	1939	98

Prices to farmers (in cents per pound) were:

1930	19.5	1935	19.3
1931	13.6	1936	26.9
1932	8.6	1937	32.0
1933	20.6	1938	19.1
1934	21.9	1939	22.3

(*Wool Statistics and Related Data,* pp. 38, 79 and 80.)

1920s, annual imports had been about 100 million pounds per year. By 1932, they were down to only 17 million and they remained low until 1939, except for the relatively heavy importations of 1936 and 1937, which grew out of the increased business activity of that period. Imports dropped back sharply to 31 million pounds in 1938 and were up to only 98 million pounds in 1939.

The outbreak of World War II brought a demand for wool that was far in excess of the amounts the U.S. sheep industry could supply. From 1942 to 1946, wool imports were at unprecedented levels and substantially in excess of the amounts produced in the United States.[14] Even in the postwar years, imports were larger than the amounts produced domestically. The current level of domestic production is much below the amounts required for domestic consumption when employment and business activity are at high levels. However, the amounts imported during the war years and after were greatly affected by considerations other than market demand, as explained later (see pp. 338–45).

Wool Markets and Problems in the 1920s

The wool market was badly demoralized in the period following World War I. Prices had fallen to little more than a quarter of what they had been at the peak of war demand and wool was almost unsalable in the summer of 1921. Though the wool producers were in desperate circumstances, there was no very general demand for direct government intervention, other than that of reimposing wool tariffs. The general attitude was that of wanting the government out of the wool business as soon as it could get out without wrecking the market entirely. The government agencies sought to ease the transition by rationing the amounts of government-owned wool put on the market and timing their sales so as to avoid competition with new clips coming from the country. They auctioned only limited amounts at a time and held off during periods when deliveries of domestic wools were at their peak. However, the general objective was to liquidate government stocks as soon as that could be done practically and thereafter to leave the industry free of government interference.[15]

14. Imports in these years were as follows (in millions of pounds, grease basis):

1940	223	1947	528
1941	614	1948	596
1942	783	1949	347
1943	643	1950	551
1944	582	1951	469
1945	725	1952	439
1946	924		

(*Agricultural Statistics, 1953,* p. 378.)

The data given above do not include some half billion pounds imported duty-free in the years 1942 to 1946 and later re-exported. The wools so handled were not available for domestic use. See explanation in later sections.

15. The operation was complicated by a somewhat capricious shift in demand. The market showed a marked preference for the fine wools and tended to neglect the

Instead of looking to the government for assistance, except in the form of tariffs, the wool growers turned more and more to an emphasis on improvements in methods of marketing and financing. The National Wool Warehouse and Storage Company, a grower-owned selling agency which had been set up earlier, in Chicago, was forced into liquidation in 1924 as a result of overadvances made to growers in 1919 and 1920. However, steps were taken almost at once to organize a new corporation, the National Wool Exchange, along somewhat similar lines but with headquarters in Boston instead of Chicago.[16]

The Exchange served as the selling agency for a number of state wool grower cooperatives and also sold on commission for some of the larger growers who were not members of cooperatives. Though the Exchange was organized as a stock corporation, the methods it used were more like those of a central cooperative selling agency. It operated successfully during the late 1920s but did not achieve a volume of sales or a position in the market comparable to that of the government-sponsored National Wool Marketing Corporation, which succeeded it in 1930.

In the meantime, there was an extensive development of small cooperative wool selling organizations through the Middle West, many on a county basis, and some larger cooperatives such as the Pacific Cooperative Wool Growers Association of Portland, Oregon, and the Ohio Wool Growers Cooperative Association.

Wool in the Farm Board Program [17]

At the time of the stock market crash in 1929, ambitious plans were just taking shape for the creation of a nationwide cooperative selling agency designed to handle the bulk of the domestic clip. Under the sponsorship of the Federal Farm Board, this new organization, the National Wool Marketing Corporation, was launched in December 1929. It was made up of 30 member associations, most of them organized on a state basis. A National Wool Credit Corporation was also organized as a way of handling advances and other financial arrangements.[18]

---

coarser wools, which constituted the bulk of the supply. The fine wools, that is, the combing wools suitable for worsteds and other high-grade fabrics, come largely from Australia and New Zealand and from the specialized sheep-producing areas of the Plains and Mountain states. (Much of the wool grown in Ohio is also of the fine type.) The coarser wools come more largely from the farm flocks of the Middle West.

16. The Exchange began operation in 1926.

17. Both in the Farm Board program and in those undertaken later, mohair (obtained from goats) was included along with wool. Since imports and exports of mohair are not important and since mohair is mainly a concern of Texas and neighboring states, it is not discussed separately in this analysis of the wool industry. The prices of mohair have tended to follow a pattern somewhat similar to wool prices. The amount of mohair produced is ordinarily in the order of 15 to 20 million pounds, 7 or 8 per cent of the over-all production of animal fibers in the United States in recent years.

18. For a somewhat fuller discussion of this operation, see Murray R. Benedict, *Can We Solve the Farm Problem?*, Twentieth Century Fund, New York, 1955, pp. 96–98. Of the 30 member associations (as of June 1930), 13 were in existence before 1929 and 17 were organized in 1929–1930.

The National Wool Marketing Corporation was not conceived as a government stabilization agency but rather as a step toward a more efficient, more highly centralized arrangement for selling wool. It was thought that if a considerable part of the domestic wool clip could be handled through a single, large cooperative selling agency, the bargaining power of the growers could be increased, lower selling costs could be achieved and prices could be stabilized within the marketing year. The organization was not intended or designed for carrying wool over from year to year in an attempt to offset the effects of a major depression.

However, the course of events very quickly forced both the Corporation and the Board into the role of price-stabilizing agencies, using government funds that probably could not be repaid. The price of wool (to farmers) had begun to ease off as early as April 1929. By September it was down to 29 cents as compared with 35.9 cents in January and February. Partly because of the support anticipated from the Farm Board and the new organization then being set up, the price held moderately firm during the fall and winter of 1929–30. It had declined only to 25.9 cents by February 1930.

The National Wool Marketing Corporation got under way in time to solicit the 1930 wool crop on consignment and to make advances on it. It advanced about 90 per cent of current prices in 1930 and 80 to 85 per cent in 1931. This high advance was made possible through loans from the Farm Board's revolving fund which made up the difference between the amounts the Corporation could borrow from the banks and the amount of the advances to growers. The Farm Board's portion of the loan was, of course, junior to the obligations held by the banks and consequently the absorber of losses if they occurred, which they did when the price of wool continued to decline.

The Board's participation was similar in principle to the assistance given to cotton and wheat by way of the cotton and wheat stabilization corporations, though no stabilization corporation was established for wool. The operation also was in some respects a forerunner of the nonrecourse loans later provided by the Commodity Credit Corporation.[19]

Problems Encountered

The high advances made in the summer of 1930 were intended in part as a means of checking the downward drift of wool prices and encourag-

19. The advances to the wool growers were not officially nonrecourse loans. The growers were legally obligated to repay advances that were in excess of the returns realized from the wool. In practice, it has always proved difficult and expensive to recapture overadvances made to farmers, especially in times of severe depression. Many of them have no money with which to pay and, under conditions such as those of the early 1920s and early 1930s, might even be out of business. In many cases, the advances made were actually in excess of 100 per cent of current value because of the difficulty of appraising accurately the quality of the clip at the time the advance was made. Wool clips vary widely in quality and condition. Accurate grading calls for a degree of technical skill which a fieldman authorizing advances is not likely to possess.

ing widespread participation by growers in the cooperative selling program. The second of these purposes was substantially achieved. The National Wool Marketing Corporation did receive on consignment about a third of the 1930 domestic wool clip and around 85 per cent of the mohair clip.

However, these large consignments tended to be an embarrassment rather than an asset. They did not constitute a large enough portion of the total wool stocks to make it necessary for the mills to draw heavily on supplies held by the National Wool Marketing Corporation for meeting their current operating needs. Since the Corporation was endeavoring to hold for higher prices, the tendency was for the Corporation's stocks to remain inactive while other stocks moved into consumption. Thus the Corporation was, to some extent, left "holding the bag" and eventually had to close out much of its wool at the very low prices that came to prevail later.[20]

Wool prices (to farmers) averaged 19 to 20 cents during the summer of 1930 as compared with about 30 cents a year earlier. They continued to decline during the marketing year and were only 15 to 16 cents in February and March of 1931. The price was around 13 to 14 cents in the summer of 1931 and sank to an all-time low of 7 cents in July 1932.

The Farm Board eventually wrote off about $12.5 million of the over-advances made in 1930 and 1931, including about $6 million in losses on mohair. Mohair became almost unsalable at any price. A change was made in the management of the National Wool Marketing Corporation. With the marked improvement in wool prices that came in the latter part of 1933, the Corporation was able to strengthen its financial position and has functioned effectively in the years since, operating as a cooperative selling organization rather than as a stabilization agency.

Results Achieved

The operation as a whole probably delayed somewhat the full impact of the price decline so far as wool and mohair were concerned but apparently did not affect materially the over-all returns to growers, except for the $12.5 million subsidy provided by the Farm Board. In the 1920–21 decline, virtually all of the price drop occurred between May 1920 and May 1921 (from 50.3 cents to 16.0 cents). The 1929–1932

20. This is obviously an oversimplified description of the events of that period. The National Wool Marketing Corporation was, of course, trying to sell throughout the year. However, it was to some extent committed to an effort to stabilize the market. With the uncertainty then prevailing as to the future course of prices, it seemed logical to move cautiously in selling at the seemingly low prices of the early part of the marketing year. The Corporation also was handicapped by the fact that its management was new and inexperienced and that it had to rely on an outside sales agency to market its product. (For a fuller discussion of some of the problems, see Murray R. Benedict, "An Evaluation of the Cooperative Wool Program," *American Cooperation,* American Institute of Cooperation, Washington, 1931, Vol. II, pp. 265–86.)

decline was more gradual, from 35.5 cents in March 1929 to 7.0 cents in July 1932.

Government intervention ceased to be a factor in the wool market from 1932 until the outbreak of World War II, except for such protection as was afforded by the tariff and a modest loan program made available in 1938 and 1939.[21] Prices were low on the 1934, 1935 and 1938 clips but were well above parity in 1936 and 1937. They were still moderately below parity in early 1939 (about 90 per cent) but moved up to about 120 per cent of parity by the end of that year.

The production of shorn wool held about steady at approximately 360 million pounds, which was about 40 million above the high level attained in 1928 and 1929. Wool prices, though less than satisfactory to growers in some of the years, averaged well above the general level of farm prices in all of the years except 1935, even though no special wool program was in effect.

WOOL IN WORLD WAR II

The outbreak of World War II brought an abrupt change in the wool situation. Almost immediately, decisions made by the American and British governments became the principal determinants of price and storage policies both in the United States and abroad. That situation continued throughout the war and for some years thereafter.

The policies followed in the war years were modified and improvised from time to time as conditions changed. A basic objective was, of course, to assure adequate supplies to meet military and civilian needs. Another was to provide outlets for the wool being produced in Australia, New Zealand and South Africa, and a third was to shift stocks from outlying areas to locations where they could be drawn on if needed. The initial success of the Japanese effort to gain control of the Pacific made it important that reserve supplies not be in positions where they could be cut off if trans-Pacific shipping lanes were made unusable. Later, actual or potential shortage of shipping capacity became a factor.

Mill consumption began to increase in 1939 and 1940. By 1942, it was nearly double the amounts used in the late 1930s. Takings remained at that level or higher through 1946 and did not slack off importantly until 1949. U.S. production, though high in the early 1940s, was not large enough to meet current requirements and could not contribute at

21. Wool prices fell off sharply in the late fall of 1937 and early 1938. They remained low until September 1939. Ten-month, nonrecourse loans at 75 per cent of parity were offered by the Commodity Credit Corporation at 4 per cent. About 83 million pounds of wool went under loan in 1938 and the program apparently steadied prices somewhat. By late 1938, prices rose above the loan rate and most of the loans were redeemed. Loans were again offered in 1939 but not much use was made of them as the price of wool was above the loan rate. No wool program was in effect during the years 1940–1942 as prices were rising rapidly.

all to the sizable stockpiles considered necessary (except as it was replaced by supplies imported).

Management of Stockpiles in the War Years

The actions taken during the war years were designed mainly to further the war program rather than the interests of wool growers. However, the pricing arrangements made were presumed to be on a basis that would be equitable to wool producers. Since the government took over exclusive management of wool stocks and prices, there was no free market to which the prices paid can be related. The most logical criterion of fairness appears, therefore, to be the relation of wool prices to the general level of farm prices.

As of April 1, 1941, the United States had only about 200 million pounds of wool on hand (grease basis). A new clip of around 450 million pounds (including pulled wool) was about to come on the market. It was estimated that annual wartime requirements would be 900 to 1,000 million pounds. Inventories would have to be built up and at least 500 million pounds of foreign wool per year would be needed.[22]

In 1940, the National Defense Advisory Commission recommended that an emergency stockpile of foreign wools be built up in the United States to insure supplies in the event that foreign shipments should be cut off.[23] The British government had taken over control of all wool in Australia and New Zealand, in October 1939. Control was extended to South African wools in August 1940. These actions put approximately three quarters of the available foreign apparel wool under United Kingdom control. Arrangements made thereafter with respect to foreign wools were almost wholly through United States–British governmental agreements. At the request of the United States, the British government agreed, in December 1940, to store in the United States 250 million pounds of Australian wools, which could be made available to U.S. mills in an emergency.[24]

In 1942, the Office of Production Management authorized a stockpile of one billion pounds. As part of this program, the Defense Supplies Corporation acquired 302.5 million pounds of Australian wool and 34.7 million pounds of Uruguayan wools. It had previously agreed, in October 1941, to accept South African wools for storage on a consignment basis, with the understanding that they would be available for U.S. consump-

22. See John W. Klein, *Wool during World War II,* U.S. Bureau of Agricultural Economics, War Records Monograph 7, May 1948, pp. 8 and 9.

23. This action had been recommended by a U.S. interdepartmental committee as early as 1939, after the war broke out in Europe, but no action was taken at that time. (*Ibid.,* p. 19.)

24. The British Ministry of Supply retained ownership, but the U.S. Defense Supplies Corporation agreed to pay transportation and storage costs. (For a fuller description of these and succeeding actions, see *ibid.,* and James Gilbert Evans, "American Wool Import Policy," *Department of State Bulletin,* November 3, 1946, pp. 783–86.)

tion if needed. This agreement was terminated on June 30, 1942, at which time 122 million pounds of Cape wool were in storage in the United States.[25]

The British agreement was modified in 1942 by an informal arrangement whereby the Defense Supplies Corporation agreed to accept for storage and transhipment to England whatever amounts of Australian, New Zealand and Cape wool the British Ministry of Supply might choose to ship. The formal agreement with the United Kingdom was amended in 1943, by placing an upper limit of 900 million pounds on the amount the Defense Supplies Corporation would accept for storage, and obligating the Ministry of Supply to keep a minimum of 400 million pounds in the stockpile. The stocks were to be available to either country if needed for "strategic" purposes.[26] Shipments under this agreement were terminated in September 1943.

It was also agreed that, after suspension of hostilities, this stockpile would not be disposed of in the United States except by agreement between the two governments.[27] Nevertheless, wool grower representatives in the United States were much concerned about the possibility that these stocks might eventually find their way into the U.S. market and cause a price break similar to that of 1921. This apprehension was heightened by the fact that the size of the stockpile was a closely guarded military secret.

The maximum quantity in the stockpile was 518 million pounds. Most of it had been re-exported by the terminal date of the agreement.[28] In December 1943, the War Production Board approved release of the stocks of foreign wool that had been purchased by the Defense Supplies

25. The summary here presented is derived largely from Evans, *op. cit.*

26. Transportation and storage charges were to be shared equally by the Ministry of Supply and the Defense Supplies Corporation until one year following the close of hostilities.

27. In all, there were five international agreements between the United States and British governments in respect to the handling of wool stocks. The first provided for stockpiling British-owned wools in the United States as described above. That agreement was superseded by one that provided that the United States would buy all wool then stored by the British in the United States and some that was to arrive later. Agreement No. 3, signed at the same time, provided that the United States would store British-owned South African wool, this to be available for U.S. consumption if needed. No. 4 authorized the British government to ship and store in the United States, for its own account, Australian and New Zealand wools. The fifth agreement, entered into in March 1943, was a consolidation of Nos. 3 and 4. The U.S. preferred to spend some $7.5 million on storage costs rather than to lay out some $90 to $100 million for outright purchase. The U.S. government realized a substantial profit on the wool eventually purchased as a means of bolstering the United Kingdom's dollar exchange position, probably more than enough to offset the cost of storage. A few minor agreements for purchase of other foreign wools were also entered into, e.g., with Uruguay, Argentina and Iceland. These were largely for the purpose of supporting the economies of those nations. (See *Wool during World War II*, pp. 20 and 21.)

28. These arrangements were facilitated by the fact that the United Kingdom had entered into agreements with other members of the Commonwealth whereby she would purchase their exportable surpluses of wool during the war years and for one wool year thereafter.

Corporation. They were subsequently liquidated through auction sales and transfers to the United Nations Relief and Rehabilitation Administration.

On the whole, the wool supply situation was relatively easy throughout the war. This was due, however, to the fact that the United States was able to keep the Pacific supply lines open. Had these been cut off, the precautionary measures taken early in the war would have assumed much larger importance.

The Domestic Wool Program

The prices of domestic wools moved up moderately in late 1939 and stayed up through 1940 (approximately 28 cents as compared with 20 cents in the preceding year). This amount of advance did not imply any marked shortage or fear of shortage in wool supplies. It was mostly a reflection of reviving business activity. There was some strengthening effect as a result of the Buy American Act of 1933, which required that wool textiles purchased for the armed services be made from American-grown wool. An administrative order issued in November 1940 permitted the use of foreign wools in filling government contracts but some domestic wools bought at a premium continued to be used.[29]

Prices to U.S. growers continued to advance in 1941 and stood at about 37 cents at the end of that year. There was a further small advance even after ceilings were established. The price in 1942 was about 40 cents from February and March on to the end of the year. This was about 55 per cent above the 1939 price.

The demand for domestic wools began to falter in 1943. Military requirements were declining and labor was becoming scarce. Mill operators showed a preference for foreign wools because of their relative cheapness and because they required less labor, having been better prepared for market before shipment.

To overcome the uncertainty in regard to outlets for domestic wools, the Secretary of Agriculture directed the Commodity Credit Corporation to purchase the entire domestic clip of 1943 at ceiling prices and required that all domestic wool, with minor exceptions, be sold to CCC (Food Distribution Order No. 50, April 25, 1943). This provision was extended year by year until April 1947.

The support prices thus maintained were favorable as compared with past prices of wool, but growers were running into high costs and were especially handicapped by the shortage of skilled help. Sheepherders, always a limited group, were becoming more and more scarce. Some

29. The effect of this provision probably cannot be measured precisely as many other factors enter into the pricing of wool for given uses. Evans states that there was an average spread of 17 cents per clean pound between domestic and imported wools at the time the Office of Price Administration established ceilings on wool prices on February 28, 1942. (*Department of State Bulletin,* November 3, 1946, p. 785.)

were drafted. Others shifted to high-paying jobs in the defense industries and no new ones were coming in.[30]

The government's purchase price in 1943 was 41.7 cents per pound, which was 141 per cent of parity.[31] At that time the farm price of cotton was 112 per cent of parity, of wheat 105 per cent, of corn 118 per cent and of beef cattle (a competitor of sheep in the range areas) 140 per cent. The buying price remained at approximately that same level through 1949. However, most other farm products rose rapidly from 1945 on. Thus the price of wool, though relatively favorable at the time the government started its purchase program, became less and less favorable as time went on. By 1949, meat animals were 183 per cent above their 1939 levels and farm products as a whole were up 160 per cent. Wool prices had increased about 120 per cent.

As a result of high costs, labor shortages and relatively low prices, the production of shorn wool fell off rapidly from 1942 on. The amount produced in 1942 was 388 million pounds. Output was down to 213 million pounds by 1949. This decline was not entirely due to unsatisfactory returns. Though wool did not share in the rapid price advance of the postwar years, as shown above, lambs, another product of the same flocks, rose in about the same proportion as other meat animals but not as much or as fast as choice steers.[32] Among the inhibiting factors in the sheep industry was a widely prevalent fear that the wool stock situation was getting out of hand and that there might be a disastrous break in prices after the war like the one that had caused such havoc among sheep raisers in 1921. World wool stocks were known to be very high and the prospect of a smooth transition to peacetime conditions did not appear bright.

30. Many of the larger sheep ranches have long relied heavily on Basques recruited from Spain, or their descendants, as a source of supply for skilled sheepherders. This source of supply had now dried up and wool production began to decline even though returns, as compared with those of earlier periods, seemed favorable. Sheepherding is not only an occupation that requires special skills but also one which, because of the isolation and loneliness of the work, does not appeal to most young men of native birth. In addition, the demand for beef was pushing up the prices of cattle even more rapidly than those of most other farm products. Since beef cattle are to some extent competitors for the same productive resources as sheep, there was some tendency for growers to shift out of sheep and into cattle. The sheepherder problem was, of course, mainly confined to the western states where flocks are large and growers are heavily dependent on hired labor. However, various other factors were tending to discourage sheep production. (See *Achieving a Sound Domestic Wool Industry,* A Report to the President of the United States from the Secretary of Agriculture, December 1953, pp. 7–10.)

31. The support prices given here and elsewhere are for national averages, not necessarily the prices received by any particular grower or for any specific lot of wool.

32. The income from wool is estimated to be only about 40 per cent of the total income from sheep, lambs and wool. (See Walter W. Wilcox, *The Farmer in the Second World War,* Iowa State College Press, Ames, 1947, p. 234.) However, the percentage varies from region to region, more of the total coming from meat in the Middle West and more from wool in the specialized wool-producing areas of the Plains and Mountain states.

CCC Stocks Pile Up

Toward the end of the war, mills turned to the production of civilian goods.[33] However, the use of domestic wools dropped off sharply and Commodity Credit Corporation stocks of these wools increased since the CCC selling price was higher than the prices of comparable imported wools. CCC held 327 million pounds, grease basis, on July 1, 1945 and 499 million pounds on July 1, 1946, which was more than the equivalent of a year's domestic production. This inactivity on the part of domestically produced wools increased still more the apprehensions of the sheep producers about the future of their industry and led to growing concern over the situation that was developing.[34]

As a way of meeting the problem, the Commodity Credit Corporation announced in November 1945 that it would sell domestic wools at the price of duty-paid foreign wools. That concession still was not sufficient to make the domestic wools move freely as most mills prefer the better-prepared foreign wools to those grown domestically if they can be obtained on a comparable price basis.[35] The price was further reduced in February 1946. CCC sales of domestic fine-combing territory wools for the first half of 1946 were about 19 cents (clean) below the purchase price. The loss was absorbed by CCC. As a result of this concession, domestic wools began to move more freely and the market for them took on a healthier tone.

WOOL IN THE POSTWAR YEARS

During the war years, world production of apparel wools exceeded consumption. On July 1, 1945, world carry-over stocks amounted to around 5 billion pounds, about three times the average carry-over of the prewar years. The United Kingdom Ministry of Supply owned more than two thirds of these stocks as a result of its wartime agreements to

33. U.S. mills operated near capacity during 1946, producing a record volume of woolen fabrics, but even so were not able to supply the demand. Mill consumption continued high in 1947 but not so high as in 1946. Thereafter, it fell off to a 1949 level that was little more than half that of 1946. There was a sharp revival of wool manufacturing in 1950.

34. This low rate of mill consumption of domestic wools was in marked contrast to the over-all situation. C. J. Fawcett, General Manager of the National Wool Marketing Corporation, stated in June 1945 that "Our consumption in 1944 was about 1,400,000,000 pounds, of which 74.1% was of foreign origin. We imported and consumed over 650,000,000 pounds of foreign wool in 1944 while using only 50% of our 1944 domestic clip. . . . Practically the only market for domestic wool since the beginning of the war has been furnished by the Army Quartermaster through orders for cloth specifying the use of liberal portions of domestic wool in their raw material blends." (Paper for American Farm Bureau Federation, June 1, 1945, mimeo.)

35. The Australian and New Zealand wools are more uniform in quality than those grown in the United States and the established practice of "skirting" them provides a fleece that can be handled by the mills with less labor and trouble than if the whole fleece is used. Skirted wool has the breech wool, tags and other low-grade portions trimmed off before shipment.

purchase the export surpluses of Australia, New Zealand and South Africa.[36]

To deal with this situation, and to help in stabilizing the world wool market, the United Kingdom and the Southern Hemisphere wool-exporting members of the Commonwealth established, in 1946, a joint organization known as U.K.-Dominion Wool Disposals Limited. Under this agreement, the stock of dominion-grown wools owned by the United Kingdom Ministry of Supply in each of the countries was transferred to joint ownership by the United Kingdom government and the dominion government concerned. The excess stocks were to be fed onto the market in such a way as to cause a minimum of disturbance to the market and to keep prices relatively stable.[37]

At that time, it was generally expected that orderly liquidation of these stocks might take ten years or longer. This estimate proved much too pessimistic. Wool auctions were resumed in September 1946, but with reserve prices established. (Auctions in the British and dominion markets had been suspended in 1939.) The current clips in the dominions were to be taken over by the Joint Organization if not sold at prices equivalent to the auction reserve prices.[38] The Joint Organization undertook to maintain the prices then current, unless it should become necessary to adjust to a definite trend that seemed likely to continue.[39]

Demand turned out to be much stronger than was anticipated. The operation was skillfully handled. The current productions of Australia, New Zealand and South Africa were disposed of and Joint Organization stocks were reduced more rapidly than had been expected. The wool textile industry of western Europe recovered rapidly and by the end of 1946 was at about the level of 1938. Prices in the foreign markets advanced and Joint Organization stocks were reduced about 500 million pounds by June 1947. By July 1950, Joint Organization stocks were down to only about 150 million pounds, as compared with 3,210 million pounds on hand at the end of July 1945.[40]

36. There was some decrease in these stocks during 1945–1946. In the five Southern Hemisphere wool-exporting countries, stocks declined from about 3 billion pounds, grease basis, on July 1, 1945 to around 2.7 billion on July 1, 1946. (*Department of State Bulletin*, November 3, 1946, p. 786.)

37. Since many other countries were concerned with this problem, the International Wool Textile Organization and representatives of the major consuming countries were invited to form a consultative committee to advise with the Board of U.K.-Dominion Wool Disposals Limited. Close contact was also maintained with agencies concerned with such matters as rehabilitation of the wool textile industry in consuming countries.

38. U.K.-Dominion Wool Disposals Limited came to be generally referred to as the Joint Organization or J.O.

39. The prices which the Joint Organization thus sought to maintain were, of course, much lower than those prevailing in the United States, since these foreign wools had been moving into the United States, after payment of duty, and still were selling at less than the U.S. prices for domestically grown wools.

40. U.S. Department of Agriculture, *The Wool Situation*, July 1950, p. 12. In 1945, the British government held about 3.6 billion pounds of the 5.1-billion-pound world stocks. This was equivalent to more than two years' production for Australia, New

In the meantime the market had continued strong with generally rising prices. Had it not been for the large supplies available from Joint Organization stocks, this would apparently have been a period of desperately short supply and boom prices. World consumption was running substantially above world production. That disparity became much more apparent in 1950 and 1951 when the greatly increased demand that followed the outbreak of war in Korea was superimposed on a world market in which no large carry-overs remained.[41] Wool prices (to farmers) rose by nearly 100 per cent between June 1950 and June 1951. This, however, was in large part a speculative rise. U.S. mill consumption rose about 30 per cent in 1950 but had dropped back to about the 1949 level by 1952. Prices fell as abruptly as they had increased and by March 1952 were about at the levels of early 1950.

Efforts to Establish a U.S. Postwar Policy on Wool

Hearings on the wool situation were held in November and December 1945 by a Special Senate Committee to Investigate the Production, Transportation and Marketing of Wool. The principal alternatives suggested to this committee were: (1) an increase in the rate of duty sufficient to offset differences in the cost of producing foreign and domestic wools, (2) the establishment of quotas on foreign wools, limiting importation in any one year to the amount by which consumption exceeds production, (3) purchase of all wool, foreign and domestic, by a government agency which would sell at the average cost of procurement, and (4) maintenance of prices on domestic wools by having the Commodity Credit Corporation sell at prices in line with duty-paid foreign wools, with reimbursement to the Corporation, for losses sustained, out of funds derived from import duties on wool.

The tariff increase and quota proposals were opposed by the State Department as being contrary to the spirit of American economic foreign policy, which was directed toward the reduction of world trade barriers and opening up channels of trade. Assistant Secretary Clayton, speaking for the Department, expressed doubt that the American people would favor state trading, such as that implied by the third alternative, except in time of war.[42]

Zealand and South Africa. Most of the good-quality combing wools, suitable for shipment to the United States, had been liquidated by the end of 1947. The coarser fleece wools, and inferior qualities of combing wools, were still in long supply but could not have a large influence on the U.S. market since they are not the types usually exported to the United States.

41. A wool committee was set up in April 1951 under the International Materials Conference, but, since the prewar auction system of selling had been re-established, the other governments concerned resisted a U.S. proposal to set up an allocation system combined with ceiling prices. Prices declined in the succeeding twelve months and no action was taken.

42. This plan had been proposed by Dean J. A. Hill of the University of Wyoming

The government's proposals were put forward in a letter from President Truman to Senator O'Mahoney, the chairman of the Committee, in March 1946.[43] He suggested: (1) that the parity price of wool be revised so as to take account of the unfavorable price situation of wool in the period 1909–1914, (2) that the Commodity Credit Corporation support incomes to wool producers through purchases, loans or payments at the same percentage of the revised parity prices as it was directed to support prices of "basic" agricultural commodities, (3) that CCC be authorized to continue to sell wool at prices competitive with duty-paid, imported foreign wools and (4) that losses incurred on payments made by CCC be reimbursed out of funds derived from the customs duties on wool.[44]

The Seventy-ninth Congress did not enact a wool bill before adjournment, but the Senate Committee on Agriculture and Forestry reported out favorably S. 2033, which included the principal features of the President's proposal.

U.S. Prices and Program, 1947–1950

Since S. 2033 did not come to a vote, and no other wool legislation was passed in the meantime, the wartime wool program expired on April 14, 1947.[45] It was resumed on August 14, 1947, through an act which directed CCC to support the price of wool until December 31,

---

and had a good deal of support from farm organizations, among them several of the wool grower associations, the American Farm Bureau Federation and some of the livestock marketing associations. Under it, the Secretary of Agriculture would have been directed to support the price of wool through purchases at a price no lower than (a) comparable prices as of January 15, 1946 or (b) the current comparable price. The Secretary would also have been directed to acquire by foreign purchase or from foreign-held stocks in the United States enough wool to meet the requirements of domestic manufacturers. The wool would then have been sold to the manufacturers at the average cost of acquisition.

43. This was in response to a letter sent to the President by Senator O'Mahoney in January. He had urged cooperation with the Committee in framing a long-term government policy in regard to wool. The Truman proposals grew out of a request by him to the Office of War Mobilization and Reconversion and other interested government agencies for suggestions as to the kind of program that might be mutually satisfactory.

44. Senate Doc. 140, 79th Cong., 2d sess. The letter also suggested that the marketing agreement and order program be made applicable to wool, that a research and development program for improving the quality of domestic wool be initiated, and that the executive agencies discuss with interested foreign governments the possibility of working out an international wool agreement with a view to achieving coordinated action and more unified supervision of world wool marketing and price policies. The idea of an international wool agreement was later given some consideration, but the proposal met with so little encouragement from the representatives of the other nations concerned that the idea was dropped.

45. At the end of December 1946, CCC holdings amounted to 480 million pounds (grease basis), which was more than 100 million pounds in excess of a full year's production, both shorn and pulled. Total stocks, including those in the hands of mills and dealers, amounted to 895 million pounds, which was about 100 million pounds more than the stocks of a year earlier and more than three times the amounts customarily held in the years 1935–1939. (*The Wool Situation,* March 1947, p. 3.) However, mill consumption of apparel wool was at an all-time high of 610 million pounds (scoured basis) in 1946. (*Wool Statistics and Related Data,* p. 58.)

1948 at the same rate as in 1946.[46] The portion of the 1947 crop for which price supports were applicable was much smaller than in previous years since only that part of it still owned by producers on August 15 was eligible for purchase. However, the brief lapse in the support program, from April to August 1947, apparently had no significant effect on the prices paid to growers, as the monthly prices for that year show almost no change.[47]

As a means of restoring health to the market for domestic wools, the most important feature of the 1947 act was an authorization for CCC to sell its stocks on a competitive basis with foreign wools. These stocks had been relatively inactive and the market was still being largely supplied by the more attractively priced foreign wools.[48] This action, together with the very active demand of the postwar period, led to gradual reduction of CCC holdings. However, the demand was uneven as between types of wool. Fine wools were in active demand both in the United States and abroad while medium wools were sluggish. About 90 per cent of the 1947 sales from CCC stocks was of the fine-wool types. Thus the principal need for price concessions was in the holdings of coarser wools.

CCC holdings of domestic wools had been reduced to only 67 million pounds (scoured basis) by April 1, 1949 and to 17 million by April 1950. This was in relation to peak holdings of 196 million pounds in 1946.[49] Under the act of August 1947, wool prices to growers were supported by means of CCC purchases in 1948 at the same level as in 1946 and late 1947, that is, at an average level of 42.3 cents.[50] That level of support, in the same form, was continued through 1949 by a

46. Public Law 360, passed August 5, 1947.

47. *Wool Statistics and Related Data,* p. 78.

48. CCC holdings of both domestic and foreign wools had reached a peak of 540 million pounds (grease basis) in October 1946. (*The Wool Situation,* October 1950, p. 4.)

49. *Wool Statistics and Related Data,* p. 53. The figures given here and in some other places are on a scoured basis since that is the form in which they appear in the official sources. There is no dependable conversion factor for translating weights in the grease to weights of clean wool since the shrinkage varies greatly in different types and lots. Some of the coarse wools may shrink as little as 40 per cent; some of the fine wools as much as 70 per cent or more. As a rough approximation, the clean weight may be taken as about 45 per cent of the grease weight. Since clean content is a much more accurate specification than grease weight, it is the one mainly used in the trade and in recent years is the form specified in tariff schedules.

50. As pointed out earlier, this price was relatively favorable in terms of percentage of parity in the war years (141 per cent in 1943) but, as the prices of things bought by farmers rose in the postwar years, the percentage of parity represented by this stationary price for wool declined sharply. It was only 101 per cent in 1947 and dropped to 94 per cent in 1948 and 1949. A "National Wool Act of 1948" was passed by the Congress but was vetoed and so did not come into effect. It provided for direct payments to growers similar to those later authorized in the National Wool Act of 1954. Also, the Department of Agriculture recommended on two occasions the imposition of import quotas or higher tariffs, under Section 22 of the Agricultural Adjustment Act. On the first of them, the Tariff Commission did not make a recommendation. In connection with the second, it recommended an increase in import duties but its recommendation was not approved by the President.

provision in the Agricultural Act of 1948 (Section 1c) which extended its termination date to June 30, 1950. However, the supports available in 1948 and 1949 were of little significance as the prices received in the market were above support levels. (See Table 43.)

TABLE 43

WOOL: LEVELS OF SUPPORT, PERCENTAGES OF PARITY AND PRICES RECEIVED BY FARMERS, 1938–1954

Marketing Year	Level of Support		Season Average Price Received by Growers	Type of Support		Authority	
	Average Support Level	Per Cent of Parity		Loan	Purchase	Mandatory	Permissive
	(Cents per Pound)		*(Cents per Pound)*				
1938 [a]	18.0	75 [b]	19.1	L	—	—	P
1939	18.0 [c]	78 [b]	22.3	L	—	—	P
1940 [d]	—	—	28.4	—	—	—	—
1941 [d]	—	—	35.5	—	—	—	—
1942 [d]	—	—	40.1	—	—	—	—
1943	41.7	141 [b]	41.6	—	P	—	P
1944	42.4	135 [b]	42.3	—	P	—	P
1945	41.9	132 [b]	41.9	—	P	—	P
1946	42.3	129 [b]	42.3	—	P	—	P
1947	42.3	101 [b]	42.0	—	P	M [e]	P [e]
1948	42.3	94 [b]	49.2	—	P	M	—
1949	42.3	94 [b]	49.4	—	P	M	—
1950	45.2	90	62.1	— [f]	P	M	—
1951	50.7	90	97.1	— [f]	P	M	—
1952	54.2	90	54.1	L	P [g]	M	—
1953	53.1	90	54.9	L	P [g]	M	—
1954	53.1	90	53.2				

Sources: Derived from U.S. Production and Marketing Administration, *CCC Price Support Statistical Handbook,* November 1953, p. 55, and later reports; also U.S. Agricultural Marketing Service, *Wool Production and Value of Sales,* 1955, p. 2. (Season average prices 1940–1950 are as shown in U.S. Department of Agriculture, *Agricultural Statistics, 1954,* p. 347.)

a. 1938 loans available on 1937 wool on hand April 15, 1938 as well as on wool produced in 1938.
b. Computed on basis of announced support level.
c. Support continued at 1938 clip level.
d. No program.
e. Permissive to April 15; no program April 15 to August 15; mandatory after August 15.
f. Program inoperative—no purchases made.
g. Pulled wool only.

Changes in the Agricultural Act of 1949

The Agricultural Act of 1949 gave wool a special status as among the "nonbasic" commodities, which, in general, were to be supported at rates of from 60 to 90 per cent of parity. The Secretary of Agriculture was directed to support the price of wool at not less than 60 per cent of parity or more than 90 per cent, but "at such rate as he determines will encourage an annual production of approximately 360 million pounds of shorn wool." [51] This meant, in effect, a directive to support the price at 90 per cent of parity since production was then much below the indicated 360 million pounds.

Also, a change was authorized in the method of computing the parity price of wool which increased the computed parities by some 5 or 6 cents,[52] thus raising the support level as compared with that provided under the formula previously in use. The authorization for CCC sales at less than cost of acquisition was renewed [53] thus leaving the way open for continuing purchase of domestic wools at premium prices without building up burdensome stocks, but under continuous subsidy if wool prices fell below the foreign price plus tariff.

The Wool Situation, 1950–1953

Under the provisions of the Agricultural Act of 1949, support prices at 90 per cent of parity (45.2 cents) were authorized for 1950 but CCC did not acquire any wool as open-market prices were above the support level. War broke out in June and the principal problem became that of holding prices in check rather than of raising them. The Defense Production Act of 1950 authorized price controls on wool and mohair as well as on other farm products but was not immediately implemented. The act provided that no ceiling could be established on agricultural prices at less than the higher of two prices—parity or the highest price received by producers between May 24 and June 24, 1950.

The Office of Price Stabilization issued a general ceiling price regulation on January 26, 1951. It established ceiling prices for most commodities and services on the basis of prices in effect during the period December 19, 1950 to January 25, 1951. However, raw wool, when sold by the producer, was one of the commodities specifically exempted.[54] Some wool products, if sold to defense agencies, were also exempted. From time to time thereafter, OPS established dollar-and-cent ceilings for various types of wool and wool products but a 1951 amendment to the Defense Production Act of 1950 provided that no ceiling should be

51. Title II, Section 201 (a).
52. *The Wool Situation,* November 1949, pp. 6 and 7. However, wool producers in the West, where most of the wool is grown, contended that the parity price increase did not reflect adequately the increased costs to them as a result of higher wage rates for sheepherders. Wages constitute 25 to 30 per cent of their costs whereas, for the United States as a whole, they constitute only 10 or 12 per cent of farm costs. Since farm wages had risen more than any other cost item, this change if fully reflected in the parity price for wool would result in a higher parity standard for that product.
53. Title IV, Section 407.
54. *The Wool Situation,* January 1951, p. 3.

established on any agricultural product at less than 90 per cent of the price prevailing on May 19, 1951.[55] Since wool prices to producers were then above a dollar a pound, this meant, in effect, that no meaningful ceiling could be established. The price of wool to farmers had moved up rapidly during 1950. Standing at 49.6 cents in January, it was up to 57.3 cents by June and had risen to 82.8 cents by December. The rise continued during the early months of 1951, reaching $1.19 in March.[56] Thereafter, it fell off gradually to March 1952 when it was at about the same level as in March 1950 (53.8 cents as compared with 52.4 cents).

Under these circumstances, there was no occasion for CCC purchases of wool as a way of supporting prices. However, the Production and Marketing Administration did announce a support price of 50.7 cents per pound to be effective from April 1, 1951 through March 31, 1952. No wool was acquired under this program. Some foreign wools were purchased as part of the 100-million-pound (clean basis) reserve, which had been authorized in the late summer of 1950. CCC announced in April 1951 that it was suspending further purchases for the reserve. Up to that time, about 12 million pounds (grease basis) had been acquired for the Department of Defense.[57]

In January 1952, the Office of Price Stabilization issued a new Price Regulation (No. 35, Revision 1), which reduced ceilings about 20 per cent for sellers of grease wool, other than growers. That order was made effective as of April 8 but had little effect as OPS announced on April 22 the suspension of price controls on greasy wool, scoured wool, wool top and various other types (but not mohair), to take effect on April 28.[58] The suspension of price controls at that time was of no significance so far as the growers were concerned as their prices had already dropped back to 51.5 cents, about the 1949 level.

The rapid decline in wool prices that occurred between June 1951 and April 1952 caused a good deal of concern on the part of growers but was actually a return to normal after a period of heavy military purchasing and speculative activity.[59] The underlying situation was basically

55. *Ibid.*, October 1951, p. 8.

56. This was 211 per cent of parity. (*Ibid.*, p. 6.)

57. *Ibid.*, April 1951, p. 11. At about the same time, the Department of Defense announced that it was introducing measures designed to reduce military requirements substantially, possibly as much as 15 per cent.

58. *Ibid.*, April 1952, p. 7.

59. There was also uneasiness over the changing valuations placed on foreign currencies in terms of U.S. dollars. The "soft-currency" problem had been a very disturbing factor in international markets throughout the postwar period. Most of the free world was short of dollars, and changes in the dollar valuations of foreign currencies as well as outright controls over dollar purchases were frequent and in some cases drastic. In August 1949, the value of the British pound was reduced from $4.06 to $2.80. Since the Australian and New Zealand currencies were tied to the pound, this, of course, affected to some extent trading relations with the United States. In some countries, the need for U.S. dollar exchange was so acute that special export concessions or currency revaluations were used as a means of increasing dollar sales. Concern was ex-

sound. The last of the CCC holdings carried over from World War II had been liquidated in the summer of 1950 and no domestic wool was acquired under the 1950 and 1951 support programs. World production was up slightly and world consumption was down from the high levels of the preceding year. However, the situation was in reasonably good balance and U.S. prices to growers moved up slightly during 1952 and 1953.

The Production and Marketing Administration announced price supports averaging about 54.2 cents per pound to growers for the 1952 clip. This was 3½ cents above the 1951 support level, the difference being due to an increase in parity prices. Two types of loans were offered, the regular nonrecourse loan to mature on January 31, 1953 and "advance loans" at 70 per cent of the nonrecourse loan value with a maximum maturity date of five months from the date of the loan. The advance loans could be made prior to the appraisal of the wool. These could be converted to nonrecourse loans, but if they were not so converted the government would take steps to collect on them at maturity rather than to take over the wool.

As of December 31, 1952 about 77 million pounds, approximately a third of the clip, were under loan. The due dates of these loans were later extended to cover an additional three months. The amount eventually acquired by CCC was about 101 million pounds, of which 95 million were shorn wool and the remainder pulled wool.

Price-support arrangements on the 1953 clip were substantially the same as those for 1952. Nonrecourse loans were made available from May 1, 1953 through March 31, 1954, and "advance" loans on a recourse basis at 70 per cent of the nonrecourse rate. The advance loans were to have a five-month maturity or to run until April 30, 1954, whichever was earlier. Nonrecourse loans were to mature on April 30, 1954. Pulled wool, to the extent that support was required, was to be on a purchase basis.[60]

Early in 1954, the Administration proposed a new approach to the wool problem. Direct payments would be made to growers at the end of the season in amounts sufficient to make up the difference between the average prices received by growers and the incentive prices specified. The payments would be made from the general revenues of the govern-

---

pressed also over the alleged practice of some manufacturers of using wools imported without duty as carpet wools in the manufacture of other types of woolen goods.

The unbalanced exchange situation almost all through the world was, of course, a disturbing influence in the wool markets. So also was the extensive resort to state trading, by both exporting and importing nations. These difficulties became less significant as more normal trading arrangements developed and the various national economies recovered from the unsettled conditions brought about by the war.

60. Under the 1953 program, CCC took over about 36 million pounds of wool. CCC holdings as of May 31, 1954 were about 123 million pounds as compared with 101 million pounds a year earlier. Prices to farmers were approximately the same as in 1952.

ment but could not exceed the unobligated tariff receipts from imports of wool and wool products. Similar supports were proposed for pulled wool and mohair, with appropriate differentials.

In principle, the Administration plan, which was later incorporated in the Agricultural Act of 1954, is somewhat similar to the one used in making payments to sugar producers. The main differences are that the wool program, following the precedent established in the Agricultural Act of 1949, contemplates encouragement for U.S. growers to produce more wool, whereas the sugar program looks more specifically to the stabilization of production and prices and includes import quota provisions.[61]

Since the 1954 legislation was still in a formative stage, the Secretary of Agriculture announced, early in 1954, a support program for shorn wool which was essentially the same as those in effect in 1952 and 1953. It included both advance and nonrecourse loans. The support price specified was 52.1 cents, subject to later upward adjustment if the parity price should increase.[62] The average price received by growers for the 1954 clip was 53.2 cents.[63]

The National Wool Act of 1954

The National Wool Act of 1954 (Title VII of the Agricultural Act of 1954)[64] set up approximately the plan which the Administration had proposed earlier in the year. Its declared purpose is to encourage annual domestic production of approximately 300 million pounds of shorn wool, in the grease, "at prices fair to both producers and consumers in a manner which will have the least adverse effect on foreign trade."[65]

Support is provided through the Commodity Credit Corporation, by

61. Also, the wool program is related to customs duties collected on wool and its products whereas the sugar program includes a domestic excise tax. However, the effect on the price paid by the consumer is much the same in either case.

62. *The Wool Situation,* February 24, 1954, p. 7. The support price was later advanced to 53.2 cents. (*Ibid.,* April 20, 1954, p. 3.) Beginning with 1954, prices of pulled wool were supported through loans rather than by purchases.

63. U.S. Agricultural Marketing Service, *Wool Production and Value of Sales,* 1955.

64. Public Law 690, 83d Cong., 2d sess., approved August 28, 1954.

65. A primary reason for the position taken by the Administration and the Congress was the need for building closer economic and security ties with Australia and New Zealand and a desire to avoid conflict between the policy relating to wool and the over-all national policy of seeking to stimulate and facilitate world trade. Wool is so important to the Australian economy that an increase in tariffs or even the imposition of quotas under Section 22 would have been disturbing to the Pacific area security efforts. The wool growers generally would have preferred an increase in the tariff rate. That, however, would have run counter to a much broader national policy to which the United States had been committed from 1934 on. A secondary objective was to avoid further build-up of CCC stocks, while at the same time giving relief to wool producers and furthering the declared policy of increasing domestic wool production. Since the President had assured the wool grower representatives of his desire to help them if a workable plan could be devised, the government departments were under strong pressure to seek some new type of solution rather than to continue with the kind of program then in effect.

means of loans, purchases, payments or other operations, "at such incentive level as the Secretary, after consultation with producer representatives, and after taking into consideration prices paid and other cost conditions affecting sheep production, determines to be necessary in order to encourage an annual production consistent with the declared policy of this title." Such support prices may not exceed 110 per cent of parity.

If the support price is put at 90 per cent of parity or below, it is to be at such level between 60 and 90 per cent of parity as will encourage the production of approximately 360 million pounds of shorn wool. The period covered by the act, if not changed in the meantime, is April 1, 1955 to March 31, 1959. Pulled wool and mohair are to be supported at such levels as will maintain normal trading practices and approximately the same percentage of parity for mohair as for shorn wool. No support other than through payments may be provided at more than 90 per cent of parity.

The total amount of such payments may not exceed 70 per cent of the accumulated totals of specific duties on wool and wool products collected after January 1, 1953 under Schedule 11 of the Tariff Act of 1930 as amended.[66] Payments may be made through the marketing agencies to or through whom the grower sold his wool. Payments to individuals or in total which are too small to justify the expense of making them need not be made.

The Secretary of Agriculture is also authorized to enter into or approve agreements between marketing cooperatives, trade associations and others whose memberships are engaged in handling wool, mohair, sheep or goats, or the products thereof, for the purpose of carrying on advertising and sales promotion campaigns. For these purposes, deductions from the returns to growers may be made, subject to specified forms of approval or referendum. In accordance with this section of the act (Section 708) the Secretary of Agriculture submitted for grower referendum a proposal that such deductions be made for promotional purposes. The required percentage of yes votes was obtained and the grower-financed promotional program was authorized in the fall of 1955.

Support Set at 62 Cents for 1955 Wool

Acting in accordance with the provisions of the new act, the Secretary of Agriculture announced in the spring of 1955 an average support level of 62 cents on shorn wool in the grease. This was 106 per cent of parity as of September 15, 1954. It was 8.8 cents per pound, or 16.5 per cent, above the national average loan rate for 1954 and 15 per cent above the national average price received by growers in 1954. The support levels

66. However, no payment was authorized for any wool or mohair produced prior to January 1, 1955.

for 1950 through 1954 had been at 90 per cent of parity. Support commitments for mohair and for pulled wool were on a comparable basis.

No loans or price-support purchases are contemplated under the new procedure. Wool prices are to be allowed to find their own level in a free market, except for the price-supporting effect of the tariff. Supplementary payments on the wool sold in a given year are not to be made until the summer of the year following. At that time a determination will be made of (1) the average price received by growers and (2) the percentage by which this must be increased to yield an average national return equivalent to the announced support price, that is, 62 cents for the 1955 clip.

Each grower, either directly or through his marketing agency, must file a claim at his local county Agricultural Stabilization and Conservation office giving date of sale, net price received and other pertinent information. His statement must be supported by appropriate documents. The national average percentage by which the announced support price exceeds the average return to growers by way of the market is applied to each grower's net sales proceeds to determine the amount of supplementary payment due him. Similar but somewhat more complex arrangements are provided for making supplementary payments on pulled wool.[67]

Administratively, the new program has both advantages and defects, as compared with the one in effect from 1950 through 1954. It avoids the accumulation of stocks in the hands of CCC. On the other hand, it involves more detailed and extensive administrative arrangements in the field since each grower's account must be handled separately. Under the previous plan, only those growers who obtained loans had to be dealt with individually. Under the CCC purchase plan used during the 1940s, even that amount of direct dealing with the individual grower could be dispensed with.

The new plan, under the price provisions announced for 1955, provides a substantially higher price to growers than that authorized in the Agricultural Act of 1949. The price to consumers should be no higher than under the earlier plans. Since CCC was allowed to sell its acquisitions at prices competitively related to those on foreign wools, the prices paid by consumers were presumably about at free-market levels, except for the differentials resulting from tariffs. Whatever influence the tariff rates may have on domestic prices will still apply under the new plan.[68]

67. For details, see *Federal Register,* Vol. 20, No. 63 (March 31, 1955), pp. 2011-14. The specific regulations are, of course, subject to change from time to time. As experience is gained, it may be found desirable to modify and simplify the regulations established for the 1955 clip.

68. However, the public as a whole will, of course, pay a higher price than under the plans previously in effect but in a different form, namely, through a reduction in net returns to the Treasury from wool duties. The total cost will be higher because of the larger subsidy to wool growers.

The loss to the government in the period 1950-1954 was relatively small, only the amount resulting from resale, at lower prices, of wool acquired under the nonrecourse loan programs of 1953 and 1954. Under the new plan, the cost to the government is certain to be larger and may well be as much as $30 to $40 million per year, if wool prices are maintained at as much as 106 per cent of parity or more.[69]

LOOKING TO THE FUTURE

The over-all policies relating to agriculture are obviously in a controversial stage and the shape they will take in the years ahead cannot be stated with any assurance. It is quite possible that wool and sugar, the most important of the deficit crops, will continue to be dealt with in ways that are dissimilar from those relating to the major export crops. The heavy accumulation of stocks of the export crops in the hands of CCC is of great concern to farm leaders of all shades of opinion, and to the general public as well. However, proposals for dealing with the problem differ markedly.

One school of thought places primary emphasis on price and would accept such amount of production restraint as might be required to maintain relatively high prices without increasing materially the stocks now held. For those who hold that view, governmental support of farm prices at 90 per cent or even 100 per cent of parity is a logical and reasonable approach. Generally speaking, the proponents of that policy minimize the significance of price as a guide to volumes and kinds of production.

For the export crops, national farm policy has taken a turn in the direction of lower and more flexible price supports, and more reliance on price as a guide to production. The amount of flexibility introduced is moderate and probably insufficient, in itself, to bring about needed adjustments, particularly in wheat production, except as it may be supplemented by other measures. There is strong opposition even to this amount of relaxation of the high and rigid type of price support carried over from the war period.

The policy adopted in 1954 is likely to be highly controversial for some years to come and will no doubt be affected importantly by changes in relative party strengths. However, the divergence in attitude does not follow party lines closely. In general, there appears to be increasing support for more reliance on open-market prices as a guide to production. This tendency, if it exists, could be quickly reversed if there should be

69. There was a realized gain on wool as reported by CCC, amounting to $142,596 in 1951, and a loss of $86,610 in 1952 (for fiscal years ending June 30 as reported in Commodity Credit Corporation, *Report of Financial Condition and Operations,* December 31, 1952, p. 23). The corresponding losses for 1953 and 1954 were $15,290 and $452,501. (*Ibid.,* April 30, 1955, p. 24.) Consumers have, of course, paid an additional subsidy as a result of the tariffs on imported wools.

a severe decline in farm prices generally, as a result of reduced domestic or foreign demand. The direction taken might also be reversed by new alignments in the Congress.

So far as wool is concerned, the warrant for the high level of support now provided must rest primarily on the assumption that it will affect the amounts produced. It cannot be justified in terms of equity alone.[70]

Quantity to Produce and Level of Support

Assuming that the amount of wool produced will be affected by the prices received, the question arises as to how much domestic wool is needed in terms of national interest. The legislation now in effect implies strongly that, if production is less than 300 million pounds of shorn wool, price incentives should be provided to bring it up to that level; and support at not less than 90 per cent of parity is authorized if production is less than 360 million pounds. If production increases to more than 360 million pounds, support is to be provided at 60 to 90 per cent of parity as the Secretary of Agriculture may decide. The legislation thus provides in a rough way a flexible price-support procedure though one that is geared to relatively high levels of production.

There is no clear basis for deciding how much wool should be produced domestically. Both the 300-million-pound level and the 360-million-pound level have been selected arbitrarily, though with some consideration of past performance. Shorn wool production was approximately 300 million pounds per year in 1909–1911 but was beginning to fall off just prior to World War I. It passed the 300-million-pound mark in 1928 and moved up rather consistently to 388 million pounds in 1942. There is fairly clear evidence in this behavior that wool production does respond to price incentives. During most of that period, except in 1930–1932, wool prices were more favorable than those of most other farm products.

It is evident, however, that domestic wool production cannot, at any reasonable level of prices, be made adequate to supply U.S. needs in wartime or in periods of high domestic demand such as 1945–1955. Domestic production supplied less than half of the wool used in World War I and World War II and imports were in excess of domestic production during the ten-year period following World War II. Hence the United States must count on heavy supplies from abroad in peacetime as well as in war periods, except in times of very low business activity. There is much to be said for having a domestic wool industry that is

70. The unfavorable cost situation in wool production has been noted earlier. However, the price policies in effect in recent years have not, in general, taken account of cost variations for individual products. They have been based on previously existing price relationships. An attempt to base price supports, in terms of equity, on the constantly changing relative cost situations for different commodities would involve the government in impossibly complex and controversial computations that would be almost certain to break down.

large enough so the nation could squeak through in the event of a very severe strain on its wool resources, but it would be difficult if not impossible to make a case for a wool industry big enough to supply all domestic needs.

The reserve of woolen goods in the hands of consumers and the armed forces is now so large that almost all newly produced domestic supplies probably could be channeled to military uses for a time if necessary. In terms of this criterion, an attempt to maintain domestic production at or near 300 million pounds does not appear unreasonable. Question can be raised as to the warrant for artificial stimuli to raise it much above that level, assuming reasonably adequate foresight in stockpiling to meet war contingencies.

It seems clear that an attempt to increase domestic wool production to a level of U.S. self-sufficiency, even if it could be achieved, would be highly uneconomic and almost certainly a disservice to wool producers. Such a policy would result in enormous oversupplies and price gluts in ordinary times. The wool industry can be far more stable if the ups and downs of demand and production can be absorbed by the very extensive world market rather than concentrated within the United States. Except for a minimum supply adequate to meet the most urgent needs, both the U.S. government and U.S. consumers can, for the present at least, be supplied more economically by the very efficient, low-cost producers of Australia, New Zealand and elsewhere than by sheep producers in the United States.

Sheep-Producing Areas Declining

It is not to be expected that wool production in the United States will continue to supply as large a part of U.S. consumption as it did in earlier times when land was much more plentiful and population much smaller. However, there are very large areas in the United States that are probably best used for sheep production. Where they are suited also for raising beef cattle, it can well be argued that they should be shifted to that type of use, except as strategic considerations call for the maintenance of specific minimum levels of wool production. With a rapidly growing population, the increased pressure for larger quantities of beef points to maximum use for that purpose of resources suitable for beef production. Beef cattle, without significant tariff protection, have been able in recent years to bid higher for the use of resources suited to their needs than have sheep, even though the wool industry has long had artificial protection through tariffs.

There is, however, in the present situation a significant argument that has seldom been brought out which points in the opposite direction. Much of the Plains area has been recently converted to wheat production, a product that is obviously in long supply. As a part of the wheat adjustment program, there is need for re-extensifying the agriculture on sizable parts of that area.[71] If livestock production can be made relatively more attractive and crop production relatively less attractive, there is little doubt that considerable areas in the Plains region could be used to better national advantage, except in wartime, in the production of livestock, including sheep, than in grain production. This is especially true for those areas that are subject to high risks because of frequent droughts.

Here a well-organized livestock industry, with adequate supplemental resources in the way of associated irrigated feed-producing areas, would almost certainly be more stable and more socially desirable than the very hazardous types of grain production now carried on. Assuming a reasonable amount of responsiveness to price incentives, adjustments can be encouraged by raising the prices of alternative products as well as by lowering the prices of products that are being overproduced.

The two types of incentive can be used conjointly, and the encouragement of cattle and sheep production as a replacement for some of the grain production of the Plains region may be no more expensive than other measures that might be considered. Almost certainly it would be a more defensible approach than to continue heavy expenditures for the production of wheat that is not needed or desired.

Production Efficiency Could Be Increased

Another approach to the sheep and wool problem that many feel has been neglected is that of research designed to increase the efficiency of the sheep industry itself. In terms of improvements in production per unit of input, the sheep industry stands at the bottom of the list for the period 1930–1933 to 1950–1953. During that period output per unit of input for wheat, small-grain and livestock farms in the Northern Plains area increased by 69 per cent; for cotton farms in the Mississippi Delta, 49 per cent; for hog-beef farms in the Corn Belt, 32 per cent; and for dairy farms in the Central Northeast states, 13 per cent. In the same period output per unit of input on sheep ranches in the Northern Plains area not only did not increase but dropped back to only 95 per cent of what it had been in 1930–1933.[72]

This points to the need for intensive effort to improve the efficiency of sheep production and to increase the attractiveness and salability of the products derived from sheep. A recent interagency wool study group of the U.S. Department of Agriculture describes a number of fields of research which offer promise as ways of increasing the efficiency and

71. That is, for converting it back to types of agriculture in which both the input per acre and the return per acre will be smaller than if it is used for crop production.

72. *United States Agriculture: Perspectives and Prospects,* a report prepared for the American Assembly, Graduate School of Business, Columbia University, 1955, p. 36.

profitableness of the sheep industry.[73] These include, among others, studies looking to more effective control of parasites and infectious diseases, intensified research on nutritional problems, improved breeding, range improvement, control of predators and so on.

The study group also outlined a number of promising fields of study in the marketing and processing phases of the wool industry, including those which would make wool fabrics more attractive to consumers and thus might check the shift to substitute fibers used for similar purposes. Included also was the proposal, later incorporated in the National Wool Act of 1954, for an expanded and improved program of public relations and promotion.

These and other measures designed to improve efficiency in wool production and to increase the demand for wool undoubtedly merit serious consideration in an industry that has lagged so far behind in technological progress. Action along these lines obviously cannot be expected to bring quick or sensational gains and hence is not a solution for acute or short-run problems. Over a longer period it may well prove to be among the most important steps that can be taken in creating and maintaining a sound and prosperous wool-growing industry.

How High Should the Price Be?

If the purpose of the support provided is to influence production, the level of support chosen obviously should be based on its effect on production. This is the stated objective of the current program. It is, in effect, an experiment in forward pricing. As such, it has numerous precedents, mainly in the programs put into effect in the two world war periods. The World War I wheat program was in part a price-stabilizing operation. In part, however, it was also a guarantee of an announced price designed to bring about increased production. Somewhat similar devices were used in the government's pledge to try to maintain a specified relationship between the price of hogs and the price of corn. In the early part of World War II, Secretary Wickard pledged himself to support a hog price of $9.00 per hundredweight at a time when hogs were selling at about $6.00. The price supports authorized for the Steagall commodities and some of the incentive payments provided were of similar character.

A forward pricing approach is quite different from that of supporting prices at a fixed percentage of parity. The fixed percentage of parity looks to past price relationships, regardless of whether the resulting

73. *Achieving a Sound Domestic Wool Industry,* a report to the President of the United States from the Secretary of Agriculture, prepared by an Interagency Wool Study group in the Department of Agriculture, December 1953; see especially pp. 44–53. The report was prepared mainly as an aid to the President in arriving at conclusions in regard to the various proposals for assistance to the wool industry that had been or were expected to be presented to him at about that time.

output is too much or too little. Forward prices and incentive prices presumably seek to guide production in desired directions. They may imply differential downward adjustments in price supports as well as differential upward revisions. Tariffs, by implication at least, have similar objectives though their use for this purpose has long been severely distorted by pressures designed to achieve larger returns for the groups concerned, without reference to the desirability of increasing or decreasing production.

The Wool Act of 1954 permits forward prices as high as 110 per cent of parity so long as domestic production does not exceed 300 million pounds. Obviously, there will be wide differences of opinion as to how high a support price for wool is warranted and how large a production is needed. These are matters that can be settled only by the Congress, though it is evident that self-interest, group pressures and other factors not in keeping with the national interest will continue to influence the decisions made.

If, instead of an incentive-price approach, the criterion of equitableness of return is used, there appears to be no important reason why wool should be treated differently from other farm commodities. Under existing price-support policies, that would imply an upper limit of 90 per cent of parity and possible downward modifications of that level if stocks become redundant. Under this criterion, it would be hard to make a case for support of wool prices at a level in excess of 90 per cent of parity.[74]

Without far more detailed study than is feasible here, it is impossible to measure accurately the relative returns from sheep production and those from competing products. The index of prices received by farmers for meat animals as a whole stood at 292 in 1954 (1910–1914=100); the index for wool at 298.[75] It appears, therefore, that the increase authorized in the 1955 price of wool, if warranted, must be justified in terms of the announced policy of stimulating wool production, rather than on grounds of equity.

The level of support provided for wool rests, therefore, on a congres-

74. The problem of equitable returns to sheep producers is further complicated by the fact that wool producers have income from lambs and mutton as well. The prices of wool did not advance proportionately with those of other farm products in the period 1946–1949 but prices were high in 1950 and 1951. The drop in 1952 was to a level roughly in line with the prices of other farm products. However, even in the early postwar years, the price of lambs increased sharply though not at so fast a rate as for beef cattle. The price of lambs at Chicago (December to April average) stood at $14.71 per 100 pounds in 1945. By 1948 it was up to $26.92, an increase of about 83 per cent. The price of choice steers increased in the same period by 150 per cent. Sheep prices, at Chicago, increased about 57 per cent. (*Agricultural Statistics, 1953*, pp. 348, 374.) Meat animals as a whole rose from an index of 207 in 1945 (1910–1914=100) to 340 in 1950, an increase of 64 per cent. They were up to 411 in 1951 but dropped back to 358 in 1952. (*Ibid.*, p. 602.)

75. U.S. Department of Agriculture, *Agricultural Prices,* May 27, 1955, pp. 50, 53.

sional determination of national need.[76] A more general adoption of the policy established for wool in 1955 would constitute a very significant reversal of past policy: a shift to forward pricing with price supports related to officially determined national needs. Such a policy, which has been strongly advocated in some circles, would imply reductions in the levels of support for some commodities, notably wheat and probably cotton, as well as the type of increase authorized for wool. However, the flexible support program authorized, within limits, in the Agricultural Act of 1954 does point in that direction.[77]

Relation to Wool Tariffs

If the policy established in 1954 is continued, the importance of tariffs to wool producers presumably will decline. Assuming a willingness on the part of the government to support wool prices on an incentive basis, the level of tariff would apparently be immaterial to wool growers as long as 70 per cent of the amount of duty collected is adequate for carrying out the program.[78] However, it is scarcely to be expected that the interest of wool growers in the tariff will suddenly be eliminated.[79] The new arrangement makes the industry somewhat more heavily dependent on decisions made by the Congress or by government officials. These probably can be more easily changed than can the rates of duty on wool.[80] However, the forward pricing arrangement would seem to

76. Or, of course, on a recognition of sufficient political strength on the part of wool producers to maintain preferential treatment for wool.

77. On the basis of logic, ignoring political considerations, the justification for support of wool prices at a level as high as 106 per cent of parity still rests, of course, on the conclusions reached by the individual, the group or the Congress as to how much domestic wool production is needed in the national interest.

78. It is quite conceivable that the cost of the program could be high enough to require more than 70 per cent of the income from wool tariffs. If that should happen, the wool growers would, of course, have a strong incentive for advocating the maintenance or increase of wool tariffs.

79. That wool growers have not yet fully adjusted their thinking to the new program is evident from some of the current comments of their representatives. See, for example, "Wool Act Lowering Prices, Says Wilson," *California Livestock News,* June 14, 1955, pp. 1, 3, which is quoted from an article by J. Byron Wilson, Secretary of the Wyoming Wool Growers Association in the *Wyoming Wool Grower* of June 4, 1955. Here it is suggested that the wool act has resulted in a reduction of domestic wool prices in relation to those of foreign wools, duty-paid. There does not appear to be any logical reason why manufacturers would pay either less or more for domestic wool under the new program than under the one previously in effect when CCC was presumably releasing stocks at prices that were competitive with those of foreign wools.

Whether this be true or not, the returns to growers under the 1955 type of program would not be affected. It is probable, however, that the market has not yet fully adjusted itself to the new set of conditions posed by the legislation of 1954 and it seems likely that more stable relationships between the prices of domestic and foreign wools will develop unless the situation should again be disturbed by depression or war. It is to be expected that domestic wool prices will be more sensitive to temporary influences under the free-market pricing now in effect than in the period when government nonrecourse loans tended to keep them at or above the support prices established by the government.

80. Proposed changes in the tariff on wool, whether upward or downward, have nearly always encountered strong resistance. Wool growers have long advocated higher

assure wool growers of more stable prices than those that have prevailed in the past when principal reliance was on the level of tariff protection.

The arrangement put into effect in 1955 does open the way for tariff adjustments in line with the government's announced policy of promoting freer world trade without at the same time cutting down support for an important industry that has long been encouraged and maintained by means of tariffs, provided the government is willing to accept the loss of revenue and the costs involved in supporting the price of wool.[81] Furthermore, it has improved relations between U.S. sheepmen and those in Australia. The two have many interests in common but in the past they have tended to be pitted against each other because of the tariff issue. With that bone of contention pushed into the background, there may be opportunities for mutually advantageous teamwork on the part of growers in the two areas instead of the antagonisms and distrust that have so often affected their relations in the past. This approach, if applied to all deficit crops now relying on tariff protection, could be an expensive undertaking. However, it is already, in essence, being used in supporting the two major deficit crops, sugar and wool.[82]

If such a policy were to be applied to all protected industries, farm and nonfarm, the costs and complications would undoubtedly be on such a scale as to be of major concern to the Congress and the general public. Hence, except as a national need for the increase or maintenance of production can be shown, it is difficult to justify such procedures merely because the products concerned are produced on farms.

The protection afforded by the tariff, on which so much reliance has been placed in the past, has operated, so far as it was effective, as a sales tax paid by consumers for both domestic and foreign wools. That part

---

tariffs and have succeeded in having hearings held by the Tariff Commission several times in recent years, and many bitter attacks have been made on the wool tariffs by groups opposed to them. The wool grower organizations and representatives from the sheep-producing states have not been able to get increases in tariffs in the period since 1930 and only one decrease has been made, that of 1948 when the duty was reduced from 34 cents to 25.5 cents per clean pound. That adjustment was made under the powers granted to the President under the Trade Agreement Act of 1934 as amended and renewed by succeeding congresses. For critical views about the demands of the wool growers for increased tariff protection and other subsidies, see "The Trouble with U.S. Wool . . . ," *Fortune Magazine,* January 1947. See also Wilcox, *op. cit.,* pp. 230–34.

81. The new policy also makes possible a pricing arrangement that should tend to improve the competitive position of wool as compared with that of synthetic fibers. Per capita consumption of wool has declined sharply from the wartime highs (from 5.14 pounds in 1946 to 2.93 pounds in 1952). Consumption in 1952 was slightly below the 1939 level (2.93 as compared with 2.99). (*Agricultural Statistics, 1953,* p. 80.) It is obviously important from the standpoint of the wool-growing industry to maintain price relationships that will not encourage unduly the substitution of synthetic fibers for wool in the clothing industry.

82. It does not follow, of course, that equally strong arguments could be made for high supports on the minor deficit crops. Also, these other groups almost certainly would not be able to muster as much political strength as can be brought to bear by the growers of wool and sugar.

collected as duties on imported wools has been income to the U.S. Treasury. The part which consisted of higher prices to domestic wool growers has gone to them in higher prices.

It would be a mistake, however, to assume that the tariff has been continuously effective in raising prices to U.S. wool producers or, when it is effective, that prices are necessarily raised by the full amount of the duty. The wool market is very complex and many factors affect the spread between foreign and domestic prices at any given time. It seems entirely clear that high tariffs have not in the past operated to maintain wool prices at times when the industry was most in need of assistance. However, they have apparently helped the industry to make quicker recoveries following severe slumps than the recoveries that have characterized the major export crops. In the event of a major war, it can be taken for granted that wool almost all through the world will become a state-traded commodity. Hence the levels of tariff in effect at such times will be of little significance.

CCC's Place in the Program

Since the market for raw wool may at times be severely depressed by a sharp falling off of demand, there is continuing need for stand-by arrangements whereby domestically grown wool can be acquired and held until mill demand picks up. For this, an organization of the CCC type is well suited. It has much larger resources and more flexibility than the Farm Board stabilization corporations that preceded it. Also, it can hold stocks for longer periods. There is abundant evidence that rather large wool stocks can be liquidated in an orderly and constructive way if the holding agency has sufficient time and financial resources. The successful and orderly liquidation of U.S. and world stocks of wool after World War II is a case in point.

A stabilizing operation of that kind might be desirable and helpful even under the type of program initiated in 1955, though not as important to growers as if the government were not supporting prices. Such an acquisition and holding operation could reduce government losses from a temporary glut in the wool market, which might result in very low prices and correspondingly high payments out of government funds.

Because of the tendency for wool prices to recover as soon as pipeline stocks have been used up, stabilizing purchases of that kind may not involve much loss provided they are handled in such a way as merely to ease the impact of large but temporary fluctuations in demand rather than as a method of keeping prices continually above their open-market levels. Wool acquired in that way must usually be held for more than a year and worked off gradually. Hence that type of operation is not well suited to the financing arrangements customarily used by cooperative and other selling agencies in their efforts to carry out "orderly marketing" within the production year.

The top-heavy stocks of the National Wool Marketing Corporation in 1930–1932 probably could have been worked off without much loss if the operation could have been extended over a period of two or three years. But financial arrangements were not set up with that in mind and could not well be, under ordinary commercial and government loan agency types of financing. By the fall months of 1933, wool prices to farmers had recovered to within about 5 cents of the 1929 levels and liquidation could probably have been carried out without severe loss to the government or much adverse effect on the market.[83]

In 1921 also, if there had been in existence an agency of the CCC type, wool which was virtually unsalable could have been absorbed temporarily and probably could have been moved later with only very moderate loss, if not carried in at unwarrantedly high prices. While wool was selling at only 15.5 cents in July 1921, it was up to 32.5 cents a year later.[84]

Even under the type of program put into effect in 1955, growers may find price-stabilizing activities helpful under some conditions. If wool production should reach a level such that supports are put at less than 90 per cent of parity, growers would very likely be adversely affected by a very stagnant market and might then find it highly advantageous to have some stand-by arrangement for the absorption and holding of temporarily redundant supplies. If wool price supports were to be discontinued or lowered drastically, some provision of that kind would become especially important for wool because of the predominant influence of changes in demand as compared with the effect of fluctuations in supply.

Cost of the Program

The cost of the wool program during the war years can hardly be regarded as meaningful in a price-support sense. Many of the steps taken were for the purpose of assuring adequate supplies for military and civilian use and as a means of stabilizing conditions in the British Commonwealth of Nations and elsewhere. However, a substantial con-

83. It should be noted that the statements here made pertain particularly to wool, a deficit crop. Such a plan is worthy of serious consideration even for crops not ordinarily imported, but it is not likely that excess stocks of those crops could be worked off as smoothly and quickly as surplus stocks of wool. It is also necessary to re-emphasize the comment that such a program is suitable for stabilization activities but not for keeping prices continuously above the market.

84. Psychological factors must, of course, be considered in situations of that kind. Heavy stocks depress prices, but that effect is not likely to be important unless the trade expects the stocks to be moved by a certain time. Where financing is through commercial channels, the financing agencies usually exert pressure for early liquidation. Hence the tendency for buyers to hold off and drive hard bargains. These considerations would not necessarily apply to any great extent if the stocks were held by CCC or some similar agency. It would be important, however, that liquidation policies be carefully devised and fully understood by the trade.

sideration in the operations relating to domestic wool was that of supporting prices to growers and avoiding a disastrous break in prices after the war ended.

Only negligible losses were incurred by CCC in the years 1933–1941. The only program in effect in those years was the wool loan authorization of 1938 and 1939. The total amount loaned was less than $17 million and the realized loss amounted to only $176.[85] However, the loan level in that period was only 75 per cent of a parity level that was lower than it would be if computed under the formulae now being used. Between July 1, 1941 and June 30, 1946, realized losses amounted to $15.8 million. But a much larger potential loss had been incurred as a result of building up stocks in CCC ownership. This showed up in the succeeding period, July 1, 1946 to June 30, 1951, when realized losses came to $76.3 million. Wool, unlike cotton, did not experience a sharp price rise in the immediate postwar years. This was due, of course, to the abundant supplies available in both the U.S. and world markets. Prices did rise sharply in 1950 and 1951, but by that time the wartime stocks held by CCC had been closed out so it did not have postwar gains on wool to offset losses as it did on some other commodities, notably cotton.

Since market prices and CCC loan rates were very nearly in balance in 1952 and 1953, and the amounts of wool taken over under the loan programs were small, losses incurred by CCC were very moderate, $86,610 in 1952 and $15,290 in 1953. Losses mounted again in 1954, reaching $452,501 for that year. The over-all cost as reported by CCC for the period 1933 through 1954 was $93.3 million.[86] Though this is considerably less than the $266 million on wheat (and the much larger loss in prospect on wheat now held), or the $267 million loss on cotton, the amount in proportion to the size of the industry is very much greater. Cotton accounted for about 8 per cent of gross cash receipts from farming in 1952, wheat for about 6.5 per cent, whereas wool and mohair accounted for less than four tenths of 1 per cent.[87]

Also, the cost borne by way of the Commodity Credit Corporation does not reflect the full cost to the public of the contributions made to wool producers. Part of the cost is paid in the form of higher prices resulting from tariffs. It is difficult if not impossible to measure the effect

85. Data here shown are from Commodity Credit Corporation, *Report of Financial Condition and Operations as of April 30, 1955,* p. 24. They do not include costs incurred by the Defense Supplies Corporation, a purely wartime operation which was closed out soon after the end of the war. (However, the National Wool Marketing Corporation sold over 300 million pounds of foreign wools for Defense Supplies Corporation in the period 1944–1947. See U. S. Department of Agriculture, Farmer Cooperative Service, *Sales Method Problems of Wool Cooperatives,* June 1954, p. 2.)

86. However, CCC still held, as of June 30, 1955, 152 million pounds of wool acquired under the 1952–1954 price-support programs. (*The Wool Situation,* August 11, 1955, p. 13.) Additional losses on the wool so held were probable.

87. If the wool crop were of a size comparable to that of the wheat crop, and if losses were proportional to those incurred in the 1933–1954 period, the cost to CCC would have been in the order of $1.8 billion.

of the tariff on prices to wool producers and wool consumers. That is especially true for a period like that of the 1940s when state trading, stockpiling for war, price ceilings and many other factors were involved. Even in more normal times, the tariff is not uniformly effective in raising the level of domestic wool prices. For short periods in times of severe depression its effect may be negligible.

If we assume as a very rough approximation that wool tariffs are as much as 75 to 80 per cent effective in ordinary times, the annual subsidy provided to U.S. growers by this means would be in the order of $25 million (20 cents per pound on about 130 million pounds, clean basis).[88] This, of course, does not reflect the full cost of the tariff to U.S. consumers since the price of imported wool as well as domestic wool is increased in a similar way. However, the higher price paid on imported wools as a result of the tariff is essentially an excise tax on wool consumers, with the proceeds going to the U.S. Treasury, not to wool growers. Also, it should be recognized that the price increases thus brought about are pyramided in the manufacture and sale of woolen goods and that other tariffs apply on manufactured wool.

The cost to the Treasury of the wool program undertaken in 1955 cannot be estimated with any assurance at this time. Presumably the price to growers will be about 8 cents above the price prevailing in the market in 1954. This, together with a corresponding increase on mohair, would indicate a cost of something in the order of $30 to $35 million for the 1955 program.[89]

Both of these estimates obviously are subject to very wide margins of error. However, if we accept them as being roughly in accord with the facts, it would appear that the people of the United States are now providing annual subsidies to the wool-growing industry that are in the order of $50 million to $60 million. That cost must be weighed against (1) the importance to the United States of maintaining domestic wool production at the levels set up as goals in the legislation of recent years, (2) just treatment to growers who have made large investments under protective policies established in the past, and (3) encouragement that may be desirable in converting to other uses cropland now used in

88. The full duty in effect, since 1948, is 25½ cents (clean). Prior to 1948 it was 34 cents. During 1953, domestic wools were selling from as low as 77 per cent of the price of comparable imported wools (duty-paid) for some of the finer wools to as high as 115 per cent on some of the coarser South American wools. (See Albert M. Hermie, *Prices of Wool at Boston,* A Comparison of Prices of Domestic and Imported Wools, U.S. Agricultural Marketing Service, Agriculture Information Series, Bulletin 118, 1954, pp. 27–41.)

89. If wool tariffs were to be lowered and if prices received in the market by domestic wool producers were correspondingly reduced, the cost of the direct subsidy would, of course, be larger since the government has pledged itself to make up the difference between the average price received and a 62-cent average. However, costs to consumers for both domestic and imported wools would be reduced. Treasury receipts would be smaller because of the lower tariff on imported wools. Thus the drain on general revenues of the government would be larger than the increase in direct payments to growers.

growing wheat and other surplus crops and the maintenance of prosperity in communities built up in areas that are heavily dependent on sheep production.

World Wool Situation Roughly in Balance

The world wool situation appears to be roughly in balance at about present levels of prices (tariffs considered) or a little lower. World production has been increasing moderately in recent years. Inventories are about normal and the severe distortions in market conditions that grew out of World War II and the Korean War seem largely to have disappeared. With a growing world population, it would seem that increasing demand should absorb such amounts of increased production as appear to be in prospect, unless depression or war should again throw production, demand and stocks out of balance or synthetics should make heavier inroads on the markets customarily supplied by wool.

Whether the incentive prices now provided will actually stimulate U.S. production materially, only time will tell. If they do, the change is likely to be gradual. A continuing policy problem will be that of how much subsidy, in addition to the tariff, the nation feels warranted in providing as a means of maintaining or increasing wool production and what level of wool production is actually required in the national interest.

9

Marketing Agreements: Fruits and Vegetables

DURING THE 1920s, the thinking in regard to methods of aiding agriculture was in a formative stage. Many different approaches were presented and discussed. Among them were proposals for strong national and regional producer cooperatives, operating without government assistance; the several versions of the McNary-Haugen and export debenture plans for subsidizing exports; and, in the late 1920s, the plan adopted by the Federal Farm Board.

As a result of these efforts and controversies, two rather distinct approaches to the farm problem emerged, particularly from 1931 on. One group, keenly aware of the difficulties encountered by the Federal Farm Board, stressed control of production. The other placed more emphasis on control and improvement of marketing procedures.[1]

As the inadequacy of the procedures available to the Federal Farm Board became evident, and especially after the elections of 1932, congressional representatives and farm leaders undertook the drafting of new legislation, which was adopted in the spring of 1933. Here the primary emphasis was on production control, especially for the major export crops. George Peek, the leader of the drive for the McNary-Haugen Plan and, later, first administrator of the Agricultural Adjustment Administration, was not convinced that controls on production were necessary or desirable. He still placed principal emphasis on improvements in distributive and processing practices and, of course, would have preferred some type of export subsidy financed by an equalization fee to any of the plans actually adopted.

Emergence of the Marketing Agreement Idea

Considering a marketing agreement approach preferable to production controls, Peek brought up at a late stage in the drafting of the Agricultural Adjustment Act a proposal for including an authorization for the

1. For a more detailed discussion of the way in which these divergent points of view developed, see Edwin G. Nourse, *Marketing Agreements under the AAA,* The Brookings Institution, Washington, 1935, pp. 1–23. Also see the more general account in Murray R. Benedict, *Farm Policies of the United States, 1790–1950,* Twentieth Century Fund, New York, 1953, Chapters 9–12.

Secretary of Agriculture to enter into marketing agreements with producers, handlers and processors of farm products. Stress was to be placed on aggressive efforts to dispose of surpluses through every available outlet and on agreements with processors and distributors that would result in the highest feasible prices to growers in any given situation of market outlets and marketing conditions.

This general philosophy was in accord with the philosophy shaping up in a companion measure which was to apply to nonfarm businesses, namely, the National Industrial Recovery Act. It discarded almost completely the long-accepted policy of government opposition to combinations to fix prices and restrain trade, and proposed instead that the government itself participate in and approve combinations of that kind. Presumably, the public interest would be protected by the fact that agreements would have to be approved and supervised by public agencies, thus insuring against antisocial types of action. In other words, the plan then proposed, and later adopted, accepted the view that cartel types of arrangement could, under certain conditions, be beneficial to society if properly managed and controlled.

The Peek Amendment was accepted by the drafters of the Agricultural Adjustment Act but in more inclusive form than Peek had contemplated.[2] It authorized the Secretary of Agriculture to enter into marketing agreements relating to *any* agricultural commodity or product thereof, thus extending the possibility of direct benefits to a much wider constituency than was contemplated under the crop adjustment portions of the act.

Antitrust and Licensing Features

To protect participants in such agreements from prosecution under the antitrust laws, the act declared that "the making of any such agreement shall not be held to be in violation of any of the antitrust laws of the United States, and any such agreement shall be deemed to be lawful." [3] At the suggestion of Secretary Wallace, a further provision was added which was to prove much more controversial than the marketing agreement idea itself. This section, 8 (3), authorized the Secretary "to issue licenses permitting processors, associations of producers, and others to engage in the handling, in the current of interstate or foreign

2. The amendment was worked out in collaboration with Frederick P. Lee and Charles J. Brand, who were helping the committee draft the bill. Under the original plan, the marketing agreement approach would have been limited to the "basic" commodities, with other grains and meat animals included if they were subsequently declared to be "basic" commodities. However, the American Farm Bureau Federation, largely at the urging of the California federation, moved to have the act broadened to include "nonbasic" crops. The California federation represented growers of many specialty crops, some of which had already been handled under unofficial procedures of somewhat similar type, and later under the California Prorate Act, which was passed in the spring of 1933. (See Nourse, *op. cit.*, pp. 15 and 127.)

3. The act also stated that the parties to such agreements would be eligible for loans from the Reconstruction Finance Corporation for aid in carrying out the agreements.

commerce, of any agricultural commodity or product thereof." Such licenses were to be "subject to such terms and conditions . . . as may be necessary to eliminate unfair practices or charges that prevent or tend to prevent the effectuation of the declared policy (as stated in the Agricultural Adjustment Act) and the restoration of normal economic conditions in the marketing of such commodities or products and the financing thereof." [4]

The Secretary could suspend or revoke such licenses, after due notice and opportunity for hearing, and his action was to be final, if in accordance with law. Any person engaged in such handling was to be subject to a fine of not more than $1,000 for each day during which the violation continued. A further provision required licensees under the act to furnish reports on quantities bought and sold and the prices thereof and to keep such records as the Secretary might require.

Business Groups Opposed to Licensing Powers

It was natural that the grant of such broad powers to the Secretary of Agriculture would be opposed by the business groups likely to be affected. Some of the proponents of the measure, including Secretary Wallace, stressed the necessity of having some such procedure in order to make the marketing agreement plan work. Others looked upon it as a means whereby aggressive and far-reaching reforms might be achieved. Though strongly opposed by some groups, the licensing section was included in the act as passed, together with the more general provisions described above. Administrative procedures and penalties provided in Sections 8, 9 and 10 of the Federal Trade Commission Act of September 26, 1914 were made applicable to the jurisdiction, powers and duties of the Secretary of Agriculture in administering this portion of the act.

The authority for licensing handlers, processors and others could be used even in the absence of a marketing agreement and thus was regarded as a means of strengthening the Secretary's hand in effecting agreements that would be acceptable to him, and also as a way of achieving regulation in situations where agreements could not be effectuated. The granting of these broad powers, and the lack of unanimity in concepts as to their objectives, caused this section of the act to be a center of controversy throughout the early years of the program. There was widespread criticism of the marketing agreement features of the act of 1933, and some doubt as to their legality. As a result the legislation was extensively modified in 1935. However, the earlier marketing agreement programs were carried out under the original provisions. The subsequent modifications are therefore discussed in later sections.

4. If not in conflict with then existing acts of Congress or regulations pursuant thereto.

Administrative Arrangements—First Period

In view of the known preference of the first AAA administrator, George Peek, for an approach oriented largely to the marketing phase of the farm problem, it is not surprising that marketing agreements came in for early attention. Four main divisions of the Agricultural Adjustment Administration were set up, one of which was the Processing and Marketing Division. The other three were Production, Finance, and Information and Publicity. For three of the commodity groups, wheat, cotton, and corn and hogs, there were corresponding sections in the Processing and Marketing Division and in the Production Division. The Processing and Marketing Division also had sections on Licensing and Enforcement, Foreign Trade, Food Products, Fisheries and Alcoholic Beverages.[5]

Shortly after Chester Davis became AAA administrator in December 1933, the plan of organization was drastically overhauled. All of the commodities were brought under a single Commodities Division, which carried out both the production and marketing activities. This meant de-emphasizing the marketing phase of the program and putting more emphasis on production control, at least in respect to those commodities for which production control programs were authorized.[6]

Proposals for using the marketing agreement features of the act began to pour in as soon as it came into effect. They came from processors and handlers, many of whom had opposed the marketing agreement legislation, as well as from the original proponents of that method of attacking the farm problem. The reasons back of these proposals varied widely. One was that crops were already well advanced and it was evident that the slower, long-term program of production adjustment could not have much effect on 1933 output. Another was that processors and handlers, fearful of oversupplied markets and cutthroat pricing practices, saw in the code and marketing agreement procedures a means whereby markets could be stabilized and marketing margins protected.

Within the AAA, and in the NRA as well, some of the government representatives were eager to make a start on reforms directed toward more extensive regulation of prices, margins and practices. Others, both in and out of government, were earnestly hoping to find a way of dealing with the farm price problem that would be quicker and less cumbersome

5. Since the agricultural processing industries were eligible to apply for codes under the NRA, Administrator Peek and Co-Administrator Brand asked the President to put jurisdiction over codes for the agricultural processing and handling groups in the hands of the Secretary of Agriculture, to avoid confusion and overlapping. This was done. However, shortly after Mr. Peek's resignation as administrator of the AAA (December 8, 1933), the codes covering agricultural commodities beyond first processing were transferred back to NRA.

6. See charts of the 1933 and 1934 organizations in Nourse, *op. cit.*, pp. 26, 27. There were, of course, other extensive changes in AAA organization in succeeding periods, but they are not relevant to this discussion.

than individual contracting with each of the hundreds of thousands of farmers growing the major crops. Some of the fluid milk cooperatives felt that the licensing feature of the act might enable them to overcome the difficulties arising from sales by nonmembers and price cutting by distributors. Still others saw in the marketing agreements a way of supplementing the longer-term programs or perhaps even of avoiding the need for processing taxes and benefit payments.

Fluid Milk and Basic Crop Agreements

Between August 1 and December 20, 1933, fifteen marketing agreements relating to fluid milk were put into effect. The Chicago agreement was terminated on December 20, 1933 and the New Orleans agreement on February 1, 1934, at the request of the participants. The other thirteen were terminated by the Secretary of Agriculture on February 1, 1934.[7] These and the later milk agreements are discussed in Chapter 11, which deals with the fluid milk program as a whole, and hence they are omitted in the following discussion, which is limited to the programs relating to fruits, vegetables and other specialty crops.

The marketing agreements for basic crops, and others closely related to them, are also omitted since they are covered in the chapters dealing with those commodities. These include the agreements pertaining to wheat, rice, tobacco, potatoes, peanuts and naval stores. In addition, nineteen codes were approved in the period 1933–1935, most of them for commodities not within the scope of this discussion.[8]

1933–1935, Tryout of New Approaches

The period 1933–1935 can be regarded, on the whole, as one of experimenting with a great variety of untried methods for relieving the distress in agriculture. Not only in the market agreement phase but in the major crop programs as well, mechanisms, personnel and policies had to be developed at top speed, and many assumptions had to be made as to the underlying philosophy that should govern decisions. With hundreds of administrators occupied with scores of commodities, each presenting a special set of problems, it is not surprising that inconsistencies, operating difficulties and questions of legal interpretation soon came to the fore.

The widely divergent views of Secretary Wallace and Administrator Peek with respect to the place and functions of marketing agreements made consistent and well-considered policies difficult to arrive at. Wallace looked upon the licensing provision as a means whereby the pyramiding of processing taxes could be avoided by controlling trade

7. *Ibid.*, p. 50.

8. The codes dealt with such things as the imported-date-packing industry, alcoholic beverages, commercial and breeder hatcheries, grain exchanges, and so on.

practices. Peek, who had long advocated diversion rather than production control, was more interested in using marketing agreements as a way of disposing of export surpluses in the world markets at prices below those maintained in the domestic markets. He regarded licenses as a device for regulating processors' practices and reducing margins, which he felt were unduly high.[9]

Neither of these views fitted well with the set of problems shortly to be faced by the administrators of the marketing agreement programs. In such complex marketing situations as those relating to fluid milk and other perishable commodities, diversion to export markets was not involved and even control over processing and handling charges was not a primary consideration.

Under the fluid milk agreements, it soon became evident that the spread between the prices of fluid milk and the prices attainable from converting milk into manufactured dairy products had been widened, thus increasing the problem of enforcement. The law was vague as to what provisions could or could not be enforced, and the ever-present problem of interstate versus intrastate business made the administrators hesitant about bringing violation cases into court. Presumably, federal control could be exercised over interstate shipments but not over intrastate transactions. Yet many of the fluid milk markets were so constituted that intrastate shipments could make unworkable the provisions relating to interstate shipments.

The fluid milk phase of the program went through several stages, each representing a new approach to the problem.[10] As the broader agricultural program developed, especially after the resignation of Administrator Peek, the marketing agreement provisions of the legislation came more and more to be looked upon as a means of assisting the producers of specialty crops and perishables rather than as an aid to growers of the major field crops (see other chapters). Furthermore, since important changes in the laws governing marketing agreements were made in 1935 and after, primary emphasis in the discussion here presented is on the programs of the later years rather than on those of the early period.

The Amendments of 1935

Violations of marketing agreement provisions became increasingly difficult to cope with. The ability of the Secretary to enforce regulations through the licensing powers assigned to him came to be widely doubted

9. Edwin G. Nourse, Joseph S. Davis and John D. Black, *Three Years of the Agricultural Adjustment Administration,* The Brookings Institution, Washington, 1937, pp. 218–19.

10. See Chapter 11 of this study and *Three Years of the Agricultural Adjustment Administration,* pp. 224–27; also Nourse, *op. cit.,* pp. 48 and 49. For a more extended description and analysis of the dairy programs of this period, see John D. Black, *The Dairy Industry and the AAA,* The Brookings Institution, Washington, 1935.

after some of the lower courts held against the government in enforcement cases.[11] A lack of full agreement between the Agricultural Adjustment Administration and the Department of Justice, and within the Adjustment Administration itself, further complicated the situation. Enforcement virtually broke down following the unfavorable opinion of the Supreme Court in the Schechter case (May 28, 1935), which terminated the NRA program.[12]

As early as 1934, the administrators of the AAA and the Department of Agriculture had sought, unsuccessfully, to have the marketing agreement provisions of the law amended and strengthened. By the summer of 1935, it had become evident that the law as then drawn could not be made workable. Part of the difficulty, from a legal standpoint, lay in the delegation of powers to the Secretary of Agriculture and, through him, to local supervisory bodies. In the Schechter case, which involved similar legal concepts, Mr. Justice Cardoza, in his concurring opinion, had referred to the (NIRA) act as "delegation run wild."

To overcome these difficulties, the Congress included in the August 24, 1935 amendments to the Agricultural Adjustment Act several changes in the legislation pertaining to marketing agreements. The most important change was that which discontinued the licensing authority and substituted a "Secretary's order" procedure. The Secretary could issue an "order" regulating marketing operations in interstate commerce, either as implementation of a marketing agreement or without a marketing agreement. This specified that each such action must be an official act of the Secretary and thus avoided the vagueness and diffusion of authority that had characterized the earlier procedure. It also was somewhat less punitive. A violator could be fined but could not be put out of business by having his license withdrawn.

The act as amended was also much more narrowly restricted than in its original form. It now could apply only to "milk, fruits (including pecans and walnuts but not including apples and not including fruits, other than olives, for canning), tobacco, vegetables (not including vegetables, other than asparagus, for canning), soybeans, and naval stores as included in the Naval Stores Act." [13] However, the wording pertaining to interstate commerce was broadened by stating that such orders shall regulate only "such handling of such agricultural commodity as is in the current of interstate commerce, or which directly burdens, obstructs, or affects, interstate or foreign commerce in such commodity or product thereof." [14]

The specific authorizations were in three parts, one relating to milk,

11. See Nourse, *op. cit.*, pp. 267–90.

12. *A.L.A. Schechter Poultry Corporation* v. *U.S.*, 295 U.S. 495 (1935).

13. This narrowing of the scope of the act reflected, in the main, the strength of the opposition from canners and processors, who objected strongly to being subjected to the marketing order procedure.

14. Public Law 320, 74th Cong., Sections 8c (1) and 8c (2).

one to fruits and vegetables, and one which was applicable to both types of product. The part applying to fruits and vegetables gave authority for grade, size and quantity limitations, allotment of quotas to handlers and producers and proration of shipments, equalization of losses and so on, but did not authorize the fixing of minimum prices to producers or the fixing of resale prices.[15]

Later Marketing Agreement Legislation

The Agricultural Adjustment Act of 1933, including the 1935 amendments, was invalidated, in part at least, by the Supreme Court's decision of January 6, 1936.[16] The Department of Agriculture held that the marketing agreement legislation was not affected, since the Court's decision dealt primarily with the processing tax and acreage control features of the act. However, since technical objections relating to the validity of the sections applying to marketing agreements were sustained in some of the lower courts, a new act known as the Marketing Agreement Act of 1937 was passed. In the main, it followed the lines of the 1935 amendments and served merely to provide positive congressional affirmation of the separability of the crop control and marketing agreement parts of the Agricultural Adjustment Act.

An attempt was made in the 76th Congress (1939) to broaden the act so as to make it applicable to any agricultural commodity, or product thereof, but the bill proposed (H.R. 6208) failed of passage, though it was strongly supported by the American Farm Bureau Federation. The canners, chief spokesmen for the processing industries, contended (1) that federal market controls on canning products had been unsuccessful except on cling peaches and asparagus, (2) that production control would be essential, (3) that such programs would require either historical or current bases, both of which would be inequitable, (4) that

15. Normally, an order could not be promulgated unless approved by the handlers of at least 50 per cent of the volume of the commodity within the area covered by the agreement and two thirds of the producers, by number or volume. However, in the event the signatures of the required 50 per cent of the handlers could not be obtained, an order could be issued if (a) it was approved by the President, (b) the Secretary of Agriculture determined that failure to effectuate the order would prevent carrying out the declared policy or (c) promulgation of the order was the only way of making the policy effective, provided two thirds (by number or volume) or more of the growers affected had approved the agreement. (Slightly different and higher requirements were to apply to California citrus fruits.)

It was this provision for issuance of orders without the acquiescence of a majority of the handlers that resulted in specific enumeration of the commodities to which orders could be applied. Processors recognized that their interests and those of the producers, with respect to control of shipments, might not coincide and that the producers' interests would be likely to take precedence in decisions made by the President and the Secretary of Agriculture. (For a fuller discussion of procedures and protective features provided in the act, see George L. Mehren, *Agricultural Market Control under Federal Statutes*, Giannini Foundation of Agricultural Economics, Berkeley, California, Mimeographed Report No. 90, 1947, pp. 7–9.)

16. *U.S.* v. *Butler et al., Receivers of Hoosac Mills Corporation*, 297 U.S. 1 (1936).

controls for canning crops must be prepared a year in advance and that weather and yield variations would preclude accurate estimates, (5) that secondary outlets for restricted crops are inadequate, (6) that the carry-over problems for staple canned goods would be unsolvable, (7) that they were opposed to control instruments in the formulation of which they had little part, and (8) that the necessity for harvesting many of the fruit crops within a few hours precludes effective grade and size control. These were essentially the same arguments that they had used successfully in 1934 and 1935.[17]

After the close of World War II, a further attempt was made to extend the marketing agreement powers of the Secretary of Agriculture to all agricultural commodities but it, like the 1939 attempt, was unsuccessful. However, a bill making other amendments to the act was finally passed and was approved on August 1, 1947 (Public Law 305, 80th Cong.). It made no substantial changes in the legislation already on the books, but did spell out somewhat more fully the Secretary's powers in regard to inspection and allotment by grades, sizes and qualities of the amounts handlers might ship in any given period. A further slight change in the act was made in 1949 by adding almonds and filberts as commodities that might be made subject to the Secretary's orders.

The Agricultural Act of 1954 added a new subsection which broadened somewhat the declaration of policy and made some additions to the list of commodities to which marketing orders might be applied. The new subsection authorized the Secretary of Agriculture ". . . to establish and maintain such orderly marketing conditions [for any of the enumerated commodities] as will provide, in the interests of the producers and consumers, an orderly flow of the supply thereof to market throughout its normal marketing season to avoid unreasonable fluctuations in supplies and prices."

The principal addition affecting the commodities discussed in this chapter was that which authorized the issuance of marketing orders relating to processed grapefruit (canned or frozen) if such action is favored by processors who have canned or frozen more than 50 per cent of the total volume so processed during a representative period chosen by the Secretary.

The act also provided for the regulation of containers (for commodities covered by orders) and for market research and development projects financed with funds collected pursuant to marketing orders. Provision was also made for regulations in respect to imports of certain of the commodities with a view to maintaining standards for the imported commodities comparable with those applied under marketing orders.[18]

17. Mehren, *op. cit.*, p. 11. However, S. 1096, making Washington, Oregon and Idaho apples eligible for marketing agreements, was passed and approved (Public Law 98, 76th Cong., May 31, 1939).

18. The Administrative Procedures Act of 1946, which applied generally throughout the government, also affected in some ways the procedures used in hearings relating to marketing agreements and the handling of supplementary regulations.

Related Programs and Legislation

Other activities carried on by the government have had a bearing on some of the specialty crop programs, particularly those financed under Section 32 of the AAA amendments of August 24, 1935. That section authorized assignment to the Secretary of Agriculture of 30 per cent of the gross revenue received from customs duties for use by him in encouraging exports of agricultural products, encouraging domestic consumption and financing adjustments. The Secretary was given wide discretion in the use of these funds.

Some of the funds have been used to provide export subsidies and other assistance in disposing of the major field crops. However, they have come to be regarded more and more as special funds for aid to the growers of the minor crops. Surplus removal operations either in conjunction with or separate from marketing agreement programs have been undertaken from time to time. Among them were transfers for school lunches, aid in setting up the food stamp program of 1939–1941 and some export operations.[19]

The foreign-aid programs of the late 1940s also included some special arrangements for giving assistance to growers of specialty crops heavily dependent on foreign outlets since the international markets were not able to absorb all of the available supplies through normal marketing arrangements. Even before passage of the 1935 amendments (which included Section 32), some assistance of that kind was authorized. An appropriation of $150 million was provided in 1934 for diversion programs of various kinds and relief purchases were made in such ways as to aid in disposing of farm surpluses. Until 1935, these were handled by the Federal Surplus Relief Corporation. After that corporation was liquidated, the Federal Surplus Commodities Corporation carried on a similar program. Its purchases were made with funds provided under the Jones-Connally Cattle Act and the LaFollette amendments relating to dairy products, as well as with those assigned from tariff revenues under Section 32.[20]

OBJECTIVES OF THE PROGRAMS

Marketing agreements, like the production control programs, were designed to raise prices to farm producers. However, they differed from the major crop control programs in that, though they provided a mechanism for using self-imposed regulations sponsored and supplemented by the government, they did not include provisions for government payments

19. For a fuller explanation of these activities, see Murray R. Benedict, *Can We Solve the Farm Problem?,* Twentieth Century Fund, New York, 1955, Chapter 8.

20. Until 1937, purchases were made by the Commodities Purchase Section of the Agricultural Adjustment Administration and distributed by the Surplus Commodities Corporation. After that, the Corporation, with greatly expanded powers, handled purchasing as well as distribution. (Mehren, *op. cit.,* p. 10.)

to growers.[21] The licensing and Secretary's order procedures were, in effect, an attempt to use the government's police powers to make non-signatory handlers adjust their operations to the program provisions prescribed.[22]

Presumably, the growers and handlers concerned could undertake similar quantity- and quality-stabilizing activities without government assistance if they could act with sufficient unanimity and if the actions taken were not of such nature as to be in conflict with the applicable provisions of the antitrust laws.[23] Such plans had been tried many times in earlier periods but nonparticipating minorities could wreck them, even while reaping some of the benefits from them. Seldom could enough of the growers be induced to follow the plans laid down by the majority to make such plans workable. Hence the proposal that the government step in to aid grower groups in carrying out programs that they were unable to make successful on their own. The policy implied was entirely in keeping with the philosophy that found expression in the NRA codes, the various crop control programs, and the labor laws passed in the 1930s. The parallel with the union-shop principle in organized labor is obvious.

Collateral benefits were, of course, expected to accrue to farmers, handlers and processors, and the general public. Among these were improvement of quality, elimination of waste by preventing shipment of low-quality and unwanted products, greater uniformity in packs and more even pressure on the markets. Handlers also were expected to benefit to some extent through protection against price cutting, more stable margins and allocation of amounts handled. However, there was also an implication that handlers' margins might be reduced if considered too high by the administrators in charge of the government agencies concerned.

The aim was to manipulate supplies in such a way as to eliminate seasonal and weather-induced gluts in the markets for perishables, to maintain a steady flow of the product during its appropriate season, and to preclude shipment of quantities and qualities of product that would depress the market unduly or that might more profitably be diverted to other uses or outlets. Some concerted effort in stimulating demand was

21. Except for minor administrative expenses.

22. While this states in broad terms the underlying principle, it must be recognized that under some conditions the wishes of specified majorities of the growers may be dominant even though a majority of the handlers are opposed to the regulations and procedures agreed to by the Secretary of Agriculture and the growers. Also, the powers granted to the Secretary of Agriculture are not limited to collaboration in carrying out formally adopted marketing agreements.

23. While the Capper-Volstead Act and other federal legislation relating to agricultural cooperatives give such organizations some latitude in respect to freedom from prosecution under the antitrust laws, producer groups have from time to time been prosecuted for attempts to regulate volume of sales and prices. The marketing agreement legislation specifically exempted them from such prosecution if they were acting in accordance with agreements approved by the Secretary of Agriculture.

contemplated and also, in some cases, control over the amounts produced or marketed.

METHODS OF OPERATION

Marketing agreement programs are developed at the request of the industry and are thoroughly discussed by the various industry groups concerned. They are then reviewed by the Department of Agriculture and usually are modified on the basis of experience gained in other programs. A public hearing is held to receive evidence for and against the proposal and to obtain suggestions for further changes. If the Secretary of Agriculture considers the final version to be in harmony with the objectives set forth in the act and to have substantial industry support, it usually is submitted to a vote by the producers. However, in some cases, the views of producers have been obtained in other ways.

Each agreement establishes an administrative organization, specifies the control devices to be used and contains many other provisions. Much of it relates to the mechanics of operation. A first problem is to determine what is to be done and a second, and quite different, problem is to decide how it is to be done.

The Control Board, which usually is dominated by producers, supervises the program and acts as an intermediary between the industry and the Secretary of Agriculture. Also, it works up regulations and recommends them to the Secretary for issuance as Secretary's orders. For some of the programs, a second committee, composed largely of handlers, serves in an advisory capacity and furnishes information about current marketing conditions.

Members of these committees, together with alternates, are selected by the Secretary of Agriculture from nominees chosen by the industry. An attempt is made to have the committees broadly representative of the areas involved, the organizations affected and the types of marketing agencies concerned. The Control Board selects a program manager (and staff of clerical and field workers) to carry out its policies, to investigate and report violations to the Department for possible enforcement action, and to collect assessments and disburse monies.

Control Measures Used

The Marketing Agreement Act authorizes a number of different control devices. Most of those used are of four general types:

1. Establishment of minimum prices to producers. (This has been used mainly in the fluid milk agreements.)
2. Rate-of-flow regulations. (These are used to level out alternating periods of glut and scarcity in the markets for perishables.)
3. Grade, size and quality regulations. (This device is used to reduce interstate shipment of "inferior" portions of perishable crops.)

4. Surplus controls. (These are used to divert "excess" quantities of durables from normal channels to secondary outlets.)

At one time or another, nearly all of the procedures authorized in the act have been tried, including controls over auction marketing, establishment of maximum service charges, prohibition of "unfair" trade practices and methods of competition, and provisions for filing and posting prices. These techniques, in general, have been found ineffective. Price fixing is now limited to milk orders. Most of the recent programs for other perishables rely mainly on grade and size restrictions, occasionally combined with rate-of-flow regulations, as a means of increasing prices to producers. For tree nuts, dried fruits and other durables, surplus control devices are more commonly used.

Usually the Control Board is required to prepare, at the beginning of each crop year, a marketing policy statement which sets forth the type of program that is to be carried on during the ensuing season. These statements, however, are often rather superficial, and are looked upon as a chore rather than as an opportunity to perform a real service by making a penetrating analysis of the problems facing the industry.

Thereafter, specific orders are prepared. These may apply to the entire season or to only a portion of it. The Control Board, in conjunction with such other committees as may be established, reviews the immediate situation in prospect (supply, demand, availability of competing commodities and so on) and *recommends* orders that it deems appropriate. These recommendations are reviewed by the unit of the Department of Agriculture responsible for the program concerned and are approved or disapproved in the name of the Secretary of Agriculture. If approved, the orders are issued immediately and become binding on the industry. If disapproved, the controls become inoperative or the Department of Agriculture issues a different set of orders.

NUMBER AND KINDS OF AGREEMENTS

In the period 1933–1955, well over a hundred marketing agreements of various kinds were approved and put into operation. This does not mean, however, that the number of commodities affected was equally large. No less than fifteen of the early agreements had to do with fluid milk markets, eight dealt with various types of tobacco, three with rice and two with packaged bees. Over-all numbers are not meaningful since some agreements operated for a single season or less while others were continuous or were reinstated after being suspended for a time.

In the first flush of enthusiasm following passage of the Agricultural Adjustment Act, agreements relating to a diverse array of commodities were entered into. This was the period in which George Peek and Charles J. Brand, strong proponents of the marketing agreement approach, were in charge of the Agricultural Adjustment Administration.

During that period and the one immediately following it (to May 1934), agreements were adopted for the fifteen fluid milk areas mentioned above and for several other nonhorticultural commodities. (See Table 44.) Nearly all of these agreements were terminated after only a brief period of operation. Since most of them are dealt with in other chapters, they are not discussed further at this point.

The current use of orders accompanied by agreements (aside from those in the fluid milk markets) is confined largely to fruits, tree nuts and potatoes, particularly those grown in specialized production areas for sale in distant markets. Many of the programs relating to these products have been continued over considerable periods, some for fifteen years or longer. The scope of marketing agreement operations was, of course, substantially curtailed through the restrictions written into the legislation in 1935 which made the marketing agreement approach inapplicable to most canning crops, including nearly all of the canning vegetables, and to the major field crops.

The scope and nature of the operation was still further limited by operating difficulties encountered in the early stages of the program. Some of the groups, particularly the citrus producers, visualized the marketing agreement technique as a means of coordinating shipments from the different producing areas in such a way as to result in national stabilization of the industry.

Such an approach had been fully worked out as early as December 1933 and the early citrus area agreements contained provisions for connecting up with other areas to bring into effect a national stabilization plan sponsored and aided by the government. That idea was abandoned shortly thereafter. It was found virtually impossible to achieve agreement on methods of allocating shipments from the various producing areas. The interests of the different groups were often in conflict and the problems arising out of the relation of old established areas to newer, developing areas and the sharp fluctuations in year-to-year production presented difficulties which, at least at the time, seemed insuperable.[24]

Between 1933 and December 31, 1955, some thirty-three agreements relating to fresh fruits had been set up. In addition, there were sixteen for vegetables and twenty-two for canned and dried fruits and other nonperishable specialty crops. (These are listed in Tables 45, 46 and 47.) In a few cases, Secretary's orders (or licenses in the first period) were promulgated in the absence of a marketing agreement. (The number of agreements in operation in each of the years 1933–34 to 1954–55 and the number of seasons in which they were operated are summarized in Table 48.)

24. Similar difficulties were encountered by the asparagus and Bartlett pear growers. So far as is known to these writers, no undertaking of that kind has thus far been carried out successfully.

TABLE 44

MISCELLANEOUS COMMODITIES: FEDERAL MARKETING AGREEMENT PROGRAMS

Commodity and Area	Number: Agreement	Number: License or Order [a]	Effective Date: Agreement	Effective Date: License or Order	Termination Date [b]	Composition of Administrative Committee [c]: G	P	H	N	Other Commodities Included?
Wheat, North Pacific	14		10/11/33		4/ 1/36	4	2	2	1	
Rice, California	10	96L	9/26/33	12/12/34	9/14/35		7		1	Yes [d]
Rice, milling, southern	17	11L	10/16/33	10/17/33	3/ 6/34		7			
Rice, milling, southern	39	11L	3/ 6/34	10/17/33	4/ 1/35		7			
Peanut millers	35	29L	1/27/34	1/27/34	10/ 1/34	5	5			
Tobacco, flue-cured	15		9/25/33		3/31/34				[e]	
Tobacco, burley	34		12/11/33		4/15/34				[e]	
Tobacco, fire-cured and dark air-cured	37		12/ 1/33		7/15/34				[e]	
Tobacco, dark air-cured	38		12/ 1/33		7/15/34				[e]	
Tobacco, fire-cured and dark air-cured	41		3/26/34		7/15/34				[e]	
Tobacco, cigar-leaf	46		12/ 1/33		6/30/34				[e]	
Tobacco, shade-grown, Connecticut Valley	28	28L	12/11/33	1/17/34	8/15/41			[f]		Yes [g]
Tobacco, cigar-leaf, Type 62 shade-grown, Fla.-Ga.		83		6/ 3/52						
Alcoholic beverages importing	25	19L	12/ 1/33	12/10/33	10/22/40				[h]	
Distilled spirits	27	21L	12/10/33	12/13/33	4/18/34				[h]	
Gum-turp and gum-rosin processors	36	37L	2/21/34	3/13/34	11/ 3/37		9			Yes [i]
Wood-turp and wood-rosin processors		55L		5/13/34	12/31/36		7			
Gum, gum-turp and gum-rosin agents		77L		7/14/34	12/31/36			5		
Gum, gum-turp and gum-rosin distributors		78L		7/14/34	12/31/36			5		
Packaged bees and queens	43	54L	5/ 6/34	5/ 6/34	9/ 6/38			5		
Packaged bees and queens	79	29	9/ 6/38	9/ 6/38	8/29/39			6		

Sources: Summarized from copies of marketing agreements, licenses and orders, and termination orders issued by U.S. Department of Agriculture; and annual reports of the Department.

a. Suffix "L" denotes a license, others are orders. No orders issued to accompany MA 14, 15, 34, 37, 38, 41 and 46. No agreement issued to accompany licenses 55, 77 and 78 and order 83.

b. Each license or order was terminated on the same date as the marketing agreement it accompanied except license 11, which was continued for the duration of marketing agreements 17 and 39.

c. Abbreviations: G—Grower, P—Processor, H—Handler, N—Neutral.

d. Crop Board of 7 grower representatives plus Chairman of Marketing Board.

e. Administered by Secretary of Agriculture.

f. Executive Committee of Connecticut Valley Shade Growers Association plus proportional representation of contracting handlers not members of the Association.

g. Acreage committee of 5 members—2 from control committee, 2 selected by growers who are not parties to the marketing agreement, 1 chosen by first 4.

h. Administered by Federal Alcohol Control Administration.

i. Advisory Council of 6 members—2 selected by processors, 2 by dealers and 2 by Secretary.

Notes to Table 45 continued:

d. Abbreviations:

GS—grade and size limitations (G—grade only; S—size only)
RF—rate of flow, i.e., period proration, including regulation of daily shipments
MC—maximum rate on marketing service charges
TP—control of unfair trade practices and competition
H—holidays (packing, loading or shipping)
PP—price posting or fixing
Misc.—Miscellaneous provisions include: auction control in MA 16, 29 and 55; volume control in MA 87; maturity control in MA 99; coordination of activities by citrus producing areas in MA 29, 30, 33 and 55; maturity and container regulation in MA 121; and container regulation in MA 126.

TABLE 45

FRESH FRUITS: FEDERAL MARKETING AGREEMENT PROGRAMS, 1933–1955

Commodity and Area	Number: Agreement	Number: Order [a]	Effective Date [b]	Termination Date [b]	Seasons Operated (Beginning in Year Shown) [c]	Regulations Permitted [d]
Citrus, Fla.	29	22L	12/18/33	8/13/34	1933	GS, RF, MC, TP, Misc.
Citrus, Fla.	55	95L	12/18/34	7/15/35	1934	GS, RF, MC, TP, Misc.
Citrus, Fla.	64	7	5/ 8/36	7/31/37	1936	GS, RF
Citrus, Fla.	84	33	2/22/39		1939–1955	GS, H
Limes, Fla.	126	101	6/15/55		1955	GS, Misc.
Citrus, Calif.-Ariz.	30	23L	12/18/33	5/17/47	1933–1935	RF, MC, Misc.
Citrus, Calif.-Ariz.	30	2	1/13/36	5/17/47	1936–1941	RF
Lemons, Calif.-Ariz.	94	53	4/10/41		1941–1955	RF
Grapefruit, Calif.-Ariz.	96	55	5/26/41		1941–1955	GS
Oranges, Calif.-Ariz.		66	10/26/42	3/ 8/52	1941–1952	S, RF
Navel oranges, Ariz.-Calif.	117	14	9/22/53		1953–1955	S, RF
Valencia oranges, Ariz.-Calif.		22	3/31/54		1954–1955	S, RF
Citrus, Texas	33	26L	12/26/33	11/14/35	1934	GS, MC, TP, Misc.
Citrus, Texas	71	15	7/13/37	1/ 1/40	1937–1939	GS, RF
Deciduous tree fruits, Calif.	6	7L	10/ 9/33	8/ 1/35	1934	RF
Deciduous tree fruits, Calif.	61	7L	7/20/35	11/ 8/38	1935	GS, RF, MC
Deciduous tree fruits, Calif.	66	9	5/25/36	4/ 1/38	1936, 1937	GS, RF, H
Deciduous tree fruits, Calif.	85	36	5/29/39		1939–1942, 1945–1955	GS, RF, H, TP
Grapes, Calif. Tokay	11	9L	10/14/33	9/14/35	1933	RF, MC
Grapes, Calif. Tokay	93	51	8/20/40		1940–1942, 1947–1955	GS, RF
Apples, Calif. Gravenstein	51	82L	8/20/34	12/ 2/36	1935	RF, MC
Pears, Calif. Hardy	87	38	6/20/39		1939–1941	GS, Misc.
Deciduous fruits, Northwest	16	27L	10/28/33	10/18/35	1934	RF, TP, PP, Misc.
Prunes, Northwest fresh	77	26	7/23/38	6/30/52	1939–1942	G, RF, PP
Pears, Pac. Coast winter	81	31	10/11/38	6/ 1/39	1938	GS
Pears, Pac. Coast winter	89	39	8/26/39		1939–1942, 1948–1953, 1955	GS
Strawberries, Fla.	50	81L	8/20/34	12/19/35	None	GS, MC
Peaches, Colo.	54		11/ 6/34	10/ 3/39	None	RF, MC, PP
Peaches, Colo.	88	40	8/15/39		1939–1941, 1949–1955	GS
Grapes, Ark.	76	25	7/19/38	2/19/39	1938	G, RF
Peaches, Utah	91	50	7/24/40		1940, 1941, 1951–1955	GS
Peaches, Ga.	99	62	4/27/42		1942, 1945–1947, 1950–1954	GS, Misc.
Avocados, Fla.	121	69	6/11/54		1954–1955	G, Misc.

Sources: Summarized from copies of marketing agreements, licenses and orders and termination orders issued by the U.S. Department of Agriculture; annual reports of the department supplemented by information furnished by the Fruit and Vegetable Division, U.S. Agricultural Marketing Service.

a. Suffix "L" denotes a license, others are orders. No order issued to accompany MA 54. No marketing agreement issued to accompany orders 22 and 66.

b. Same dates for license or order and accompanying agreement except effective dates for MA 29 (12/14/33), 30 (12/14/33), 6 (9/2/33), 11 (9/30/33), 16 (10/14/33), 50 (8/5/34) and 51 (8/5/34). Also license 7 continued for duration of both MA 6 and MA 61 and license 23 terminated on 10/15/36, after being superseded by order 2 (on 1/13/36).

c. In addition, programs were maintained for data collection in some years: MA 93 in 1944–1946 and MA 54 in 1934–1935.

(*Footnote d opposite*)

TABLE 46

FRESH VEGETABLES AND MELONS: FEDERAL MARKETING AGREEMENT PROGRAMS, 1933–1955

Commodity and Area	Number: Agreement	Number: Order [a]	Effective Date [b]	Termination Date [b]	Seasons Operated (Beginning in Year Shown)	Regulations Permitted [c]
Asparagus, Calif. fresh	40	39L	3/20/34	4/ 6/35	1934	RF, Misc.
Asparagus, Calif. fresh	58	39L	4/ 3/35	11/21/36	1935	RF, Misc.
Cantaloupes, Ariz.-Calif.	75	24	5/17/38	7/31/38	1938	S, Misc.
Cauliflower, Oregon	72	16	7/19/37	4/23/39	None	RF, GS
Celery, Fla.	42	51L	5/ 1/34	12/ 7/35	1935	RF, MC
Celery, Fla.	73	21	11/ 9/37	10/15/38	1937	RF
Onions, Utah	70	14	4/26/37	5/18/45	1939	GS
Onions, Colo.	90	43	12/ 5/39	5/23/46	1939	GS
Tomatoes, Miss.	86	37	6/ 5/39	6/ 1/45	None	GS
Tomatoes, Fla.	125	45	10/ 8/55		1955	GS
Vegetables, Colo.[d]	56	97L	1/15/35	12/ 7/35	1935	RF, FS, MC
Vegetables, Colo.[d]	67	10	8/ 9/36		1936–1942; 1946–1955	GS, H, RF, FS
Vegetables, Wash.[e]	49	79L	7/21/34	3/ 8/40	1934–1935	GS
Vegetables, Wash.[e]	63	6	5/ 4/36	3/ 8/40	1936	RF, H, GS, Misc.
Watermelons, Fla., Ga., N.C., S.C.	52	83L	8/ 6/34	1/ 3/39	1935	RF, H, GS, MC
Watermelons, Fla., Ga., N.C., S.C.	65	8	5/12/36	5/ 2/41	1936, 1937, 1939	GS

Sources: Summarized from copies of marketing agreements, licenses and orders and termination orders issued by U.S. Department of Agriculture; annual reports of the department supplemented by information furnished by the Fruit and Vegetable Division, U.S. Agricultural Marketing Service.

a. Suffix "L" denotes a license, others are orders.
b. Same dates for license or order and accompanying agreement except MA 40 effective 3/17/34 and terminated 4/6/35 and MA 42 effective 5/1/34 and terminated 12/7/35; MA 52 effective 8/6/34. License 39 continued for duration of both MA 40 and MA 58.
c. Abbreviations:

GS—grade and size limitation (S—size only)
RF—rate of flow, i.e., period proration
MC—maximum rate of marketing service charges
H—holidays (packing, loading or shipping)
FS—Federal-state inspection and U.S. grading required
Misc.—Miscellaneous provisions include: container standardization under MA 63 and MA 75; and coordination of activities with MA 59 (canning asparagus) under MA 40 and 58 (fresh asparagus).

d. Applicable to peas and cauliflower.
e. Applicable to lettuce, peas and cauliflower; regulations, however, issued only for lettuce.

TABLE 47

NONPERISHABLE HORTICULTURAL PRODUCTS: FEDERAL MARKETING AGREEMENT PROGRAMS, 1933–1955

Commodity and Area	Number: Agreement	Number: Order [a]	Effective Date [b]	Termination Date [b]	Seasons Operated (Beginning in Year Shown) [c]	Regulations Permitted [d]
Peaches, Calif. canning cling	2	2L	8/17/33	7/12/34	1933	SC, PP, Misc.
Peaches, Calif. canning cling	47	75L	7/12/34	10/18/35	1934	SC, PP
Olives, Calif. canning ripe	26	20L	12/13/33	11/19/35	1933, 1934	SC, PP
Asparagus, Calif. canning	59	36L	3/ 6/34	2/20/36	1934, 1935	SC, Misc., QC
Raisins, Calif.	44	59L	5/31/34	9/14/35	1934	SC, PP
Raisins, Calif.	109	89	8/18/49		1949, 1951–1955	SC, QC [e]
Dates, Calif.	45	61L	6/11/34	10/ 9/35	1934	QC, PP, PS, Misc.
Dates, Calif.	127	103	7/15/55		1955	SC, QC
Prunes, Calif. dried	53	87L	8/17/34	8/21/39	1934	SC
Prunes, Calif. dried	110	93	8/25/49		1949–1955	SC, QC
Figs, Calif.	123	64	3/22/55		1955	SC, QC
Walnuts, Pac. Coast	12	8L	10/11/33	10/15/35	1933, 1934	SC
Walnuts, Pac. Coast	62	1	10/15/35	7/31/48	1935–1947	SC, PS
Walnuts, Pac. Coast	105	84	8/ 1/48 [f]		1948–1955	SC, PS, QC
Pecans, Southeast	57		3/13/35	9/30/35		QC, PP
Pecans, Southeast	111	94	9/20/49		1949–1954	QC
Filberts, Northwest	115	97	10/ 1/49		1949–1955	SC, QC, PS
Almonds, Calif.	119	9	8/ 4/50		1950–1955	SC, QC
Hops, Pac. Coast	78	28	8/15/38	7/31/40	1938, 1939	SC
Hops, Pac. Coast	92	49	8/ 5/40	9/ 1/42	1940, 1941	SC
Hops, Pac. Coast	100	63	9/ 1/42	9/ 1/45		SC
Hops, Pac. Coast	107	86	7/ 2/49	7/ 1/53	1949–1952	SC, QC

Sources: Summarized from copies of marketing agreements, licenses and orders and termination orders issued by the U.S. Department of Agriculture; annual reports of the department supplemented by information furnished by the Fruit and Vegetable Division, U.S. Agricultural Marketing Service.

a. Suffix "L" denotes a license, others are orders. Order 9 is a reassignment of an order previously terminated. No license issued to accompany MA 57.

b. Same dates for license or order and accompanying agreement except MA 47 effective 7/6/34 and terminated 6/30/35, MA 59 effective 4/3/35, MA 44 effective 5/29/34, MA 45 effective 6/8/34, MA 12 effective 10/9/33, and MA 2 terminated 7/31/34.

c. In addition, programs were maintained for data collection in some years: MA 109 and MA 119 in 1950 and MA 100 in 1942–1944. Includes period 10/2/43–3/31/47 when MA 62 was superseded by WFO 82.

d. Abbreviations:

- SC—surplus (and/or volume) control
- PP—price posting or fixing
- PS—pack standards or specifications
- QC—quality control, including grade and size limitations
- Misc.—Miscellaneous provisions include: control of unfair trade practices in MA 2, maximum rate on marketing service charges in MA 45, and synchronization of activities under MA 59 with those of MA 40 and 58.

e. QC began in 1955; previously QC only on deliveries of surplus tonnage.

f. Amended, effective July 10, 1954, to include shelled walnuts.

TABLE 48

FRUITS AND VEGETABLES: FEDERAL MARKETING AGREEMENT PROGRAMS[a] IN EFFECT AND OPERATED, BY GROUPS,[b] AUGUST 1933–DECEMBER 1955

Period or Date	Fresh Fruits	Fresh Vegetables	Nonperishables	Total
Marketing Programs Issued (except by Renewal) for Years Shown				
Total	17	11	12	40
1933–1934	9	4	7	20
1935–1938	3	4	2	9
1939–1942	3	2	0	5
1943–1946	0	0	0	0
1947–1950	0	0	2	2
1951–1955	2	1	1	4
Marketing Programs Terminated (except by Renewal) for Years Shown				
Total	6	9	4	19
1933–1934	0	0	0	0
1935–1938	3	3	3	9
1939–1942	2	3	0	5
1943–1946	0	3	0	3
1947–1950	0	0	0	0
1951–1955	1	0	1	2
Marketing Programs in Effect on Date Shown[c]				
December 31, 1934	9	4	7	20
December 31, 1938	6	5	3	14
December 31, 1942	10	4	2	16
December 31, 1947	10	1	1	12
December 31, 1950	10	1	7	18
December 31, 1955	11	2	8	21
Number of Seasons Operated				
1 season or less	5	6	1	12
2 to 4 seasons	4	4	4	12
5 to 8 seasons	1	0	6	7
9 to 14 seasons	4	0	0	4
15 seasons or longer	3	1	1	5

Sources: Summarized from copies of marketing agreements, licenses and orders and termination orders issued by U.S. Department of Agriculture; reports of the Department; and supplemental information furnished by Fruit and Vegetable Division, U.S. Agricultural Marketing Service.

a. A series of agreements and licenses or orders is considered to be a single program if a particular commodity or group of commodities is covered for substantially the same production area. All lapse periods are disregarded, including the following which extended for more than one year: Florida citrus 7/37 to 2/39, California-Arizona oranges 3/52 to 9/53 for valencias and to 3/54 for navels, Texas citrus 11/35 to 7/37, California deciduous tree fruits 4/38 to 5/39, California Tokay grapes 9/35 to 8/40, Florida

RESULTS ACHIEVED

There is relatively little in the way of quantitative studies designed to show the price and other effects of marketing agreements. Attempts to appraise their effectiveness must therefore be mainly qualitative and based largely on the conclusions of well-informed observers. Since a case-by-case listing of the numerous agreements would be repetitive and would contribute little to clearer understanding of these operations and the problems they present, the procedure followed is, instead, to describe in some detail the experiences in a number of representative cases and to draw from them such conclusions as seem warranted.

The reasons for the lack of quantitative data on program results are not hard to find. One is that few of the agreements have been in continuous operation for any considerable number of years. A more significant reason is that there is almost no dependable basis for judging what prices and marketing conditions would have been like if no program had been undertaken. Market conditions, demand, production, quality and timing all vary greatly from year to year and even between different periods within the year. Hence, any attempt to relate prices received to those that would have prevailed had there been no marketing agreement is beset with great difficulties.[25]

The California Deciduous Tree Fruit Agreements

One of the first marketing agreements approved was that relating to interstate and foreign shipments of fresh deciduous tree fruits other than apples (that is, pears, peaches, plums and cherries). The problems and results stemming from that agreement are typical of those encountered in a number of the other fruit and vegetable operations. The program has passed through two rather distinct phases. The first, covering the

25. However, there is need for further study of that problem. Regulations still are issued largely on subjective judgments as to what the situation is and how prices will be affected by the controls. Much reliance is placed on guesses, guided by the experience and "feel" of the industry members of the committees. The development of a small research unit within the Department of Agriculture to work on these problems would be helpful and more research of that kind could well be carried on in the state experiment stations, particularly in those states where the problems are important.

Notes to Table 48 continued:

celery 12/35 to 11/37, California raisins 9/35 to 8/49, California dates 10/35 to 7/55, California prunes 8/39 to 8/49, Southeast pecans 9/35 to 9/49 and Pacific Coast hops 9/45 to 7/49.

All programs on California-Arizona citrus are treated as a single program. The initial program covered operations for lemons, grapefruit and oranges. Beginning with 1941, separate orders were used to cover the three fruits. Now there are four orders (see Table 45).

b. Nonperishables include canned fruits and vegetables, dried fruits, tree nuts and hops. Dates are included with dried fruits, melons with fresh vegetables and strawberries with fresh fruits.

c. Fewer programs are shown to be in effect than indicated by figures on issuance and termination because some programs were not in effect on the specified dates although they were initiated earlier and continued subsequently.

period October 1933 to March 1938, was one of experimentation in which control mechanisms were substantially modified. Three marketing agreements (Nos. 6, 61 and 66) were adopted in rapid sequence.[26] After a season of disastrously low prices in 1938, growers were willing and even eager to accept a fourth agreement, which was inaugurated in the following year (No. 85, effective May 29, 1939). This new agreement differed from those previously adopted and has continued in operation.

The first agreement was for the purpose of raising prices above the unsatisfactory levels of the three preceding years, when the prices paid, especially for inferior and small-size fruits, yielded almost no net return. Under the agreement, shipments could be limited whenever a "surplus" was determined to exist. The plan was based on the assumption that the marketing of smaller amounts, within reasonable limits, would result in higher net returns to growers. In order that such limitations on amounts shipped should bear equally on all growers benefited, it was considered necessary to license all shippers.

At that time, the elimination of low grades was considered inadvisable as it was felt that such a restriction would result in gross inequities in some years. A whole district might be penalized by severe restrictions on the only quality and size of fruit it had been able to produce in that year.[27] Consequently, quantity restrictions were across the board and included high-quality as well as low-quality fruits.[28] Charges for marketing on consignment were limited to 7 per cent of the gross delivered price or 10 per cent of the net f.o.b. price. However, foreign brokerage charges could also be deducted, on shipments outside of continental North America.

The administrative arrangements were relatively simple. All program operations were put in the hands of three committees composed of members selected by the shippers, subject to approval by the Secretary

26. Marketing Agreement No. 6 and License No. 7 (effective September 2 and October 9, 1933) were not put into operation until the 1934 season. In July 1935, they were superseded by a new agreement, No. 61, and a complete revision of the license. Marketing Agreement No. 66 and Order No. 9 became effective on May 25, 1936. They were terminated by an automatic expiration clause on April 1, 1938. The license and order provisions were issued for the purpose of extending the provisions of the agreement to the entire industry.

27. Based on an unpublished manuscript, *Concerning Marketing Agreement for California Deciduous Tree Fruits* by H. R. Tolley (A Report for the Special Crop Section of AAA), undated (about August 1933). This view was rather generally held by California marketing specialists at that time.

28. Reduction in shipments was to be brought about by holding back some carloads during the weeks when peak movements would normally occur and would tend to overburden consuming markets. Under this procedure, which is known as a "car-concentration" plan, cars are released from railroad and cold storage assembly points in the order of their arrival and at rates designed to steady the flow onto the market. However, time limits on the length of the holding period are usually specified in the agreements.

of Agriculture.[29] Expenses were met through pro rata assessments on each shipper. All shippers were directed to maintain and furnish such information as might be required by the control agency and the Secretary.[30]

The 1934 operation related to Bartlett pears, freestone peaches and plums. For pears, the "car-concentration" plan, operated on a voluntary basis in 1933,[31] was again used in the same way and results were considered satisfactory. There was no restriction on peach shipments except that "price-arrival" sales were prohibited and the number of "rollers" was limited to the number of cars loaded by the shipper in the preceding 24-hour period.[32] The purpose of this control was to keep the trade informed in the hope that the price would become stabilized. It was considered moderately successful as a means of improving market conditions.[33]

For plums, a comprehensive proration scheme was initiated, but after only a few days it became evident that the proration committee could not estimate satisfactorily the supplies available for shipment. Consequently, the program was discontinued.[34]

29. These were: (1) an Executive Committee consisting of one representative for each shipper who shipped 500 cars or more in 1932 plus three members selected by all other shipper signatories; (2) a Proration Committee of seven members, at least three of whom were to be growers or representatives of grower cooperatives though the members were chosen by the signatory shippers (this committee assembled production and marketing data, decided on amounts to be shipped and made the actual pro rata allocations); and (3) a Sales Managers' Committee of seven members, at least one of whom was to be associated with a grower cooperative association. The Sales Managers' Committee was elected by the shippers and was to act in advisory capacity to the proration committee.

30. Period proration of shipments was handled by relating amounts it was considered advisable to ship in any specified period to the amounts available for shipment in each district. If a "surplus" was found to exist, allotments were made to the individual shippers in each district. A shipper's undershipment could be carried over to increase his allotment in the next succeeding period. Overshipments were deducted from the allotment for the next period. Each shipper was expected to see that his allotment was fairly distributed among the growers of the fruit handled by him. That provision caused some resentment among growers on the ground that it tended to give shippers too much discretion. Growers contended that shippers would tend to give priority to fruit they produced themselves and possibly to some favored growers for whom they handled fruit.

31. Since plans were not matured early enough for the program to go into effect in 1933, the pear growers operated a "car-concentration" plan on a voluntary basis in that year.

32. It was felt that a "price-arrival" arrangement was putting the grower too much at the mercy of the consignee, especially where sales are not made by the auction method. However, much of the fresh fruit and vegetable business has long been handled on a "price-arrival" basis. "Rollers" are cars that are en route to market but, in some cases, may be diverted to different destinations while on the way.

33. It should be kept in mind that in this period many of the agricultural markets were badly demoralized. Heavy and uneven shipments of perishables could result in glutted markets, much waste and severe losses to shippers and growers.

34. There was too much incentive for growers to inflate their production estimates in order to get larger bases against which allocations were made. This padding of figures worked to the disadvantage of those who attempted to report accurately. Also, those growers who pruned and thinned heavily were, in effect, doing their restricting during the growing season. They were thus put at a disadvantage as compared with those who produced a larger tonnage of inferior fruit.

The 1935 and 1936 Agreements

Under the agreement adopted in 1935 (No. 61), grower participation in the administration of the program was increased and the regulatory provisions were drastically overhauled. The limitation on marketing charges was continued but the method of making prorations was extensively revised.[35]

For pears, the "car-concentration" plan and shipping holidays were retained but regulation by means of grade and size limitations was finally accepted. This was a significant change since there had been vigorous opposition to such a provision when the original agreement was discussed and drafted. The 1935 agreement was used to regulate Bartlett pear shipments by the "car-concentration" method. Elberta peaches were handled on the basis of grade and size restrictions. No control on plums was attempted as the 1934 operation had been very unsatisfactory and the 1935 crop was small.

The 1935 agreement was looked upon as a transitional arrangement to be used until such time as the differences among growers from different districts, and of different kinds of fruit, could be reconciled and a more suitable plan developed. Delay in reaching agreement and getting the agreement approved made it impractical to apply it to the movement of the earlier varieties, since they had already gone to market before it could come into effect. However, it was felt that the curtailment of peak movement of Bartlett pears saved many growers who otherwise would have faced disaster as a result of glutted and demoralized markets.[36]

The third marketing agreement (No. 66), in operation during the 1936 and 1937 seasons, did not differ materially from the 1935 agreement. However, many annoyances and inequities resulted from it. It was allowed to expire on April 1, 1938, after growers had cast a large negative vote in the referendum conducted to determine whether to continue it.

The 1938 Agreement

During 1938, farm prices declined substantially from those prevailing in the two preceding years when marketing controls were in operation. It is clear in retrospect that this was part of the general drop in prices and business activity which occurred in that year. Farm prices as a whole fell from an index of 122 (1910–1914 = 100) to 97. Industrial production and national income also receded and the prices of commodities

35. The Sales Managers' Committee was retained but the Executive Committee was changed to a Control Committee consisting of twelve shippers and thirteen growers. Also, the Proration Committee was replaced by several commodity committees, each concerned with the marketing of a specific fruit.

36. See *Pacific Rural Press,* November 23, 1935, "1936 Tree Fruit Agreement—More Red Ink—Which?"

bought by farmers declined from an index of 131 to 124.[37] Consumer prices generally were down about two points.

However, the cause of the lower level of prices in 1938 was not evident to the growers affected by the control program. Much of the decline was undoubtedly attributed to the discontinuance of controls. But even though the cause of the price decline may have been misinterpreted, the depressed condition of the markets may well have increased the need for some regulation of shipments.[38] At any rate the antagonism on the part of growers, which had been so much in evidence earlier, soon disappeared and a new program was established.

The new program was limited to Bartlett pears, Elberta peaches and plums. Committees similar to those used previously were set up, that is, a Control Committee of shippers and growers, a Sales Managers' Committee and a separate commodity committee for each of the three fruits. The limitations on marketing charges and the period proration arrangement no longer appeared. Regulation was by means of grade and size restrictions and control over daily shipments, that is, through shipping holidays and "car-concentration" plans. In addition, the use of deceptive packaging and containers in the sale of Elberta peaches was prohibited.

This last agreement (No. 85) has been continued and at least one of the three fruits has been handled under it during some portion of each season since it was instituted in 1939, except in 1943 and 1944 when prices were above parity. However, even in those years, some control was exercised by means of War Food Administration orders.[39]

California Grape Agreements

A California Tokay grape agreement (No. 11) was put into effect in 1933. It was essentially a formalization and revision of a voluntary pro-

37. The index of industrial production fell off from 113 (1935–1939=100) in 1937 to 89 in 1938. National income was down from $73.6 billion to $65.5 billion. (U.S. Department of Agriculture, *Agricultural Statistics, 1953,* p. 546.)

38. Changes of that kind illustrate the reasons for the great difficulty encountered in attempts to measure the results of marketing agreement programs. In these highly distinctive markets, no general measure of consumer demand can be used with any degree of assurance. A general decline in over-all buying power may not affect prices and purchases of fruits in the same way it affects other commodities. It is probable that fruit purchases are more sensitive to changes in consumer buying power than are purchases of some other farm products which are regarded as necessities.

At any rate, farmers are likely to attribute both higher and lower prices to the existence or absence of widely discussed mechanisms, such as marketing agreements, to a greater extent than their importance warrants. However, farmer votes for or against such procedures stem from the results they think flow from them, not necessarily from any clearly demonstrable gain or lack of gain. Thus broad national and regional influences such as a general decline in buying power are much less apparent than the less significant but more direct influences arising from the things they do themselves or see operating close at hand.

39. In 1949, the agreement was amended so as to confine the regulation of daily shipments to Bartlett pears. Also, plums were separated into two commodity groups on the basis of season of marketing. Separate designations of "early plums" and "other plums" were established in order that the parity price curb would not be used to deny

gram used in 1932. It limited marketing charges and provided for period proration. The accompanying license became effective on October 14 when the season was at its peak and when prices were just high enough to cover harvesting and marketing costs. The program was credited with strengthening prices and stabilizing the market. It is quite possible, however, that early rains and the resumption of wine making had as much to do with the improvement noted as did the marketing agreement.

In 1934, a smaller crop was produced and controls were not applied though growers urged that they be invoked during the peak season. The growers wanted a new agreement in which they would have a majority voice. Consequently, the first agreement was terminated in September 1934.

A new agreement (No. 93), the one currently in effect, was developed in 1940. It provides for an Industry Committee of seven members to administer the program and a Shippers' Advisory Committee of seven members. Control is by means of grade-size restrictions, regulation of daily shipments, minimum standards of quality and maturity, and volume regulation. The second agreement provided for packaging and loading limitations in conjunction with the "car-concentration" regulation. This "holiday" provision was deleted by an amendment passed in 1953 when another form of volume regulation was adopted. The agreement was made operative in the 1940–1942 seasons and from 1947 to 1955.

Procedures such as those outlined above have many and sometimes unpredictable effects on such things as physical operations, production and utilization, selling and buying practices, and equitableness as between different shippers. For example, they may result in poor use of labor or even, in times of tight labor supply, in the loss of workers to other farms and industries in short periods of enforced idleness. Crops may go past their time of optimum quality and some shippers and areas may be penalized because of the specific time of maturing for their crop while others may suffer little inconvenience. Possibly even more important, prices may vary in such a way that shipments delayed en route may have to be sold at disadvantageous prices, unless the industry is so organized that returns can be pooled. Hence, the management of such programs requires skill, good judgment and flexibility if widespread grower dissatisfaction is to be avoided. Because of problems of that kind, and the difficulty of measuring results, some members of the Tokay industry are not convinced that the controls are beneficial, even in the short run.[40]

---

the benefits of marketing controls to the producers of late varieties merely because the price of early plums was high.

40. The existence of such doubts is evidenced by the fact that the Tokay Industry Committee, in 1949, asked the Giannini Foundation of Agricultural Economics (University of California) to make a study of the effectiveness of the Tokay program. A study was made and a preliminary report issued. (See Jerry Foytik, *Some Information Bearing on the Car-Concentration Plan for California Tokay Grapes*, Giannini Foundation, Berkeley, July 1950, 40 pp., mimeo.)

Several attempts have been made to extend controls to other types of California grapes but no programs have been adopted, except for raisins. Several elaborate proposals for regulating the activities of shippers and vintners handling wine grapes have also been discussed but not put into effect. Among the features considered were minimum price schedules, limitations on sales and surplus control funds. For table grapes, the principal evidence of interest has been on the part of the growers and shippers of Emperors. An attempt was made in 1948 to bring these under control and a hearing was held, but support was insufficient to warrant undertaking a control program.

Other Pacific Coast Deciduous Fruits

Soon after the first agreement for California deciduous tree fruits was set up, marketing programs for California Gravenstein apples and Northwest deciduous fruits (Washington and Oregon) were adopted.[41] These were terminated after operating for only a single season. For the 1938–1940 seasons, new programs for Northwest fresh prunes, Pacific Coast late pears and California hardy pears were inaugurated. These agreements have been used during several seasons when conditions seemed to warrant the use of controls of that kind.

Thus a considerable part of the Pacific Coast deciduous tree fruit industry has been, at least briefly, under federal marketing programs. However, the principal operations have been in pears, plums, Elberta peaches and Tokay grapes in California, and in fresh prunes and pears in the Pacific Northwest.

The Citrus Programs

Important parts of the citrus industry have operated under federal marketing programs over the past two decades. In December 1933, the principal citrus areas adopted separate agreements with similar provisions. It was thought that these could later be coordinated so as to operate as a national stabilization plan. Though a mechanism for interregional cooperation was fully worked out, such a program was not undertaken for reasons already mentioned. Within a few years, the idea of a national program was dropped.[42]

41. Apples had been omitted from the California deciduous tree fruit agreement because the growers of Gravensteins were already operating under a voluntary program set up under the California Prorate Act. However, a separate agreement covering Gravensteins grown in Sonoma and Napa counties was adopted in August 1934. It was not used in 1934 as the crop was small, and was in operation for only three weeks in 1935. The crop of that year was late and the growers lost the seasonal advantage they normally enjoyed because of early season shipments. The agreement was terminated in December 1936. A program was later developed, under state law, for regulating sales to both fresh and cannery outlets.

42. The plan called for two National Stabilization Committees, one for oranges and one for grapefruit, and for a National Citrus Coordinator. Difficulties arose in the

Three main agreements, with various modifications, were entered into: one for Florida oranges, grapefruit and tangerines; one for California-Arizona oranges and grapefruit; and one for Texas oranges and grapefruit.[43] For the 1933–1935 period, the agreements limited marketing charges to the average amounts charged in the preceding three years and established weekly prorations of shipments. Various restrictions on trade practices were included in the Florida and Texas agreements.[44]

Operations under the Florida agreement were halted within a few weeks by a district court injunction. That ruling was reversed by the appellate court but not until late February 1934. By that time, the marketing of the 1933 crop was well advanced. Furthermore, numerous disagreements within the industry had arisen. The attempt to use market prorates had not worked out smoothly. In the 1934–35 season, control was limited to compulsory grading and inspection.

In Texas, the 1933 crop was small because of hurricanes that destroyed much of the crop. In the following season, controls were used only for about a month, largely as a means of trying out procedures and seeing what difficulties would be encountered. The Florida and Texas agreements were terminated in July and November 1935. The reason for termination was largely that the administrative and economic arrangements had been worked out hurriedly in 1933 and were not found workable.

The California-Arizona agreement was launched under more favorable conditions, partly because of the longer and broader experience of the growers with the techniques and principles of cooperative marketing. Proration of shipments was begun in mid-January 1934 and was continued for two years thereafter. Although some conflicts arose, they did not prove insurmountable.

Citrus Operations from 1936 On

This initial phase of control in the citrus industry was brought to a close by January 1936 and new programs were initiated. The national stabilization plan, controls over marketing charges and trade practices,

---

selection of a formula for allocations, agreement on a National Coordinator, resolving conflicts between the established areas and those just coming into production, and so on. It would have been necessary to grant very wide powers to the Coordinator and there was much doubt about the willingness of the various groups and areas to accept his decisions.

43. The Florida agreements were Nos. 29 and 55 with supporting licenses No. 22, effective December 18, 1933 to August 13, 1934, and No. 95, effective December 18, 1934 to July 15, 1935. The California agreement, No. 30, was effective from December 18, 1933 to January 12, 1936. (The accompanying license was No. 23.) The Texas agreement (No. 33) was for the period December 26, 1933 to November 14, 1935 (supported by License No. 26).

44. For Florida citrus, auction market allocations were permitted (with a view to stabilizing prices at the different large markets) and federal grading and inspection were required.

auction prorations, and compulsory grading and inspection were dropped. The rate-of-flow provision was retained. However, it was supplemented by grade and size restrictions in Florida and Texas. These new agreements, as later modified, have continued to be used successfully in the California-Arizona area, and most of the time in Florida, since 1936.[45]

A third Florida agreement (No. 64, effective May 8, 1936 to July 31, 1937) was used in handling the 1936–37 crop. After a lapse of one year, a continuing program was adopted in February 1939. This new program has been used each year since 1939 to regulate the marketing of Florida citrus. It retained grade and size limitations but replaced the period proration technique with one that provided for shipping holidays. A new agreement for Texas citrus was adopted in July 1937. It was in operation during the 1937, 1938 and 1939 seasons but was discontinued in January 1940. Its termination has not affected importantly the citrus controls in recent years because the severe freeze of January–February 1951 destroyed a large part of the Texas acreage.[46]

Other Fresh Fruit Agreements

Seven other agreements relating to fresh fruit crops were entered into. The strawberry industry of Florida began consideration of a marketing agreement early in 1933. It was not pushed in that season as the 1934

45. For California-Arizona, the original agreement was retained but the accompanying license was replaced by an order on January 13, 1936. Operations were continued under this order until May 1941, when a separate program was adopted for grapefruit (Agreement No. 96 and Order No. 55) and one for oranges in October 1942 (Order No. 66). The grapefruit program provided grade and size restrictions and permitted different minima on shipments to Canada. It has been used in each year since its adoption. For oranges, since the requisite number of handlers could not be induced to sign the agreement, an order was issued. The order, which authorized weekly proration on a district basis, was amended on November 1, 1942. Operations were continued during the 1942–1952 seasons under this order. New orders providing for size restrictions and for volume regulation by weekly prorations of shipments were issued on September 22, 1953 and March 31, 1954 to cover programs for navel oranges and valencia oranges respectively. These regulations were used for the 1953–1955 and 1954–55 seasons. Lemons, from the California-Arizona area, were brought under control in April 1942 (Agreement No. 94). The simple weekly proration plan established has been used in each season since.

46. A brief comment on the reasons for some of the changes mentioned above will give a clearer view of the situation. The Florida and Texas programs were altered so as to provide for increased participation by growers. Originally, both programs were dominated by shippers. Under the revisions of 1936, the administrative committees were composed entirely of growers selected from and representing specific districts. They were assisted by advisory committees made up of shippers.

In the California-Arizona area, a different problem was posed. The bulk of the citrus grown in that area was handled by the California Fruit Growers Exchange (now Sunkist Growers, Inc.). Much of the remainder was handled by another cooperative, Mutual Orange Distributors. There was no important conflict between grower and shipper interests but the problem was that of representation on committees. This was worked out by assigning approximately half the membership of each committee to the Exchange and distributing the other memberships in such a way as to give appropriate representation to M.O.D. and the noncooperative groups. In order that the program would not become merely an instrument in the hands of the Exchange, restrictions on voting arrangements were spelled out in considerable detail.

crop in prospect was small. An agreement was made effective on August 3, 1934 but was not put into operation prior to its termination date, December 19, 1935.

During 1938, shipments of grapes from Northwest Arkansas were handled under a marketing agreement. However, the program remained in effect only for a short period, July 1938 to February 1939. It provided for period proration and for grade regulation combined with federal-state grading on a compulsory basis.

There were three separate agreements for fresh peaches grown outside of California. These were in Colorado, effective August 15, 1939, Utah, effective July 24, 1940, and Georgia, effective April 27, 1942. Though each is applicable to only a small part of the total peach crop, all three have been in operation in several of the years since their adoption.[47] In general, regulation is by means of grade and size restrictions administered by a committee composed mainly of growers. The Georgia agreement also specifies minimum maturity standards.[48]

Florida avocado growers adopted a program in June 1954 which provided for grade restrictions and for maturity and container regulations. In June 1955, Florida producers of limes adopted a program that provided for container regulations and grade-size restrictions. These programs have been in operation since their adoption.

THE FRESH VEGETABLE AND MELON AGREEMENTS

Most of the vegetable and melon crops, like the fresh fruits, are characterized by perishability, wide fluctuations in output, and periods of glut and famine in the consuming markets. The problems encountered in establishing marketing controls and managing regulatory devices are similar to those in the fresh fruit industries. However, marketing agreements have not been used extensively in the vegetable and melon industries and have not in general been successful where tried. This is probably due in large measure to the greater dispersion of producing areas, the larger numbers of growers and handlers, less specialization in production, and to some of the characteristics of the commodities themselves.

Eleven programs were adopted, five in 1934, five in the period April 1937 to December 1939 and one in October 1955.[49] Only two of these were in force on December 31, 1955. One, the Florida tomato agreement, was adopted and used in 1955. The other, the Colorado vegetable agreement, has been used extensively since 1935. None of the other nine

47. Colorado in 1939–1941 and 1949–1955, Utah 1940–1941 and 1951–1955, and Georgia 1945–1947 and 1950–1954.

48. An earlier agreement for Colorado peaches, adopted November 6, 1938, was not put into operation. It limited marketing charges to the average of the three preceding seasons, required the posting of prices and established period proration.

49. This excludes the potato programs, which are discussed in Chapter 10.

programs was in operation after 1939 and all of them have been terminated.

The California Fresh Asparagus Agreements

In the 1930s, California produced two thirds of the United States asparagus crop, including all of the canned asparagus and half of that marketed in fresh form. Furthermore, fresh asparagus from California reached the markets from four to six weeks earlier than asparagus from New Jersey and adjoining states, the principal competing area.

Under these conditions, the California producers considered the situation appropriate for a control program, particularly if an over-all plan could be developed which would coordinate shipments to both the cannery and fresh markets. Such a program was developed and was in operation for the 1934 and 1935 seasons.[50] The plan used was mainly a simple proration scheme to regulate shipments. Allocations were made on a district basis and pro rata quotas were assigned to individual handlers and grower-shippers.[51] The program was administered by a Control Committee of handlers. This Committee was authorized to "negotiate with representatives of handlers of asparagus produced in other states and areas with regard to marketing agreements contemplating joint proration of shipment."

Such coordination did not materialize and the program was terminated after only two years of operation. The growers and handlers apparently felt that it did not have sufficient advantages to warrant the rather cumbersome arrangements required and the annoying restrictions on individual action.

The Washington and Colorado Vegetable Agreements

Another attempt to coordinate sales from different areas was made in the western Washington and the Colorado vegetable agreements (Washington lettuce, peas and cauliflower and Colorado peas and cauliflower). The Control Committees established under these two programs were authorized to confer with a view to setting up agreements that would provide for proration of shipments as between different areas. Some degree of coordination on a voluntary basis was achieved in

50. The 1934 crop was handled under Agreement No. 40 and License No. 39 for fresh sales, and under License No. 36 for cannery sales. Experience gained in the first year led to several changes which were incorporated in the 1935 program (agreements 58 and 59, and parallel amendments to licenses 36 and 39). The program was terminated on February 20, 1936 for canning asparagus and on November 21, 1936 for fresh asparagus.

51. The 1935 agreement provided a second allocation procedure, based on acreage, which could be combined with the control of car movements from concentration points. It was similar to that used in the fresh pear industry. The control over car movements was intended as a way of equalizing out-of-state shipments when weather conditions caused a "bunching up" in harvesting operations.

1934.[52] The western Washington operation was considered successful. However, it was carried out largely under state law rather than federal. The state program included tomatoes, melons, cantaloupes and early potatoes as well as the commodities covered in the federal agreement.

Proration of shipments under the state program began in May, whereas the federal agreement was not approved until July 21. The state law was later declared unconstitutional. Operations under the federal agreement were carried out in 1934–1936 but with a new agreement for 1936 (No. 63, approved May 4, 1936). The 1936 agreement was terminated in March 1940.

The Colorado agreement was used in the years 1935–1942 and again in 1946–1955. It is the only federal program for vegetables or melons (except the new Florida tomato agreement) that has been in operation in the period since 1938. Operations under the federal program were suspended during the war but were continued in 1944 and 1945 under state law.[53]

The Southeast Watermelon Agreement

Watermelon growers in Florida, Georgia, South Carolina and North Carolina set up an agreement in 1934 (No. 52, effective August 10, 1934). Watermelons are very perishable and demand for them may fluctuate sharply because of weather conditions. The four states concerned furnish half the spring and early summer supply. The agreement provided for limitations on marketing charges, federal grading and inspection, grade restrictions, and for shipping holidays (not to exceed forty-eight hours and not to be spaced less than five days apart).

Because of disease and bad weather, the 1934 production was smaller than had been expected and grower returns were relatively good. Production was expanded in the following year. Grade and size restrictions were applied in 1935 and two shipping holidays were ordered. However, it is doubtful that the regulations kept any large number of melons off the market. Nevertheless, the growers considered the controls beneficial in stabilizing the market. A new agreement was adopted in 1936 and was in operation in 1937, 1938 and 1939 but was terminated in May

52. Nourse, *op. cit.*, p. 139.

53. The Washington agreements were Nos. 49 and 63. Colorado had two agreements, No. 56, approved in January 1935, and No. 67, approved in August 1936. The Control Committee includes three shippers, three cauliflower growers and four growers of fresh peas (as compared with three under the first agreement). Four district committees, to advise the Control Committee, were provided in the first agreement but were omitted from the second one. The effort to coordinate control arrangements as between areas in different states seems not to have been successful enough to warrant its continuance. The first agreements established period proration and compulsory U.S. grading and inspection. The Colorado agreement also placed limits on marketing charges. The 1936 revisions put the controls on a grade and size restriction basis and, for Washington, permitted standardization of containers. The limitation on marketing charges was eliminated from the Colorado agreement.

1941. Two other agreements of this general type were put into operation briefly, No. 42 (May 1, 1934) for Florida celery, and No. 75 (May 20, 1938) for Imperial County, California, and Yuma County, Arizona, cantaloupes and other melons.

Other Vegetable Programs

Since the Florida celery season was already well advanced, no program was put into operation until 1935, when shipments were put under limitation for eleven weeks. Grower returns were better than in the preceding three years but, apparently, the gains were due largely to improved economic conditions and smaller crops in competing areas. The agreement did not curtail volume. Estimates of available supplies were overstated and growers did not ship their full quotas. A new agreement, adopted in November 1937, discontinued the limitation on marketing charges and changed the make-up of the Control Committee. It was put into operation for only one season (1937) but was dropped shortly thereafter. A hearing was held on another Florida celery program in 1946 but it failed of approval in the referendum held in connection with it. Another hearing was held in 1955 and a program was presented for vote but again did not receive a sufficient number of votes to become effective.

The Imperial-Yuma melon agreement, administered by a committee of nine grower-shippers, placed restrictions on the marketing of small sizes and held off the market about a quarter of the 1938 crop. The prices received were considered satisfactory, but the agreement adopted on May 20, 1938 provided for automatic termination on July 31, 1938. No further attempts to establish market controls have been made; apparently the growers did not consider the gains sufficient to offset the disadvantages.

Four other vegetable agreements were worked out and approved. They were No. 75 (1937), the Utah onion agreement; No. 72 (1937), for Oregon cauliflower; No. 86 (1939), for Mississippi tomatoes; and No. 90 (1939), for Colorado onions. The two onion agreements were used only in the 1939 season. The Oregon cauliflower and Mississippi tomato agreements were issued but were not put into operation.

PROGRAMS FOR NONPERISHABLES

For the nonperishables (canning crops, tree nuts, dried fruits and hops) somewhat different procedures are possible than for the perishables. Some part of the crop can be carried over with a view to equalizing supplies from one season to another and there is more opportunity for diverting part of the crop to other markets or to abnormal outlets. When the marketing agreement legislation was passed, the growers of a number of these products immediately showed interest in using that procedure as a method of raising prices.

The procedure most commonly considered, and later employed, was to control quantities determined to be in surplus relative to normal demand at some "reasonable" price. After World War II, quality, grade, maturity and packaging regulations were also incorporated as permanent features of the programs. These are used even when surplus controls are not or cannot be applied.

In all, twelve programs for nonperishables were established, eight in the period prior to April 1935, one in 1938 and three in 1949–1955.[54] Except for pecans, the U.S. production of each of the crops was localized in a few producing areas on the Pacific Coast, at considerable distance from the principal markets. The early agreements covered Southeast pecans, Pacific Coast walnuts, California raisins, California prunes, California dates and three of the California canning crops (cling peaches, ripe olives and asparagus). The canning crop agreements were discontinued after the 1935 season. The early pecan, raisin, prune and date agreements were used for one season or less and then were allowed to lapse. However, controls on pecans, raisins and prunes were reimposed in the fall of 1949. A new date program was authorized in 1955.

In the later period, four additional programs were inaugurated: Pacific Coast hops (1938), Northwest filberts (1949), California almonds (1950) and California figs (1955). The Pacific Coast walnut agreement has been operated continuously since its adoption in late 1933. The hop program was terminated in 1953. The new date and fig programs were used in 1955. As of the close of 1955, eight programs were in use, those for almonds, walnuts, filberts and pecans, raisins, prunes, dates and figs.

The Canned Peach Agreement

Several programs for limiting the packs of canning crops and establishing minimum prices were discussed but only three were adopted, those relating to cling peaches, olives and asparagus. The California cling peach and ripe olive programs were in operation for the years 1933 and 1934 and the canned asparagus program in 1934 and 1935. In 1935, the canners fought vigorously and successfully to have canning crops excluded from the list of commodities that might be made subject to Secretary's orders. Olives and asparagus were left in as these two groups were satisfied with the program.

The clingstone peach agreement is of particular interest because of its early date and the fact that it served as a model for a number of later agreements. It was used to test the feasibility of the control devices then being proposed. The cling peach situation became chaotic in 1932, when returns to growers were barely sufficient to cover the cost of harvesting

54. Including the one for canned asparagus.

the crop and hauling it to market, even with fantastically low wage rates for labor. Only half the crop was harvested. For the peaches marketed, growers received a return of about $9 per ton as compared with $22 in 1928, $68 in 1929 and $20 in 1930.[55] The carry-over of canned peaches and of competing canned fruits was large, thus further complicating the situation.

The canning peach agreement, adopted on August 17, 1933, prohibited unfair trade practices, required the posting of prices, and prescribed minimum and maximum f.o.b. prices for canned peaches. However, the major provision was one establishing volume control as a means of raising prices to both growers and canners. The use of peaches grading below No. 1 was prohibited. Canner quotas were limited to a pack of 10 million cases out of an estimated 13-million-case crop. A price of $20 per ton for No. 1 peaches was prescribed. In addition, canners were to pay $2.50 per ton on peaches purchased for a stabilization pool. This fund was expended for the purchase of surplus peaches at $15 per ton for No. 1's. These peaches were not to be harvested and the $5 per ton differential was an allowance for harvesting costs that did not have to be incurred.

Several objections were raised in the first year of operation and a new program was developed for the 1934 crop. Only two regulatory provisions were retained and even these were considerably modified. The minimum grade requirement was changed so as to exclude all small sizes. Canner quotas were replaced by grower allocations. Each orchard was assigned a deliverable tonnage based on total available tonnage and the amount it was agreed could be canned.

Under the 1933 and 1934 programs, canners' year-end inventories were reduced to normal and returns to growers were increased sharply, from $1.5 million in 1932 to $5.5 million in 1933 and to $9.0 million in 1934. Nevertheless, the program was discontinued when the second agreement expired on June 30, 1935.[56] The task of assigning individual allotments proved extremely difficult and there was much dissatisfaction.[57] A short crop was in prospect for 1935. Also, during the control

55. S. W. Shear, *Deciduous Fruit Statistics,* Giannini Foundation of Agricultural Economics, Berkeley, California, Mimeographed Report No. 76, January 1941, p. 76. The 1929 price was much out of line on the up side because of a very short crop in that year, 180,000 tons as compared with 414,000 in 1928 and 542,000 in 1930. However, it did cause growers to be acutely conscious of the enormous decline in prices, since 1930 and 1931 were depression years. Even in comparison with the usual run of peach prices, the 1932 price was less than half what would normally be expected.

56. Canning peaches were, of course, not eligible for a marketing agreement after passage of the AAA amendments of August 24, 1935. After a lapse of a decade, a new program was worked out under state law and this has operated in the years since. It is designed to broaden the market for canned cling peaches and to avoid excess production through joint effort by producers and processors. Consumer advertising, trade promotion, quality improvement and surplus control are the mechanisms currently used.

57. The program was administered (in 1933) by a Control Committee of ten, eight of whom represented the canners, one the California Farm Bureau Federation and one

period the planting of peach trees had increased and the canning of competing fruits had expanded, thus indicating trouble ahead for the peach producers.

Canned Asparagus and Canned Olives

The California olive and asparagus industries were also in distress in the early 1930s. However, their problem was somewhat different. Both had two-way outlets. Expanding production and low demand were forcing more and more olives into crushing, where the returns were much lower than for canned olives. Since the U.S. supply of canned ripe olives is domestically produced while a large part of the olive oil used is imported, it was expected that a shift of more olives to the crushers would enhance the prices of canned olives without depressing the price of oil materially. In the asparagus industry, there is keen competition between the canning and fresh markets.

The olive stabilization program, put into effect in December 1933, was in operation for the 1933 and 1934 crops. It was terminated in November 1935. The Control Committee was authorized to establish the size of the pack by means of canner quotas, grower allocations and specification of minimum prices to growers in terms of size and variety. In addition, a schedule of minimum f.o.b. prices was established.

To make these price schedules effective, restrictions on allowances, brokerage fees and other terms of sale were spelled out. The establishment of minimum prices at the f.o.b. level was considered necessary as the bulk of the pack is sold by grower-processors and by cooperatives, who do not buy olives at fixed prices. The minimum-price feature was thought to have a favorable effect on prices to growers for the 1933 and 1934 crops. However, all of the increase cannot be ascribed to the program since production was low in those years. Size of pack was not affected. The agreement was adopted too late for it to affect the 1933 pack and that feature of it was not used in 1934.

For canning asparagus, the intention was that the agreement would be synchronized with the parallel agreement covering fresh asparagus. Minimum grades were established for asparagus that was to be canned. Limitation of pack was achieved by confining canning operations to a specified period rather than through canner quotas or grower allocations as in the peach and olive industries. An elaborate mechanism was devised to prevent diversion of supplies from the fresh market to canneries,

---

the general public. In the second year, the Committee was expanded to fifteen; seven growers, seven canners and one representative of the general public. In 1933, canner quotas were arrived at by a Board of Allocation, which consisted of three members selected by the Secretary of Agriculture. In the second year, a Receiving and Grading Committee, consisting of five growers, five canners and an eleventh member selected by the other ten, supervised the delivery of peaches to the canners. Prorations were handled by the Control Committee.

and the Control Committee, which watched the situation closely, announced, with three days' notice, the date at which packing would be completed.

In 1934, the canners would not sign an agreement but were willing to operate under a license embodying the same provisions. Accordingly, License No. 36 was issued on March 6. Growers were obligated to make cannery deliveries, after the opening date, in the quantities desired by the canners. Since each canner wanted to can as much as possible before the total designated pack was attained, deliveries on a large scale were requested even when the fresh outlet continued to be more profitable.

An agreement was negotiated and the license amended on April 3, 1935 so that no canner could take delivery from any grower except from acreage in excess of that which would supply the amount the grower was permitted to ship fresh under the companion agreement. Both the problem and the solution devised illustrate the complexity of arrangements of that kind and the improvising that is necessary if controls are to be made effective.

Considerable interest developed in similar programs for other two-outlet products. The Pacific Coast Bartlett pear industry attempted in 1934 and again in 1935 to devise a joint canning-pear–fresh-pear plan but was not able to agree on a workable procedure for synchronizing the California and Pacific Northwest industries. The canners of sour cherries tried to get agreement on a schedule of minimum f.o.b. prices to be made binding on all canners by means of a license but were unable to gain enough support to bring it into effect.

Proposals were made in 1934 for limiting the packs of sweet corn, peas, tomatoes and tomato products and for the establishment of minimum grower prices. However, since adequate statistical information was not available, the problem of devising an equitable plan for district quotas proved insurmountable. Canners, of course, lost interest when it became evident that proposals were being trimmed down so as to consist only of guarantees of minimum prices to growers.[58]

The Dried Fruit Agreements

The date, raisin and prune agreements were discontinued after operating only in the 1934 season. Programs for raisins and prunes were re-established in 1949, in conjunction with government purchase activi-

58. These attempts were made shortly after the Agricultural Adjustment Administration succeeded in raising the prices of several of the 1933 vegetable crops. In August, canners were asked to increase grower prices for certain canning vegetables above the levels specified in their contracts with the growers, since these were drawn earlier in the year when economic conditions were very unsettled. Prices for lima beans, cabbage for kraut, corn, peas and tomatoes were raised some 20 to 40 per cent. Considerable cooperation was also achieved in getting wholesalers and other buyers who had forward contracts to make revisions roughly compatible with those made by the processors.

ties designed to reduce excess supplies. In 1955 an agreement for California dried figs was adopted and the date program was revived.

The date program adopted in June 1934 was mainly a way of establishing minimum prices for sales by distributors. Such minimum prices on a monthly basis were specified by a Control Committee of eight shippers. Its purpose was to eliminate price cutting and to distribute supplies as they came forward from the growers. Controls over marketing charges, cash discounts, minimum grades and packaging standards were provided. These supplementary controls were considered necessary if the pricing provisions were to be made effective.

The agreement contemplated protection of quality and the establishment of price floors rather than the control of surpluses. Subsequently, adverse weather reduced date production well below the large crop that had been in prospect, and increased sharply the percentage of low-quality dates. Consequently, results were disappointing and the program was discontinued in October 1935.[59] The new agreement (No. 127), adopted on July 15, 1955, provides for surplus and quality controls. It was used to regulate marketings from the 1955 crop.

Programs for marketing raisins and prunes were adopted in May and August 1934. Both established controls over surpluses. In essence, the plans contemplated putting a portion of the crop at the disposal of a control board, which was authorized to dispose of it on a pooling basis. Provisions relating to the delivery and handling of these supplies were spelled out in great detail. Under the raisin program, a schedule of minimum prices to growers, applicable for the entire season, was provided.

Though raisin prices were satisfactory in 1934, because of a small crop, enforcement difficulties were encountered in the late part of the season. The 1934 prune crop contained an abnormally high percentage of low-quality fruit. Prices were not raised, but the program may have prevented further declines which would have brought chaos to the industry. Both programs were terminated in 1935.

In August 1949, these programs were revived with approximately the same control procedures as were previously used. For prunes, the Administrative Committee (consisting of fourteen growers and seven handlers) recommends to the Secretary of Agriculture the establishment of a salable percentage for the current crop, based on estimates of production, carry-over, consumptive demand, foreign outlets and other factors. Each handler is then free to dispose of that portion of his deliveries as he sees fit.

The surplus tonnage is eventually diverted into outlets that do not compete with normal marketings, that is, sales to the U.S. government and to foreign governments, commercial exports, and sales for manu-

59. A code designed to prevent price cutting in the imported-date industry was approved by NRA in November 1933. A large part of the U.S. supply of dates is imported.

facturing purposes in excess of the amounts used in establishing the figure for salable percentages. Some is diverted for use as animal feeds, for distillation, and so on.

A similar, though more complicated, program is used for raisins. Both agreements permit the maintenance of minimum-quality standards and such grading and inspection requirements as will result in "orderly marketing" of the product "in the public interest" in periods when prices are above parity.

The California fig agreement (No. 123), adopted March 22, 1955, provides for surplus and quality controls. It was in operation in the 1955 season.

The Programs for Tree Nuts

Surplus control programs similar to the one described for prunes have been in operation for Pacific Coast walnuts since 1933, for Northwest filberts since 1949 and for California almonds since 1950. For Southeast pecans, quality controls have been used since 1949. These four programs cover almost the entire U.S. output of tree nuts. Though they vary in administrative arrangements, they have a common objective, namely, the limitation of sales of unshelled nuts to amounts the domestic markets will take at prices that are considered "reasonable." The walnut program was amended on July 10, 1954 so as to include shelled walnuts in computing the total supply to which surplus controls are related.

Though the 1933 walnut crop was small, the supply of merchantable nuts was large. About 40 per cent of the previous year's large crop had been carried over. Ruinously low prices were in prospect. The two cooperatives that handled about 90 per cent of the crop announced that they would not continue to carry the entire burden of disposing of surplus through low-price, diversion outlets.

After some controversy between the two cooperatives and with the independent groups, an industry plan was developed. Under that program (Marketing Agreement No. 12 and License No. 8), adopted October 11, 1933, a surplus pool was established. Quantities so earmarked were to be diverted for shelling or exporting or were to be carried over into the following season. Though the establishment of minimum and maximum trade prices was permitted, it was not considered necessary to specify minimum prices to growers as the bulk of the crop was handled cooperatively and it was believed that an improvement in wholesale prices would be reflected back to the growers.

The 1935 program was amended to simplify operations. The minimum price arrangement was dropped, in compliance with the 1935 amendments to the Agricultural Adjustment Act. The third and current plan was adopted in August 1948. It continues approximately the same program except that minimum standards are prescribed for maturity and pack as well as for quality.[60]

The almond industry tried to develop an agreement in 1935 but the program discussed was not adopted. The pecan distributors concentrated their efforts on getting a code of fair competition similar to that for dates. However, after much agitation, an agreement (No. 57) was finally adopted on March 13, 1935. The program applied only to paper-shell pecans. It contained a schedule of minimum prices to growers and emphasized the use of U.S. grades. It was adopted primarily to enable the Control Board to organize and to recommend a course of action for the 1935 season.

The situation was different from that in walnuts and almonds in that pecan production is widely scattered and there are two varietal groups. Production of the improved, paper-shell varieties is centered in Georgia, Alabama, Mississippi and Louisiana whereas the seedling or wild varieties are grown mainly in Oklahoma and Texas. The two types are highly competitive. Many farmers produce only small quantities and sell in a variety of ways.[61]

So little progress was made that the agreement was not supplemented by the customary license. The agreement was allowed to expire on September 30, 1935 without being put into operation. A new program covering five of the southern states was adopted in September 1949. It established minimum standards by grade and size, and required federal grading and inspection.

Agreements relating to Northwest filberts and California almonds were adopted in 1949 and 1950.[62] Both use surplus control procedures similar to those for walnuts. The quantities withheld are diverted into export and shelling outlets. The programs for pecans, filberts and almonds have been operated almost continuously since their adoption.

Pacific Coast Hops

The price of hops fluctuates widely from year to year because of variations in yield and a relatively inelastic demand. To cope with this situation, a surplus control program was initiated in 1938. The program has evolved through four separate agreements.[63] Its aim was to increase

60. The program has been in operation continuously since 1933 except for the period October 2, 1943 to March 31, 1947, when prices were above parity. However, War Food Order No. 82 was put into effect in that period as a means of maintaining minimum standards of quality.

61. For a description of the industry, now somewhat out of date, see S. A. Jones, V. C. Childs, *et al., An Economic Study of the Pecan Industry,* U.S. Department of Agriculture, Technical Bulletin 324, September 1932.

62. Agreement No. 115 (October 1, 1949) for filberts and No. 119 (August 4, 1950) for almonds.

63. It was expanded in 1942. The first two agreements, Nos. 78 and 92, covering hops grown in California, Oregon and Washington, were in effect for the 1938–1941 seasons. A third agreement, No. 100, adopted on September 1, 1942, extended the coverage to

prices by limiting the amount sold from each crop. Each grower received an allotment representing his pro rata share. Sales were limited to hops (and hop products) bearing certificates issued to growers. The program was in operation during eight seasons, 1938–1941 and 1949–1952. It was discontinued on July 1, 1953.

At the request of the U.S. Hop Growers Association, a study of the effects of the hop program was made by the Giannini Foundation of Agricultural Economics in 1952. The authors of the report state that:

> The program, if not always successful in achieving "parity" price, has at least made the price higher in some seasons than it would have been without the control program. However, there is evidence that, at the same time, the higher prices have induced some growers to expand acreage and production and have induced new growers who were previously producing other crops to begin producing hops. This has led to an expansion of production which, in combination with a static or declining consumption, has resulted in continuation of a problem for whose solution the control program was originally introduced.[64]

SOME GENERAL CONCLUSIONS

So broad and diverse a program as that discussed in the preceding sections obviously cannot be reduced to any simple set of conclusions. Neither is it practical in a single chapter to analyze in detail more than a hundred marketing programs operating under a great variety of conditions and relating to commodities as diverse as watermelons and walnuts. However, some broad generalizations do seem to be warranted, and it is these that are of principal interest to the general reader.

For the participants in the programs, many specific and very detailed studies are needed in order that they may see more clearly whether the establishment and operation of marketing arrangements of this kind are likely to prove beneficial and whether techniques, administrative procedures and policies can be improved. The general public also has an interest in the effects of such programs on supplies and prices. For these purposes, individual commodity studies are appropriate and desirable. Unfortunately, not many have been made.[65]

Idaho and to hop products. No controls were put into effect under that agreement. It was terminated in September 1945. A fourth agreement, No. 107, was adopted on July 2, 1949. It included the Idaho area and established minimum standards of quality and compulsory federal inspection as permanent features.

64. Sidney Hoos and J. N. Boles, *Hops: Statistical Analysis of Marketing*, Giannini Foundation of Agricultural Economics, Berkeley, California, Mimeographed Report No. 139, September 1952, p. 27.

65. For a general, qualitative analysis of the effects of prorates and marketing agreements, see H. E. Erdman, "Market Prorates as Restrictions on Internal Trade" (and discussion by Budd A. Holt), *Journal of Farm Economics*, February 1938, pp. 170–87; George L. Mehren, "Some Economic Aspects of Agricultural Control," *ibid.*, February 1948, pp. 29–42; and *idem*, "Elementary Economic Theory of Marketing Control," *ibid.*, November 1949, pp. 1247–54. See also Nourse, *op. cit.*, particularly Chapters 14 and 15. A somewhat different approach is made by Frederick V. Waugh, "Market Pro-

One comment that seems warranted is that many of the industry groups have relied too heavily on hunches, general impressions and grower attitudes, and have not set up adequate arrangements for collecting, analyzing and disseminating needed statistical and other information. All too easily, a general upsurge in consumer income or a short crop that results in higher prices may be looked upon as a result of a control program, while a drop in demand or a large or poor-quality crop may lead growers to discredit an operation that, on the whole, has worked reasonably well.

The essential distinction is between the situation under the marketing program and what it would have been had the program not been in effect. But this is an extremely difficult judgment to arrive at and even more difficult to demonstrate empirically. In large measure, results and possibilities will continue to be based on "informed guesses" rather than on statistical computations.

Though the lack of precise information about individual programs is apparent, it is also true that one of the very significant gains from the programs is that growers participating in them have, in general, a much better understanding of the economic factors affecting their businesses than they had before. A few of the larger organizations, especially those having well-developed cooperatives to base on, have gone far in developing highly competent statistical departments. Some of the processing industries, too, have made significant progress in that direction. Generally speaking, it has been the less well organized groups, operating on a noncontinuous basis, that have been least well serviced in arriving at decisions, checking compliance and broadening their markets.

Market Controls v. Curtailment of Production

The marketing agreement technique as originally conceived placed much emphasis on control of marketing methods and margins. More and more, however, experience has led to greater emphasis on the regulation of supply, but at the marketing stage rather than in the production process, whereas the major field crop programs have relied heavily on acreage controls and government subsidies.

Basically, the difference is not great. Both types of program are designed to raise prices to growers and, in most cases, to increase the amounts paid by consumers.[66] The differences are due more to the nature of the industries and the kinds of products handled than to differences in underlying philosophy. Both constitute a form of government-sponsored monopoly.

---

rates and Social Welfare," *Journal of Farm Economics,* May 1938, pp. 403–16. However, this deals with the idea of differential prices for different income groups, a principle not contemplated in the marketing agreement programs actually developed.

66. Either directly or through taxes. In some cases, government funds have been used to supplement surplus removal programs initiated through marketing agreements. (See pp. 414–15.)

It does not follow, however, that all such operations work to the disadvantage of the consumer. Many of the crops for which marketing agreements have been developed are perishables. Some evening up of flow may be advantageous to both consumers and producers. Also, the elimination at the farm of poor qualities, offgrades and small sizes may be advantageous to consumers and socially desirable as a means of preventing waste in handling.[67]

It can be argued too that the extreme variations in supply that characterize some of the perishable crops and bring disaster to producers or short rations to consumers are not in the public interest if they can be overcome by organizing the industry in a more comprehensive way than is feasible for individual suppliers or cooperatives. Where the control of shipments does not result in waste of the commodity, both growers and consumers are probably benefited.

But can such arrangements be authorized without setting the stage for monopoly pricing arrangements that will be socially undesirable? Here opinions differ. However, so long as individual producers can come in or go out, or can increase or decrease their production at will, there is not much prospect that prices can be held at unwarrantedly high levels for very long.[68]

Generally speaking, strong controls can hold the price in the upper range of the spread within which production will not be increased or consumption decreased significantly, whereas it might be lower if there were no control. This spread, however, is usually narrow and must be judged very accurately if such gains to producers are to be achieved. If they are achieved, the modest gain to producers is not likely to be a serious burden to consumers. In nearly all cases, an attempt to hold prices very much above the free-market level tends to stimulate production and may cause the program to disintegrate.

On the whole, it seems safe to say that the opportunities for monopoly gains in the perishable crops are not great enough to be grounds for serious public concern. In the nonperishables, such as nuts and dried fruits, the surplus control arrangements, especially if they involve export dumping or heavy government purchases, may be such as to warrant careful scrutiny from the standpoint of consumers.[69]

67. However, the elimination of small sizes and offgrades may deprive consumers of lower-cost supplies that are equally nutritious though technically inferior, and thus may reduce over-all consumption. Also, these methods of control at times result in inequities and discrimination as between producing areas, especially in some years. However, the desirability of quality maintenance and rigorous standardization has long been accepted in most other lines, particularly in manufactured products. (For a fuller comment, see *Three Years of the Agricultural Adjustment Administration*, pp. 228–29.)

68. There are a few exceptions, mainly in those crops which are highly concentrated in small areas and therefore can be easily manipulated.

69. It is also quite possible for the control agencies to become so much concerned about prices for the amounts to be sold through regular channels that they overdo the diversion to inferior uses, thus operating to the disadvantage of both consumers and producers. However, such misallocations are not likely to persist very long. Producer

Marketing Agreements Not Uniformly Successful

The experience outlined in preceding sections demonstrates that the desirability and effectiveness of the marketing agreement technique are by no means universally accepted by growers and handlers. In general, the agreements have worked best for products grown in compact, specialized areas far from their principal markets, and better for the less perishable than for the highly perishable commodities.

The Pacific Coast specialty crop growers, particularly in California, have shown the greatest interest in setting up agreements and, in general, have had the best results from them. This is probably due in part to the need for reaching distant markets with a well-standardized, high-quality product and perhaps even more to the long and successful experience of these groups with cooperative organizations. Basically, the popularity of both types of market organization stems from the same causes. The marketing agreement procedure is, in effect, a more comprehensive form of the programs undertaken by many of the cooperatives before government aid became available. It has many similarities to the union-shop arrangement in organized labor since the licenses and orders tend to compel all growers and handlers to operate in accordance with rules established by the majority.

The attempts to regulate marketing charges and practices and to operate on the basis of posted prices have been abandoned at an early stage in nearly all of the agreements. Relatively simple flow regulations, quality controls and diversionary arrangements have been the ones that have stood the test of time wherever marketing agreements have continued in effect.

Surplus controls have been used in all but one of the programs for nonperishables but in only one of those relating to fresh fruits and vegetables. In the sixteen agreements (or orders) issued for fresh fruits and vegetables in the first two years of operation, a rate-of-flow provision was included in thirteen, including two where this was in conjunction with grade-size restrictions. Three called for grade-size restrictions without rate-of-flow provisions. After June 1935, grade-size limitation became the major regulatory device for perishables. It was included in thirty of the thirty-three agreements (or orders) adopted since mid-1935. In half of them such restriction was used in combination with the rate-of-flow provision. The rate-of-flow arrangement without grade-size restrictions was used in only three agreements.

---

pressure is almost always for larger allotments. The big problem, from the standpoint of the administrators, is to induce growers to hold back enough, rather than the danger of causing them to curtail too severely. Extreme restrictions lead to grower dissatisfaction and to difficult enforcement problems. The restraints that can be applied practically are almost certainly no greater than those that apply in ordinary nonagricultural, competitive businesses.

Interarea agreements on a national basis have in general proved unworkable. In fact, the number of regional and state agreements terminated after very short periods of operation, especially in perishables, makes clear the great difficulty of holding growers and handlers together even in localized areas, unless there are very evident advantages and unless the agreement is soundly based economically. However, some of the very recent efforts to develop interarea cooperation under potato marketing agreements have apparently shown somewhat better results than the earlier attempts of that kind, though mainly through improved contact by means of informal interarea agreements.

Marketing agreements have not required large expenditure of government funds, except when supplemented by government-financed surplus removal programs. They are sometimes referred to as "private price programs." [70] In this they differ markedly from the major crop programs, which have involved heavy inputs of federal funds. However, they do require fairly substantial administrative expenses, which are derived mainly from assessments on the growers and handlers rather than from the government, and a good deal of donated time. Also, operation under the rules set up may involve considerable inconvenience, some extra expense and, at times, significant disturbance to normal production and marketing processes. Undoubtedly, these disadvantages, when set off against such gains as can be shown or anticipated, have in many cases caused agreements to be discontinued or not put into operation.

Grower Control Essential

The experience to date seems to indicate that confidence in the management cannot, in most cases, be maintained unless the growers have majority representation on the project committees. Nearly all of the agreements that were started with handler domination of committees were quickly terminated and replaced by agreements that provided more grower representation.

The significance of this change may be more apparent than real. In many cases, advisory committees made up of handlers are provided. It is likely that the decisions arrived at are similar to what they would have been under the earlier form of organization, since the grower-dominated project committees obviously want the programs to be workable from a

70. However, the really meaningful device is the companion "Secretary's order," which is in terms equivalent to those of the agreement. For some fifteen years, no agreement has been issued without a parallel order. Since an order cannot be approved without concurrence of two thirds of the growers by volume or number, the issuance of an order implies support on the part of a substantial portion of the industry. Agreements can be established for any agricultural commodity, but orders are limited by law to milk, tobacco, tree nuts, a designated list of unprocessed fruits and vegetables, and some specialties. The list is thus limited because, at present, orders can be issued even though handlers fail or refuse to sign an agreement. Processors and handlers oppose vigorously any broadening of coverage in the act unless they can be assured that no program substantially affecting their operations will be put into effect without their consent.

handler standpoint. However, there are psychological advantages in having the official decisions made by grower-dominated committees.

On the whole, administrative procedures seem to have shaken down into stable patterns. Most of the problems encountered in the earlier years have been resolved to the mutual satisfaction of different groups within the industries. In some programs, there is still a feeling that the impact is not equitable. In several cases, the support given the program may stem from intangible but nevertheless important benefits such as getting growers and handlers together for better understanding of the industry's problems, alleviating mutual suspicion and disseminating information. The programs do not require large private or governmental expenditures and their continuance may be justified on the basis of rather meager benefits. Over the past twenty years, much has been learned concerning the kinds of situations in which controls are likely to be useful and the types of regulation that are appropriate.[71]

Over-All Results Inconclusive

Though proof is lacking, there is a general belief on the part of those close to the programs that some of them at least have resulted in increased returns to growers and some gains in the form of more stable markets. For example, it is generally believed that the diversion of portions of the nut crops to secondary markets on a "discriminatory price" basis increases somewhat the over-all returns to growers.

It is often contended that the programs may have induced larger plantings. Here also there is lack of conclusive evidence that plantings have been expanded more than they would have been without a control program. However, it is clear that if such programs can be and are used to extort from the public high monopoly prices, they are likely to result not only in expanded production but in increased use of substitute products. In the history of market control, there are examples of markets for controlled products which have been affected in both of these ways.

The longevity of operations under the programs affords some indication of the views of participants as to their effectiveness. Many have been terminated after only a brief period of operation. Others have been in operation during five to ten seasons or even longer. Some of these variations undoubtedly are due to differences in industry conditions, others to the experience of the growers with such programs and to the amount of cohesiveness in the group. Some, no doubt, can be traced to differences in the quality of management and the wisdom and cooperativeness of the individuals making up the control committees.

71. However, little is known about the economic aspects of these programs. Reliance still is placed on guesses, guided by the instincts and knowledge of industry members long experienced in the marketing of the commodities controlled. There is little empirical evidence about the effects of the programs on prices and still less about their influence on net income to growers for the crop as a whole, including amounts withheld or diverted as well as amounts sold through regular channels.

The devices used currently do not seem to be adequate for dealing with serious surplus situations and have not had any significant effect in narrowing distributive margins. In essence, they are designed primarily to make possible the distribution of available supplies in such a way as to take full advantage of the demand that exists. Only part of the supply is controlled.

Unregulated outlets, outside producing areas and competing commodities exert a substantial restraining influence on the prices that can be achieved by means of controls. Enforcement of regulations is likely to be difficult even where there is strong management. Grower expectations often are not realistically related to what the programs can reasonably be expected to accomplish.

More Realistic Goals Needed

The achievement of parity price, which is the specified goal and principal governing criterion in the marketing programs, accords only accidentally with the achievement of other goals. It is inflexible and sometimes very unrealistic. Other objectives are more important.

For example, if a program is put into operation, it should be reasonable to expect that:

1. Producer returns will be improved in the short run without long-run damage.
2. Unfavorable production and demand shifts will not occur.
3. The program will not threaten significant injury to processors and handlers.
4. Consumers will not be exploited by a powerful monopoly.[72]

Too rigid adherence to parity price as a goal may run counter to any one or even all of these objectives.

If some such governing policy could be established legislatively, the law might well be broadened so as to cover all commodities that qualify under the criteria chosen.[73] As of now, programs are restricted to the smallest practicable areas. In few if any of the programs embracing several areas have the committees in charge been able to reach agreement on policies and procedures that were in the interest of all of the areas concerned. Such programs had, in fact, proved unworkable even before the law prohibited them.

On the whole, enforcement has been easiest and operation most successful if:

1. Contact with the control agency could be maintained easily.

72. Jerry Foytik, "Private Price Programs in Agriculture," in *Kansas State College Bulletin,* January 1954, pp. 119–28, paper read at the Kansas Farm Policy Forum, Manhattan, Kansas, October 6, 1953.

73. Such a change would imply some modification of other provisions of the law, for example, those relating to the conditions under which Secretary's orders are permissible. Agreements without orders are meaningless, though the retention in the law of authorization for them is harmless.

2. Producer and distributor interests were somewhat similar.

3. Production was concentrated, or at least not scattered too widely.

4. There was some bottleneck in the distributive system which could be overcome through orderly management of the distributive process.

5. No large local market for the primary product was readily accessible.

6. A secondary outlet was available for diverted portions of the crop.

In short, marketing controls work best in situations where selling cooperatives work best. If applied to situations in which there are long-run surpluses, caused by excessive production capacity rather than by annual fluctuations in yield, marketing agreements are not likely to be successful. If close substitutes for the product exist, the prolonged use of marketing controls may worsen the very problems they are designed to solve.

Other Types of Aid—Fruits and Vegetables

In addition to the aid given in the "self-help" programs, through assistance in setting up and administering marketing agreements and the provision of licenses and orders, price supports through direct government expenditure have been sizable. These have been mainly in the form of Section 32 programs and losses taken by the Commodity Credit Corporation on purchases made by it. For the period June 30, 1936 to June 30, 1950, such expenditures were reported as follows (in thousands): [74]

Dried fruits	$ 74,136
Apples	65,144
Citrus fruit	58,195
Other fruit	25,425
Garden vegetables	47,827
Tree nuts	14,523
Total	$285,250

These funds were used mainly for surplus removal operations, some of which involved transfers to the school lunch program. Others were in the form of export subsidies of various kinds. Nearly a third of the price-support expenditure on perishables was in the fruit operations. Apples were in almost continuous oversupply because of a downward trend in domestic demand and increased use of citrus products and other fruits and vegetables. Foreign demand also dropped off sharply in the

74. *Price Supports for Perishable Products: A Review of Experience,* U.S. Senate, 82d Cong., 1st sess., Committee Print, October 17, 1951, p. 3. These activities were continued in 1951–1954 on an over-all scale somewhat similar to that of the late 1940s. For a more complete summary covering the years 1932 through 1953, see *Can We Solve the Farm Problem?,* Appendix B.

1930s. Citrus production was expanding, sometimes more rapidly than demand was increasing.

Dried fruits were in trouble because of reduced foreign demand. Before the depression of the 1930s, about 40 per cent of the dried fruit output (mostly prunes and raisins) was exported. Most of the expenditure on tree nuts was for the purpose of financing export and diversion programs.

Such price analyses as are available indicate that government expenditures on perishables as a whole may have raised prices by 1 to 2 per cent. For a few crops, the increase in grower returns may have been much larger: for such crops as prunes, pears, onions and snap beans, perhaps as much as 10 to 25 per cent in some years. The total amount spent was about 1 per cent of the value of all perishables sold.[75]

75. *Price Supports for Perishable Products,* pp. 10 and 11.

10

Potatoes[1]

OF ALL the farm price-support programs, the potato program has undoubtedly been the most widely discussed and criticized in the public press. During the brief period of its operation it was the most expensive of the crop programs and, because of the nature of the product, the one which consumers were most aware of.

The potato crop is not one of the most important sources of agricultural income, but it is a basic food crop, used almost daily in nearly every home in the country, and mostly in unprocessed form. It ranks about sixth in importance among the crops as a source of cash income to farmers. In recent years, it has ranked below soybeans but above sugar beets and peanuts.

The program relating to potatoes grew largely out of the fear of shortage in the war years and was confined mainly to the years 1942 to 1950. The net cost to the federal government was more than $600 million, even though there was no support program in the depression years when such aid would have seemed most appropriate, and in spite of the fact that the principal potato support program was terminated at about the time farm prices began to decline in the postwar period.

Characteristics of the Industry

Potato production has long been recognized as a highly speculative business. Demand for the product is very inelastic but production varies greatly from year to year.[2] Consequently, there are wide fluctuations in year-to-year prices, in the opposite direction from the changes in quantities produced. The pronounced variations in output of potatoes have in the past resulted mainly from two factors: (1) sharp increases and declines in yield, and (2) changes in acreages grown.

The relation of the crop to other enterprises on the farms that grow potatoes has some bearing on the fluctuations in acreages planted. Pota-

1. Potatoes have, of course, many of the characteristics of other perishable crops such as those discussed in the preceding chapter. However, since the principal programs relating to them were quite different from those described in Chapter 9, the potato programs are treated as a separate group of operations.

2. Not only is demand inelastic on a year-to-year basis but also per capita consumption has been declining for several decades. Though population has increased by more than 50 per cent during the past forty years, the food market for potatoes is almost the same as it was in the period around 1910.

toes are grown very widely on the farms of the United States, often as a side line that requires only a small portion of the total acreage of the farm. Under these conditions, very large percentage increases or decreases in potato acreage can be made without disturbing seriously the organization of the farm business as a whole.[3] The total acreage harvested was as low as 3,030,000 in 1929 and as high as 3,599,000 in 1934. The variation in planted acreages was even larger, from 3,068,000 to 3,789,000. The acreage harvested in 1954 was only 1,408,000.[4]

Another element in the situation is that, when price supports are not in effect, a good deal of the adjustment in supply occurs on the farms where the potatoes are grown. If prices are very low, some of the acreage may not be harvested, since a sizable portion of the total cost is for harvesting and marketing. Grading may be more rigorous, with more of the small and damaged potatoes left on the farm, and so on. When prices are supported at specified levels, adjustments of that kind are less likely to be made and the cost of absorbing the excess is transferred to the government instead of being borne by the industry as was customary in the past.

However, the elimination of price risk may cause growers to be willing to produce more potatoes at a given price than if they themselves had to carry the cost of risks of that kind. That effect, if it exists, could result in a gain to society if price supports were adjusted to the level needed to induce growers to produce the amounts the public really wants. On the other hand, if the price is supported in a fixed relationship to prices prevailing in some earlier period, and if that price is high enough to result in larger production than is needed, the result is merely to waste resources and impose a financial burden on society. The price maintained in some of the postwar years seems to have had that effect.

Other important characteristics of the crop are that it is bulky, expensive to ship and store, and cannot be carried over from one year to the next. The portion of the family food budget required for the purchase of potatoes is such that most families buy about as many potatoes as they want regardless of price. Consequently, price adjustments, if they are to

3. This applies, of course, mainly to adjustments on farms that depend primarily on other enterprises for their income. Some areas rely heavily on potato production as a major enterprise. Here, large adjustments in acreage are less feasible and more difficult to bring about. That is particularly true for specialized potato-producing areas such as those in Maine and in parts of Michigan, New Jersey, New York, Wisconsin and Idaho. However, in the more diversified farming areas of states like Minnesota, California and Wisconsin, rather large changes in potato acreage can be and are made as growers see prospects of larger or smaller profits in potato production. For example, the acreage harvested in the Michigan, Wisconsin, Minnesota and Dakota area declined from 858,000 in 1943 to 699,000 in 1944, a drop of 20 per cent. In Maine, the decline was from 205,000 to 201,000, only 2 per cent. (U.S. Department of Agriculture, *Agricultural Statistics, 1945,* p. 227.)

4. U.S. Agricultural Marketing Service, *Crop Summary as of August 1,* August 10, 1955, p. 4. Planted acreages in the preceding sentence are from *Agricultural Statistics, 1951,* p. 253.

have much effect on consumption, must be very large. Alternative uses for the product are limited and values in such uses very low. Hence the opportunities for diversion to other outlets at prices that can be considered acceptable are almost nil.

Yields Have Increased Sharply

An important factor in the difficulties encountered in the late 1940s was the fact that potato yields increased in a quite unprecedented way. This probably was due in part to the program itself. Less rigorous culling at the harvesting and marketing stages contributed to higher reported yields, and, more important, the elimination of price risk and the assurance of relatively favorable prices encouraged the use of fertilizer, the use of sprays and the rapid introduction of improved methods of production.

Some considerable part of this yield increase would no doubt have occurred without a price-support program, since technological advances were being made at a very rapid rate throughout the agricultural industry. The price-support program probably served to speed up that type of change. Costs also were being reduced sharply as a result both of increased yields and of much wider use of power machinery. Changes of that kind gave rise to strong incentives for increased production under a pricing system that did not provide for downward adjustments to offset cost reductions.

Whatever the reasons for the yield increases, they were large and contributed markedly to the burdensome surpluses that developed. In the period around 1930, yields per harvested acre were, for the most part, in the order of 100 to 110 bushels per acre. By the late 1940s, and in 1950 and after, they were ranging from about 225 to 250 bushels per acre. This was a much larger percentage increase than had occurred in any other important farm crop, in fact one of the most striking changes of that kind in the whole history of American agriculture.

Contrary to widely held views, very significant adjustments in acreage were made, but they were not large enough to compensate for these huge increases in yield per acre. In the late 1930s, planted acreages were in the order of 2,800,000 to 3,000,000. Concern over the adequacy of supplies and special incentive programs initiated by the government led to a stepping up of acreage to a peak of 3,355,000 in 1943. The increase in yields did not become an important factor in the situation until 1945 and after. By 1948, acreage was down to about 2,000,000 and by 1951 it had declined to 1,359,000, less than half that of the 1930s.

THE PRICE-SUPPORT PROGRAMS

Early Attempts to Aid Potato Growers

During the Farm Board period, potatoes were designated as a commodity for which loans could be made. Some of the cooperatives applied, and loans in the amount of about $400,000 were made while the Board was still operating. Loans to potato cooperatives were continued under the Farm Credit Administration, after the transfer of that activity to the banks for cooperatives. The loans made by the Farm Board were mainly for the purpose of improving merchandising operations.

The price had fallen from an average of $1.32 per bushel in 1929 to $.38 in 1932. The most important factor in this change was the decline in the general level of prices. However, the low prices of 1931 and 1932 were due partly to larger than average crops, though the excess was moderate as compared with the amounts produced in the 1920s. The 1929 crop was unusually small and the price abnormally high.[5]

There was some reduction in plantings and a lower yield in 1933. Production dropped back from 375 million bushels to 343 million and the price more than doubled. Part of the recovery was due to increased economic activity and an upward movement in farm prices as a whole. The general level of farm prices moved up from an index of 55 in February 1933 (1909–1914=100) to 80 in November.[6]

The relatively high price of 1933 led to an increase in plantings. Yields were higher and total production reached 406 million bushels in 1934, as compared with 343 million in 1933. The price dropped back to 45 cents, which was only slightly above the extremely low price of 1932.[7]

First Program under AAA

The first program for potatoes under the Agricultural Adjustment Administration was in 1933, under the marketing agreement provisions of the act. Potatoes were not classified as a "basic" crop and hence were not eligible for aid under the processing tax and production control sec-

5. The amounts produced in the years 1929 to 1940 were as follows (in thousands of bushels):

1929	333,392	1935	378,895
1930	343,817	1936	323,955
1931	384,317	1937	376,448
1932	374,692	1938	355,848
1933	343,203	1939	342,372
1934	406,482	1940	376,920

(*Agricultural Statistics, 1951,* p. 253.)

6. *Agricultural Statistics, 1937,* p. 402. Industrial production rose from 58 in January (1935–1939=100) to 85 in July, but receded thereafter to 70 in December. Factory employment increased from 65 (1923–1925=100) to 80 and above in the latter part of the year (seasonally adjusted data as given in U.S. Bureau of the Census, *Historical Statistics of the United States, 1789–1945,* 1949, pp. 328, 330).

7. It should be recognized that the potato market is not a single, homogeneous one. There are somewhat noncompetitive markets for early and late potatoes and there may be wide geographic variations in the prices for either early or late potatoes in any given year. Hence the over-all averages presented for the United States may not be representative of prices received in a particular area. Prices, production, acreages and yields by regions, states and types are given in U.S. Bureau of Agricultural Economics, *Potatoes,* Statistical Bulletin 122, March 1953, in much greater detail than can be presented in a general summary of this kind.

tions of the act. The southeastern potato growers developed a marketing agreement and license program to become effective in July 1934.[8] It was not considered satisfactory, so later in the year these growers appealed to Washington for a more effective plan of operation.

They had observed the apparent success of the cotton and tobacco control programs in raising prices to growers and wanted something similar for their industry. Growers from other areas joined them in advocating legislation for the improvement of conditions in the potato industry. The very low price of 1934 reinforced these arguments and a Potato Control Act was included in the package of amendments to the Agricultural Adjustment Act that was passed in August 1935.

The Potato Control Act of 1935

The Potato Control Act designated potatoes as a basic commodity and included provisions for control over quantities marketed that were similar to those of the Bankhead Cotton Control Act. A tax was to be levied on marketings in excess of producer allotments. The act never came into operation because of the January 1936 decision of the Supreme Court in the Hoosac Mills case, which resulted in the abandonment of control measures of that type.[9] However, Section 32 of these same 1935 amendments made funds available (from customs receipts) with which the Secretary of Agriculture could, if he chose, give some support to potato prices.[10]

The 1936 crop was small and no surplus existed. Prices rose to $1.14, as compared with 59 cents in 1935 and 45 cents in 1934.[11] A high yield in 1937 (on a slightly smaller planted acreage) resulted in a surplus for that year though not a large one.[12] In the years that followed, except in the short-crop year 1939, small quantities were purchased annually for distribution in the school lunch and relief programs.[13] Also,

8. Marketing Agreement No. 48 accompanied by License No. 76.

9. The Potato Control Act was repealed on February 10, 1936 but the method of computing parity prices for potatoes which was contained in that act was used in the later computations of potato price parities. The parity base was specified as August 1919 to July 1929 instead of 1909–1914 as provided for most other crops.

10. Even before these funds became available, the AAA formulated a plan for diverting part of the prospectively large 1935 crop for use as livestock feed and for industrial uses. However, as a result of a severe freeze in several of the late potato states, the diversion plan was abandoned. (See Edwin G. Nourse, Joseph S. Davis and John D. Black, *Three Years of the Agricultural Adjustment Administration*, The Brookings Institution, Washington, 1937, p. 203n.) The AAA also, in the fall of 1935, applied quotas on imports of potatoes (from Canada) under Section 229 of the Potato Act. (*Ibid.*, p. 207n.)

11. *Agricultural Statistics, 1951*, p. 253. Data from this source vary slightly from figures appearing in later annual issues (see note 21).

12. Marketing orders (Nos. 17 and 19) relating to potatoes from Colorado, Nebraska, Wyoming and Idaho were issued on October 19, 1937 but were canceled on July 31, 1938.

13. Potato growers, in diversion areas, were also eligible for diversion payments under the Soil Conservation and Domestic Allotment Act and in nondiversion areas as well for

some small amounts from the 1937, 1940 and 1941 crops were purchased for diversion to livestock feed and starch manufacture. Only small quantities of potatoes were distributed under the food stamp plan, which was initiated in 1939 and terminated in 1943.

The most significant operation of these years was in 1940, when production amounted to 377 million bushels and the price fell to 53 cents. Of this amount, the government bought a total of 21 million bushels, of which about 16 million were diverted to livestock feed and starch production. These purchases do not appear to have affected the price to growers to any great extent. The 376-million-bushel crop of 1937 brought a return of 53 cents per bushel and the 356-million-bushel crop of 1938 about 55 cents. The 21 million bushels purchased by the government from the 1940 crop brought the commercial supply down to about the 1938 level. Prices were similar in 1938 and 1940. However, 1938 was a recession year whereas business recovery was beginning to exert some influence in 1940.[14]

The shorter crop of 1939 (342 million bushels) brought about 70 cents per bushel. It seems probable that the price would have gone lower in 1940 if the government had not stepped in, but the evidence is not strong. Some of the potatoes bought for relief distribution probably would have been bought anyway and even some of those diverted to starch manufacture would perhaps have been bought and used in the same way. Sales for livestock feed are more likely to have reduced supplies, but this also is a use that is often resorted to by growers if supplies are excessive.

Some informal estimates put the probable effect on price at about 3 cents per bushel, that is, a price of 50 cents without government support as compared with 53 cents actually received. The operation cost the government about $7 million. If the above estimate of its price effect is accepted, it added about $10 million to the returns to growers. Consumers paid most of whatever that increase amounted to, in the form of higher prices for potatoes.

Whether this very modest effect on prices was sufficient to reduce the cutback of acreage in the following year when potatoes were in greater demand and shorter supply seems doubtful. The acreage planted was cut back slightly in 1941 and yields were slightly lower, resulting in a crop of 356 million bushels, which was about the same as that of 1938. There probably were some significant temporary and local effects in clearing away surpluses and improving prices, but the operation was

---

payments under the conservation practice features of the act. The crop was first put on an allotment basis in 1938, as a result of a nationwide referendum conducted in 1937. Allotments and/or acreage goals were continued in later years for the commercial areas and price supports were made conditional on compliance with allotments in the period from 1943 on.

14. Factory employment in 1940 was well above that of 1938 and about as high as in 1937.

apparently not large enough, or sufficiently effective in actually decreasing over-all supplies, to have a very large effect either on the returns to potato growers as a whole or on costs to consumers.[15]

THE WAR PERIOD

Efforts to Stimulate Production

In the early part of the war period, the demand for potatoes increased, and prices rose sharply, to 79 cents per bushel in 1941 and to $1.14 in 1942. There was little change in acreage, and production remained about at prewar levels. The prices of foodstuffs generally were advancing and there was not much incentive for farmers to increase potato acreage since farm labor shortages and higher wages were already making the labor-intensive crops less attractive. As early as November 1942, the Secretary of Agriculture included potatoes in a list of products which farmers were asked to produce in larger amounts. He announced that the 1943 crop would be supported at 90 per cent of parity.[16]

By the spring of 1943, the supply of late potatoes was so low that many families in the large cities were unable to buy them in the amounts they were in the habit of using. Also, government officials and the public had, by then, become much more interested in the general food supply problem.

The Secretary's request and the promise of price support at 90 per cent of parity, plus the high price received in 1942, resulted in a large increase in plantings and a record crop in 1943. For that year, the 90 per cent of parity support worked out to a little over a dollar per bushel. The very large increase in output caused the government to be heavily involved in support operations, including purchases, diversions and direct distribution by means of dealer agreements.[17]

15. During these years there was some effort to use marketing agreements in improving the marketing of potatoes. Marketing Agreement No. 97 and Order No. 58 were made effective as of August 30, 1941 for Colorado potatoes. Idaho and Oregon adopted Marketing Agreement No. 98 on September 5, 1941 (Order No. 57 was issued on the same date). This agreement (and the order relating to it) was amended on January 19, 1950. There had also been for a brief period in 1938 an order (No. 23) relating to Louisiana, Texas, Mississippi, Alabama and Florida potatoes. It was issued on May 12, 1938 and terminated on July 31, 1938.

16. The first price-support announcement for potatoes in which the support level was related to parity had been made in 1942. It related only to designated commercial areas. The support level was at 75 per cent of parity, equivalent to 76 cents in the early and intermediate areas and to 81 cents in the late areas. However, prices advanced enough so that no price-support purchases were made in 1942.

17. The problem became particularly acute in the early potato areas of the Southeast since these very perishable types with high water content could not be held for any length of time and were not well suited for processing into starch. Abnormal weather conditions delayed the North Carolina crop and brought it onto the market at the same time as crops from the Eastern Shore of Virginia and Maryland became available. Very hot weather during the shipping season intensified the problem and caused considerable spoilage. Similar difficulties arose in Oklahoma, Arkansas and northeastern Texas. (*Continued opposite page.*)

These operations involved disposal of some 36 million bushels and a net cost to the government of about $22 million.[18] The price was kept somewhat above the required support level and averaged 108 per cent of parity for the season ($1.28 as compared with $1.14 in 1942). However, farm prices as a whole were by that time up to 112 per cent of parity.

Acreage Reduced in 1944 and After

From 1943 on, acreage was reduced markedly, dropping from 3.4 million in 1943 to 2.9 million in 1944 and to 2.7 million and 2.6 million in 1945 and 1946. The 1944 crop was only moderately above prewar levels but high yields brought the 1945 outturn up to 419 million bushels and that of 1946 to a record-breaking total of 487 million.

The 1944 crop was large enough to supply the civilian population and the military services at prices that were above parity but not so high as to press strongly against the established price ceilings. However, the crop was below the estimated requirements. The 1945 crop provided a surplus of about 18 million bushels, including 8 million bushels for export, 3 million for alcohol and 3 million for starch. The net cost of support operations on the 1944 crop was about $3.3 million and on the 1945 crop about $15 million. The total for the war crops of 1943–1945 amounted to about $40 million.[19]

In potatoes, as in most other crops, the goals established by the government agencies proved unrealistic. The 1944 estimate of requirements was for a 10 per cent increase over that of 1943 and the announced goal called for a corresponding adjustment in acreage. However, farmers reduced the acreage planted about 14 per cent. Production was nearly 17 per cent below that of 1943. The price increased but it still was necessary for CCC to purchase a small quantity of potatoes in order to maintain the announced level of support prices.[20]

In general, the price guarantees of the war years apparently contributed to the maintenance of a high level of production that, for the most part, was needed. Though the 1943 and 1945 crops were large enough

---

Starch factories were overloaded and could not absorb the surplus fast enough to keep the markets cleared. In order to prevent waste, some of the early potatoes were canned and later supplied to British and American troops engaged in desert fighting, but only through use of considerable quantities of steel and tin that were desperately needed for other purposes. Government purchases through June 30, 1943 amounted to 1,645 cars. (See *Report of the Director of the Food Distribution Administration, 1943*, pp. 77–78.)

18. Commodity Credit Corporation, *Irish Potatoes, Price Supports and Related Operations, Commodity Credit Corporation and Section 32 Funds, January 1, 1943–June 30, 1952*, U.S. Production and Marketing Administration, Fiscal Branch, Financial Analysis Section, Schedule 5.

19. *Ibid.*

20. It is only fair to say, however, that nearly all production plans in wartime tend to err on the up side rather than the down side since a supply that is larger than proves to be needed causes much less concern than one that turns out to be too small.

to have caused serious trouble in ordinary times, the shortages of some foods, the high level of domestic consumption and the large military requirements resulted in most of the crop being used. The costs of the surplus removal operations were not large as compared with the subsidies provided in stimulating production of some of the other farm commodities.

TROUBLES IN THE POSTWAR YEARS

The relatively high prices of 1944 and 1945 did not cause an increase in the acreages planted. The 1946 acreage was, in fact, about 5 per cent smaller than that of 1945 and well below the 1943 and 1944 acreages. However, a sharp increase in yield (from 157 bushels to 193) resulted in a record crop of 487 million bushels.[21] The government was committed to support the price at 90 per cent of parity, which was interpreted to mean $1.15 for the early and intermediate crops and $1.23 for the late crop.

The announcement of goals had called for a reduction in acreage and production for the 1946 crop. Growers reduced the acreage by more than the recommended amount but produced 100 million bushels more than the goal called for. CCC took over about 10 per cent of the crop at a cost of $65.8 million. In addition, about $25.5 million of Section 32 funds was used, making a total cost for the season of $91.3 million.[22]

The acreage planted in 1947 was reduced sharply, partly as a result of the 18-cent decline in potato prices (from $1.40 in 1945 to $1.22 in 1946) but also because of the extremely favorable prices for competing crops and the scarcity and high cost of labor. Farm products as a whole were at 115 per cent of parity in 1946 whereas potato prices, as of January 15, 1947, were at 81 per cent of parity as computed under the special formula provided by law for potatoes.[23] The 1947 planted acreage was 2,034,000 as compared with 2,571,000 in 1946, a drop of about 20 per cent. Production was down to 389 million bushels.

Under these conditions, price-support operations were required only in some areas.[24] The season average price, $1.61, was well above the

21. The data given here are from *Agricultural Statistics, 1953,* p. 252; they are revised and are somewhat higher than those published in earlier reports.

22. *Irish Potatoes, Price Supports and Related Operations,* Schedule 5. The season average price for the United States as a whole is given as $1.22 (*Agricultural Statistics, 1953,* p. 252), which is slightly higher than the weighted average of the computed support prices. It should be noted, however, that in order to carry out government commitments, price-supporting purchases may have to be made in some areas or in some parts of the season even though prices may be above support levels in other areas or at other times.

23. That is, using the high prices of 1919–1929 as a base instead of the 1910–1914 base, which applied to most of the other farm products. (U.S. Agricultural Marketing Service, *Agricultural Prices,* January 29, 1947, p. 29.) Potatoes were not actually low in price but their price had gone down at a time when the prices of most other farm products were rising.

24. These operations as a whole involved purchase and diversion of about 34 million

1946 average and high enough to maintain acreage in 1948 at about the 1947 level. With the sharp increase in yields that was by then occurring, costs per bushel were declining and profits per acre were increasing.

The 1948 Crop

A further very large increase in yields brought the 1948 crop up to 450 million bushels, which was well above the amounts needed to supply the demand. Since the 90 per cent of parity support prices guaranteed in the war years were still in effect, the government was obligated to undertake to maintain prices at that level. The general inflationary upsurge in prices was raising the parity index so that 90 per cent of parity in 1948 was interpreted to mean $1.65 for the early crop and $1.67 for the late crop.

The situation was further complicated by a marked decline in per capita consumption of potatoes, from 1947 on. This was a resumption of a trend that had begun in the early part of the century. Consumption was in the order of 180 to 190 pounds per capita just prior to World War I. It was around 130 pounds in the 1930s and about 125 pounds in the war years. By 1948, it was down to 104 pounds and it has remained at about that level since, despite the large surpluses that have existed in some years.[25]

Though production was large in 1948, the quantities put on the market for ordinary commercial use were smaller than in the years 1941 and 1942 when production was about at the level of the 1930s.[26] The Commodity Credit Corporation bought about 136 million bushels, approximately 30 per cent of the total crop produced and about 36 per cent of the amounts sold. Considerable quantities of the potatoes produced in any given year do not go onto the market. Some are used for seed, some are fed to livestock and some disappear as a result of spoil-

---

bushels and a net loss of $54 million. CCC purchases amounted to $41,135,000 and Section 32 fund expenditures to $12,771,000. The latter figure includes $1,373,000 in diversion payments, from Section 32 funds, in disposing of 2,395,000 bushels (*Irish Potatoes, Price Supports and Related Operations,* Schedule 5).

25. *Agricultural Statistics, 1953,* pp. 252 and 274–75. The low consumption of 1948 may have been partly due to the price-support program, since prices were held high and the large quantity produced did not actually reach the market. The abrupt drop from an annual consumption of 124 pounds per capita to 104 is striking. The price was slightly higher in the preceding year. However, many consumers complained that the quality of potatoes in the market in 1948 was poor. There is some indication that the program itself may have resulted in adverse selection, some of the better potatoes going to the government for diversion or destruction and the poorer ones to market. Whatever the reason for it, potato consumption per capita has been substantially lower in the years since 1948 than in any previous period for which data are available (only slightly more than 100 pounds as compared with nearly 200 pounds in the early 1900s).

26. About 240 million bushels in 1948 as compared with 242 million in 1941 and 261 million in 1942. Data on CCC purchases and cost of the program are from *Irish Potatoes, Price Supports and Related Operations,* Schedule 5; data on sales are from *Agricultural Statistics, 1951,* p. 252.

age, shrinkage and so on. The cost of the program in that year was $206 million.[27]

Much Public Criticism of the Program

The 1948 program was so widely and vigorously criticized in the public press, and by consumers and taxpayers generally, that it was recognized as a serious threat to the price-support program as a whole. However, there was little that could be done about it so far as the 1948 crop was concerned. The Congress had made a commitment on which it could not well renege once farmers had made their plantings and invested their labor and materials in the production of the crop.

Administrators had no choice but to carry out the program as provided by law. They were required to buy up potatoes with a view to maintaining the prices specified. Since the potatoes so purchased could not be absorbed in the regular commercial markets and there was almost no secondary use for them, huge quantities were virtually given away for livestock feed or destroyed. They could not be carried over or exported and the amount that could be absorbed by the processing industries was inconsequential in terms of the deluge of potatoes forced into government ownership.

The basic difficulties were three. One, the type of support program provided by the Congress, in the form of general legislation designed mainly for other products, was wholly unsuited to potatoes; two, the phenomenal increases in yields that occurred in these years could not be foreseen by either the Congress or the administrators in charge of the program; and three, the price commitment proved to be much too high in view of the cost reductions that were occurring and the static character of the demand.[28]

The industry was greatly overstimulated and its public relations badly strained. The adverse reaction of the public may have contributed to a lower level of per capita consumption, though some downward trend was apparent even if there had been no price-support program. However, a decline of 16 per cent in one year in the per capita consumption of any commodity is most unusual. The lower level of consumption has persisted in the years since.

Public antagonism to the program did not rest mainly on the price consumers had to pay. They had experienced high prices in times past

27. The amount of loss reported for any given year on these operations varies in different sources, partly because fiscal year reports do not coincide entirely with crop years and partly because of the vague and obscure methods of reporting.

28. The unwarrantedly high parity price was due largely to the manipulation of the base period in the Potato Act of 1935. Had parity for potatoes been computed on a 1910–1914 base period, much of the pricing part of the difficulty would have been avoided. (See p. 432.)

when the potato crop was small.[29] Resentment centered more on the wastefulness of the program and the fact that consumers were having to pay high prices at the same time that huge amounts of government funds were being poured into the industry and large payments were being made to some individual growers.[30] Complaints about the quality of the potatoes available to consumers also were numerous.

Support Levels Reduced in 1949

Public and congressional opposition to the program became so vigorous that the 1948 and 1949 agricultural acts provided for a reduction in the percentage of parity at which the price of potatoes would be supported. Supports were thereafter to be at 60 to 90 per cent of parity, as the Secretary of Agriculture might determine to be needed or appropriate. The modernized parity formula authorized in those acts would have resulted in a further significant reduction in support prices had it

29. For example, the price to farmers was $1.32 in 1929, and even in 1936, when almost all farm prices were low and the economy in depression, it was $1.14. Prices had been even higher, ranging up to $1.91 in the World War I period and in the early 1920s. (See *Agricultural Statistics, 1937,* p. 189, and *1951,* p. 253.)

30. For example, *Time Magazine* carried a widely discussed item in its August 29, 1949 issue (pp. 15 and 16), which read in part as follows: "*Potatoes & Gravy*—Maine's Aroostook County, dotted with neat white farmhouses and big gambrel-roofed barns, is the most northeasterly county in the U.S. Its richest farmers have become rural capitalists, with offices in town, four-hole Buicks in the garage, sons at Harvard, and winters in Florida. It was all thanks to potatoes—and, in recent years, to the wild generosity of the U.S. Government. *$15,000 Apiece*—By the end of June, the Government had in one year poured a whopping $64 million into the pockets of Aroostook potato men, to buy up the surplus from Maine's biggest cash crop. Some of the takes were eye-popping examples of the nation's weirdest experiment in farm pharmacy (total U.S. cost last year: $225 million). At least two Aroostook potato shippers collected Government checks for around $500,000; a dozen or so got more than $150,000 each; at least 31 over $100,000 apiece. In all Maine, 4,503 farmers averaged $15,000 apiece in Government bounty, *Washington Post* Newsman John W. Ball reported last week. Those who didn't sell their crops to the Government benefited by the artificially inflated price in retail markets. One potato farmer salted away $13,160 from a 30-acre farm which cost him only $3,000 ten years ago. Another made $50,000 in four years off his 144 acres. Farm laborers were doing almost as well: up to $25 a day for following the digging machines; $15 to $25 a day for planting."

The adverse reaction continued even after support prices were reduced under the 1949 program. The *San Francisco Chronicle,* in its *This World* section of February 12, 1950, carried a full front-page picture of acres of potatoes being spread out on the desert to get rid of them, together with a wry article stating that "The Government was grappling with a monster of its own creation last week. The monster's shadow reached from Maine to California, and its threat gave U.S. officials nightmares. The monster was Solanum Tuberosum commonly called the Irish potato. U.S. farmers in 1949 had grown some 70,000,000 bushels of surplus potatoes. They could not be dumped on the domestic market, lest they collapse the price. Few could be channeled into free lunches for school children or to Indians on Federal reservations. Fewer still could be shipped abroad. Most of the surplus would find no normal outlet. Such huge potato surpluses during the past five years had cost the U.S. public half a billion dollars, and there was more to come."

Similar news stories and comments were carried widely throughout the country, particularly in 1949 and 1950.

TABLE 49

POTATOES: ACREAGE, YIELD PER ACRE, PRODUCTION AND PRICE, 1939–1955

Year	Acreage Planted	Acreage Harvested	Yield per Acre Harvested	Production	Season Average Price to Farmers
	(Thousands)	*(Thousands)*	*(Bushels)*	*(1,000 Bushels)*	*(Per Bushel)*
1939	2,867	2,813	121.7	342,372	$0.694
1940	2,886	2,832	133.1	376,920	0.526
1941	2,749	2,693	132.1	355,697	0.788
1942	2,755	2,671	138.1	368,899	1.14
1943	3,355	3,239	141.7	458,887	1.28
1944	2,878	2,780	138.1	383,926	1.47
1945	2,729	2,664	157.4	419,399	1.40
1946	2,571	2,527	192.9	487,315	1.22
1947	2,034	2,001	194.4	388,985	1.61
1948	2,007	1,981	227.1	449,895	1.53
1949	1,778	1,759	228.8	402,353	1.28
1950	1,712	1,696	253.4	429,896	0.917
1951	1,359	1,334	240.3	320,519	1.63
1952	1,421	1,401	249.0	349,098	1.96
1953	1,549	1,524	249.3	380,075	0.797
1954	1,423	1,408	252.8	356,031	1.30
1955	1,434	1,406	271.3 [a]	381,631 [a]	0.945 [a]

Sources: Agricultural Statistics, 1953, p. 252; U.S. Agricultural Marketing Service, *Annual Summary, Acreage, Yield and Production of Principal Crops, 1953,* p. 94, *1954,* p. 99, *1955,* p. 97; and *Season Average Prices and Value of Production, 1951 and 1952,* p. 18, *1952 and 1953,* p. 18, *1953 and 1954,* p. 16, *1954 and 1955,* p. 21.

a. Preliminary.

not been for the transitional adjustment provision which permitted reductions of only 5 per cent in any one year.[31]

The reduction in support levels for the 1949 and 1950 crops tended to discourage production in some areas, but higher yields resulted in continuing over-all surpluses. The yield in 1949 was 228.8 bushels per acre and the 1950 yield was 253.4 bushels, nearly 120 bushels per acre above the general level of yields in the early 1940s. Acreage was cut back further but not enough to offset these heavier yields. (See Table 49.)

31. However, the relation of potato prices to other prices, under the modernized formula, would still have been considerably distorted because of the high support prices maintained in the preceding years. For an explanation of "modernized" parity, see Murray R. Benedict, *Can We Solve the Farm Problem?,* Twentieth Century Fund, New York, 1955, Appendix A.

The purchase program for the 1949 crop was designed to support a national average price of $1.08, or about 60 per cent of the January 15 parity price, which was computed as $1.81.[32] The reduction still was insufficient to cause either a cut in production or an increase in consumption that would bring the two into balance. Government purchases amounted to some 75 million bushels, about 22 per cent of the total quantity sold by farmers and about 18 per cent of the total crop produced.

The purchase program resulted in a net loss to the government of $80,534,000. Such outlet as there was for the surplus was mainly in the form of feed for livestock at prices that provided almost no net return to the government. Efforts were made throughout the year to divert potatoes for alcohol production but that was found impractical. Other raw materials were available from which alcohol could be manufactured more cheaply than from potatoes purchased at 1 cent per hundred pounds at the farm.[33]

Supports Continued at 60 Per Cent in 1950

The 60 per cent of parity support was still in effect for the 1950 crop and again the government incurred heavy losses because of excess production. Planted acreage, though reduced moderately, still was large enough to result in a crop of 430 million bushels, which was far above what the market would take at even a 60 per cent of parity price. The yield increased still further, to 253 bushels, which was by far the highest ever recorded, as a national average, up to that time. Government purchases amounted to about 100 million bushels and program losses to $65,122,000.[34] The average support price was approximately $1.00 per bushel, the January 15 parity being computed at $1.67.

32. The comparable parity in 1948 was $1.86. *Agricultural Prices,* January 30, 1948 and January 28, 1949, p. 26, mimeo., and Commodity Credit Corporation, *Review of Operations,* p. 16.

33. See *Report of the Administrator of the Production and Marketing Administration, 1951,* p. 35. There was a change in policy for the 1950 crop in that purchasers were required to absorb the cost of grading, sacking and loading, except on potatoes for export. These costs had previously been borne by CCC. This contributed to the high proportion of the 1950 crop that was dumped, as the value for feed was not sufficient to warrant feeders in paying these costs. The values recovered on potatoes sold as feed were only about 6 per cent of the amounts paid to the growers by CCC for potatoes so used. About 38 million bushels went to feed use, about the same amount was dumped and about 17 million bushels were used in starch production. Donations amounted to 5.5 million bushels.

34. The year-by-year losses and volumes purchased vary somewhat in different reports depending on the time covered by the report and the timing of the operation. The figures used here are, in the main, from *Irish Potatoes, Price Support and Related Operations.* Of the 1950 purchases, 43 per cent were used as livestock feed, 32 per cent were destroyed, 5 per cent were donated to school lunches, 16 per cent were used for starch and the remaining 5 per cent went to potato flour, exports and miscellaneous. (See *Price Supports for Perishable Products: A Review of Experience,* U.S. Senate Committee Print, 82d Cong., 1st sess., 1951, p. 19.)

Price Support Abandoned in 1951

By 1951, opposition to the program had become so strong that the Congress directed that no further price support should be provided on potatoes unless marketing quotas were in effect (Public Law 471, 81st Cong., 2d sess.). Since there was no legislation providing machinery for marketing quotas on potatoes, this meant that there could be no price supports thereafter unless new legislation was passed.[35]

Recognizing that price supports would not be available on potatoes in 1951 and after, producers reduced plantings sharply, to 1,359,000 acres. This was less than half the acreage grown in 1939.[36] With yields somewhat lower than in the preceding year (240 bushels as compared with 253 in 1950), the resulting crop, 321 million bushels, was more than 100 million bushels below that of 1950.

The amount put on the market for human consumption was about 266 million bushels, about the same as in 1950. However, in the meantime, the Korean War had begun and the prices of nearly all farm products rose. Potato prices to farmers averaged $1.63 as compared with $.917 in 1950. The 1951 price was the highest since 1919 but only moderately above 1947 and 1948 prices, when supports were at 90 per cent of parity. The farm value of the crop in 1951 was $522 million as compared with $393 million in 1950.[37] Consumers paid very high prices in 1951 and still higher ones in 1952, when the price to farmers averaged $1.96, the highest of record. However, government outlays had been discontinued.

The high prices of 1951 brought the first reversal of the long and steep downward trend in potato acreage. The 1952 planted acreage was 1,421,000, as compared with 1,359,000 in 1951. There was a further increase of about 128,000 acres in 1953. Yields held around the peak level established in 1950. (See Table 49.)

35. The wording of the act also was interpreted to mean that the Secretary of Agriculture could not use Section 32 funds for purchases or other types of aid to potato growers. Such funds would, of course, have been inadequate for purchases on a scale that would have affected the potato situation importantly. A provision in the Agricultural Act of 1954 which repealed the special provision relating to potatoes in the act of 1949 was interpreted as clearing the way for the use of Section 32 funds in supporting the price of potatoes if the Secretary of Agriculture chose to take such action.

36. There was some increased interest in marketing agreements during the late 1940s and early 1950s but they seem not to have been found useful except for dealing with special problems in local areas. The Maine potato area adopted a marketing agreement in 1948 (Agreement No. 108 and Order No. 87) but discontinued it in June 1951. A new Order (No. 70) was issued in September 1954. An Order was issued for Massachusetts, Rhode Island, Connecticut, New Hampshire and Vermont in November 1951. New Jersey developed a marketing agreement (No. 116 and Order No. 98) in April 1950, but terminated it in April 1952. Oregon and parts of California have experimented to some extent with marketing agreements and also the southeastern states and South Dakota and Washington. Such agreements were said to result in holding back from 5 to 25 per cent of the low grades and less desirable sizes. (See *Price Supports for Perishable Products: A Review of Experience*, p. 20.)

37. *Agricultural Statistics, 1953,* p. 252.

In 1954, acreage was again reduced, to about the 1952 level, and production was down moderately. Preliminary 1955 figures show a further large increase in yields (to 271.3 bushels) on approximately the same acreage as that of 1954. The preliminary estimate of production is 382 million bushels, about the same as the amount produced in 1953.

THE POTATO PROGRAMS IN RETROSPECT

The potato programs of the past two decades (to June 30, 1953) resulted in an over-all cost to the government of $635.8 million.[38] The results achieved have not, on the whole, been pleasing either to the public or to the industry. However, there were many unforeseeable circumstances that contributed to the unsatisfactory experience with the program. The most significant one was the phenomenal increase in yields, which made previous data for estimating the response of production to price virtually unusable.

The program itself had serious defects. By its nature, it was not well suited to a perishable crop with few important secondary uses. The base period used in computing parity prices for potatoes was unrealistic and could not contribute to logical relationships between the prices of the various farm products in this period. The crop was sufficiently different from most of the other Steagall commodities to indicate a need for special legislation instead of lumping it in with a great number of miscellaneous products with different production conditions and price relationships.

It is apparent that the support levels for potatoes in the early postwar years were too high. However, the difficulties that arose could not well have been foreseen either by the Congress or by government administrators at the time the program was launched. Once it got under way, commitments had been made that could not well be withdrawn.

The origin of the wartime program must be considered in light of the conditions that existed at that time. The situation in 1942 was grim and many decisions had to be made without adequate knowledge of their probable effects.[39] It is clear now that the production incentives provided in 1943 were larger than they needed to be. Acreage was increased from 2.75 million to 3.35 million. Production was increased by nearly 25 per cent, but, with most carbohydrate foods in plentiful supply, there

38. U.S. Department of Agriculture, *Realized Cost of Agricultural and Related Programs, by Function or Purpose, Fiscal Years 1932–1953,* in U.S. Senate Committee on Agriculture and Forestry, *General Farm Program,* Hearings, 83d Cong., 2d sess., Part I, 1954, pp. 74–89 (reproduced in Appendix B in *Can We Solve the Farm Problem?*).

39. For example, no one knew how long the war would last or how severe the strain on U.S. food resources would be. Wheat supplies were abundant at that time, but losses from enemy action were very severe and the ample production of ensuing years could not be foreseen. If food supplies became tight, potatoes, both as an important item of diet and as a substitute for wheat, might become more important in the United States as they had already become in Britain and Russia. Hence it was considered better to risk a surplus than to take a chance on critically short supplies.

was little corresponding shift from other foods to potatoes as a source of calories.

There was little to go on in estimating the probable effects of a given level of incentive prices since farm prices in nearly all lines were rising rapidly and profit motivations were shifting, not only as a result of changes in relative prices but because of cost changes, labor scarcities and other factors as well.

Parity Base Chosen Was Too High

Part of the trouble was due to earlier action, largely politically motivated, which put the computation of parity prices for potatoes on an unrealistic basis as compared with that used for most other farm products. The price-support level required in the war years and for two years thereafter was a result of a provision in the Potato Act of 1935. That act specified that the base period for potatoes should be the same as that assigned to tobacco in the Agricultural Adjustment Act of 1933, namely, August 1919–July 1929. But there had been no change in consumption habits in respect to potatoes similar to the change in demand for tobacco. The base period for most other farm products was 1909–1914.

The average price of potatoes in the 1919–1929 period was $1.12, as compared with $.67 in 1909–1914. The later base period included the very high-price years 1919–1921 and also the high years 1925–1927 when prices were two to three times as high as they were customarily in the period prior to World War I. When the change in the index of prices paid by farmers was applied to this higher base price, the result was a parity price for potatoes that was some 25 per cent above what it would have been if the 1909–1914 base had been used.

The reason for the choice made is obvious, so far as the advocates of the potato act were concerned. If the pre-World War I base had been used, potatoes would have been about at parity in 1933. The representatives of the potato growers naturally wanted to set a higher goal and had sufficient political support to enable them to do so. The construction and publication of the parity price for potatoes was continued on the basis provided in the 1935 act until 1949. It put potato producers in a favored position pricewise, as soon as prices came to be supported nearly across the board at 90 per cent of parity.[40] Even so, the supports pro-

40. The Secretary of Agriculture was required to support potato prices at 90 per cent of parity from 1943 on. Prior to that time there had been no program specifically related to parity. A price-support program at 75 per cent of parity was announced for some areas in 1942 but no action to implement it was required as the price in the market was relatively favorable. It was the Steagall Amendment that forced the Secretary into the untenable position that developed later. The 1941 act extending the life of the Commodity Credit Corporation (which included the Steagall Amendment) did provide for the use of "comparable" prices for any "nonbasic" agricultural commodity "if the production or consumption of such commodity has so changed in extent or character since

vided seem not to have been high enough to cause undue expansion in either acreage or production during the war years, except in 1943 and to some extent in 1945. The serious unbalance developed in the postwar years, not from increased acreage but from increased yields.

"Modernized" Parity Formula Would Have Helped

Had Title II of the 1948 act come into effect without qualifications, a more rapid correction of the situation would have been possible. The formula provided in that act would have reduced the computed parity price (September 1948) from $1.86 to $1.61 and would have permitted support at 60 to 90 per cent, which would have brought the support price below $1.00 per bushel.

However, the act provided that, in cases where parity was lower under the new formula than under the old formula, the computed parity price could not be reduced by more than 5 per cent a year. In accordance with that provision, the Secretary established a support level for the 1949 crop which was 60 per cent of parity under the "old" formula, reduced by 5 per cent. That was the lowest level he was permitted to use under the legislation then in effect but was still around 70 per cent of parity under the new formula and would have been around 100 per cent of parity had the pre-World War I base been used in figuring parity under the "old" formula. In the meantime, the provision for including farm wage rates in the parity formula, which was part of the Agricultural Act of 1949, had raised the parity level itself to some extent.

Support for the 1950 crop was put at 60 per cent of a transitional parity that was 5 per cent lower than that of 1949. That was the minimum permitted by law but not low enough to cause any marked decline in acreage. The 1950 acreage planted was 1,712,000 as compared with 1,778,000 in 1949. It is apparent that even a 60 per cent support, based on a slightly reduced parity computation, was more than adequate to induce the production needed under the yield and cost conditions then existing.

Some Surpluses Might Have Developed Anyway

The supports provided in the postwar years unquestionably encouraged farmers to produce more potatoes than were needed. But it is not so clear that heavy surpluses would not have developed without price supports. The oversupply probably would not have been so persistent and severe cuts in acreage would no doubt have been made sooner. However, the acreage reductions that were made were by far the largest in the recorded history of the industry.

---

the base period as to result in a price out of line with parity prices for 'basic' commodities." However, that provision was actually used only in a few cases where it operated to raise parities. Courageous application of it would have provided a partial "out" for the government in the troublesome situation that arose in the postwar years.

Farmers probably would have considered them adequate, even as a response to low free-market prices, and would have continued to produce more than the market could absorb, except that a larger cut in acreage in 1950 would probably have been made. More of the adjustment would no doubt have been accomplished through failure to harvest or market the crop, whereas with price supports in effect, virtually all of the marketable potatoes were sold either to consumers or to the government.

The first reaction to the abandonment of support, in 1951, was an excessive cut in acreage and production, which, in conjunction with an inflationary upsurge in prices generally, resulted in a shortage of potatoes and very high prices to consumers. It does not follow that such low production would normally result from free-market prices. Farmers were keenly aware of the heavy surpluses of the preceding years and did not know what might happen now that price supports had been abandoned. They overadjusted.

Some correction was made in 1952 but not enough. It was not until 1953 that an abundant crop on a moderately higher acreage was produced. The 1954 crop was about adequate and the price roughly in line with those maintained under price supports in 1949 and 1950. The 1955 crop was large enough to be fully adequate to meet normal requirements but only because of a further heavy increase in yields, not from the planting of a larger acreage.

There is some indication that an assured level of prices encourages the growing of larger acreages, but the evidence is by no means conclusive. Acreages were reduced rapidly throughout the price-support period. The reductions were, in fact, much larger than those that have customarily followed years of low prices in the past.

Logic would suggest that if price risk, which is one of the costs of production, is assumed by the government, farmers would produce needed quantities at a lower average price than if they had to carry that cost themselves. However, there are many examples in the economy generally in which heavy continuing investments are made at very low average returns, partly because of the possibility of very large gains to those who strike it lucky. Mining and oil ventures are extreme examples. There is not much concrete evidence that potato production would have been adjusted much more rapidly in the absence of price supports, unless it is assumed that price supports were a principal factor in bringing about the yield increases that were the primary cause of the excess production.

Nature and Causes of the Yield Increases

The yield increases shown are the most striking feature of the potato situation from 1940 to 1954. There had been a slight upward trend in yields from 1866, when such data were first collected, to 1940,[41] but in all that period, no yield of more than 124 bushels is reported. Mostly the yields in the 1860s and 1870s were in the order of 80 to 90 bushels and in the 1930s, from 100 to 110 bushels, except for the large yields of 1937–1939 (123, 124 and 122).

Moderate gains in yield were being made from 1937 through 1944, but the big increases came from 1945 on and were on such a scale that by 1950 the highest yield ever reported prior to 1940 had been doubled (253 bushels as compared with the then record high of 124 in 1938).[42] This great increase in yields was due in part to shifts in areas of production.[43] There has been a tendency for small growers with low-yielding acres to abandon production and for acreages to be increased in the higher-yielding areas.[44]

The shifting of areas was probably the largest factor in the gains made through 1939, but the gains made since then cannot, to any considerable extent, be attributed to that cause. They have come about mainly through technological improvements. Among these are the development of varieties that are more resistant to disease and more prolific, and the use of much larger amounts of commercial fertilizer.

More and better insecticides have also helped to stabilize yields in some areas and annual yield fluctuations resulting from weather variations have been reduced to some extent by shifting production to irrigated areas, where water supplies can be controlled. While plantings have not been strictly controlled, the use of acreage allotments, with a provision that price-support purchases would be available to those who complied with them, has encouraged closer planting and concentration of the crop on the highest-yielding acres.

The price-support program almost certainly contributed to the yield increases shown, especially those resulting from closer planting and more intensive applications of fertilizer and labor on allotted acres. However, there seems little warrant for assuming that there would not have been rapid technological advance and large increases in yields even in the absence of a support program. Technological improvements were being adopted at a very rapid rate throughout the agricultural industry. Gross

41. See *Agricultural Statistics, 1937,* pp. 188–89, *1951,* p. 253, and *1953,* p. 252.

42. The 1955 yield of 271 bushels carried the production per acre well above even that phenomenally high level.

43. When growers were asked to increase production in 1943, the outlying, specialist areas increased plantings by 33 per cent whereas producers in the Lake states increased their plantings by only 19 per cent. Moreover, the Lake state producers quickly reverted to their downward trend in succeeding years while producers in the specialist states maintained their high acreages. (See University of Minnesota, *Minnesota Farm Business Notes,* November 30, 1952, p. 2.)

44. The development of technology, especially the use of expensive machines for spraying, digging and so on, has, of course, given the larger operators marked advantages over the small growers. It is not profitable to acquire expensive, specialized machinery for use on small acreages and the hiring of custom machine operations has not been an important feature of the potato industry.

farm production increased nearly 30 per cent between 1930 and 1951, even though the number of acres planted or grown had declined by nearly 12 million.[45]

Mere continuation of the trend established in the 1930s would have brought yields up to the 150- to 160-bushel level, even without the war impetus. There is little reason to think farmers would not have used improved strains, better methods of fertilizing and larger-scale machinery in a period like that of the 1940s and early 1950s. Area shifts also would no doubt have continued, though perhaps not on so large a scale.

Whatever the reasons for it, there can be no doubt that the increase in yields was the most important factor in creating the surplus problem. Acreages would have had to be cut back at a phenomenal rate if they were to offset or more than offset the higher production per acre. The drop in per capita consumption also added to the difficulty. Here also, the program itself may have intensified the problem.

Perishability of the Crop a Factor

The situation was also complicated by the perishability of the product. Loan programs such as those provided for the storables, though made available in a minor way, could not be used to advantage for potatoes. They were useful principally as a means of encouraging orderly marketing. About the only practical procedure, once an excess of potatoes had been produced, was to buy them outright for diversion or dumping in the areas where they were produced. To prevent them from being produced, even with marketing quotas in effect, would have been almost impossible with yields increasing as rapidly as they were in that period.[46]

Early potatoes, in particular, are very difficult to handle. Their high water content makes them very perishable and of little value for processing. For these reasons, they must be harvested in a short period and moved quickly. Also, shipments usually must be carefully timed to avoid competition with shipments from other areas that harvest a little earlier or a little later.

For late potatoes, there is more leeway. They deteriorate in the spring rather than at harvesttime. However, they must be kept in cold storage if serious late-season deterioration and waste are to be avoided. Since

45. For 52 principal crops. (See *Agricultural Statistics, 1951,* pp. 546, 561.)

46. However, if some type of compensatory payment had been used, consumers might have fared better in that larger quantities of potatoes would have been put on the market at lower prices, with direct payments being made to farmers to compensate for the lower prices received. If wisely conceived and well controlled, such a procedure probably would have been little if any more expensive than the one that was followed. A workable plan of that kind has not thus far been developed and brought under consideration. The question of what to do with the surplus and how to keep it off the market would still have remained. In view of the relative inelasticity of the demand, such a plan would not, of course, have made it possible to use effectively such large volumes of potatoes as were produced in the late 1940s. Also, some changes in the legislation would have been necessary.

suitable storage is expensive, the most practical procedure is to dispose of quantities that obviously will not find a market, and to do it fairly early in the season.

PROBLEM STILL UNSOLVED

Though a good deal of experience has been gained as a result of the costly program carried out in recent years, no clear and widely acceptable plan for introducing more stability into this highly speculative industry seems yet to have emerged.[47] From the standpoint of the public, a program that will assure adequate supplies of so important an item of diet seems clearly to be desirable. There is evidence that without some assurance that prices will not go disastrously low, growers may not produce enough potatoes to satisfy consumer requirements. For example, the supply available in the 1951–52 season, immediately after the discontinuance of price supports, was undoubtedly below amounts that could be regarded as reasonably adequate.[48]

The 1951 cutback was undoubtedly too severe. It was mainly an acreage cut. Yields were lower than in 1950 but well above any achieved prior to 1950. The uncertainties surrounding a return to free-market prices in an industry so recently and so severely distorted by government operations no doubt accounted for part of the excessive cutback.

Prices Even Higher in 1952

The 1952 price was even higher than that of 1951 despite a moderate increase in both acreage and production. The upward adjustment in response to the high 1951 price would almost certainly have been larger had it not been for the imposition of OPS price controls in January

47. Some attempt has been made to draw conclusions of that kind in a recent publication, *Price Supports and the Potato Industry,* University of Minnesota Experiment Station Bulletin 424, January 1954. However, the production response analyses, based on pre-World War II relationships, so evidently do not take adequate account of the great changes in yields and costs since 1945 that the conclusions arrived at are not widely accepted.

48. John W. Ball, in a feature article in the *Washington Post* for June 1, 1952, commented in part as follows: "Are you one of those millions of Americans who have said in the last few weeks, 'I have never known potatoes to be so scarce,' or 'I have never known potatoes to be so high priced'?

"If so, you are right. The good old Irish spud—the basic vegetable in most American diets—has never been so scarce or so costly as right now.

"This situation becomes positively fascinating when one remembers that since the war the government has spent more than half a billion dollars—the cost of the District of Columbia government for five years—supporting the price of potatoes and destroying the surplus.

"Here are the startling figures.

"Early in May, the average retail price for a peck of potatoes (15 pounds) was $1.16. The previous record was set in 1920—just after World War I—at 93.8 cents a peck. In 1950, the price averaged only 69.3 cents, a sharp drop from 82 cents in 1949 and 83.8 cents in 1948, when government price supports were in effect and Uncle Sam was destroying the best of the crop in lots of millions of bushels in an effort to keep prices high . . ."

1952, and the possibility of later cuts if prices seemed to be out of line. Price ceilings were announced on January 6, 1952, to become effective on January 19 (Ceiling Price Regulation No. 119). They provided for rollbacks ranging from 15 cents per hundred pounds in Maine to $1.40 in Idaho. The December 15 price had been at about 105 per cent of the high parity established under the formula then in use.

The limitation on prices was revoked on June 6, 1952, but it was then too late for the revocation to have any significant effect on farmers' decisions to plant in the 1952 season. Acreage had been increased from 1,359,000 in 1951 to 1,421,000 in 1952. With a 249-bushel yield, production amounted to 349 million bushels as compared with 321 million in 1951. However, because of the general rise in prices, the average price received by farmers for the 1952 crop was $1.96 as compared with $1.63 in 1951.[49]

The 1953 and 1954 experience probably reflects more nearly the type of production response that can be expected in the absence of either price supports or price ceilings. There appears to be more stability in yields now than in the decades prior to World War II. That is probably due to improved and disease-resistant varieties, better protection through spraying, and some shift to irrigated acreages where water supplies can be controlled. Acreage also may become more stable because of the shift of production into the specialized, larger-scale potato-growing areas. If these conclusions are correct, it is probable that both potato production and prices will be more stable, even under free-market conditions, than they were before 1940.

Parity Price Approach Not Likely to Work Well

Even if it should seem advisable to provide some type of price insurance to growers, and possibly thereby to increase stability of output and reduce costs to consumers, it is unlikely that the use of any existing parity formula will work out smoothly. The changes in yields and production techniques have been so great that some new relationship of potato prices to other farm prices, and to prices generally, is clearly in the making.[50]

49. The high prices in 1951 and 1952 were no doubt due in part to the general price inflation that occurred in those years. However, production in both years was enough below usual consumption requirements to result in very sharp price increases, in view of the very inelastic demand that characterizes the markets for potatoes. The farm value of the 1952 crop was about the same as that of the 1947 and 1948 crops and well above those of 1949 and 1950 when heavy government expenditures were still being made. Farm values for the six-year period were as follows:

1947	$628,193,000	1950	$392,901,000
1948	688,572,000	1951	521,967,000
1949	514,970,000	1952	687,101,000

(*Agricultural Statistics, 1953*, p. 252.)

50. Even the full application of the "modernized" parity formula, based on price relationships of the past ten years, is unlikely to be helpful in stabilizing the industry

A new approach, possibly in the nature of an assured minimum price designed to result in a desired level of production, would seem to offer more promise of satisfactory results. If such a procedure is contemplated, it will be desirable to give administrators a rather wide range of discretion in establishing minimum prices. A period of trial and error will undoubtedly be needed before the probable response to a given level of minimum prices can be determined with any assurance.[51]

If the use of some such forward pricing device results in a lower return to growers than the Congress deems reasonable, such funds as the government chooses to put into the industry perhaps could be better used in the form of supplemental payments, related to the returns received in the market, than in trying to buy up and divert enough of the crop to maintain a given level of prices in the market. In that case, some of the waste would be avoided and consumers would get the benefit of whatever volume of potatoes is produced. Production in areas, and of types or qualities, for which no market exists would tend to be eliminated. Closer grading and better quality would be encouraged since payments would be proportional to returns received in the market.

The incentives provided could be at such levels as the Congress and the administrators might consider in the public interest and just to the growers concerned.[52] Such a program would apparently be less cumbersome, more equitable and more in keeping with the best use of resources than to try to establish area by area and type by type some specific level of support price.

If no support program is put into effect, potato production and prices will, of course, be determined by the decisions of growers operating under the incentives provided by free-market prices, that is, in the same way as in the years prior to 1940 (except for minor modifications in the 1930s). Some grower groups have expressed a marked preference for a return to and continuance of that type of economic arrangement. That appears to be more generally true for the areas where expansion is

---

unless support levels are put at very low percentages of parity. Price relationships over the past decade have been so much disturbed by the government's own programs that they are of little value as a guide, and those of earlier periods are clearly unsuitable.

51. Either the establishment of such a program of guaranteed minimum prices or an attempt to develop a more realistic parity formula by regions and types will inevitably prove very difficult. The qualities and uses of the potatoes produced in the several regions are so different that the crop can well be classified as several commodities. The differences are not so great as in tobacco but they are distinguishable.

For example, early potatoes produced in the southern states are highly perishable and supply a distinctive seasonal market, and the markets for Maine and Idaho potatoes are somewhat distinct from those of other late-producing areas. Consequently, it is very difficult to establish support prices that will not disturb normal marketing arrangements and yet will be equitable and will result in some desired average season price for the crop as a whole. Various formulae have been tried but as yet no method has been demonstrated to be sufficiently satisfactory to warrant its adoption as an established procedure.

52. Such a plan is now being tried out experimentally in the wool industry, under legislation passed in 1954.

occurring and specialization is increasing than in the areas where methods of production are more static.

It is mainly in the expanding, specialized areas that the most rapid technological advances have been made and it is there that per bushel costs have been reduced most rapidly. So far as the public is concerned, shifts of that kind appear to be desirable, from the standpoint of stability of supply and low over-all cost. They present difficulties for the areas in which the competitive position is deteriorating and the industry declining.

In some areas and in a minor way, marketing agreements are being or can be used to some advantage. Their advantage, if successfully handled, is that quality and size standards can be made more rigorous in years or seasons of heavy production, thus keeping on the farms potatoes that would be likely to affect prices and consumer demand adversely. They also lend themselves to promotion programs designed to increase per capita consumption. There would seem to be little prospect, however, that large regional or national marketing agreements can be made workable for a crop that is produced over such wide areas and under such different conditions.

The present disposition of both the public and the Congress appears to be to revert to traditional, free-market operations so far as the potato industry is concerned, or at least to give them a more thorough trial than they have had thus far in the postwar period. The adverse reaction to the programs of the late 1940s will not be easily or quickly overcome and if any new program is adopted it will almost certainly be of a different type from that which was in effect during the early postwar years.

11

Fluid Milk

FEW IF ANY farm commodities are more widely used and more widely produced than milk. Virtually every family in the United States is a consumer of milk and more than two million farmers produce it for sale in one form or another. Of these, more than a million reported sales of whole milk in fluid form in the census of 1950. Roughly a sixth of all cash farm income is derived from the dairy industry and it constitutes an important part of the farming operations in every state in the union. In addition, some 50,000 distributors and 12,000 dairy plants are engaged in the business of handling milk and its products. The policies relating to milk are therefore of very wide interest both to the public and to farm people in all parts of the country.

Though the fluid milk industry has long had an important relationship to the welfare of the general public, widespread and detailed economic regulation of it by government is of comparatively recent origin. During World War I, milk prices were established in the Boston area by the U.S. Food Commission. In other areas, but usually only for limited periods, quasi-public committees have at times undertaken to establish or negotiate prices for milk during emergencies or after periods of prolonged economic instability. However, except in World War I, these efforts did not rest on either state or federal authority.

Dairy Products Omitted in Early Relief Proposals

Though a very important part of the farm economy, dairy products were omitted from the early proposals for direct farm relief that were put forward in the 1920s. This was due in part to the fact that the great bulk of the product of the dairy industry is consumed domestically. Since the principal emphasis in that period was on special export devices, dairy products did not lend themselves to the kinds of relief programs most vigorously advocated by the farm groups.

Dairy farmers had, however, attempted to better their situation in two other ways: (1) by securing tariffs on imported butter and vegetable oils (and to a lesser extent on milk and cream), and (2) by building strong cooperative selling and processing organizations. The tariffs on butter were seldom fully effective, except for brief periods when foreign supplies were available at very low prices. The tariffs on milk and cream were significant mainly with respect to potential imports from Ontario for the New York market. The larger tariff interest of the dairymen was in protection against the importation of foreign vegetable oils for use in making margarine.

The fluid milk cooperatives, which began to assume large importance in the 1920s, are of two general types.[1] Most of them are "bargaining" cooperatives; others are of the "operating" type. The primary function of the "bargaining" cooperatives is to negotiate terms of sale for their producer members. These include prices, time and method of payment, transportation arrangements, handling and receiving station charges, guarantees of payment and so on. They also check the weighing of milk and testing for fat content. The "operating" cooperative actually receives and disposes of the milk, manufactures butter, cheese or other by-products and may even extend its activities to the whole marketing process, including delivery of milk to consumers. Few of the associations are at either of these extremes. "Bargaining" cooperatives often engage in some of the physical operations relating to the distribution of milk, and "operating" cooperatives, though they may actually handle the major part of the milk delivered by their members, often act as bargaining agencies for some parts of it.[2]

Monopoly Charges against Cooperatives

Because of the effectiveness of cooperatives in bargaining or marketing, some of their officers and managers have at times been brought into court on charges of violating federal or state antitrust laws. Court actions of that kind occurred mostly in the 1920–1929 decade. To clarify the situation and define the rights of cooperatives, many of the state legislatures enacted laws that specifically authorized the formation of cooperatives and, to some extent, exempted them from prosecution under the antitrust laws.[3] In 1922, federal legislation in the form of the Capper-Volstead Act gave farm producers the right to sell their products cooperatively without being considered in violation of the antitrust laws, provided appropriate forms of organization were used and they did not engage in practices that were prohibited. However, the Capper-Volstead Act did not give the cooperatives unlimited rights to establish prices. They may not, through their collective bargaining and selling activities, "unduly enhance the price" of the product.

From 1929 on,[4] the federal government took a more positive position

1. The cooperative form of organization had come into wide use in the butter and cheese industries long before that time.

2. For a fuller explanation of the operations of "bargaining" cooperatives, see U.S. Farm Credit Administration, *Economic Analysis of Bargaining Problems of Milk Cooperatives,* Circular C-104, April 1937.

3. State laws could not, of course, provide immunity from prosecution under federal law.

4. And to some extent even from 1926 when the Division of Cooperative Marketing was set up in the U.S. Department of Agriculture.

in favor of cooperative selling. This form of action was no longer merely permitted; it was officially sponsored and was given financial aid by the government. Educational and research assistance was also provided. Up to that time, except for the rather modest aid provided in the form of legal authorizations and research and educational assistance, dairy farmers neither sought nor obtained federal or state help in meeting the problems of their industry, except for such small gains as might result from the tariff.

1929–1933, Chaotic Conditions in the Industry

The dairy industry, like most others, was thrown into confusion by the abrupt decline in business activity and consumer purchasing power that began in 1929. Dairy product prices held up better than the prices of most other farm products but, even so, the decline was from an index of 157 (1909–1914=100) in 1929 to 82 in 1933. The prices of farm products as a whole declined from 143 to 62.[5] However, within the dairy industry, there was considerable variation. The price of milk used for direct consumption in fluid form fell least (relative to other farm prices). The prices paid by dealers for milk for fluid use occupied an intermediate position and milk used in the manufacture of butter, cheese and similar products fell most. The price of butterfat, which was 45 cents per pound in 1929, fell to 18 cents in 1932. The prices paid for all milk declined to $1.27 per hundredweight, from $2.54. Even the price paid by distributors for Class 1 milk (the highest-price category) dropped from $2.82 per hundredweight in 1929 to $1.60 in 1933.[6]

Some cost rates, such as those for purchased feed grains, cow replacements and hired labor, also fell drastically, but fixed costs such as taxes, interest and debt repayments did not. Foreclosure rates increased, the business of village merchants fell off and the whole economies of communities based on dairying were seriously depressed. Farmers, in desperation, shifted from one type of outlet to another and often undertook to sell their products directly to the consumer. Lacking experience, their first move, in the effort to obtain customers, was usually to cut prices drastically.[7]

The price structure was demoralized. Relationships between fluid milk distributors and their suppliers were thrown into confusion. The cooperatives were especially vulnerable since producer members were in a position to force changes in management or to withdraw from the association

5. U.S. Department of Agriculture, *Agricultural Statistics, 1937,* p. 400.

6. U.S. Department of Agriculture, *Dairy Statistics and Related Series,* Statistical Bulletin 134, October 1953, p. 48. Prices paid by condensaries fell off from $2.04 to $.89. (*Ibid.,* p. 49.)

7. Milk "depots," roadside stands, milk peddlers and cut-rate stores appeared in great numbers. Other stores, especially the chains, began to use milk as a "loss leader."

whether or not the circumstances warranted such action.[8] Many formerly popular officers and managers of cooperatives were forced out by memberships that were not well informed as to the causes of their difficulties. Serious "milk strikes" developed in some areas, with trucks stopped on the highways and the contents of the cans dumped. It is not surprising, therefore, that the agricultural legislation passed in 1933 contained provisions for milk market control and that many of the states passed laws with similar objectives.[9]

But these facts do not explain fully why public intervention in the dairy marketing process has taken the form it has or why it was continued after the period of acute emergency had passed. The depression did not create the underlying need for economic regulation of the fluid milk markets. It did create pressures that revealed inherent structural weaknesses in the organization of the industry. In some markets, the strain was greater than the marketing machinery could stand and it broke down. However, the basic reason for increasing resort to public regulation lies in the nature of the demand for fluid milk, the conditions under which milk is produced and sold, and the characteristics of the product itself.

Demand for Milk Inelastic

The demand for fluid milk at retail is notably unresponsive to small changes in the retail price. Hence, both increases and decreases in price, within the usual ranges, tend to be borne by or reflected to consumers. The probable effect of a large change in price is difficult to estimate since milk prices tend to be rather stable, except when there are large changes in the price level that affect the economy as a whole. When changes in the general level of prices are occurring, it is virtually impossible to isolate price changes that are brought about by market regulation from those that are due to such other factors as deflation, inflation and increased consumer incomes.

An increase in the retail price of milk, within the ranges that actually occur, appears to have a somewhat larger effect on the amount purchased than does a decrease of similar size. However, such changes in price may have different effects in the long run than in the short run. A cutback of consumption which results from a price increase may disappear as consumers become accustomed to the higher price. Also, the effect may be different if the price change is widely publicized than if it does not attract much public attention. At any given time, many con-

8. The cooperatives succeeded for a time in holding up the price of Class 1 milk, but the returns for milk diverted to manufactured dairy products, and hence the blended price as well, fell sharply as a result of mounting surpluses. (See Leland Spencer and S. Kent Christensen, *Milk Control Programs of the Northeastern States,* Part 1, Cornell University Agricultural Experiment Station, Bulletin 908, November 1954, p. 10.)

9. The state of Wisconsin and the Canadian province of Manitoba had already (in 1932) enacted legislation of the type that later came into more general use.

sumers do not know what the price is. However, those who do know are likely to be the ones whose consumption rates are most responsive to price changes.[10]

When conditions are relatively stable, and with price changes within the narrow ranges that are likely to occur in ordinary times, the percentage change in amounts purchased is probably less than 30 to 50 per cent of the percentage change in price and is in the opposite direction. Broadly speaking, the same is true of the relationship between quantities of milk sold and changes in consumer incomes, except that here the two will move in the same direction; that is, larger consumer real incomes result in larger consumption of milk and vice versa.

There is some evidence that the effect of an increase in consumer income will be greater if it accrues to families in the lower income groups who may have been unable to afford as much milk as they wanted to buy. The sharp increase in per capita consumption of milk in the war years supports this conclusion. However, here also, the long-run effects of increased consumer incomes may differ from the short-run effects, because of consumption habits, prior commitments against income and so on. With the income changes diffused among families of markedly different levels of income, the percentage change in the quantity of fluid milk purchased is likely to be no more than a third to a half as large as the percentage change in income with which it is associated.[11]

Similarly, while there are some seasonal variations in the quantities of milk purchased, and even some day-to-day fluctuations, these are usually within a range of 6 to 8 per cent above or below the annual daily average. The outstanding characteristic of milk consumption habits is their relative stability, if other foods are abundant and conditions within the economy fairly stable.

Seasonal Fluctuations in Supply Are Large

On the supply side, the situation is in marked contrast to the continuous and stable demand described above. In many of the large fluid milk

10. For more detail (and differing views) about price elasticity in the markets for fluid milk, see George K. Brinegar, *Effect of Changes in Income and Price on Milk Consumption,* Storrs, Connecticut, Agricultural Experiment Station Bulletin 280, July 1951; Charles J. Blandford, *The Demand for Milk and Cream as Revealed by Consumer Purchases at Retail Stores in New York City,* Cornell University Agricultural Experiment Station, Bulletin 765, 1941; and E. W. Gaumnitz and O. M. Reed, *Some Problems Involved in Establishing Milk Prices,* U.S. Department of Agriculture, Marketing Information Series, DM-2, 1937. The literature on milk marketing is voluminous and includes many detailed, technical studies. Most are in general agreement on the relative inelasticity of demand for fluid milk, except as major changes in consumer purchasing power occur.

11. See, for example, Brinegar, *op. cit.; What Makes the Market for Dairy Products?,* Wisconsin Agricultural Experiment Station, Bulletin 477 (North Central Regional Publication No. 10), September 1948; R. E. Patzig and Gideon Hadary, "Relationship of Income to Milk Consumption," *Journal of Farm Economics,* February 1945, pp. 204–10; and John D. Black, "The Income Elasticity of Milk," *ibid.,* August 1946, pp. 845–48.

markets, daily deliveries in the months of heaviest production are as much as one and a half times as great as in the months of low production, usually the fall months. Sometimes the ratio is nearly two to one, and ratios of three to one in some areas are not uncommon. Supplies are also subject to rather substantial week-to-week and day-to-day variations, especially in the summer months.

Supply, like demand, is not quickly responsive to changes in price. Furthermore, production response to a decrease in price appears to be different from that resulting from an increase in price, especially in areas where there are few alternative outlets and few products that compete with dairying for the use of productive resources.[12]

The reasons for the lack of close correlation between amounts of milk produced and the price paid for it are not hard to find. The ratio of fixed to variable costs is very high on dairy farms. Consequently, in the short run (and possibly even for a considerable period), prices can fall very low and still be high enough to cover the out-of-pocket costs for purchased feeds and other variable items. Under such conditions the dairyman will lose less by continuing to produce than by stopping production. Later, if the low price continues, he will reduce the size of his herd or feed less intensively, and may even go out of the dairy business. Low prices tend to jeopardize investments rather than to curtail supplies.

The rate of long-run supply adjustment varies, of course, from region to region. In the Middle West, where alternative kinds of farming are numerous, changes may occur rather quickly. In the northeastern states, where dairying is the major and sometimes almost the only farm enterprise, adjustments are likely to be slower and smaller.

Significance of Sanitary Regulations

In the dairy industry, sanitary regulations are so important both in milk production and in milk marketing that very important economic consequences flow from them. Important and somewhat expensive requirements to safeguard the quality of urban milk supplies have been in effect in the older markets for a very long time. During the depression, the effectiveness of sanitary regulations was jeopardized, in many areas almost disastrously, by the inability of dairy farmers to meet the special costs requisite for the production of high-quality milk, such as disease elimination, cooling equipment, and barn and milk-room improvement.

This fact alone undoubtedly caused many representatives of the general public to favor legislation that would authorize economic regulation of the dairy industry. Also, the fact that the decline in dairy farmers'

12. In a state like Wisconsin, where many outlets are available (fluid milk buyers, creameries, condensaries, cheese factories and so on), the response in deliveries to any given market outlet from a change in price may be both large and immediate. In a highly specialized milkshed, such as that of New England or New York, the response may be quite different.

incomes was jeopardizing the rural social and tax structure in many areas lent support to efforts to improve conditions. The extremely wide distribution of the dairy industry has long given the dairy interests a strong voice in legislative matters.

However, our concern here is not with the reasons for sanitary regulations but with their economic effects. One effect is that they impede both expansion and contraction of supply. Producers who have not made the necessary investments for cooling equipment and other sanitary safeguards are not likely to do so unless they have reasonable assurance of continuing outlets for their product in fluid milk form. Conversely, once the investment has been made, they are not likely to relinquish a "fluid milk" outlet, and the higher price that goes with it, either quickly or voluntarily.

Other factors in the situation are that fluid milk is bulky in relation to its value and that it cannot be stored for any long period of time. Both of these characteristics contribute to heavy emphasis on transportation costs and short hauls. Hence, fluid milk tends to be so priced as to enable it to outcompete most other types of agricultural production in the areas that are within shipping distance of the large population centers. Thus the price to farmers in these areas is usually markedly higher than the price that farmers in more distant areas can obtain for milk which is to be converted into manufactured dairy products. There is therefore continuous pressure from dairy farmers just outside the recognized and regulated milksheds to have the privilege of selling fluid milk in those markets.[13]

Because of this tendency, sanitary regulations are and have been used as a way of protecting monopoly positions on the part of producers who have vested rights in the arrangements set up for supplying particular markets. The laws passed and the regulations set up are not always designed to protect the consumer. Some are, in fact, highly artificial and not closely related to the quality of the milk. While this generalization is widely accepted by students of the problem, it is difficult to prove or to quantify in most cases though specific identifiable instances can easily be cited.[14]

13. With the greatly improved modern methods of transportation, such as glass-lined refrigerated tank cars and trucks, this pressure may be exerted by areas far distant from the consuming markets, unless laws and regulations prevent such shipments.

14. Because of the wide interest in this problem, the U.S. Department of Agriculture undertook a study, published in 1955, of *Regulations Affecting the Movement and Merchandising of Milk* (Agricultural Marketing Service, Marketing Research Report No. 98, June 1955). Among the conclusions reached (see pp. vii and viii) were:

"1. That regulations of one kind or another account for most, but not all, of the amounts by which prices to producers exceeded a Midwestern base price plus costs of transportation. If free movement were to be permitted, prices to about one fourth of the producers of fluid milk would decline by an average of about 48 cents per hundred pounds. In some markets, the declines might range up to 75 cents to $1.00 per cwt. (A change of 46 cents per cwt. would be approximately 1 cent a quart.)

"2. That these declines would be partly offset by an increase of about a quarter of a billion pounds in milk consumption. Hence increases in total long-distance shipments

On the other side, it should be pointed out that many dairymen who want to intrude on established milk markets in times when milk is abundant are not prepared to accept the responsibilities implied by the right to participate in such markets. They may not be in a position to guarantee dependable supplies in periods of shortage or to meet even well-justified minimum standards of sanitation.

However, the system of sanitary regulations is undoubtedly one that lends itself to abuse in some situations and should be kept under scrutiny by the public and by the dairy groups that are excluded from markets they would like to have access to. Under some circumstances and in some areas, there would be social and over-all producer gains from more widely based interarea supply arrangements than are permitted under present laws and regulations.[15]

THE NEED FOR A UNIQUE PRICING SYSTEM

The peculiarities of the demand and supply conditions for milk, and the nature of the product itself, have resulted, first, in the adoption of a unique pricing system, and second, in a need for public regulation. Few of those closely in touch with milk marketing problems question the need either for special pricing arrangements or for a considerable amount of public regulation. The controversies and the conflicts of interest relate

---

would be relatively small, as price adjustments would make such movements less attractive than they now are.

"3. Sanitary regulations hinder or prevent the movement of milk into a substantial number of cities but in most markets they do not burden the movement of milk unduly if consistent with the requirements most widely regarded as essential.

"4. State milk controls over resale prices tend to limit opportunities for introducing innovations in marketing practices and for using aggressive methods in promoting sales. Federal milk marketing orders, as general policy, seek to avoid requirements that impede the movement of milk though some of them may have that effect."

The National Grange, on the basis of a study also published in 1955, concluded that "the net effect of (sanitary) restrictions has been to hold down consumption." (*Barriers to Increased Consumption of Fluid Milk,* A Special Report, January 1955, p. 60.) In general, the courts have tended to uphold without question the right of a municipality to establish reasonable standards in order to protect the health of its citizens but have, in many cases, invalidated regulations which, in purpose or in effect, constituted "unreasonable" trade barriers against outside milk. The general drift is toward applying as a criterion of reasonableness the standards recommended by the U.S. Public Health Service. For a fuller discussion and citation of numerous studies pertaining to the matter, see *ibid.,* pp. 60–78.

15. For example, sources in the Middle West probably could to advantage supply larger quantities of milk and cream to the eastern markets during seasons of short supply than they now do. Such an arrangement, which admittedly would have to be worked out very cautiously, might make it possible to ease down somewhat the amount of high-cost production now carried on in the eastern milksheds in order to have enough to supply the demand in periods of low production. If so, a larger part of the eastern milkshed output would go into Class 1 uses and consumers might get milk at a lower annual average cost without serious detriment to milk producers in the eastern milk-producing areas. Similar considerations may apply to the sources that supply milk to the Los Angeles area. (So far as this writer is aware, actual data demonstrating that such gains are possible have not been assembled though the general idea expressed above has frequently been put forward by students of the problem.)

mainly to the criteria used in regulating the milk markets and to specific provisions of laws, regulations and administrative decisions.

There are, of course, a number of milk markets in which public economic regulation has not been applied. However, in nearly all such situations, cooperative and industry organization has been developed in such a way that pricing arrangements and market regulation are very similar to those in the markets that are under public regulation. It can almost be said that public regulation consists more of a formalization and broadening of practices already developed under private auspices than of something new that has come from government itself.

The need for and significance of the special pricing arrangements that have grown up in the fluid milk markets can be made clearer by a brief consideration of the situation that would exist if milk were handled under some simple, one-price arrangement such as that which applies in the case of potatoes, vegetables, grains or livestock products.

If an attempt were made to establish a price that would "clear the market" of all milk delivered during the day without resorting to secondary outlets, prices would have to fluctuate greatly from season to season and even from day to day. Retail prices might range from as low as 10 cents per quart, or lower, to as high as 40 cents, or higher. Even with these extreme fluctuations, there would undoubtedly be days when part of the demand would remain unsatisfied or when not all of the milk received could be sold. The normal procedure for ironing out these fluctuations both in "regulated" and "unregulated" markets is, of course, to induce shipment of enough milk to supply the demand for milk in fluid form and to convert the surplus into manufactured dairy products that are more storable or that move into broader or more specialized markets such as those for ice cream, cottage cheese and so on.

Frequent and drastic changes in price also would lead to diseconomies in production. No dairy farmer could plan intelligently or effectively faced with price uncertainties of that magnitude. Universal dissatisfaction with such pricing systems has led to the adoption of contractual arrangements between suppliers and handlers, and to "classified price systems" in every important fluid milk market in this and other countries. Flat-price arrangements simply do not work.

Classified Price Plans

A way had to be found to assure an adequate supply of milk from day to day throughout the year and to provide returns to producers that would induce them to continue in business and to meet the demand in short seasons as well as in periods when milk production was high. At the same time, it was necessary to provide safeguards that would protect consumers against exploitation.

Thus far at least, the only system that has been devised that will meet those requirements is a class price arrangement. That is, all of the milk offered by the producers authorized to compete in a given market is received. That part of it needed to supply the market for fluid milk is paid for at a Class 1 price. The Class 1 price must be high enough to induce farmers to supply the amount of Class 1 milk needed even in the periods of lowest production. This means that there will be a considerable surplus in some parts of the year and that there must be some margin of safety even in periods of low production. This surplus is ordinarily referred to as Class 2 or even Class 3 or Class 4 milk, depending on the use that is made of it.

The excess milk over that required for Class 1 uses is disposed of through secondary outlets—in ice cream, butter, cheese, canned milk, dried milk, casein and so on—at prices approximating those prevailing for raw materials used in these wider types of dairy product market. The producer then receives a blended price based on the amount of his product used as fluid milk and that portion going into manufactured dairy products.

For example, if a particular dealer receives 1,000,000 pounds of milk in a given month and sells 900,000 pounds as fluid milk, he must dispose of the other 100,000 pounds at the price obtainable by way of manufactured dairy products. His total cost for milk in that month may be:

9,000 cwt. at $5.00	$45,000
1,000 cwt. at $3.00	3,000
Total cost	$48,000

If a simple pooling arrangement is used, each producer will receive a price that will be a weighted average of the two prices shown above, namely, $4.80 per hundredweight.[16]

This means, of course, that the larger the proportion of "excess" milk delivered, the lower the blended price will be. There is, therefore, an incentive for milk producers in the aggregate to avoid large expansion beyond the amounts that can be sold as Class 1 milk, unless the price that can be obtained for "excess" milk is high enough to be profitable,

16. In practice, there are, of course, many variations and modifications of this simple procedure. For example, milk will be paid for on the basis of its relative fat content, a specified place of delivery and so on. There may be more than two types of outlet with differential prices for each. For the larger markets, there is likely to be a market-wide pooling arrangement since a given dealer may sell as fluid milk a larger or smaller portion of the milk he receives than does some other. The blended price will then be arrived at on the basis of the relative amounts of milk going to different types of use in the market as a whole. That, of course, necessitates intramarket transfers of funds as among the various dealers so each will bear his proportionate share of the cost of removing "excess" milk from the market for Class 1 milk. Obviously, such a system requires complex and well-supervised accounting arrangements and a considerable amount of enforcement. Otherwise, it would quickly break down. Hence, the general preference on the part of milk producers, and, generally speaking, of milk distributors as well, for public control over the operation.

which it usually is not in view of the high costs incurred in supplying milk suitable for fluid use. However, the individual producer may, of course, find it profitable to produce as much as he can since any reduction of output he might make individually would not be likely to affect the average price received.

Defects of "Classified" Prices under Private Auspices

The flaw in the classified price system, especially under private auspices, is that it is inherently unstable if not subject to market-wide controls. There are always some dealers who want to buy the milk they require for sale as fluid milk at prices that may be above the "blended" price but below the price established for Class 1 milk. The greater the margin between Class 1 milk and "excess" milk, the greater the incentive for such practices and the more unstable the market. Large excesses in the form of Class 2 or lower-use-value milk also contribute to instability.

Also, especially in periods of great economic disturbance, the classified price system lends itself to abuse in that uneconomic practices may develop or be perpetuated under it. During the depression, many markets became so honeycombed with excessive charges, "special deals" on classification and accounting, excessive transportation charges, inequalities in methods of paying for butterfat, "penalties," "refunds," quota systems and so on that it was virtually impossible to determine what prices were being paid to producers on the average.

The most serious diseconomy results from the maintenance of a Class 1 price that is too high, so the average or "blended" price exceeds the price for manufacturing milk by too wide a margin. This tends to encourage dairymen to produce large quantities of milk that is paid for at the "blended" price but has an actual value, in manufacturing uses, below its cost. Whenever the cost of producing such milk exceeds its value as manufacturing milk, there is a social loss that is concealed under the pricing system used.

That loss must be borne by someone. In the first instance, it is borne by all of the producers whose returns are thus blended. If milk which costs $4.00 per hundredweight to produce must be sold through an outlet that returns only $3.00, there is a loss of $1.00 per hundredweight that pulls down the average net return. It may, of course, result in a price to consumers that is higher than it needs to be. This probably is the largest single diseconomy in the dairy industry. Some competent observers believe that it alone is larger, in total, than all others combined.

A further defect of the classified price system is that it lends itself to monopolistic exploitation. Dealers and milk producers may find that they have a community of interest, implemented by wide marketing margins for dealers and high Class 1 prices for producers, which may be adverse to consumers' interests. The opportunity for exploitation of consumers through arbitrarily established high prices is so obvious that it does not require elaboration.

The Need for Public Participation

It is clear that some sort of classified price system is virtually inescapable in the orderly handling of fluid milk. However, it is also evident that, in view of the defects inherent in such a system, both from the standpoint of the public and of the industry, some type of public regulation is needed. That need has been rather generally recognized by legislative bodies, both state and national. The principal controversies have centered on the methods of control, the policies to be followed, and the governmental level at which controls will be established, that is, state or national.

It seems likely that public regulation of some kind, in the fluid milk markets, would have developed long before 1933 had it not been for the deep and general aversion to public participation in economic activities during that period. The whole problem has now become more complex as a result of technological changes, higher quality standards, improved transportation, and so on.

It is difficult to see how any large fluid milk market could now be operated successfully without resort to a classified pricing system. Such a system would have to be either wholly private or operated by means of some combination of private and public participation.[17] Once the idea of classified prices has been accepted, there is equally evident need for some agency, public or private, to do the auditing and accounting that is necessary for maintaining a suitable balance between the interests of the producers, the dealers and the general public.

The auditing function is peculiarly well suited to performance by a public agency. Even where qualified firms of public accountants are engaged by producer cooperatives—the arrangement generally in effect prior to 1933—the results are not likely to be satisfactory. The auditing seldom applies to all distributors in the market, sometimes not even to a majority of them. Also there is an inherent incompatibility between the auditing function, which usually is controversial and may even lead to litigation, and the selling function, which is the cooperative's primary activity.[18]

Since public participation in the process of operating and supervising the fluid milk markets appears to be essential in the present complex situations in these markets, the principal problem from the standpoint of the public, and of the industry, is that of how to carry out such super-

17. Unless the public were prepared to take over the whole process of handling and distributing fluid milk.

18. As one cooperative member put it, "You usually are not very successful in selling milk to a dealer if you have to do it at the same time as you're 'lawin' or 'fightin' with him about an audit adjustment."

vision in a way that will be equitable, economical and practical. The remainder of this chapter summarizes and analyzes the experience gained under the public control programs carried on in the years since 1933, with principal emphasis on the federal rather than the state programs.[19]

FEDERAL REGULATIONS—THE FIRST PERIOD

The legislation on which the federal milk control programs are based is contained mainly in three acts—the Agricultural Adjustment Act of 1933, the August 1935 amendments to that act, and the Marketing Agreement Act of 1937. Two other acts have had some bearing on the program though perhaps only temporarily. These are the Steagall Amendment of 1941 and the Administrative Procedures Act of 1946.[20]

The laws themselves have been modified significantly from time to time as a result of weaknesses that became apparent when they were put into effect. Administrative arrangements and policies have been modified both as a result of experience gained and of legislative changes and court decisions. Also, much information has been accumulated and administrative know-how has been greatly increased.

Relevant Portions of the Agricultural Adjustment Act of 1933

The 1933 act provided general authorization for the Secretary of Agriculture to enter into marketing agreements with processors, associations of producers, and others engaged in the handling, in interstate or foreign commerce, of *any* agricultural commodity or product. This provision, therefore, authorized marketing agreements in the fluid milk industry as well as in the types of commodities discussed in Chapter 9.

Although the act required that "due notice" be given and that interested parties be afforded opportunity for a hearing when marketing agreements were being considered, it did not require the holding of hearings when licenses were being considered or when amendments to agreements or licenses were proposed. It was, in fact, very vague and general. The agreements could be expected to include only those features that promised sufficient mutual advantage to induce the various component parts of the industry to enter into them voluntarily.

The purposes and limitations of licenses, which were presumably designed to "eliminate unfair practices or charges that prevent or tend to

19. Much of the public supervision of fluid milk markets is under state auspices, but the procedures and problems are generally similar to those that appear in the federal programs. Some of the markets still are handled under producer-distributor agreements without public supervision, but usually on the basis of agreements worked out by strongly organized groups. However, even in these situations, the marketing methods and general policies tend to be similar to those found in the publicly supervised markets.

20. There have been, of course, minor amendments from time to time, but these are not discussed here except incidentally. Also, some of the World War II legislation and regulations related to milk.

prevent the effectuation of the declared policy" and were therefore regulatory measures, were not clearly defined. There was even some doubt whether both marketing agreements and licenses could be used simultaneously in the same market.

The act was also vague as to who could be parties to marketing agreements and how individual producers (as distinct from associations of producers) could be represented. What practices were "unfair" and what charges would tend to "prevent the effectuation of the declared policy"? Was there to be any effort to control production? There was even serious question whether the marketing agreements in the milk markets should come under the Agricultural Adjustment Administration or should be handled as industry-wide codes under NRA. The milk producers' associations were, in fact, influential in having the codes pertaining to agricultural products transferred to the jurisdiction of the Secretary of Agriculture.

From an economic standpoint, one of the most serious defects of the original act was that it did not provide usable guides or standards for arriving at prices to be paid and charged for milk. For example, were the prices for milk and dairy products to be established by categories of products for the nation as a whole (with appropriate regional or geographic differentials), or were they to be established on a market-by-market basis?

Could the classified price system, already developed by the producer cooperatives, be used, or would some other procedure have to be devised? There was also question as to what standards should be applied in determining prices for particular classes of milk and whether distributors' resale prices would be controlled or only the prices paid to milk producers.

If it was decided that resale prices were to be controlled, questions arose as to what dealers' margins should be permitted for each type of product, for example, in glass containers or paper containers, for Grade A and Grade B and for homogenized, vitamin fortified, advertised and unadvertised brands. There were similar problems with respect to different levels of service—home delivery, store delivery, milk depots and bulk sales.

The Marketing Agreement and License Phase

There was little time for discussion of these issues or for appraisal of alternatives. On May 12, 1933, the day the act was signed, a Chicago group, made up of representatives of the Pure Milk Association, a producers' cooperative, and of dealers operating in that market, presented to the Secretary of Agriculture an agreement they had worked out themselves. Dozens and indeed scores of others were presented soon afterward. By the end of 1933, more than two hundred agreements had been drafted and submitted, though only fifteen had been approved and made effective.[21]

Broadly speaking, the policy adopted was to enter into a separate marketing agreement and to issue a separate license for each fluid milk market that could be readily differentiated from other markets. This early period lasted only from May 1933 to about the end of that year. It can be characterized as the marketing agreement–license phase since it was only in that period that marketing agreements were of much importance in the federal regulation of fluid milk markets. From 1933 on, the emphasis shifted, first to licenses and then to fluid milk market "orders."

Administration was left largely to the local agencies. Costs were met by deductions obtained in the first instance from the dealers, but later deducted by them in whole or in part from the payments made to producers. The terms, conditions and marketing procedures were for the most part, insofar as they were considered legally and practically feasible, those suggested by the interested parties, that is, by the producers acting through their cooperative associations and by the dealers.

These programs, formulated by the interested parties, were not adopted without a struggle. The programs submitted usually included some features that were of doubtful legality. Others, though not vulnerable from a legal standpoint, were considered questionable in terms of public policy. Still others, which may have been necessary so long as producer cooperatives and dealers were negotiating the terms of sale without public agency intervention, were less essential under a system of public regulation. However, at that time no one knew how long the government would continue to participate in the fluid milk marketing process or how well the new industry-and-government team would work.

These early programs were actually much more detailed and comprehensive than those now in effect, though fewer markets were regulated. They differed from the succeeding ones in at least three important ways. One was that the government undertook not only to regulate the prices dealers would pay to producers but also the vastly more complicated task of establishing and enforcing the prices milk distributors could charge their customers. Milk is sold in many ways and in many forms, including sales through subdealers, stores and other wholesale buyers as well as to millions of individual consumers under all sorts of conditions. A second difference was that the government undertook to regulate (and sometimes to prohibit) a rather considerable number of trade practices on the part of the dealers. A third was that the early agreements

21. For an excellent and more detailed discussion of the marketing agreement and license program in this period, see Edwin G. Nourse, *Marketing Agreements under the AAA,* The Brookings Institution, Washington, 1935, especially Chapters 1, 2, 3 and 10, and John D. Black, *The Dairy Industry and the AAA,* The Brookings Institution, Washington, 1935.

and licenses usually included some provision for regulating or limiting production.

At the insistence of the dealers (since this was their major interest in having an agreement), and usually with the acquiescence or insistence of the producer representatives, the agreements invariably included a complete schedule of resale prices.[22] Dealers usually were willing to enter into agreements only if resale price and other detailed control features were included, and if there was expectation that the government would undertake to enforce them.

The dealers who did not sign the agreement often were bitterly opposed to these rigorous controls. Hence, in the fluid milk markets, licenses were invariably issued at the time the marketing agreement was approved. This was to make the provisions of the agreement applicable to all dealers whether or not they had signed the agreement.

Much Opposition to Resale Price Provisions

There was much opposition to the resale price regulations and they came eventually to be regarded as unenforceable. Many of the small distributors had customarily sold at somewhat lower prices than their larger competitors charged. They could not use advertising and other sales promotion techniques to advantage and hence resorted to price cutting, sometimes to very drastic price cuts in the depression years. Rightly or wrongly, they came to feel that the resale price provisions were designed to put them out of business. Similar controversies developed later with respect to milk sales by chain stores. During the depression, the practice of using milk as a "loss leader" had become extensive in some markets.

Many producers also were dissatisfied with the quotas assigned to them under the base-surplus plans, which were ordinarily a feature of the agreements.[23] Members of the cooperatives usually were accustomed to this procedure but "nonmember" producers often were not. Many of them regarded these arrangements as "newfangled," complicated and inequitable and as something designed by the cooperatives to deprive them of a portion of their fair share of the market. The quota system also was used frequently as a means of discouraging the entrance of new

22. Not only did they specify minimum prices at which dealers could sell to individual consumers and to stores and other agencies, but also the prices such handlers must charge for each grade of milk in each type of container and each type of delivery service. They also prohibited such things as the granting of discounts, "loss-leader" sales, omission of bottle deposits and "tie-in" sales. There were even restrictions on the advertising of marketing services and the giving of other merchandise as an inducement to buy milk. They represented, in fact, an attempt to establish probably the most extreme type of market rigidity ever imposed in the American economy.

23. A producer was assigned, or earned, a right to sell at preferred prices a specified quantity. All he produced in excess of that amount was "surplus" and would therefore have to be sold at lower prices. This came to be known as the base-surplus plan.

producers into the market. New suppliers might be required to sell all of their milk for a time at the "surplus" price, usually for three months from the time of making their first deliveries.

Another cause of dissatisfaction was that the agreements and licenses usually provided for market-wide equalization funds so designed that each distributor would have to bear his proportionate share of the cost of diverting "surplus" milk to secondary outlets. These provisions frequently gave rise to antagonism on the part of some dealers who did not customarily acquire large amounts of "surplus" milk and also among producers who were not members of the cooperatives.[24]

For all of these reasons, the experience under the marketing agreement and license phase of the program was not a happy one either for members of the industry or for the government administrators in charge of it. There were too many controversial issues to settle, too many divergent and conflicting points of view, both within the industry and in the government, and too few guides and standards. Experience was limited and there was little in the way of precedents to go on.

Beyond this, there was a deep skepticism within the Administration concerning both the legality and the wisdom, from a public policy standpoint, of attempting to regulate the resale prices charged by dealers. The tendency was for this procedure to guarantee to the dealers a fixed marketing spread while profit margins of producers, for whom the program was ostensibly designed, were not comparably protected. Had that been considered or attempted, it would have meant fixing the prices of major cost components such as feeds, hired labor and the like, and this obviously would have brought the dairy program into conflict with other parts of the over-all farm program.

Furthermore, enforcement proved extremely difficult, cumbersome and time-consuming. Close check on each of the millions of individual transactions was obviously not practical, and even when cases were brought into court, the courts were understandably loathe to apply drastic penalties for seemingly minor infractions of the law which nevertheless were serious enough to cause grave difficulty in the management of the program.[25]

24. Members of cooperatives felt concern as well. Since most of the cooperatives were financed by means of deductions from the returns made to producers by the dealers, there was fear on their part that if nonmembers received higher returns because no deductions were made for membership dues to the cooperatives, this might weaken the cooperatives. There was also some feeling that if the agreement and license procedure really worked, producers would have less reason to join the cooperatives or to continue as members of them.

25. A breach-of-contract approach was ordinarily not feasible as the dealers who had signed the agreement were co-sponsors of the program. Usually they tended to comply with the regulations, unless under pressure to "meet competition." For the others, the procedure available, aside from fines, was the revocation of licenses, after due notice and formal hearing. This was considered both too drastic and too slow. However, it has been used to some extent in California, and in some other areas, under state laws and regulations.

Changes in Administration Policy, 1934

In the latter part of 1933, the Agricultural Adjustment Administration made drastic changes in its policy relating to fluid milk marketing. After January 1934, it would not attempt to regulate dealers' resale prices (except in situations where the resale price structure was badly demoralized).[26] If resale prices were continued in the marketing agreements or licenses, they were to be low, relative to those customarily charged, and thus would be designed to prevent demoralization of the market rather than to maintain normal margins. That is, they would be lower, usually substantially lower, than the prices that might be expected to prevail in the market.

Prices for Class 1 milk were to be kept in some reasonable relationship to the prices obtainable for milk sold as butter, cheese and other manufactured milk products. No attempt was to be made to obtain "parity" prices except in conjunction with, or as a result of, a general production control program for all dairy products. The "base" and "surplus" system of payment would be retained, but mainly as a way of discouraging large seasonal variations in supply. There was also to be more emphasis on local responsibility in the formulation and administration of marketing agreements and licenses, but licenses were to be rigorously enforced.

As soon as it was announced that the government would not continue to establish resale prices, there was a marked decline of dealer interest in the program. Dealers, of course, were still concerned about the prices they would have to pay producers, but their interest was largely in keeping producer prices as low as possible. They refused thereafter to become parties to marketing agreements. The Agricultural Adjustment Administration announced that the marketing agreements then in effect (which contained the minimum resale price provisions) would be terminated on February 1, 1934. Reliance then came to be placed entirely on licenses. This phase also was short-lived as the licensing authority was soon supplanted by the power to issue milk market "orders."

Production Control Not Undertaken

Because of the complexity of the problem, and also because of strong opposition from dairymen, the Adjustment Administration did not undertake to control the production of dairy products. The decision to relate the price of fluid milk to that of manufactured dairy products also proved very difficult to carry out, especially after it became apparent that a dairy control program would not be undertaken. That policy was not actually put into effect.[27] There was, in fact, no well-defined policy in

26. This pertains only to the federal program. The control of resale prices has been continued in some of the state programs.

27. In later periods, many of the formulae did include provision for relating milk

respect to milk prices in that period. The price of fluid milk in the regulated markets probably was higher than it would have been if there had been no federal intervention. However, the general trend of prices was upward and the severe drought of 1934 undoubtedly strengthened the prices of dairy products generally, so there is little on which to base estimates of the specific effects of the control programs themselves.

The plan to shift more responsibility to local agencies also proved impractical. The trend was, in fact, in the opposite direction. This was due largely to strenuous resistance from the "independent" dealers and the producers who sold milk to them (that is, producers who were not members of cooperatives). Furthermore, there was opposition within the Agricultural Adjustment Administration to the adoption, without a good deal of modification, of programs submitted by the dominant agencies in the various markets. This opposition extended also to efforts to decentralize administration of the programs.

In addition, there was growing criticism of attempts by the Secretary of Agriculture to delegate authority in these and other marketing programs (see pp. 373–75). The practice was adopted, and is still followed, of appointing a "Market Administrator" responsible directly to the Secretary.[28] This meant centralization of authority rather than decentralization of it.

Despite the changes made, or perhaps even because of them, vigorous opposition continued, especially from the dealers, who objected to the abandonment of resale price-fixing, and from the cooperatives which, for the most part, supported the dealers' position. There was continuing strong opposition to the equalization of returns, mostly by the "independent" dealers and their suppliers; to "market-service" deductions; and to the reports and disclosure of records required of dealers who had not been accustomed to having such audits.[29] The base quota and surplus system also continued to draw fire, especially from producers who had not previously been accustomed to that method of payment, and even from some who were familiar with it but felt that the quotas allotted were not fair.

---

prices to those of manufactured dairy products but, of course, with a premium on deliveries for the fluid milk use.

28. In practice there was, of course, in virtually all cases, consultation between the Administration and the people in the industry before such an appointment was made.

29. Much resentment was stirred up within the industry by a speech of Secretary Wallace at Madison, Wisconsin, in January 1934. He disclosed the results of audits made of the books of milk dealers in St. Louis, Chicago, Boston and Philadelphia, which purported to show profits ranging from 14.6 to 30.8 per cent for the year 1933, a year of acute general depression. While Secretary Wallace presented these figures as an explanation of the government's decision to abandon the policy of fixing resale prices, he also used the occasion to criticize the leaders of some of the producer cooperatives for urging the continuance of that policy. This latter criticism created so much resentment among producers and their organizations that many of them later supported the Feisinger Bill (H. R. 8988), which would have required the Secretary to fix resale prices and to give local control committees much more authority. Though the bill was not passed, it did give rise to discussions that had considerable effect on later legislation.

Despite the complaints, controversies and difficulties, licenses were requested for more markets than the Adjustment Administration was prepared to handle. Experienced personnel was lacking and in many instances the volume of milk actually moved in interstate commerce was so small that federal regulation did not seem warranted. Nevertheless, some 48 markets were licensed in 1934.

LEGISLATIVE CHANGES, 1935 AND AFTER

Legislative Revisions of 1935

Troubles in the milk program were an important element in the decision to revise the marketing agreement sections of the Agricultural Adjustment Act in 1935. Opponents of the program then in effect contended that the act involved "unconstitutional delegation of powers by the Congress" and that it "attempted to regulate intrastate commerce." In addition, violations of license provisions had become numerous and many law suits had been adjudicated or were before the courts. Some decisions in the lower courts were adverse to the government and hence a source of encouragement to violators.

Nonviolators watched their competitors continue to refuse to make payments to equalization funds and decline to pay "market-service" charges, file reports or keep and make available appropriate books and records. Some did not pay producers in accordance with the terms of the licenses. Court action against them was slow, ponderous and uncertain as to outcome. Yet if the violators could continue their violations with impunity, they had enormous competitive advantage over those who abided by the regulations.

There were also, of course, many errors both of commission and omission on the part of administrators, some due to haste or inexperience, others to the lack of guides and standards or of adequate information and understanding of the issues. However, even if administration and planning had been "perfect," it can be doubted that there would have been much less acrimony and litigation. Milk dealers, like other businessmen, were not accustomed to regulation, did not like it, and were determined to resist it. Only a comprehensive review by the courts could resolve some of the controversies and clarify questions about the powers, duties, rights and obligations of the various participants.

These controversies, and the inability to secure compliance, had two major effects on the program. One was that the Administration tended to work more closely with the producers' cooperative associations, and with the milk dealers and handlers; the other was an increased determination on the part of the Administration and the dairy industry to seek new legislation from the Congress.

This legislation, though actually passed as part of the Agricultural

Adjustment Act amendments of 1935, was so extensive that the enactments later were designated collectively as the Marketing Agreement Act of 1935. Their general nature and significance have already been described. With respect to milk specifically, the new act provided for the following:

1. The classification of milk "in accordance with the form in which or the purpose for which it is used."

2. "Fixing, or providing a method for fixing, minimum prices for each such use classification which all handlers shall pay, and the time when payments shall be made, for milk purchased [by them] from producers or associations of producers." [30] The act further provided that "such prices shall be uniform as to all handlers," subject only to adjustments for "volume, market, and production differentials customarily applied by the handlers subject to such order; the grade or quality of milk purchased"; and "the locations at which delivery of such milk, or any use classification thereof, is made to such handlers."

3. A method whereby all producers or associations of producers delivering milk to specified handlers or on a market-wide basis would be paid a uniform price for the milk delivered by them regardless of the use made of it (subject, of course, to quality and locational differentials).

4. Making adjustments in payments as among handlers so that the total sums paid by each handler would equal the value of the milk purchased by him at the prices fixed in accordance with the price-fixing powers prescribed. This was a necessary corollary to the market-wide pooling system and provided authorization for establishing an "equalization fund" in each market where the market-wide system of pooling was adopted.

5. Authorization to deduct from payments to producers the amounts required to pay for certain marketing services and for supplying market information.

6. Payments to "new producers" for a limited time (not over three months) at the price established for the lowest-priced use classification. This presumably would discourage entrance into the market if the producer wanted to enter only on a seasonal or temporary basis rather than as a permanent supplier. On the other hand, the Secretary of Agriculture was directed not to enter into any marketing agreements or issue any order that would prohibit or limit the marketing in that area of any milk, or any product thereof, purchased in any production area in the United States.

Under the general sections of the act (also applicable to milk), there was a provision that an order could not become effective until the handlers of not less than 50 per cent of the volume marketed within the area had signed a marketing agreement. However, this limitation was

30. 49 Stat. 750, Sections (5)A and (5)B.

modified by two other provisos: (1) that an order could not become effective unless favored by at least two thirds of the milk producers supplying the market (by number or volume) if a market-wide pool was contemplated (three fourths if the plan called for a pool applying to specified handlers); and (2) that if an order was favored by the prescribed number of producers it could become effective even if the handlers refused to sign a corresponding marketing agreement. In that case, however, the Secretary, with the approval of the President, had to determine (1) that the refusal of the handlers to sign an agreement tended to prevent the effectuation of the declared policy of the act and (2) that the issuance of the order was the only practical means of advancing the interests of the milk producers selling in that market. This was the same provision as was described earlier (see Chapter 9) in connection with marketing agreements for fruits and vegetables.[31]

Some Further Changes Made in 1937

The 1935 act provided a reasonably adequate legal basis for federal regulation of milk marketing. Most of its provisions are still in effect. A description and analysis of the operations carried out under that act and later modifications of it provides, therefore, in broad outline, a record of the development of federal regulation of milk marketing in the years since.[32]

However, since doubt had been cast on the constitutionality of the marketing agreement features of the Adjustment Act both by the Schechter decision and the Hoosac Mills case, the Marketing Agreement Act of 1937 was passed with a view to (1) reaffirming the separability of the marketing agreement sections of the original act, (2) disavowing the idea of regulating production, (3) emphasizing the idea of market regulation and (4) redefining in broader terms the concept of interstate trade.

For the most part, the 1937 act was a reaffirmation of the 1935

31. This provision was opposed vigorously by the milk handlers as they naturally preferred a market agreement and order procedure under which they could have more influence. However, the adverse decision of the Supreme Court in the Schechter case made it clear that "codes" formulated and administered by an industry—and hence presumably marketing agreements as well—could not be enforced. Consequently, for effective regulation of milk marketing a different procedure was needed. The Schechter decision, more than any other argument or consideration, diverted the interest and attention of the dairy industry away from marketing agreements and toward more definitely regulatory programs.

32. The fact that an adequate legal basis for regulating the milk markets had come into being was not generally recognized at that time. Decisions unfavorable to the government were rendered by some of the lower courts and violations of orders and other regulations continued to be a problem. Consequently, producer cooperatives and government administrators were reluctant to undertake new programs in markets not already under regulation. Hence, for some years after the passage of the 1935 act, the program was going through a period of adaptation, court review and evolutionary development.

act. However, some changes were made. The objective of achieving parity prices through establishing an appropriate balance between the production and consumption of the specified agricultural commodities was abandoned and, instead, emphasis was put on the maintenance of "orderly marketing conditions for agricultural commodities in interstate commerce . . ."

There was some further spelling out of the standards to be used by the Secretary of Agriculture in establishing prices for milk in the markets to which orders applied. Account was to be taken of the prices of feeds, the available supply of feeds, and other economic conditions which would affect the supply and consumption of milk in the area concerned. In short, if "parity" prices proved not to be a reasonable standard, some other standard might be applied which would "insure a sufficient quantity of pure and wholesome milk and be in the public interest." This introduced a needed element of flexibility but also placed on the Secretary of Agriculture added responsibilities in exercising the discretion thus conferred on him.[33]

Wartime "Emergency" Legislation

World War II had a very significant impact on the milk program as well as on other federal agricultural programs. Whereas the problem in the 1930s was one of devising methods for dealing with surpluses, the problem in many markets came to be that of assuring adequate supplies to meet the rapidly growing demand. Not only did the increased employment and higher level of consumer incomes give rise to larger per capita consumption of milk but there was also a greatly increased demand for cheese, dried milk, butter and other manufactured dairy products. Part of it stemmed from the need for increased shipments abroad under lend-lease and the relief agencies, as well as from the higher level of domestic consumption.

The first of the acts pertaining to this situation was the Steagall Amendment of July 1941. That amendment directed the Secretary of Agriculture, if he found it necessary to encourage an expansion in the production of any "nonbasic" agricultural commodity, to support the price of that commodity through loans, purchases or other operations at not less than 85 per cent of parity. This was later raised to 90 per cent and was to be continued for two years after the close of hostilities.

In contrast, the price controls established under the Emergency Price

33. The attempt to broaden the definition of interstate commerce involves numerous highly technical legal and economic concepts, which are not discussed here. Many of them still are not fully resolved or clarified. The interests of the farm groups were not entirely consistent on this point. In their efforts to make eligible for federal regulation more of the farm products moved, they advocated a broad though still vague definition. In other connections, such as federal regulations pertaining to wages and hours or social security, some of the farm groups urged strongly a much narrower concept of what constituted interstate commerce.

Control Act of January 1942, and later legislation, established "parity" price, or some alternative level, as a ceiling beyond which prices of farm products were presumably not to be allowed to rise.[34] Though not rigorously enforced, particularly in respect to farm products, these limitations on prices that could be charged or paid eventually put milk producers in a squeeze which threatened a reduction in output at a time when more milk was urgently needed.[35]

During the war years, the price mechanism was not the principal factor in allocating milk among its various uses. Other devices were used, such as rationing, limitations on sugar and fat used in making ice cream, and prohibition of the sale of heavy cream to consumers. "Set-aside" orders also were used as a means of obtaining supplies required by the government.

Even these measures, designed in part to channel more of the over-all milk supply into fluid uses, were insufficient to keep milk supplies in balance with the sharply increased demand. As a means of stimulating, or at least maintaining, milk production in the face of rising feed and labor costs, heavy subsidies were provided during the war years. Some subsidies were paid to the manufacturers of cheddar cheese and butter, but the major subsidy provided was on fluid milk.

Subsidy rates differed by sections of the country and also by seasons. In general they ranged from 25 cents to 90 cents per hundredweight. For the war period as a whole, the subsidies on dairy products were the largest provided to any agricultural industry, amounting in all to more than $1.3 billion.

While the war regulations modified drastically the functioning of the price mechanism in the fluid milk markets, the basic problems and legislation here under consideration were not changed importantly. Such carry-over effect as existed was mainly on the prices of manufactured dairy products, through the continuance of wartime price-support legislation (see Chapter 6). Their relation to fluid milk prices was mainly an indirect one. Heavy government purchases of butter and cheese did, of course, ease pressure on the fluid milk market and enhanced, at least temporarily, the prices received by fluid milk producers for Class 2 milk converted into manufactured dairy products.

34. For a more complete description of the legislative and other actions taken in this connection, see Murray R. Benedict, *Farm Policies of the United States, 1790–1950,* Twentieth Century Fund, New York, 1953, pp. 408–30.

35. Price controls on milk were at first applied only at the retail level but eventually were extended (in February 1943) to provide for maximum prices which dealers might pay producers. At first, the regulations specified certain base periods and established the prices then prevailing as the maxima which could be charged. Later, more detailed regulations and other criteria were used. Full description of the complex legislative and administrative arrangements of that period would be much too voluminous for presentation here and in fact would have no important significance in tracing the development of the program now in effect. Consequently they are treated only in barest outline. For a more detailed account of the wartime dairy programs, see Gertrude Foelsch, *Federal Milk Marketing Orders and Dairy Programs in World War II,* U.S. Production and Marketing Administration, Agriculture Monograph No. 12, August 1951.

The Administrative Procedures Act, 1946

As the first period of creating new programs and new agencies for the relief of agriculture drew to a close, more emphasis began to be placed on improvement in administrative procedures, organizational relationships and so on. That emphasis became more prominent at the close of World War II when the problem of liquidating emergency war agencies had to be faced.

Many of the agencies set up hurriedly during the depression and war years were organized for fast action, and arrangements were often worked out on a basis of expediency rather than of the functional relationships that were customary in governmental operations. Consequently, there had been a growing volume of criticism of the methods and organizations so hastily devised. In an effort to correct that situation, the Congress passed in 1946 a general act known as the Administrative Procedures Act. It did not apply specifically to agriculture but did have a bearing on a number of the agricultural programs, including those pertaining to fluid milk.

The complaints made were, in general, of the following types: that the operation of regulatory agencies often included functions of incompatible types, such as acting as a legislative agency (in formulating and issuing regulations), as an executive agency (in administering the program), as prosecuting attorney or advocate (in carrying out investigations and presenting evidence) and, finally, as judge and jury in the adjudication of issues and controversies.

Other criticisms were that some of the agencies were "power hungry" or that their actions were arbitrary and capricious. There were complaints that public hearings were not held or, if they were, that little attention was paid to the testimony of any except the people affiliated with the agency. Regulations were said to be vague, complicated and confusing and often were not published or got lost. It was also contended that affected parties were given little opportunity to participate in the rule-making process.

That some of these criticisms, at least in respect to certain federal agencies, were well founded can scarcely be doubted. In general, they were directed less at Department of Agriculture operations than at some other government agencies. The Department of Agriculture, for the most part, showed a high degree of responsiveness to criticism of its activities and usually sought quickly to alter or improve its procedures if well-founded objections were raised. Some of the difficulties noted, however, were due to defects in the legislation rather than to administrative inadequacies. Others were due to difficulties inherent in the regulatory process itself. And, finally, some difficulties resulted from inadequate or inefficient functioning of administrators.

OPERATING PROCEDURES

No useful purpose would be served by presenting here a detailed description of the regulatory machinery and the functions performed by the milk control agencies. However, a brief general sketch of the arrangements will enable the reader to grasp more fully the complexity of the problem and of the mechanisms required for carrying out a program of this kind.

The primary authority rests with the Secretary of Agriculture, and official actions, such as the issuance of orders, must be in his name and on his responsibility. Within the Department of Agriculture the analysis of proposals, preparation of orders and general supervision of orders in effect are handled by specialists in the Dairy Branch. In addition, the Department has a legal staff, responsible to the Solicitor, which reviews all orders and also provides "reviewers" who preside over public hearings and certify as to the accuracy of the public records of such hearings.

Whenever a legal issue relating to a specific order is raised, the facts pertaining to it are presented at a formal, quasi-judicial hearing before a "Judicial Officer." If his decision is favorable to the Department of Agriculture and unfavorable to the opposing litigants, they may appeal to a federal court of competent jurisdiction.

The key unit in the system at the local level is the "Market Administrator." He is appointed by the Secretary of Agriculture, usually after consultation with local proponents of the order. Most of his salary, and all of his employees' pay, is derived from assessments on the industry, which are provided for in the marketing order. He is the primary link between the industry and the office of the Secretary of Agriculture and a channel for information and official actions moving both ways.

The Market Administrator receives reports from the handlers relating to their receipts and utilization of milk, audits their books and records, calculates and announces the prices to be paid to producers, and checks the weighing and testing of milk at the receiving plants. He also provides market information, helps carry out public programs relating to milk (as, for example, in wartime) and performs many consultative and mediatory functions. By far the largest of his tasks is that of auditing the many and complex records relating to the operation.

He also must keep the administrators in the Department of Agriculture adequately and realistically informed as to the special problems and conditions in his market area. It is this task of following an intermediate course between the role of an autocrat carrying out the programs developed by the Department of Agriculture and, on the other hand, that of an overzealous advocate of the wishes of his constituents that constitutes one of the most delicate and exacting phases of his work. The success of the whole complex regulatory operation depends heavily on the wise selection of experienced and able market administrators.

DEVELOPMENT OF MILK MARKET CONTROLS, 1936–1954

The period 1933–1936 was one of experimentation and controversy in the federal milk control program. Thereafter the situation became more stable and many of the more burdensome or unworkable features of the program were discontinued. Here, as in the marketing agreements for fruits and vegetables, many of the procedures and policies considered appropriate or desirable were found impractical and had to be abandoned.

Since 1936, the number of federally regulated markets has grown year by year to a coverage of 58 markets in 1955, as compared with 6 in 1936. (See Table 50.)

TABLE 50

MILK: NUMBER OF FEDERAL MARKETING ORDERS IN EFFECT DURING ALL OR A PART OF THE FISCAL YEAR, 1936–1955

Fiscal Year	Number	Fiscal Year	Number
1936	6	1946	29
1937	7	1947	30
1938	10	1948	30
1939	14	1949	35
1940	19	1950	39
1941	20	1951	46
1942	22	1952	50
1943	22	1953	49
1944	24	1954	53
1945	27	1955	58

Sources: U.S. Agricultural Marketing Service, *The Dairy Situation,* April 1954, p. 28, and September 6, 1955, pp. 23, 29.

Most of the large markets, except those in California, are now covered by federal marketing orders, for example, New York, Chicago, Boston, Philadelphia, Detroit, Minneapolis, St. Paul, St. Louis, Kansas City and Cincinnati.[36] In addition, many of the smaller markets of the Middle West are now under that type of regulation, mainly in states that do not have state milk control laws. These include such cities and combinations of cities as Duluth-Superior; Clinton, Iowa; Dubuque, Iowa; Lowell-

36. There is, however, continuing controversy in nearly all of the federal milk control areas as to what the boundaries of the area should be. In many of them, the marketing orders have been amended from time to time to enlarge or contract the area, usually to enlarge it. For a discussion of this point, see R. W. Bartlett and W. H. Alexander, *The Practice of Establishing Federal Order Marketing Areas as Related to Economic Theory,* Department of Agricultural Economics, University of Illinois, Urbana, AE 2957, August 1953, mimeo.

Lawrence, Massachusetts; and Fall River, Massachusetts. Some 40 million people reside in the areas covered by federal milk market orders.[37]

State Milk Control Laws

State milk control laws began to take shape even before the federal program came into effect. The first steps were taken in 1932 and by July 1933 seven states had adopted milk control legislation. Between 1933 and 1940, nineteen other states passed legislation of that kind. Ten of them later discontinued state control and either operated without public regulation or turned to federal orders.[38]

In general, the state milk controls apply on a statewide basis, whereas federal marketing orders regulate operations only in specified urban market areas. The coverage through federal and state regulation as of April 1954 is shown in the accompanying map.

The state milk marketing laws came into being largely in the period when the constitutionality of federal regulation was under attack, or threat of attack, and also, in part, as a result of unsatisfactory experience with the early federal agreements and licenses. In a number of states they have been retained, but the trend seems now to be in the direction of more reliance on federal regulation and less on state action. The number and scope of federal orders has increased consistently since 1936 while the area covered by state regulations has declined.[39]

37. As of September 1955, federal orders were in effect in 58 milk marketing areas. They regulated the minimum prices paid to about 185,000 producers for about a third of all whole milk delivered to plants, that is, to fluid milk distributors and manufacturing plants. (See *The Dairy Situation*, September 6, 1955, p. 23.) The handlers operating in these markets produce and sell almost every type of dairy product known and used and include almost every type of marketing organization. Some of the milk sold by the federally regulated handlers is sold by them in markets that are not under federal regulation. (They may be under state regulation or not under regulation of any kind.) Some, probably most, of the milk purchased by the federally regulated handlers is bought in areas where other buyers are also purchasing milk. These intermarket purchase and sales arrangements create many economic interrelationships between regulated and unregulated markets and handlers. Also, the extensive network of state and municipal sanitary regulations and the considerable number of state milk regulatory arrangements add to the complexity of the market structure.

38. The states which discontinued state controls are Delaware, Indiana, Maryland, Michigan, Ohio, South Dakota, Texas, Utah, Washington, Wisconsin and Oregon. North Carolina recently adopted a state milk control law. Of the sixteen states operating under state milk control laws in 1955, eleven exercised control not only over prices paid to producers but also over resale prices to consumers. In 1933 and after, several attempts were made to bring about joint federal and state regulation in the New York market, but that form of control was not adopted until 1938. Some New York dealers were shifting their purchases to Pennsylvania, Vermont and other out-of-state areas and could not be effectively controlled by New York laws and regulations. It became virtually impossible for a dealer to comply fully with the New York regulations without losing business to cut-rate competitors.

39. However, there was some resurgence of interest in state controls in the early and middle 1950s, for example in North Carolina, South Carolina, Arkansas and Ohio. There are sound reasons for retaining or adopting state controls in areas where there is not much interstate movement of fluid milk, for example in states like Texas, California, Colorado and possibly Ohio. Under the federal system, if a policy is adopted for one

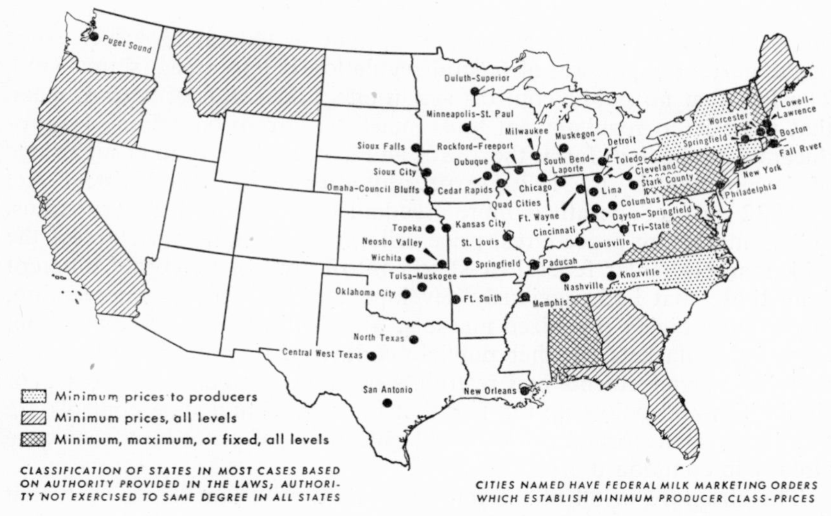

Source: U.S. Department of Agriculture

GEOGRAPHY OF FLUID MILK PRICE REGULATIONS, AS OF APRIL 1954

This shift has no doubt been due in part to the broadening of the definition of interstate commerce, both through legislative action and by judicial interpretation. In many areas where federal action was formerly considered of dubious validity, the right of the federal government to exercise authority has come to be generally recognized. Furthermore, the modifications made in the federal program during the middle 1930s have made it much more acceptable to the industry than it was in the first years of its operation.

The federal program does not provide for the fixing of resale prices to consumers whereas a number of the state laws do include such authorization. This may have had some influence on decisions as to which of the two approaches to use, but, if so, its significance is not clearly apparent. It seems more likely that state regulation is largely a survival of a procedure adopted at a time when federal regulation was considered of dubious legality and merit, and was continued thereafter because it seemed to be working reasonably well and was not strongly opposed.[40]

state it may have to be applied in 47 other states whether it fits or not. Also, it is a simpler matter to get adjudication of disputes in state courts than in federal courts and costs only about a half or a third as much. The possible advantages of genuine federal-and-state action in this realm have been very little explored.

40. The constitutionality of federal regulation of milk markets that operate wholly within a state rests upon somewhat tenuous reasoning, namely, that milk so used is "in the current of or affects" interstate commerce in butter, cheese and other manufactured dairy products. This, together with the desire to keep control closer to home, may have some bearing on decisions to continue to rely on state regulation.

The more sparsely settled states have not until recently shown much interest in milk market regulation either state or federal. However, some of the current expansion of federal regulation is into areas of that kind. The fact that no public controls are in effect does not, of course, mean that there is no regulation of those markets. Group bargaining by producers dates back as far as the 1880s and had reached a rather high stage of development by the 1920s, especially after the Capper-Volstead Act of 1922 gave cooperatives more freedom of action and clearer status.

The marketing procedures, price criteria and general structure of the milk markets under federal or state control are not markedly different from those that had previously developed, without public intervention, in the more highly organized markets. This is not to say, of course, that any of the markets whether publicly controlled or not are free of monopolistic arrangements and restraints on trade. It merely stresses their similarities and points up the fact that the federal and state controls are to a large extent formalizations and legalizations of procedures that were already in common use.

The structure of all of the important fluid milk markets is such that dominance by a comparatively few large distributors virtually requires some type of oligopsonistic pricing procedure which the milk producers have had to meet through more or less monopolistic types of organization. Public controls do tend to make more enforceable the rules of the game and, at least theoretically, provide for some measure of public participation in the bargaining process.

The problem is not primarily one of prices. It is rather one of maintaining orderly relationships in a very dynamic industry that affects large numbers of people and has great economic significance. Controversies in regard to it can reach a stage of intensity that may jeopardize the interests of the public as well as of farmers, business organizations and employees. A means appears to have been found whereby these conflicts of interest can be channeled into a place (the office of the milk market administrator) where they can be reconciled in such a way that farmers, handlers and the consumers can live with them and be reasonably free of the more violent types of controversy. Though the system does not work perfectly it appears to have had a stabilizing influence; there has been no milk strike or other serious disturbance in the industry during the twenty years in which the milk control programs have been in operation.

Though the federal and state governments have interceded in a large way, they have succeeded in providing procedures and specialized personnel, such as economists, attorneys and hearing officers, that contribute to orderly handling of most of the kinds of controversy that arise. Despite the high degree of regulation involved, the programs have been handled in such a way as to retain a considerable amount of the vitality which stems from local participation and interest.

Whatever its merits or demerits, public regulation of the more important fluid milk markets appears to have become well established and there is little indication of a reversal of the trend of recent years. More than 60 per cent of the fluid milk sold for direct consumption is now under direct public control, and the prices and policies established in respect to these controlled supplies no doubt have some influence on prices in the areas not under control. The problems requiring consideration are therefore largely in the realm of how to make the system more equitable and more efficient socially rather than of whether or not to have public regulation of the fluid milk markets.

PRICE EFFECTS OF THE PROGRAMS

Public and industry interest in federal and state milk controls centers around the following questions: How have they affected returns to producers? What has been their effect on wholesale and retail margins and the prices paid by consumers? Have they contributed significantly to stability in supplies, prices, market conditions and equitable relationships as among producers, handlers and consumers? Have they had any identifiable influence on the amounts of milk consumed, the efficiency of production and progress in marketing methods?

It would be a hardy investigator indeed who would attempt broad generalizations in regard to an industry so complex and varied. Nevertheless, the numerous and voluminous studies available do throw some light on these questions and it is possible now for the layman to consider them in a more informed way than could have been done at the time such programs were first initiated.

It must be recognized, however, that production and marketing conditions vary widely from area to area even when no public controls are involved. For example, in 1930 dealers' average buying prices for standard-grade milk for city distribution as milk and cream ranged from $1.90 per hundredweight at Denver to $4.00 at Miami, Florida.[41] The price at Boston was $3.98 while the Minneapolis price was $2.36 and the Chicago price was $2.67.

These large differentials in price are due mainly to great differences in production conditions, lengths of haul, supplies in relation to fluid milk requirements and so on. In part, too, the divergencies in 1930 may well have been due to the relative strengths and effectiveness of producer organizations in holding prices stable in the face of a major disturbing influence such as the onset of depression.

These intermarket differentials have become markedly smaller in recent years but there is little warrant for attributing the change to public controls, since a number of the markets that are not under either state

41. *Utilization of Farm Crops, Milk and Dairy Products,* U.S. Senate, Hearings before a Subcommittee of the Committee on Agriculture and Forestry, 2d sess., pursuant to S. Res. 36 and S. Res. 198, Part 4, 1950, p. 2044.

or federal control have made the largest relative gains. For example, the price at Denver, where public controls were not in effect, was $4.94 in 1949 as compared with $5.82 at Boston and $7.09 at Miami.[42] The Miami price, for various reasons, was much above those of any of the other markets. Omitting Miami and New York, the range of prices in 1949, in the markets reported, was only from $3.77 at Chicago to $5.99 at Richmond, Virginia.

The marketing margins within the various markets are also affected by almost innumerable variations in conditions, which make comparisons difficult. However, the range in dealer margins is far smaller than the range in prices to producers. Among the things that affect costs of delivering and selling are differences in wage rates, topography, delivery density and size of firm.

Public Controls and the Producer

Milk producers have rather generally favored public control, at least with respect to prices paid to producers and the methods of payment used. Where producers are so organized as to be able to bargain effectively with the milk distributors, public regulation helps them to avoid undercutting of prices and other disruptive influences stemming from nonmember suppliers and also enables them to force all dealers to pay the same prices for given grades and classes of milk.

These considerations are more important in times of severe depression since it is then that the milk markets may become demoralized and chaotic. However, the problem of the noncooperating producer and dealer is serious enough even in ordinary times for most producer groups to prefer to see them brought under control.

Efforts to measure the effects of milk controls on prices paid to producers are inevitably highly speculative. Not many researchers have even attempted to arrive at specific figures on this point. Such studies as are available seem to indicate some rather modest price gains to producers as a result of the control programs. Spencer and Christensen concluded, on the basis of studies in New York state, that gains averaging about 5.2 per cent, for the period 1933–1953, were achieved.[43]

Their findings indicate that prices were affected through increases in Class 1 prices paid by dealers and through the requirement that dealers who formerly bought on a flat-price basis pay the full Class 1 price for that portion of the milk sold for use in fluid form. They have assumed that some 40 per cent of the fluid milk sold in the New York markets would have been bought at flat prices if there had been no milk controls

42. *Ibid.* The Denver price for 1930 was only for a seven-month average and hence may not be representative of the price for the full year. It is given here because Denver is the only one of the markets listed that has not since come under public control.

43. Leland Spencer and S. Kent Christensen, *Milk Control Programs of the North-*

and that 66 to 72 per cent of the milk so purchased would have been sold as fluid milk.

If these assumptions are accepted, prices paid by these dealers for Class 1 milk were raised by some 3 to 9 cents per hundredweight. Milk controls apparently raised the over-all prices paid by dealers who normally buy on a classified basis by a little more than half a cent per quart. For the others, the increase in the price paid to producers was estimated at a little more than one cent per quart.[44]

For the most part, the gains to producers from milk controls appear to be of a less tangible kind. Market orders have apparently tended to stabilize the markets, to prevent milk price wars and to protect producers against unethical practices of various kinds on the part of milk handlers. To the extent that these ends were accomplished, the producer has had a better basis for planning and financing his business and adjusting his output to the seasonal ups and downs of the market than he would have had had there been no public controls in effect.

On the negative side, the controls may have tended to result in excessive spreads between the prices of Class 1 milk and those for "surplus" milk. Also, if the prices to consumers were increased by the amounts indicated above, there may have been some slight reduction in the amounts of fluid milk bought by them.[45]

---

eastern States, Cornell University Agricultural Experiment Station, Bulletin 908, November 1954, p. 80. The Spencer and Christensen estimates, by periods, were as follows:

Period	Type of Control in Effect	Net Gain in Price Paid to Producers: Amount per Cwt.	Net Gain in Price Paid to Producers: Per Cent
July–December 1933	State	$0.24	15
January–December 1934	State	0.25	15
January 1935–March 1937	State	0.19	10
September 1938–January 1939	State and federal	0.26	15
July 1939–May 1942	State and federal	0.11	5
July 1946–June 1948	State and federal	0.02	—
July 1948–December 1950	State and federal	0.27	6
January 1951–December 1953	State and federal	0.16	4
Average for all periods		0.166	5.2

44. *Ibid.,* p. 82. If increases of these amounts did occur, and if those in other federally controlled markets were similar (an assumption that is of very dubious validity), the increase in returns to producers nationwide (for those supplying federally controlled markets) may have been in the order of $20 million per year. Presumably, most of this would be passed on to consumers. It must be emphasized, however, that the basis for any such estimate on a national scale is so extremely nebulous that not much significance can be attached to it.

45. A recent study by the National Grange gives a somewhat more inclusive list of advantages which the persons interviewed considered to be traceable to controls at the producer level. Several of them, however, are based on the assumption that the control programs do result in higher prices to producers, a conclusion which, as pointed out above, rests on very limited and rather questionable evidence. For the Grange viewpoint, see *Barriers to Increased Consumption of Fluid Milk,* A Special Report by the National Grange, Washington, January 1955, pp. 82, 83.

Controls from the Consumer Point of View

The consumer is concerned with the milk situation primarily in terms of adequacy and dependability of supply, quality, price and service. As pointed out earlier, supplies will be adequate at all times of the year only if more than enough is produced in the flush seasons. Even very drastic seasonal variations in prices to consumers would not adjust demand to supply on a seasonal basis. Therefore, some special pricing arrangement is essential. It has taken the form almost universally of a stable price to consumers and a variable price to producers, with excess supplies diverted to lower-value outlets.

Consumers quite evidently prefer a stable price throughout the year for milk sold at retail, except for downward continuing adjustments that may be possible or upward adjustments that may be necessary. The adequacy of supply has not been a problem except for a short period during World War II. It can be assumed that dairymen will provide enough milk to meet the demand at prices approximating those now prevailing and probably would do so at somewhat lower prices, even though they themselves would not consider lower prices equitable.

Quality can be controlled without resorting to market controls and hence does not enter importantly into the problems here under discussion, except to the extent that sanitary regulations may be used to achieve economic ends. Service arrangements do have a bearing though one that is not easy to define. Some consumers object to arrangements which they regard as enforced contributions for services they do not use or desire (that is, to costs for home delivery if part of that cost falls on consumers who buy on a cash-and-carry basis). In the federally controlled markets, where resale prices are not regulated, the relations between prices associated with different levels of service are presumably on a competitive basis though there are undoubtedly institutional factors that affect these relationships in various ways. In some of the state-controlled markets, the differentials between home-delivered and store milk are officially determined as are also the allowances permitted on bulk sales.

In the main, however, the consumer's primary concern is with the price he must pay for milk used in the home. For the most part, changes in the retail price of milk will be made only in one-half-cent or one-cent amounts. These, if passed on directly to the producer, involve rather large decreases or increases in the return to him, in the order of 25 cents to 50 cents per hundredweight. This may mean a change of from 6 or 7 per cent up to 15 per cent or more in gross income, and in an industry with high fixed costs this may mean the difference between profit and loss.

As pointed out earlier (pp. 444–45) the response of consumers to moderate changes in price tends to be small, either in the way of increases or decreases in consumption. Consequently, in markets where resale prices are unregulated, there is some tendency for distributors to maintain retail prices when the cost of milk goes down or when supplies become overabundant, and to seek to maintain or increase sales by means other than price concessions.

This may result in the maintenance of an unduly high price for Class 1 milk, to the disadvantage chiefly of consumers but to some extent of producers as well. To the extent that such results do occur, there is an argument, from the consumer's standpoint, for the control of resale prices as well as of prices to producers, provided the consumer's interest is adequately represented in the decision-making process.[46]

The Resale Price Control Problem

Few of the issues relating to milk control have been more hotly and widely debated than the provisions for control over resale prices. They were a continuing source of friction and difficulty in early federal licensing arrangements and have been prominent in the controversies over retention or discontinuance of state milk control laws in Oregon, New Jersey and elsewhere. The federal government dropped the attempt to control resale prices at an early stage in the program. Several of the states have eliminated that feature, even where controls at the producer level were continued. As of 1955, eleven states still had controls at every level of production and distribution.[47]

Many have assumed that the fixing of resale prices tends to widen the spread between the prices paid to producers and those charged consumers. A recent study by Bressler and Clarke raises considerable question as to the truth of this assumption.[48] The National Grange study

46. That condition cannot be taken for granted under the procedures now in use. Virtually all of the milk control legislation and regulatory machinery has come about as a result of producer and handler influence and tends to be more responsive to the interests and wishes of these groups than to those of the consumer. In general, consumers have not been organized to participate effectively in policy-making in this field and, except in isolated instances, have not shown a keen interest in it.

There are, of course, some exceptions. Very wide interest can develop suddenly, as is evident in the public reactions of recent years to some of the state milk control laws. The individual dairyman or handler naturally has a much larger stake in the results of the policies adopted than does the individual consumer. Consequently, he spends more time and money on the matter and exercises far greater pressure on legislators and administrators in developing policies that are favorable to him.

47. They were Alabama, California, Florida, Georgia, Maine, Montana, New Hampshire, Pennsylvania, Rhode Island, Vermont and Virginia. (See *Barriers to Increased Consumption of Fluid Milk,* p. 81.) Oregon recently abandoned all types of control and there has been some criticism of resale price controls in California.

48. R. G. Bressler, Jr. and D. A. Clarke, Jr., "Resale Milk Price Control—Outmoded and Antisocial?," *Journal of Farm Economics,* May 1955, pp. 280–91. This finding is in general agreement with that of the Temporary National Economic Committee, which, in the late 1930s, compared dealers' margins on home-delivered milk in selected cities before and after resale price-fixing became effective. The Committee concluded that, on the whole, the margins on home-delivered milk were not affected significantly by the public regulation of resale prices. (See Spencer and Christensen, *op. cit.,* p. 114.)

(*Barriers to Increased Consumption of Fluid Milk*), participated in by several close students of milk marketing problems, presents arguments that, on the whole, are unfavorable to resale price maintenance. So also do most of the federal administrators concerned with milk market regulation. It is contended that such controls are handicaps to efficiency and innovation, that price differentials between store and home-delivered milk are so fixed as to deny the consumer price advantages for self-service to which he is entitled and that inefficient dealers are enabled to perpetuate their inefficiencies.

These are serious charges and the general trend seems clearly to be away from the attempt to regulate resale prices. However, there seems to be little evidence that, either with or without fixed resale prices, possible economies will be passed along to consumers and producers. The fact remains that prices to consumers are relatively inflexible and that competitive forces alone may not reduce spreads or adjust price relationships in ways that would be in keeping with the public interest.[49]

Though accurate comparisons are difficult if not impossible, because of the widely varying conditions in different markets, the Bressler and Clarke study shows that there is at present no significant difference between the average spreads in controlled and uncontrolled markets.[50] If anything, their findings point to a slightly smaller average spread in the markets in which there is public control of resale prices.

Their findings indicate, however, that the range in spreads tends to be greater in the uncontrolled markets and that price discounts for out-of-store sales and multiple-unit sales (rather than for single quarts) tend to be somewhat larger in the unregulated markets (about 0.8 cent per quart on the average). However, this higher average discount rests largely on the situations in 7 of the 67 unregulated markets included in the study. In these 7 markets, maximum store differentials ranged from 3 to 5 cents per quart.[51]

49. This does not mean, necessarily, that the striking uniformity and the similarities of timing in raising or lowering milk prices are a result of secret, collusive agreements, though that has often been charged and the Department of Justice has at times brought legal action against dealers on the basis of circumstantial evidence of that kind. Actually, the uniformity of prices noted is a result of basic competitive conditions. No dealer can afford to be undersold by an important competitor. If one competitor cuts prices, the others are virtually compelled to follow suit. The product is highly standardized and the services offered by different dealers are practically identical. Consequently, there is almost no basis for price differentials based on brand names or quality differences. This does not mean, of course, that the prices or price spreads arrived at are ideal from the standpoint of the public or the industry. (For fuller comment, see Spencer and Christensen, *op. cit.*, pp. 132–33.)

50. "Resale Milk Price Control—Outmoded and Antisocial?," pp. 284–91.

51. Those who advocate elimination of existing resale price controls, particularly some of the larger chain stores, contend that the discounts on store milk could and would be increased if such action were permitted. There is reason to think that some at least of the larger chains would adopt that policy. However, the findings to date do not indicate that such price concessions have been made very generally in the markets in which

Possible Effects in a Declining Market

The differentials existing at any given time do not, however, tell the whole story. It may well be that public controls act as a delaying influence when major changes in the market situation occur. That would be consistent with the idea that controls are primarily a stabilizing mechanism. They were originally introduced, under public auspices, in an effort to check a disastrous decline in fluid milk prices.

It would be reasonable to expect that in either an advancing or a declining market officially established prices, at either the producer or consumer level, would not be adjusted as quickly as would prices in uncontrolled markets. If that is true, the spreads now permitted in markets where resale price controls are in effect may represent adjustments to an earlier wage and price situation and the current similarity of spreads in controlled and uncontrolled markets may be somewhat deceiving.

The price paid by dealers for standard-grade milk for city distribution in fluid form has moved up consistently since public controls were first initiated. The only exceptions are two periods of recession, 1938–1940 and 1949–1951. Starting with a low of $1.60 per hundredweight in 1933, the average price was up to $2.40 in 1941. By 1945, it had reached $3.26 and it has continued to advance, except for moderate recessions in 1949–1951 and 1953. The price in 1952 was $5.46.[52] Wage rates also increased almost continuously throughout that period.

Under these conditions, when demand was increasing enough that producer pressure and market requirements forced prices up in the unregulated markets, it is understandable that prices would advance in much the same way in the regulated markets. Thus the influences affecting prices in both the regulated and unregulated markets were undoubtedly similar, though possibly with some lag in the regulated markets.

If prices should decline markedly, as they did in the early 1930s, there is reason to believe that both producer prices and dealers' spreads would prove more resistant to change in the regulated markets than in the

there are no resale price controls, that is, in the markets that now handle the great bulk of the fluid milk business. Even in those markets, of course, strong forces exert an influence against larger discounts for store-delivered milk, among them the well-organized milk-drivers' unions that have been developed in nearly all of the larger markets whether controlled or uncontrolled.

52. *Dairy Statistics and Related Series,* 1953, p. 48, and *Agricultural Statistics, 1954,* p. 386. The year-by-year average prices were as follows:

1933	$1.60	1940	$2.21	1947	$4.71
1934	1.89	1941	2.40	1948	5.17
1935	2.05	1942	2.79	1949	4.76
1936	2.13	1943	3.16	1950	4.57
1937	2.32	1944	3.24	1951	5.14
1938	2.26	1945	3.26	1952	5.46
1939	2.17	1946	3.92	1953	5.15

unregulated ones. Whether that is considered desirable or undesirable depends on the point of view. Certainly producers and handlers would favor such resistance to downward adjustments in the returns to them. Consumers might prefer a quicker and more complete adjustment to the new price-cost situation, though in a period of severe readjustment there is apt to be strong public sentiment for protection of customary wage rates, prices and margins, as there was in the period when the NRA was trying to provide such protection and, in fact, even during the depression years prior to 1933.

It is apparent that neither public sentiment nor the dairy industry generally would subscribe to the idea that fluid milk prices and handlers' margins should be kept unchanged if prices declined generally. The realism and public desirability of actions taken to cushion price declines of that kind would depend on the appropriateness and wisdom of the formulae used in determining the prices to be maintained through regulatory devices. Some delaying and stabilizing action would undoubtedly be in the interest of producers and handlers, and probably of the public as well, provided it did not result in extreme distortion of the price structure and undue hardship to consumers or excessive reductions in fluid milk consumption.

It must be kept in mind, of course, that much the same price pattern might result from strong producer-distributor organization and collaboration even in markets not under public regulation. Under such conditions, prices for Class 1 milk and handlers' margins might well be held higher than the interests of the public or even those of the dairy industry as a whole would call for.

In summary, the conclusion seems warranted that majority sentiment in the industry, among milk market administrators and on the part of the general public, is somewhat adverse to the continuance or expansion of public regulation of resale prices. That attitude, as of the present, does not seem to be based on a clear showing that wider spreads have resulted from such controls. There may, however, be longer-term diseconomies such as inhibitions that prevent new developments and more efficient methods of marketing. Resale outlets and procedures in the handling of fluid milk are extremely complex, and regulation, unless very detailed and very wisely conceived, can easily lead to social inefficiencies and retardation of progress.[53] Possibly more persuasive is the argument that, if resale price regulation does not affect materially the price margins in the various markets, the public expense of maintaining such controls might well be eliminated.

53. Some students of the problem argue that public controls can be used to bring about increases in efficiency since they provide a mechanism whereby concerted action can be taken in some situations in which individual action by a given firm might not be practical—for example, a shift to every-other-day delivery, certain types of quantity discount and so on.

More Adequate Criteria Needed

This still leaves a problem of considerable importance, however, both in the publicly regulated markets that do and in those that do not involve resale price maintenance,[54] namely, that of devising ways by which the public will be supplied with milk at the lowest prices consistent with adequate returns to producers and reasonable profit opportunities for handlers. The fluid milk markets have moved some distance in the direction of a regulated public utility. Yet few students of the problem advocate complete adoption of that approach.

With prices established by public agencies at either the producer or handler level, or both, and in the absence of a full public utility regulation procedure for determining prices, there is need for legislative or administrative formulation of the criteria to be used in establishing prices. Much study has been given to formula pricing schemes of various kinds, but there still is much controversy over the form such formulae should take.

Some of the older approaches in terms of a relationship between fluid milk prices and the price of butter have been made unworkable by disturbances to the butter market that have come about through the extensive shift to margarine as a substitute. The shift of fluid milk from minor to major status as an outlet for milk produced has also given rise to a need for a method of pricing that will recognize the dominant role of fluid milk in many areas.[55]

54. And, of course, also in markets not under public regulation if private bargaining results in much the same price pattern as public regulation.

55. The obsolescence of older approaches to this problem has led to extensive study and fairly widespread adoption of various types of formula pricing designed to regulate supplies rather than to maintain some pre-existing relationship to the prices of manufactured dairy products. Among the most carefully worked out of such plans is that devised by the Boston Milkshed Price Committee in 1947 (with later supplements). That committee, which consisted of agricultural economists, marketing specialists and industry representatives, proposed a plan for pricing Class 1 milk which is known as the "Boston Formula." It and modifications of it have been put into effect not only in the Boston market but in many others as well. The Committee's analyses, conclusions and recommendations are set forth in *A Recommended Basis of Pricing Class 1 Milk in the Boston Market,* a condensed report by the Boston Price Committee, September 1947; *Consumer Income as a Factor in Pricing Fluid Milk in the Boston Market,* processed, November 1951; and *Recommendations of the Committee to be Made at Public Milk Hearing,* Boston, Week of May 12, 1952, mimeo.

The plan takes account of the effects of price and cost relationships on production and deliveries, of the influence of consumer incomes and other factors on consumption, of seasonal variations in supply and of reserve supplies needed as a safety factor in the seasons of lowest production.

Many other studies of this general problem have appeared in recent years. See, for example, U.S. Farm Credit Administration, *Formula Pricing of Fluid Milk,* Misc. Report 127, December 1948. Also Kentucky Agricultural Experiment Station Bulletin 558, *Formula Pricing of Fluid Milk* by John B. Roberts and Grant Grayson, November 1950, and R. G. Bressler, Jr., *The Use of Automatic Formulas in Pricing Market Milk,* 1948, Giannini Foundation, University of California, processed, 11 pp.

PRODUCTION, PRICES AND CONSUMPTION, 1930–1954

It is clearly impractical to estimate the price effects of the fluid milk control programs on a nationwide basis. At no time has the program been national in scope and the coverage has varied considerably from period to period. Furthermore, the general movement of prices appears to have been similar in the markets under public control and in those not under public control.

Detailed studies pertaining to specific areas can throw some light on the probable effects of the programs in those areas, but it would be unwarranted to assume that results would be the same in other markets and other areas. Conditions vary as between markets and there are differences in the effectiveness of administration, in producer and handler cooperation, and in supply and demand conditions.

However, it is possible to provide some broad indicators of how fluid milk producers have fared in comparison with other farm groups and of some of the general developments in the fluid milk markets. Changes in the dairy industry as a whole, with special reference to manufactured dairy products, have been discussed in Chapter 6. The data given here therefore relate principally to fluid milk.

Since 1930, total milk production has increased by about 15 per cent, from approximately 100 billion pounds to about 115 billion. It was higher during the war years, reaching nearly 120 billion pounds in 1945.[56] Whole milk delivered to plants and dealers has increased at a much faster rate. (This, of course, includes large quantities that do not find their outlet as milk sold in fluid form to consumers.) Whereas the amount of milk sold as whole milk to plants and dealers amounted to about 34.5 billion pounds in 1930 (about 34.5 per cent of total production), by 1952 the amount sold in that way had increased to 76.7 billion pounds, approximately two thirds of the total amount produced.

Civilian consumption of milk and cream in fluid form has increased about 30 per cent since 1930 (from 42.1 billion pounds to 54.7 billion). Most of the increase was due to the growth of population. Per capita consumption is only about 4.5 per cent larger than it was in 1930 (352 pounds as compared with 337 in 1930 [57]). The larger consumption, in fluid form, has approximately equaled the increase in production of milk going into the fluid milk markets, so the amounts diverted to manufacturing and other uses have remained nearly constant over the twenty-year period.

Price Changes

No single price can be very meaningful in complex and stratified markets such as those in which fluid milk is sold. For present purposes,

56. *Dairy Statistics and Related Series,* pp. 2 and 3.

57. *Ibid.,* p. 80; percentages computed. Per capita consumption was higher during the war years with a high of 399 pounds in 1945.

the series giving prices paid by dealers for standard-grade (3.5 per cent butterfat) milk for distribution as milk and cream is probably the most useful one.[58] The average price for this class of milk was $2.82 per hundredweight in 1929.[59] It had fallen to $2.20 by 1931 and reached a low of $1.60 in 1933. The decline was slower and less drastic than that for farm products as a whole. The average for all farm products reached its lowest point in 1932 at 44 per cent of the 1929 level while the price of fluid milk was 57 per cent of the 1929 price at its low point a year later.

This slower and somewhat more moderate decline for fluid milk was, no doubt, a result of the stabilizing influence of the institutional arrangements customary in those markets. Though less drastic than the declines in the prices of many other farm products, it was, of course, an exceedingly severe price drop, and caused widespread distress and discontent in the fluid-milk-producing areas.

The price recovered in 1934, to $1.89, and to $2.05 in 1935. By 1937, it was up to $2.32, about 82 per cent of the 1929 level. This improvement cannot, of course, be attributed to the imposition of public controls. Many other influences were at work, and coverage under public controls was spotty. Droughts affected the situation in 1934 and 1936 and there were heavy purchases of dairy cattle in the disease-eradication programs. Also, there was some general recovery in the economy as a whole.

During the years 1934 through 1939, fluid milk prices averaged about 76 per cent of the 1929 price, whereas the average price for farm products as a whole was about 70.5 per cent.[60] There are some indications that public controls may have had some stabilizing influence on the over-all price of fluid milk, but this cannot be demonstrated with any assurance.

It is clear that milk producers fared somewhat better than most other types of farmers, even though special programs were set up for them too. However, it is probable that the strong cooperative organizations operating in most of the large markets, and the buying and selling arrangements developed prior to 1933, would have exerted some stabilizing and price-raising influence even if there had been no public control program.

From 1940 on, the price moved up rather consistently to a level of $5.46 per hundredweight in 1952, which was about 193 per cent of the

58. This, as explained earlier, is not a clearly defined price since it is affected by the pricing plans used, the amounts diverted to manufacturing uses and so on.

59. *Dairy Statistics and Related Series,* p. 48.

60. Parity ratios relating specifically to milk for fluid use in homes are not available. The parity ratio for all milk delivered to plants and dealers stood at 97 in 1929. It dropped to 68 in 1932 and recovered to 97 in 1942. With government production payments included, it ranged from 109 to 120 in the years 1943–1946. It dropped back to 92 in 1949 and stood at 102 in 1952. (*Dairy Statistics and Related Series,* p. 40.) Farm products as a whole had a parity ratio of 92 in 1929 and dropped to 58 in 1932. The ratio rose to 115 in 1947 and dropped back to 100 in 1949 and 1950. It was 82 on October 15, 1955.

1929 price. The average for all farm products was about 183 per cent of the 1929 level. The over-all level of farm prices had been somewhat higher in 1948 and 1951 but declined in 1953–1955. Fluid milk also showed some decline but, in general, held its gains somewhat better than farm products as a whole. Dairying is, in fact, a more stable industry than are some of the major field crops.

Costs Also Increased

During this period, the costs of milk production also rose substantially. The cost of concentrate rations fed to milk cows on farms from which milk and cream are sold stood at $1.88 per hundredweight in 1929. It dropped to $.86 in 1932 and had increased to $3.75 by 1952.[61] This, together with hired labor, constitutes the largest item of cash cost in milk production. Farm wage rates, which stood at 187 (1910–14=100) in 1929, dropped to 89 in 1933 and had risen to 508 in 1952.[62]

Much of the labor used on dairy farms is family labor and hence is not paid for in cash. Also, in some areas a considerable part of the feed is home-produced. However, the figures cited reflect the fact that costs have risen very substantially during the past twenty years.

The price-cost situation for the dairy industry as a whole does not appear to have resulted in any marked stimulation of production. Over-all milk production in 1952 was up only about 15 per cent over that of 1930. The number of dairy cows was down substantially from that of earlier years. It was 21.6 million in 1952, slightly below the 22.2 million on farms in 1930. The dairy cow population was up to 25.6 million in 1944, a period in which milk prices were relatively favorable as compared with those of most other farm products. The increase in production noted above has come about as a result of better selection, better breeding and care of cows, and more intensive feeding.

Prices Paid by Consumers

Of special interest to consumers is the price at the retail level. The average in leading cities of the United States was 14.4 cents per quart in 1929.[63] It dropped to 10.4 cents in 1933 and has increased gradually since, to 24.2 cents in 1953. The 1953 price was about 68 per cent above that of 1929, whereas the price of fluid milk to farmers was around 90 per cent above the price received in 1929.

There was some technological advance in the fluid milk distributing industry during these years, but a major factor was the shift to every-other-day delivery, which was made possible by refrigeration and the improved quality of milk. Some of the gains were reflected in a some-

61. *Dairy Statistics and Related Series,* p. 14.
62. *Agricultural Statistics, 1951,* p. 544, and *1953,* p. 567.
63. *Dairy Statistics and Related Series,* p. 57.

what smaller percentage spread between the prices paid to milk producers and the prices paid by consumers. Part of the difference is also accounted for by the large development of secondary products such as ice cream, cottage cheese and skim milk which has enabled distributors to dispose of "surplus" milk in ways that yield them better returns than by making it into butter and cheese.

In general, the price of milk to consumers compares favorably with the prices of most other foods in respect to increases from the 1935–1939 period to 1952. (See Table 51.) This, of course, does not show

TABLE 51

FOODS: PERCENTAGE INCREASES IN RETAIL PRICES, 1935–1939 TO DECEMBER 1952

(*1935–1939=100*)

Product	Increase
Fish	233.9
Pork	103.4
Lamb	161.6
Eggs	101.8
Dried fruits and vegetables	148.8
Meats, poultry and fish	162.4
Beef and veal	192.8
Beverages	247.0
All foods	*129.9*
Fresh fruits and vegetables	154.0
Chickens	106.7
Dairy products	117.1
Sugar and sweets	90.5
Cereal and bakery products	94.5
Fats and oils	39.8
Canned fruits and vegetables	65.9
Fresh milk (retail, delivered) U.S.	102.4
Fresh milk (retail, delivered) Boston	94.5
Fresh milk (retail, delivered) Chicago	116.0 [a]

Source: U.S. Department of Labor, *Retail Food Prices by Cities,* December 1952, p. 6

a. Derived from data in U.S. Department of Agriculture, *Fluid Milk and Cream Report,* February 1945, p. 11, and December 1952, p. 2.

whether it is high or low in relation to what it could be under conditions of maximum social efficiency in producing, handling and pricing the product. It does indicate that the increase in the price of fluid milk to consumers has been rather moderate in comparison with the increases shown for many of the other foods used.

CONTINUING AND FUTURE PROBLEMS

The preceding sections have outlined in broad terms the situation which led to the use of controls and class prices in the fluid milk markets. They have also summarized the developments in this realm from 1933 on. It seems warranted to conclude that some type of public control will be continued in most of the important markets.[64]

A question still remains as to whether such control will be exercised through state governments or by the federal government and how inclusive it will be. Control of resale prices was discontinued by the federal government in 1934 and has not been reinstated. There appears to be little sentiment for revival of this feature in federal milk orders. Five of the sixteen state milk control programs do not include resale price-fixing.

As now operated, the program is a hybrid one with some overlapping of jurisdictions. Mostly, this duality of organization is a historical accident. A good many of the state systems were set up before the federal program became well established and more than half of them have been continued for one reason or another. Some markets lend themselves better to state control than others. If the supply area lies almost wholly in a single state, no important difficulties arise in supervising the market on a state basis that would not exist if it were federally regulated. Other markets which depend heavily on supplies from a number of states seem clearly best suited to federal control.

At present, there seem to be no large differences in the results achieved by the two systems, except to the extent that resale price controls are important in some of the state systems. Coordinated national programs, if desirable, could no doubt be worked out more easily and more effectively under an all-federal system than under the one now existing. There might be some small saving in the costs of general supervision, though that cannot be stated with any assurance. Supervision from Washington of markets that are located at considerable distance from the capital involves expense and lack of close contact that may not be factors in the state systems.

Furthermore, there are still some problems in regard to constitutional authority for federal regulation of markets that lie wholly within the borders of a state. This issue seems to be much less significant than it was in the 1930s but it could come up again if the judicial climate with respect to state versus federal powers should change. Generally speaking, it seems likely that the trend of the future will be toward increased reliance on federal controls and that principal emphasis might well be

64. A substantial amount of fluid milk, of course, still does not come under either federal or state regulation. However, except in the smaller markets, the volume so handled is decreasing. The number of markets under federal regulation has been increasing consistently over the past ten years and seems likely to continue to increase in the years immediately ahead. State regulation appears to be at a standstill or declining somewhat.

on ways of making the federal programs more useful, effective and socially desirable.

Many Administrative and Policy Problems Still Exist

Though much progress has been made, the management of the federal order programs is still far from a simple orderly procedure in which most decisions can be made on the basis of precedents and well-defined criteria. Basically, the mechanism set up is a device for reconciling conflicts in a very complex situation. It has some of the characteristics of a mediation service in the realm of labor-management relations. New problems are constantly arising and a body of principles and precedents is gradually being built up.

Much of this is not of great concern to the general public, so long as it does not increase prices to consumers or disrupt services and production organization. Often the disputes are between handlers, or between a particular handler and a particular group of producers, and may have little effect on the over-all market or price situation. Many of the functions carried on by the milk market administrators would have to be performed in some other way if not handled by them, possibly through more elaborate organization by producer cooperatives and distributor organizations. The cost of the program would be much the same and would be borne by pretty much the same groups, since the programs are now financed by the industry, except for a modest amount of general supervision supplied by the federal government. Supervision within a market undoubtedly would not be as complete, uniform and equitable as under the public controls now in effect.

Principles Governing Class Prices Important

The policies followed in establishing class prices are important both to consumers and producers. If the Class 1 price is unduly high, consumers are penalized by having to pay more for fluid milk than is warranted. Too large a spread between the price of Class 1 and that of "surplus" milk may be to the disadvantage of producers, as well as consumers, by inducing excessive production of milk of Class 1 quality (usually at high cost) and having too much of it go to "surplus" uses, thus reducing the blended price received by producers.

Except for diversions to take care of necessary amounts of seasonal surplus, milk for manufacturing use can ordinarily be produced more economically in outlying areas that do not have access to the fluid milk markets.[65] To produce it under conditions suited to Class 1 use involves

65. The Boston Milkshed Price Committee suggested that a surplus of 18 per cent in November would provide an ample margin of safety. Many large markets operate with much smaller reserves in the low-production months. An 18 per cent margin in November means, of course, that there will be very large surpluses at some times in the year. In

unnecessary costs and social losses and may well be unprofitable to the dairyman himself since the price actually received tends to be concealed in the blended price arrangements customarily used. Since in some markets more than half the milk delivered by producers is used by the receivers in manufacturing operations (in some seasons of the year nearly two thirds), it is apparent that diversions of milk produced in high-cost areas can result in unnecessary social and industry costs and may reduce significantly the blended price paid to producers.[66]

Other problems, such as the determination of marketing allowances and differentials, and the reports and accounting required, are of concern mainly to the members of the industry. However, a collateral gain appears to be observable in that the rigorous accounting and auditing procedures established by the market administrators seem to have done much to allay suspicion on the part of producers as to the ultimate uses made of milk for which they were paid at Class 2 or Class 3 prices. These procedures also have encouraged handlers to achieve some economies through the establishment of more effective accounting controls.

Other problems, such as that of determining the size of the area to be included under a federal marketing order, create difficulties of concept and practical policy for administrators but are not usually of direct concern to the public, except in fringe areas. In the early days of the program, the keenest competition and the most demoralizing price-cutting tendencies appeared in the areas peripheral to the large markets. It was here also, and among the producers who supplied the handlers serving these areas, that the most vigorous opposition to federal controls developed. Consequently, the tendency, at first, was to not include such areas in marketing licenses and orders. However, the establishment of orderly arrangements in the larger, adjoining markets tended to develop greater stability in these fringe areas as well and many of them have since been brought under control, probably with less hardship and opposition than if they had been forced in at the start.[67]

---

an effort to overcome in part these wide fluctuations in supply, most market controls provide for seasonally adjusted prices to producers, and some have very elaborate arrangements for making it more attractive to producers to increase their deliveries in the fall months and reduce them in the spring months. In the Boston and New York markets, June deliveries in recent years have been about 157 per cent of the amounts delivered in November. In some markets, seasonal variations have been reduced to as low as 15 to 25 per cent. However, very careful and detailed studies would be required to show whether that much adjustment was actually sound economically.

66. For example, in 1952, milk deliveries in two of the largest markets (Boston and New York) amounted to 8.5 billion pounds. Of this, 4.5 billion pounds were sold in Class 1 outlets while 4 billion had to be sold in non-Class 1 outlets, that is, as surplus. In some markets, several classes of milk are established, the classification being determined by the use to which the milk is put. Such arrangements obviously complicate greatly the administrator's job of accounting and supervision. The class price for each use needs to be adjusted to the revenue derived from such use in such a way that there will be no strong incentive for handlers to bring in large additional supplies for manufacturing beyond the amounts needed in the over-all stabilizing process.

67. However, an expansion of the marketing area usually is associated with an ex-

The Problem of Sanitary Regulations

The public obviously has an important interest in the maintenance of adequate regulations and inspection for assuring that the milk available for purchase will be healthful and of high quality. Producers also are affected by the adequacy and nature of sanitary and quality regulations. If they are inadequate, the demand for milk may be reduced. If they are unnecessarily complicated and expensive, costs go up.

There has been frequent and vigorous complaint at times that sanitary regulations were used to shut out from specific markets milk that was of adequate quality and cleanliness, as a means of maintaining a monopoly position for the producers already established in the area and equipped to meet its sanitary requirements. Producers more commonly object to what they regard as unnecessary and unduly expensive requirements and to overlapping inspections by different jurisdictions.

The problem of adequate, available and controllable inspection also creates difficulties in bringing in milk from distant areas to meet seasonal shortages in a given consuming market.[68] If such difficulties could be overcome, it often would be more economical to rely on more distant, lower-cost areas for some of the supply required in seasons of shortage than to expand year-round production in the close-at-hand, high-cost production areas.

The tendency to use sanitary codes as a means of protecting monopoly interests of local producer groups appears to be on the decline, but many of the old and now obsolete laws and regulations remain on the books. It is in the interest of consumers, and for the most part of producers as well, to support efforts to improve and simplify such regulations rather than to complicate them and allow them to be used for the attainment of economic objectives. It is also in their interest to keep the cost of meeting sanitary requirements as low as is consistent with the maintenance of quality.[69]

---

pansion of the supply area, as well as of the number of dealers, thus intensifying the problem of seasonal variations in supply.

68. During several of the shortage seasons in recent years, large quantities of so-called "emergency" milk were brought into many of the fluid milk markets from sources that are not regularly inspected for the sale of milk in fluid form in markets of that kind. That practice has created serious problems for dealers, producer cooperatives, health officers and sanitary control officials. If such milk, on arrival at the market, does not meet the applicable health and sanitary requirements, it cannot be sold as fluid milk. The handler may then be deprived of a much needed supply and at the same time may suffer a loss because the milk must be diverted to lower-grade uses. Ordinarily, inspection should be extended to enough additional farms and plants to meet the requirements of the market except in very unusual supply shortages.

69. For a fuller discussion of this problem, see the report of the National Grange on *Barriers to Increased Consumption of Fluid Milk*, pp. 60–78. The Grange did not go so far as to advocate a comprehensive federal inspection act, or other drastic steps, for overcoming the inconsistencies and inadequacies of the various sanitary and inspection arrangements now in existence. It did, however, urge positive and continuing efforts by consumers and producers to relax unnecessary restrictions on interarea movement of

Effects of Technological Changes

Technological advances are creating far wider markets for the milk produced in any given area or region than were available in earlier periods. These developments, so far as strictly economic factors are concerned, are tending to break down the natural monopolies formerly enjoyed by the areas close to the large centers of population. For example, whole milk can now be sterilized, condensed to various degrees of concentration, sealed in sterile containers and shipped almost any distance. Unsalted butter, "plastic cream" and other products can be used in making ice cream and in many other ways. Thus the old area advantages based mainly on transportation costs and the perishability of the product are becoming less important.

As a result, conflicts of interest arise, not only between producers and consumers but also between the established suppliers of the fluid milk markets and those producers whose farms are located in more distant areas that in the past had to depend on the returns obtainable from butter, cheese and other storable dairy products. The increasing competition from margarine in the butter markets is likely to give rise to even more vigorous efforts by potential suppliers outside the established milk sheds to gain access to the urban fluid milk markets.

If dairymen so located can produce milk more cheaply than the dairymen currently supplying the fluid milk markets, society may well benefit from letting them come in. However, there are many problems to be solved, among them the matter of controls over quality, timing of shipments, stability of supply and so on. Furthermore, dairymen close to the large urban markets naturally will resist changes that may jeopardize their preferred status in the fluid milk markets.[70]

Consumer Representation Not Adequate

Consumer opposition to the general idea of milk market controls has not been vigorous or widespread. Consumer representatives have at times

milk and to make sanitary regulations more uniform and more realistic. However, the tremendous improvements that have been made in the provisions for supplying wholesome, high-quality milk were recognized and commended. The Senate Committee on Agriculture and Forestry, which considered this problem in its 1950 hearings on the utilization of farm crops, recommended against a federal inspection act but did urge strongly that the U.S. Public Health Service exercise stronger leadership in resolving this complex array of problems. See U.S. Senate, Committee on Agriculture and Forestry, *Utilization of Farm Crops,* Senate Report No. 604, 82d Cong., 1st sess., 1951, pp. 18, 19.

70. Changes in consumption habits, the development of new products and so on also contribute to a demand for changes in price structures and in the number of classes recognized. For example, the increased emphasis on nonfat milk solids and the increased use of skim milk in fluid form have put skim milk into a different category from the one it occupied when it was regarded purely as a low-value product often used for livestock feeding or even dumped into sewers as worthless. Similar problems arise in establishing allowances such as those for costs of transportation and the operation of receiving station differentials based on fat content, all of which must be spelled out in marketing orders.

attacked specific policies or decisions but usually not the underlying principles of the legislation itself. This may, of course, be due to a lack of effective organization and of adequate knowledge about the workings of these complex marketing arrangements. Furthermore, a given change in milk prices usually affects the family budget of the individual consumer only in a relatively minor way whereas it may make a very substantial difference to the individual milk producer. Consequently, producers are usually much better organized and much more active in furthering their interests than are consumers.

Certainly there is need for more effective representation of consumer interest in the formulation of milk market orders and pricing formulae. A considerable element of monopoly is introduced and maintained through public action and serious diseconomies may creep in without either consumers or producers being aware of them. Here, however, as in most public utility and quasi-public utility operations, consumers must rely to a considerable extent on the protection afforded through the participation of public officials in the price-making process. That their interests are not fully represented and protected is evident from the nature of the organizational arrangements. Producer and handler influence is much more effectively implemented than consumer influence in both the federal and state programs.

Nevertheless, there are genuine and significant reasons for the consumer to favor orderliness and quality protection in the fluid milk markets. Sanitary regulations are, of course, necessary and cannot be provided by the consumers themselves, even though such regulations may at times be so manipulated as to operate to the economic disadvantage of consumers and of some of the producers. In ordinary times, a dependable and adequate supply of milk at all seasons of the year is probably more important to the consumer than any moderate reduction in the average price paid. There is, however, a continuing need for objective and penetrating study of the situation with a view to establishing more equitable criteria for pricing milk and effecting economies in the marketing and production processes.

INDEX

INDEX